PRENTICE HALL

SCIENCE EXPLORER

Human Biology and Health

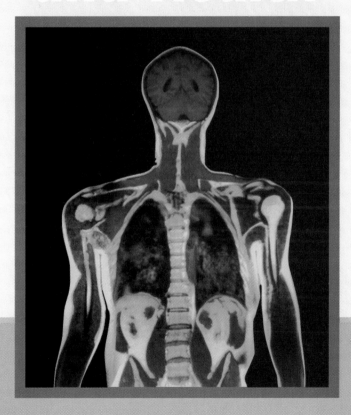

PRENTICE HALL
Needham, Massachusetts
Upper Saddle River, New Jersey

ISBN 0-13-434568-1
1 2 3 4 5 6 7 8 9 10   03 02 01 00 99

PRENTICE HALL

SCIENCE EXPLORER

GET READY FOR A CONTENT-RICH, HANDS-ON EXPLORATION!

PRENTICE HALL
SCIENCE EXPLORER
Earth's Waters

PRENTICE HALL
SCIENCE EXPLORER
Motion, Forces and Energy

PRENTICE HALL
SCIENCE EXPLORER
Animals

15 Books In All

Chart your own course.

15 motivational hardcover books make it easy for you to create your own curriculum; meet local, state, and national guidelines; and teach your favorite topics in depth.

Prepare your students with rich, motivating content...

Science Explorer is crafted for today's middle grades student, with accessible content and in-depth coverage of all the important concepts.

...and a wide variety of inquiry activities.

Motivational student- and teacher-tested activities reinforce key concepts and allow students to explore science concepts for themselves.

Check your compass regularly.

Science Explorer gives you more ways to regularly check student performance than any other program available.

Utilize a variety of tools.

Integrated science sections in every chapter and Interdisciplinary Explorations in every book allow you to make in-depth connections to other sciences and disciplines. Plus, you will find a wealth of additional tools to set your students on a successful course.

Chart the course you want with *15 motivating books* that easily match your curriculum.

Each book in the series contains:

- Complete and accessible coverage of core science topics
- Integrated Science sections in every chapter
- Interdisciplinary Explorations for team teaching at the end of each book
- Comprehensive skills practice and application—assuring that you meet the National Science Education Standards and your local and state standards

EXPLORATION TOOLS: BASIC PROCESS SKILLS

Observing

Measuring

Calculating

Classifying

Predicting

Inferring

Graphing

Creating data tables

Communicating

LIFE SCIENCE TITLES

From Bacteria to Plants
1 Living Things
2 Viruses and Bacteria
3 Protists and Fungi
4 Introduction to Plants
5 Seed Plants

Animals
1 Sponges, Cnidarians, and Worms
2 Mollusks, Arthropods, and Echinoderms
3 Fishes, Amphibians, and Reptiles
4 Birds and Mammals
5 Animal Behavior

Cells and Heredity
1 Cell Structure and Function
2 Cell Processes and Energy
3 Genetics: The Science of Heredity
4 Modern Genetics
5 Changes Over Time

Human Biology and Health
1 Healthy Body Systems
2 Bones, Muscles, and Skin
3 Food and Digestion
4 Circulation
5 Respiration and Excretion
6 Fighting Disease
7 The Nervous System
8 The Endocrine System and Reproduction

Environmental Science
1 Populations and Communities
2 Ecosystems and Biomes
3 Living Resources
4 Land and Soil Resources
5 Air and Water Resources
6 Energy Resources

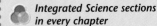

Integrated Science sections in every chapter

Posing questions

Forming operational definitions

Developing hypotheses

Controlling variables

Interpreting data

Interpreting graphs

Making models

Drawing conclusions

Designing experiments

EARTH SCIENCE TITLES

Inside Earth
1 Plate Tectonics
2 Earthquakes
3 Volcanoes
4 Minerals
5 Rocks

Earth's Changing Surface
1 Mapping Earth's Surface
2 Weathering and Soil Formation
3 Erosion and Deposition
4 A Trip Through Geologic Time

Earth's Waters
1 Earth: The Water Planet
2 Fresh Water
3 Freshwater Resources
4 Ocean Motions
5 Ocean Zones

Weather and Climate
1 The Atmosphere
2 Weather Factors
3 Weather Patterns
4 Climate and Climate Change

Astronomy
1 Earth, Moon, and Sun
2 The Solar System
3 Stars, Galaxies, and the Universe

PHYSICAL SCIENCE TITLES

Chemical Building Blocks
1 An Introduction to Matter
2 Changes in Matter
3 Elements in the Periodic Table
4 Carbon Chemistry

Chemical Interactions
1 Chemical Reactions
2 Atoms and Bonding
3 Acids, Bases, and Solutions
4 Exploring Materials

Motion, Forces, and Energy
1 Motion
2 Forces
3 Forces in Fluids
4 Work and Machines
5 Energy and Power
6 Thermal Energy and Heat

Electricity and Magnetism
1 Magnetism and Electromagnetism
2 Electric Charges and Current
3 Electricity and Magnetism at Work
4 Electronics

Sound and Light
1 Characteristics of Waves
2 Sound
3 The Electromagnetic Spectrum
4 Light

Integrated Science sections in every chapter

Place your students in the role of science explorer through a variety of inquiry activities.

Motivational student- and teacher-tested activities reinforce key concepts and allow students to explore science concepts for themselves. More than 350 activities are provided for each book in the Student Edition, Teacher's Edition, Teaching Resources, Integrated Science Lab Manual, and Inquiry Skills Activity Book.

STUDENT EDITION ACTIVITIES

Time

Long-term

1 Class Period

10–25 Minutes

Chapter Project
Opportunities for long-term inquiry—start of each chapter

Real-World Lab
Everyday application of science concepts—one per chapter

Skills Lab
In-depth practice of an inquiry skill—one per chapter

Sharpen Your Skills
Practice of a specific inquiry skill—two per chapter

Discover
Exploration and inquiry before reading—start of every lesson

Try This
Reinforcement of key concepts—two per chapter

Directed   Guided   Open-ended

Inquiry

Check your compass regularly with integrated assessment tools.

Science Explorer gives you more ways to regularly assess student progress than any other program. A wide variety of assessment tools are built into every page of the Student Edition, and ongoing assessment options are woven throughout the Teacher's Edition and program resources. Now, you'll know exactly how your students are doing every step of the way.

Prepare for state and local exams with traditional and performance-based assessment.

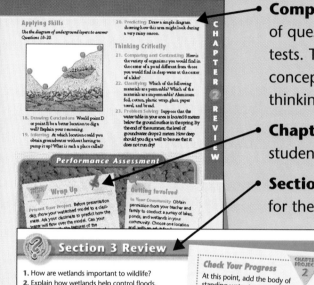

- **Comprehensive Chapter Reviews** include a wide range of question types that students will encounter on standardized tests. Types include multiple choice, enhanced true/false, concept mastery, visual thinking, skill application, and critical thinking. Also includes Chapter Project "Wrap Up."

- **Chapter Projects** contain rubrics that allow you to easily assess student progress.

- **Section Reviews** provide "Check your Progress" opportunities for the Chapter Project, as well as review questions for the section.

- Additional *Science Explorer* assessment resources: **Assessment Resources with CD-ROM** and **Resource Pro® with Planning Express®.** See page 9 for complete product descriptions.

Self-assessment opportunities help students keep themselves on course.

- **Caption Questions** throughout the text assess critical thinking skills.

- **Checkpoint Questions** give students an immediate content check as new concepts are presented.

- Plus, the **Interactive Student Tutorial CD-ROM** provides students with electronic self-tests, review activities, and Exploration activities.

Utilize a variety of tools.

Easy-to-manage, book-specific teaching resources

Teaching Resource Packages are available for each of the 15 titles. Packages contain a Teacher's Edition desk copy, Teaching Resources with Color Transparencies, Guided Reading Audiotapes, Materials Kit Order Form, and a Correlation to the National Science Education Standards.

Teacher's Edition three-step lesson plan—*Engage/Explore, Facilitate,* and *Assess*— is ideal for reaching all students. Chapter planning charts make it easy to find resources, as well as to plan for block scheduling and team teaching.

Teaching Resources with Color Transparencies are organized by chapter to make it easy for you to find what you need—when you need it.

- **Chapter Project Support**
- **Lesson Plans**
- **Section Summaries**
- **Review and Reinforcement**
- **Enrichment**
- **Skills Practice**
- **In-Text Lab Worksheets**
- **Interdisciplinary Explorations**
- **Performance Assessments with Rubrics**
- **Chapter Tests, Book Test**
- **Answer Key**
- **Color Transparencies (20 per book)**

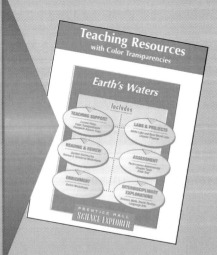

Guided Reading Audiotapes provide section summaries for students who need additional guided reading support. Also available in Spanish.

Program-wide print and technology components to support the entire program

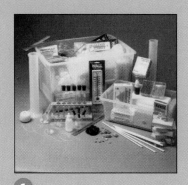
1

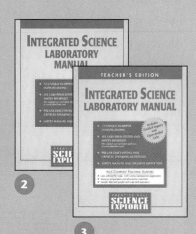
2

3

4

5

6

1. **Materials Kits**—Prentice Hall and Science Kit, Inc. have collaborated to develop a Consumable Kit and Nonconsumable Kit specific to each book. Electronic order forms make it easy for you to customize kits.

2. **Integrated Science Laboratory Manual**— 72 additional laboratory investigations, covering the entire *Science Explorer* curriculum.

3. **Integrated Science Laboratory Manual, Teacher's Edition**—information on safety, equipment, strategies, and answers to all questions in the student edition lab manual.

4. **Inquiry Skills Activity Book**—additional activities that introduce basic and advanced inquiry skills and reinforce skills on an as-needed basis.

7

8

9 **10**

11

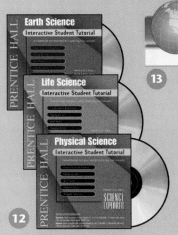

12

USING THE INTERNET

www.science-explorer.phschool.com

13

ASSESSMENT RESOURCES WITH CD-ROM

POWERFUL COMPUTER TEST BANK SOFTWARE (MACINTOSH & WINDOWS)

72 CHAPTER TESTS AND 15 BOOK TESTS

EXCLUSIVE DIAL-A-TEST SERVICE

PERFORMANCE-BASED TASKS

Instant Access to All Resources!

SCIENCE EXPLORER

14

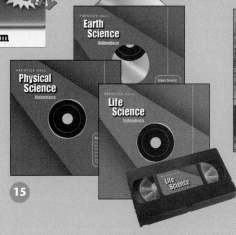

15

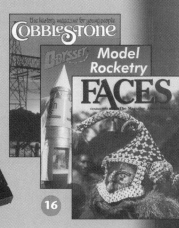

16

5. **Student-Centered Science Activities**—five regional activity books focused on the Northeast, Southeast, Midwest, Southwest, and West.

6. **Program Planning Guide**—course outlines, block scheduling pacing charts, correlations to the National Standards, and more.

7. **Product Testing Activities by *Consumer Reports***— 19 student-oriented testing activities developed by Consumer Reports and Prentice Hall. Available in ten-packs for each activity and correlated to each book.

8. **Prentice Hall Interdisciplinary Explorations**— 15 units designed to help you connect science topics to social studies, math, language arts— and students' daily lives.

9 & 10. **Professional Development Resources**— *How to Assess Student Work* and *How to Manage Instruction in the Block*

11. **Resource Pro® CD-ROM**—electronic versions of the Teaching Resources for all 15 books—ideal for creating integrated science lessons. Contains Planning Express® software and Computer Test Bank. Organized by chapter to save you time.

12. **Interactive Student Tutorial CD-ROMs**— provide students with self-tests, helpful hints, and Exploration activities. Tests are scored instantly and contain a detailed explanation of results.

13. *Science Explorer* **Internet Site**—additional activities and current data for every *Science Explorer* chapter. Check it out at www.science-explorer.phschool.com

14. **Assessment Resources with CD-ROM**— comprehensive collection of assessment resources containing **Computer Test Bank Software**, chapter and book tests, and performance assessments.

15. **Life, Earth, and Physical Science Videotapes and Videodiscs**—allow students to further explore and visualize concepts through spectacular short documentaries containing computer animations.

16. *Cobblestone, Odyssey,* **and *Faces* Magazines**— engaging magazines that support the Interdisciplinary Units and selected topics from each book.

Options for Pacing *Human Biology and Health*

The Pacing Chart below suggests one way to schedule your instructional time. The *Science Explorer* program offers many other aids to help you plan your instructional time, whether regular class periods or **block scheduling.** Refer to the Chapter Planning Guide before each chapter to view all program resources with suggested times for Student Edition activities.

Pacing Chart

	Days	Blocks		Days	Blocks
Nature of Science: Finding a Balance in Nutrition	1	$\frac{1}{2}$	**Chapter 3 Food and Digestion**		
Chapter 1 Healthy Body Systems			Chapter 3 Project What's for Lunch?	Ongoing	Ongoing
Chapter 1 Project Time for a Change	Ongoing	Ongoing	**1** Food and Energy	$4\frac{1}{2}$	2–3
1 How the Body Is Organized	$3\frac{1}{2}$	1–2	**2** Integrating Health: Healthy Eating	$2\frac{1}{2}$	1–2
2 Keeping the Body in Balance	$2\frac{1}{2}$	1–2	**3** The Digestive Process Begins	4	2
3 Integrating Health: Wellness	$2\frac{1}{2}$	1–2	**4** Final Digestion and Absorption	$2\frac{1}{2}$	1–2
			Chapter 3 Review and Assessment	1	$\frac{1}{2}$
Chapter 1 Review and Assessment	1	$\frac{1}{2}$	**Chapter 4 Circulation**		
Chapter 2 Bones, Muscles, and Skin			Chapter 4 Project Travels of a Red Blood Cell	Ongoing	Ongoing
Chapter 2 Project On the Move	Ongoing	Ongoing	**1** The Body's Transportation System	$3\frac{1}{2}$	1–2
1 The Skeletal System	4	2	**2** A Closer Look at Blood Vessels	3	$1\frac{1}{2}$
2 Integrating Technology: Diagnosing Bone and Joint Injuries	2	1	**3** Blood and Lymph	$3\frac{1}{2}$	1–2
3 The Muscular System	3	$1\frac{1}{2}$	**4** Integrating Health: Cardiovascular Health	$2\frac{1}{2}$	1–2
4 The Skin	$3\frac{1}{2}$	1–2			
Chapter 2 Review and Assessment	1	$\frac{1}{2}$	Chapter 4 Review and Assessment	1	$\frac{1}{2}$

Options for Pacing *Human Biology and Health*

Pacing Chart

	Days	Blocks
Chapter 5 Respiration and Excretion		
Chapter 5 Project Get the Message Out	Ongoing	Ongoing
1 The Respiratory System	5	$2\frac{1}{2}$
2 Integrating Health: Smoking and Your Health	$2\frac{1}{2}$	1–2
3 The Excretory System	3	$1\frac{1}{2}$
Chapter 5 Review and Assessment	1	$\frac{1}{2}$
Chapter 6 Fighting Disease		
Chapter 6 Project Stop the Invasion!	Ongoing	Ongoing
1 Infectious Diseases	$2\frac{1}{2}$	1–2
2 The Body's Defenses	$4\frac{1}{2}$	2–3
3 Preventing Infectious Disease	$2\frac{1}{2}$	1–2
4 Noninfectious Disease	$3\frac{1}{2}$	1–2
5 Integrating Environmental Science: Cancer and the Environment	$1\frac{1}{2}$	$\frac{1}{2}$–1
Chapter 6 Review and Assessment	1	$\frac{1}{2}$
Chapter 7 Nervous System		
Chapter 7 Project Tricks and Illusions	Ongoing	Ongoing
1 How the Nervous System Works	3	$2\frac{1}{2}$
2 Divisions of the Nervous System	4	2

	Days	Blocks
3 The Senses	4	2
4 Integrating Health: Alcohol and Other Drugs	$4\frac{1}{2}$	2–3
Chapter 7 Review and Assessment	1	$\frac{1}{2}$
Chapter 8 The Endocrine System and Reproduction		
Chapter 8 Project A Precious Bundle	Ongoing	Ongoing
1 The Endocrine System	$2\frac{1}{2}$	1–2
2 The Male and Female Reproductive Systems	3	$1\frac{1}{2}$
3 Pregnancy, Birth, and Childhood	$3\frac{1}{2}$	1–2
4 Integrating Health: Adolescence—A Time of Change	$3\frac{1}{2}$	1–2
Chapter 8 Review and Assessment	1	$\frac{1}{2}$
Interdisciplinary Exploration: The Olympic Games	2–3	1–2

RESOURCE PRO®

The Resource Pro® CD-ROM is the ultimate scheduling and lesson planning tool. Resource Pro® allows you to preview all the resources in the *Science Explorer* program, organize your chosen materials, and print out any teaching resource. You can follow the suggested lessons or create your own, using resources from anywhere in the program.

Thematic Overview of *Human Biology and Health*

The chart below lists the major themes of *Human Biology and Health*. For each theme, the chart supplies a big idea, or concept statement, describing how a particular theme is taught in a chapter.

	Chapter 1	Chapter 2	Chapter 3	Chapter 4
Patterns of Change		Much of an infant's skeleton is cartilage. Gradually most cartilage is replaced by bone.		
Scale and Structure	The human body contains trillions of cells that are organized into tissues, organs, and organ systems.	The skeletal system is made up of bones, ligaments, tendons, and cartilage. The muscular system is made up of voluntary and involuntary muscles.	The digestive system digests food mechanically and chemically into molecules that can be absorbed and transported to other areas of the body.	In the cardiovascular system, the heart pumps blood, blood carries needed materials and blood vessels transport these materials, to other parts of the body.
Unity and Diversity			Carbohydrates, fats, proteins, vitamins, minerals, and water are all essential to human health. Different foods contain different amounts of these nutrients.	Arteries, veins, and capillaries provide the network through which blood travels, although their structure and functions differ.
Systems and Interactions	Cells, tissues, organs, and organ systems interact in the human body, enabling it to function and maintain homeostasis.	Cardiac muscles are involuntary muscles found in the heart; smooth muscles are involuntary muscles found in other body systems; and skeletal muscles permit voluntary movement. The skeletal and muscular systems work together to enable movement.	The different organs of the digestive system interact to carry out the breakdown of foods. The circulatory system transports these foods throughout the body.	By carrying needed materials throughout the body, the circulatory system enables the functioning of all body systems.
Energy	During stress, adrenaline initiates processes that provide the body with extra energy.	The muscular system uses energy to perform its functions. Energy is required to grow new bone and muscle tissue.	Carbohydrates, fats, and proteins all supply the body with energy. Food energy is measured in Calories.	The circulatory system delivers the raw materials needed for energy to the cells and carries the waste products of energy production away from the cells.
Stability	The organ systems work together to maintain homeostasis in a changing external environment.	The skeletal system helps maintain homeostasis by storing certain minerals and releasing them when they are needed.	The digestive system helps maintain homeostasis by providing the body with nutrients and energy.	By providing the body with needed materials and removing wastes, the circulatory system helps maintain homeostasis.
Modeling		Students construct a model of the bones, joints, and muscles involved in a specific movement.	Students model the breakup of food particles in the small intestine.	Students produce a model of the path of a red blood cell through the circulatory system.

	Chapter 5	Chapter 6	Chapter 7	Chapter 8
Patterns of Change	Over time, smoking can damage both the respiratory and circulatory systems.		Cancer cells multiply uncontrollably, invading and destroying healthy tissue.	The fertilized egg divides over and over and develops into an embryo. After birth, change occurs during the individual's lifetime.
Scale and Structure	Oxygen enters the body through the alveoli, which provide a large surface for gas exchange.	The body has three lines of defenses to fight disease: barriers to pathogens, the inflammatory response, and the immune response.	The nervous system is made up of two parts—the central and peripheral nervous systems. Neurons are the specialized cells of the nervous system.	A tiny zygote eventually develops into a multicellular human.
Unity and Diversity				The male and female reproductive systems differ in structure, but the primary function of both systems is to produce new individuals.
Systems and Interactions	The respiratory and circulatory systems interact to carry oxygen to body cells and remove carbon dioxide.	The body's immune system protects the body by attacking and destroying pathogens. By introducing antigens, vaccination allows the body to fight pathogens as if the antigen had naturally occurred.	Neurons respond to stimuli from both the external and internal environments. The nervous system processes information from the senses and regulates body functioning. Drugs can interfere with the functioning of the nervous system.	The reproductive system produces sex cells needed for reproduction and hormones that regulate body activities.
Energy	Without oxygen, the energy-releasing chemical reactions inside cells could not take place.	Energy is required by the body to fight off disease.		
Stability	The respiratory system helps maintain homeostasis by providing the body with the oxygen needed to release energy, and by removing carbon dioxide.	The body's immune system helps the body maintain normal functions by attacking and destroying harmful pathogens.	The nervous system controls homeostasis in the body. Damage to the nervous system upsets the body's stability.	Hormones produced by the human endocrine system help the body maintain stability.
Modeling	Students construct a model of how the diaphragm functions in breathing.	Students model how a disease spreads, how skin acts as a barrier to disease, and how disinfectants work.		

Inquiry Skills Chart

The Prentice Hall *Science Explorer* program provides comprehensive teaching, practice, and assessment of science skills, with an emphasis on the process skills necessary for inquiry. The chart lists the skills covered in the program and cites the page numbers where each skill is covered.

Basic Process SKILLS				
	Student Text: Projects and Labs	Student Text: Activities	Student Text: Caption and Review Questions	Teacher's Edition: Extensions
Observing	22, 55, 60–61, 66–67, 76, "88–89, 112, 119, 139, 148–149, 168–169, 188–189, 216–217, 224–225, 250	16, 18, 23, 38, 40, 46, 50, 52, 56, 59, 70, 77, 82, 91, 107, 113, 120, 135, 145, 156, 170, 175, 182, 196, 204, 208, 231, 237, 260	49, 84	18, 25, 43, 48, 51–53, 57, 59, 92, 102, 114, 150, 162, 205–208, 210
Inferring	22, 112, 128–129, 250	16, 52, 56, 76, 100, 107, 110, 130, 140, 161, 190, 196, 204–205, 212, 226, 260	32, 35, 65, 97, 153, 179, 187	25, 51, 57–58, 110, 114, 121, 131, 150, 158, 166, 171–172, 178, 202, 228, 232, 236
Predicting	60–61, 76, 88–89, 112, 168–169, 188–189, 250	23, 50, 70, 82, 90, 121, 135, 260	45, 54, 65, 87, 127, 150, 153, 184, 194, 209, 223, 230	50, 74, 82, 102, 120, 123, 146, 149, 161, 228, 238
Classifying	55, 66–67	42, 77, 261	51, 71, 97, 101, 171, 200	78
Making Models	36–37, 98–99, 119, 139, 168–169, 224–225	18, 30, 85, 91, 100, 107, 116, 121, 166, 239, 261		17, 47, 53, 92, 123, 131–132, 142, 163–164, 176, 199, 209, 214, 227
Communicating	14–15, 36–37, 98–99, 112, 128–129, 154–155, 188–189, 195, 224–225	26, 44, 52, 68, 72, 90, 94, 100, 104, 121, 123, 130, 136, 163, 173, 199, 203, 208, 212, 214, 247, 261	34, 64, 96, 126, 152, 186, 222, 252	16–17, 20, 26, 29, 38, 47, 49, 53, 56, 72, 78, 80, 86, 101, 113, 123, 132, 142, 146, 156–157, 159, 164, 171–172, 177, 182, 192, 196–197, 213, 219, 227, 229, 233, 240, 246, 248
Measuring	66–67, 76, 112	59, 90, 130, 208, 239, 262–263	253	192, 218
Calculating	180–181, 250	71, 100, 108, 130, 143, 156, 263	80, 97	69, 71, 80, 108, 117, 134, 218, 238
Creating Data Tables	14–15, 88–89, 112, 119, 148–149, 168–169, 188–189, 195, 250	110, 270		
Graphing	66–67, 112, 180–181, 188–189, 250	76, 235, 270–272	187, 223, 253	
Advanced Process SKILLS				
Posing Questions	22, 128–129, 154–155	68, 159, 264		
Developing Hypotheses	88–89, 119, 139, 195, 216–217	182, 198, 210, 264	35	197
Designing Experiments	14–15, 60–61, 88–89, 112, 168–169, 188–189, 195, 216–217, 250	50, 170, 198, 210, 241, 265	35, 65	74, 197

	Student Text: Projects and Labs	Student Text: Activities	Student Text: Caption and Review Questions	Teacher's Edition: Extensions
Controlling Variables	168–169, 195, 216–217	198, 210, 265	223	
Forming Operational Definitions	14–15	120, 265		
Interpreting Data	76, 148–149, 180–181, 250	24, 76, 235, 241, 265	35, 65, 97, 127, 153, 187, 253	104
Drawing Conclusions	60–61, 88–89, 112, 128–129, 148–149, 168–169, 188–189, 195, 216–217, 224–225, 250	40, 176, 198, 241, 244, 265	127, 153, 187	162

Comparing and Contrasting	55, 66–67, 168–169, 180–181	18, 38, 40, 100, 112, 231, 237, 266	39, 65, 97, 106, 127, 153, 157, 187, 220, 236, 253	39, 42, 51, 78, 108, 176, 198, 200, 234
Applying Concepts	55, 88–89, 119, 128–129, 154–155, 216–217	18, 59, 266	21, 24, 49, 62, 65, 70, 75, 81, 91, 97, 102, 111, 131, 150, 153, 160, 164, 167, 174, 187, 192, 198, 206, 213, 223, 227, 241, 253	32, 57, 165, 178, 201, 245
Interpreting Diagrams, Graphs Photographs, and Maps	66–67, 216–217, 250	266	21, 40, 53, 58, 73–74, 83, 86, 92, 105, 117, 135, 137, 178, 205, 215, 233–234, 238	17, 43, 79, 86, 103, 114, 133, 146, 165, 193, 219, 228
Relating Cause and Effect	15, 37, 88, 112, 129, 148, 155, 168, 189, 216	267	26, 45, 57, 65, 93, 97, 118, 121, 124, 127, 138, 141, 144, 162, 166, 177, 187, 202, 211, 223, 243, 246, 253	191
Making Generalizations	119, 224–225	208, 231, 267	35, 110, 127, 242	79, 215
Making Judgments	66–67, 128–129	28, 76, 94, 140, 203, 214, 267	27, 30, 35, 62, 153, 223, 230, 248–249	124
Problem Solving	14–15, 112, 139	94, 203, 267	32, 160	31

Concept Maps		18, 268	34, 64, 222	28, 38, 140, 226
Compare/ Contrast Tables		268	126	46, 56, 234
Venn Diagrams		269		170, 226
Flowcharts		269	96, 152, 186, 252	100, 146
Cycle Diagrams		269		

The *Science Explorer* program provides additional teaching, reinforcement, and assessment of skills in the Inquiry Skills Activities Book and the Integrated Science Laboratory Manual.

Throughout the *Science Explorer* program, every effort has been made to keep the materials and equipment *affordable, reusable,* and *easily accessible*.

The *Science Explorer* program offers an abundance of activity options so you can pick and choose those activities that suit your needs. To help you order supplies at the beginning of the year, the Master Materials List cross-references the materials by activity. If you prefer to create your list electronically, use the electronic order forms at:
www.science–explorer.phschool.com

There are two kits available for each book of the *Science Explorer* program, a Consumable Kit and a Nonconsumable Kit. These kits are produced by **Science Kit and Boreal Laboratories,** the leader in providing science kits to schools. Prentice Hall and Science Kit collaborated throughout the development of *Science Explorer* to ensure that the equipment and supplies in the kits precisely match the requirements of the program activities.

The kits provide an economical and convenient way to get all of the materials needed to teach each book. For each book, Science Kit also offers the opportunity to buy equipment and safety items individually. For a current listing of kit offerings or additional information about materials to accompany *Science Explorer*, please, contact Science Kit at:
1-800-828-7777
or at their Internet site at:
www.sciencekit.com

Master Materials List

Consumable Materials

*	Description	Quantity per class	Textbook Section(s)	*	Description	Quantity per class	Textbook Section(s)
C	Adrenaline Chloride, 0.01% Aqueous Solution, 25 mL	1	7-4 (Lab)	SS	Disinfectant Products, Assortment	5	6-3 (DIS)
SS	Advertisement from teen magazine	5	8-4 (DIS)	SS	Egg White, Boiled	5	3-3 (Lab)
C	Alcohol, Isopropyl (Rubbing) 500 mL	1	6-2 (Lab)	C	Filter Paper, 15 cm Diam, Pkg/100	1	5-3 (DIS)
SS	Apple	31	3-2 (DIS) 6-2 (Lab) 7-3-SYS	C	Food Coloring, Pkg/4, 8 mL, Green, Yellow, Red, Blue	1	4-3 (Lab)
				SS	Food Packages, Assortment	5	4-4 (DIS)
C	Bag, Paper 10 × 20 × 7.5 cm	10	3-2 (DIS) 7-3 (DIS)	SS	Food Samples	5	3-1-SYS
				C	Glucose (d-Glucose) Anhydrous, 500 g, Science Grade Granular	1	5-3 (DIS) 5-3 (Lab)
C	Bag, Plastic Zip Lip 6" × 8" (1 qt)	40	2-4 (Lab) 3-1 (Lab) 6-2 (Lab)	C	Glucose Test Strips Pkg/40	1	5-3 (DIS) 5-3 (Lab)
C	Baking Soda, 454 g	1	3-4 (TT)	SS	Glue, School White, 4 oz	5	1-3 (TT)
C	Balloons, Round 13", Pkg/10	1	5-1 (Lab)	SS	Graph Paper, Sheet	10	4-2 (Lab) 8-2-SYS
C	Balloons, Round 9", Pkg/35	1	1-2 (DIS) 5-1 (DIS) 5-1 (Lab)	C	Hydrochloric Acid, 1 M, 500 mL Solution	1	3-3 (Lab)
SS	Beverages with and without Caffeine	5	7-4 (Lab)	C	Iodine (Starch Test) Reagent Solution, 100 mL	1	3-1-SYS
C	Biuret Reagent, 500 mL	1	5-3 (Lab)	C	Litmus Test Paper, Blue, Vial/100	1	3-3 (Lab)
SS	Bone, Chicken Leg	10	2-1 (TT)	SS	Magazines	30	1-3 (TT)
SS	Bone, Chicken or Turkey Leg	5	2-1 (DIS)	C	Marking Pencil, Black Wax	5	3-3 (Lab) 4-3 (Lab) 5-1 (TT) 5-3 (Lab) 6-2 (Lab)
C	Bromothymol Blue Ind Sltn., 100 mL	1	5-1 (TT)				
SS	Candy, Piece	5	7-4 (DIS)	SS	Newspapers	10	4-1 (DIS) 4-2 (DIS)
SS	Cardboard	10	1-3 (TT) 2-4 (TT)	SS	Oatmeal, Instant	1	3-1 (Lab)
SS	Cereal, Breakfast, 2 Varieties	1	3-1 (Lab)	C	Oil, Vegetable, 16 oz	1	3-4 (TT)
C	Cheesecloth, 2 M Piece	1	4-3 (TT)	C	Paper Towel Roll	1	2-3 (Lab) 3-1 (Lab) 5-3 (Lab) 6-2 (Lab)
SS	Chicken Wing, Uncooked	5	2-3 (Lab)				
SS	Chocolate, Piece	5	3-2 (DIS)				
C	Clay, Modeling (Cream) lb (water-resistant)	1	6-2 (TT)	SS	Paper, Construction, White, Pkg/50	1	2-4 (Lab)
C	Cotton Balls, Pkg/300	1	2-4 (TT)	C	Paper, Roll, 30" × 100 ft	1	1-1 (Lab)
C	Cup, Plastic, Clear, 2 oz	5	4-1 (DIS)	SS	Paper, Sheet	60	4-3 (DIS) 4-3 (Lab) 6-1 (DIS) 6-2 (DIS) 7-1 (DIS)
C	Cup, Plastic, Clear, Cocktail, 9 oz	50	4-3 (TT) 4-3 (Lab) 5-3 (DIS)				
C	Daphnia (30), Live Coupon	1	7-4 (Lab)				

KEY: **DIS**: Discover; **SYS**: Sharpen Your Skills; **TT**: Try This; **Lab**: Lab

* Items designated **C** are in the Consumable Kit, **NC** are in the Nonconsumable Kit, and **SS** are School Supplied.

Master Materials List

Consumable Materials (cont.)

*	Description	Quantity per class	Textbook Section(s)	*	Description	Quantity per class	Textbook Section(s)
SS	Peanut Butter	1	4-4 (TT)	C	Straws, Plastic (wrapped) Pkg/50	1	3-3 (TT) 5-1 (TT) 6-4 (DIS) 7-3 (TT) 7-4 (Lab)
SS	Pear	5	7-3-SYS				
SS	Pencil	5	2-4 (Lab)				
SS	Pencils, Colored, Pkg/12	5	1-1 (Lab) 4-3 (DIS) 6-4 (Lab)				
				C	String, Cotton, 200 ft	1	1-3 (TT) 3-4 (DIS)
C	Pepsin Activity 1:3000 Powder, 30 g, Science Grade	1	3-3 (Lab) 5-3 (Lab)	C	Sugar Cubes, 1 lb (Pkg/96)	1	3-3 (DIS)
C	Petroleum Jelly, 4 oz	1	7-4 (Lab)	SS	Sunscreen, SPF 30	1	2-4 (Lab)
C	Pipe Cleaners, White, 12", Pkg/30	1	6-5 (DIS) 7-3 (TT)	SS	Sunscreen, SPF 4	1	2-4 (Lab)
				C	Super Sun Kit, Refill, 15 Sheets	1	2-4 (Lab)
SS	Potato	5	7-3-SYS	C	Swab Applicators, Cotton, Pkg/72	1	6-2 (Lab)
SS	Potato Chips, Bag	1	3-2 (DIS)	SS	Tape, Masking, 3/4" × 60 yd	1	1-3 (TT) 6-2 (TT)
SS	Pretzels, Bag	1	3-2 (DIS)				
C	Rubber Bands, Assorted, 4 oz	1	4-3 (TT)	C	Toothpicks, Flat, Box/750	1	4-3 (Lab) 4-4 (TT) 6-2 (Lab) 7-4 (Lab)
C	Sand, Fine, 1 kg	1	5-3 (DIS)				
C	Stirrer Sticks, Pkg/50	1	2-3 (TT) 3-3 (Lab)	C	Vinegar, 500 mL	1	2-1 (TT)

Nonconsumable Materials

*	Description	Quantity per class	Textbook Section(s)	*	Description	Quantity per class	Textbook Section(s)
NC	Ball, Styrofoam, 1"	5	6-2 (TT)	NC	Cylinder, Graduated, Polypropylene, 100 mL	5	4-4 (TT) 5-1 (TT)
NC	Ball, Styrofoam, 2"	5	6-2 (TT)	NC	Dowel, Wood, 8 × 1"	5	3-1 (Lab)
SS	Bead	5	3-3 (TT)	NC	Dropper, Plastic	30	3-1-SYS 4-3 (Lab) 5-1 (TT) 5-3 (Lab) 7-4 (Lab)
SS	Books	10	1-1 (DIS)				
SS	Bottle, Squeeze	5	4-2 (DIS)				
SS	Bottle, Plastic, Transparent, with Narrow Neck	5	5-1 (Lab)				
NC	Cloth, Cotton, White, 18" × 22"	1	2-4 (Lab)	NC	Funnel, Plastic, 3.25"	5	4-4 (TT) 5-3 (DIS)
NC	Cloth, Flannel, White, 18" × 23"	1	2-4 (Lab)	NC	Jar, Plastic, 16 oz	10	2-1 (TT) 3-1 (Lab) 3-3 (DIS) 3-4 (TT) 4-4 (TT) 5-3 (DIS)
NC	Cloth, Polyester, 18" × 22"	1	2-4 (Lab)				
NC	Clothespin, Spring Type	5	2-3 (DIS)				
SS	Coins	30	4-3 (TT)				
SS	Compass with Pencil	5	6-4 (Lab)				
NC	Cylinder, Graduated, Polypropylene, 10 × 0.2 mL	5	3-3 (Lab)				

KEY: **DIS:** Discover; **SYS:** Sharpen Your Skills; **TT:** Try This; **Lab:** Lab

* Items designated **C** are in the Consumable Kit, **NC** are in the Nonconsumable Kit, and **SS** are School Supplied.

Nonconsumable Materials (cont.)

*	Description	Quantity per class	Textbook Section(s)
NC	Knife, Plastic	5	2-4 (Lab) 4-4 (TT)
NC	Lid, Metal, 89 mm, Screw Type	10	2-1 (TT) 3-1 (Lab) 3-3 (DIS)
NC	Magnet, Bar, Alnico w/Marked Poles, 3"	5	3-1 (Lab)
NC	Magnifying Glass, 3x, 6x	5	2-1 (DIS) 2-4 (DIS)
NC	Meter Stick, Half (50 cm in length)	5	7-1 (Lab)
SS	Objects, Assortment	5	7-3 (DIS)
NC	Pan, Aluminum Foil, 13 × 10 × 2"	10	4-1 (DIS) 4-2 (DIS)
NC	Pan, Aluminum Foil, 31 × 22 × 3 cm	5	2-3 (Lab)
NC	Paper Clips, Box/100	1	4-3 (TT)
SS	Penny	5	7-1 (DIS)
NC	Petri Dish, Disposable, Pkg/20 Polystyrene, Sterile, 100 × 15 mm	2	4-3 (Lab)
NC	Pins, Bobby, Card/60	1	2-3 (TT)
NC	Pins, Straight, Steel, Pkg/150	1	1-2 (DIS)
SS	Protractor	5	6-4 (Lab)
SS	Radio	1	7-2-SYS
SS	Rock	5	2-1 (DIS)
SS	Ruler, Plastic, 12"/30 cm	5	1-3 (TT) 2-4 (Lab) 3-4 (DIS) 6-4 (Lab) 7-4 (Lab)
SS	Scissors	5	1-3 (TT) 2-3 (Lab) 2-4 (Lab) 3-2 (DIS) 5-1 (Lab) 7-4 (Lab)
NC	Slide, Human Blood Smear	5	4-3 (DIS)
NC	Slide, Human Ovary	3	8-2 (DIS)
NC	Slide, Human Sperm Smear	3	8-2 (DIS)
NC	Slide, Ovary cs, Mammal	2	8-2 (DIS)
NC	Slide, Rat Sperm Smear	2	8-2 (DIS)
NC	Slides, Plastic, & Coverglass Set (Includes 72 plastic slides & 100 plastic coverglasses)	1	7-4 (Lab)

*	Description	Quantity per class	Textbook Section(s)
NC	Spoons, Plastic, Pkg/24	1	3-1 (Lab) 3-4 (TT)
SS	Staple Remover	5	2-4 (Lab)
SS	Stapler	5	2-4 (Lab)
NC	Stopper, Rubber, Size 2, Solid, Lb.	1	3-3 (Lab)
NC	Tape Measure, 1.5 m, Metric/English	5	5-1 (DIS) 7-3 (TT)
NC	Test Tube Support, Wood, Holds six 21 mm tubes, w/6 drying pins	5	3-3 (Lab) 5-3 (Lab)
NC	Test Tube, 18 × 150 mm, 27 mL	30	3-3 (Lab) 5-1 (TT) 5-3 (Lab)
NC	Thermometer, −40°C to 50°C/ −40°F to 120°F	10	2-4 (TT)
NC	UV Changing Beads, Pk/240	1	6-5 (DIS)
NC	Watch or Clock with Second Hand	5	3-1 (Lab) 4-2 (Lab) 7-4 (Lab)
NC	Watch, Ticking	5	7-3 (TT)

Equipment

*	Description	Quantity per class	Textbook Section(s)
SS	Apron, Vinyl	30	3-1-SYS 3-3 (Lab)
SS	Balance, Triple Beam	5	3-1 (Lab) 8-3 (TT)
SS	Calculator (Optional)	5	6-4 (Lab)
SS	Gloves, Medium, Latex, Box/100	1	2-1 (TT) 2-3 (Lab) 2-4 (DIS)
SS	Goggles, Chemical Splash - Class Set	1	2-3 (Lab) 3-3 (TT) 3-3 (Lab) 5-1 (TT) 6-2 (Lab)
SS	Microscope	5	4-3 (DIS) 7-4 (Lab) 8-2 (DIS)
SS	Stopwatch	5	4-1 (DIS) 4-4 (TT)

KEY: **DIS**: Discover; **SYS**: Sharpen Your Skills; **TT**: Try This; **Lab**: Lab
* Items designated **C** are in the Consumable Kit, **NC** are in the Nonconsumable Kit, and **SS** are School Supplied.

PRENTICE HALL
SCIENCE EXPLORER

Human Biology and Health

Program Resources
Student Edition
Annotated Teacher's Edition
Teaching Resources with Color Transparencies
Human Biology and Health Materials Kits

Program Components
Integrated Science Laboratory Manual
Integrated Science Laboratory Manual, Teacher's Edition
Inquiry Skills Activity Book
Student-Centered Science Activity Books
Program Planning Guide
Guided Reading English Audiotapes
Guided Reading Spanish Audiotapes and Summaries
Product Testing Activities by Consumer Reports™
Prentice Hall Interdisciplinary Explorations
Cobblestone, Odyssey, and *Faces* Magazines

Media/Technology
Science Explorer Interactive Student Tutorial CD-ROM
Resource Pro® (Teaching Resources on CD-ROM)
Assessment Resources CD-ROM with Dial-A-Test®
Internet site at www.science-explorer.phschool.com
Exploring Life, Earth, and Physical Science Videodiscs
Exploring Life, Earth, and Physical Science Videotapes

Science Explorer Student Editions

- *From Bacteria to Plants*
- *Animals*
- *Cells and Heredity*
- *Human Biology and Health*
- *Environmental Science*
- *Inside Earth*
- *Earth's Changing Surface*
- *Earth's Waters*
- *Weather and Climate*
- *Astronomy*
- *Chemical Building Blocks*
- *Chemical Interactions*
- *Motion, Forces, and Energy*
- *Electricity and Magnetism*
- *Sound and Light*

Staff Credits

The members who made up the *Science Explorer* team—representing editorial services, design services, field marketing, managing editor, market research, marketing services, on-line services/multimedia development, product marketing, production services, and publishing processes— are listed below. Bold type denotes core team members.

Kristen E. Ball, **Barbara A. Bertell, Christopher R. Brown, Greg Cantone,** Christine A. Caputo, Jonathan Cheney, **Patrick Finbarr Connolly,** Loree Franz, **Paul J. Gagnon, Joel Gendler,** Elizabeth Good, Kerri Hoar, **Linda D. Johnson,** Katherine M. Kotik, Russ Lappa, Marilyn Leitao, David Lippman, **Eve Melnechuk, Natania Mlawer,** Paul W. Murphy, **Cindy A. Noftle,** Beth A. Norman, Julia F. Osborne, Caroline M. Power, Suzanne J. Schineller, **Susan W. Tafler,** Kira Thaler-Marbit, Robin L. Santel, **Mark Tricca,** Diane Walsh

Acknowledgment for page 256: Excerpts from *A Kind of Grace* by Jackie Joyner-Kersee. Copyright ©1997 by Jackie Joyner-Kersee. Reprinted by permission of Warner Books, Inc.

ISBN 0-13-434568-1 Teacher's Edition

ISBN 0-13-434487-1 Student Edition
1 2 3 4 5 6 7 8 9 10   05 04 03 02 01 00 99 98

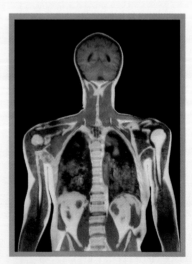

Cover: A magnetic resonance image (MRI) reveals structures within the human body.

Program Authors

Michael J. Padilla, Ph.D.
Professor
Department of Science Education
University of Georgia
Athens, Georgia

Michael Padilla is a leader in middle school science education. He has served as an editor and elected officer for the National Science Teachers Association. He has been principal investigator of several National Science Foundation and Eisenhower grants and served as a writer of the National Science Education Standards.

As lead author of *Science Explorer*, Mike has inspired the team in developing a program that meets the needs of middle grades students, promotes science inquiry, and is aligned with the National Science Education Standards.

Ioannis Miaoulis, Ph.D.
Dean of Engineering
College of Engineering
Tufts University
Medford, Massachusetts

Martha Cyr, Ph.D.
Director, Engineering
    Educational Outreach
College of Engineering
Tufts University
Medford, Massachusetts

Science Explorer was created in collaboration with the College of Engineering at Tufts University. Tufts has an extensive engineering outreach program that uses engineering design and construction to excite and motivate students and teachers in science and technology education.

Faculty from Tufts University participated in the development of *Science Explorer* chapter projects, reviewed the student books for content accuracy, and helped coordinate field testing.

Book Authors

Elizabeth Coolidge-Stolz, M.D.
Medical Writer
North Reading, Massachusetts

Dawn Graff-Haight, Ph.D., CHES
Associate Professor, Health Education
Linfield College
McMinnville, Oregon

Contributing Writers

Douglas E. Bowman
Health/Physical Education Teacher
Welches Middle School
Welches, Oregon

Patricia M. Doran
Science Teacher
Rondout Valley Junior High School
Stone Ridge, New York

Jorie Hunken
Science Consultant
Woodstock, Connecticut

Reading Consultant

Bonnie B. Armbruster, Ph.D.
Department of Curriculum
    and Instruction
University of Illinois
Champaign, Illinois

Interdisciplinary Consultant

Heidi Hayes Jacobs, Ed.D.
Teacher's College
Columbia University
New York City, New York

Safety Consultants

W. H. Breazeale, Ph.D.
Department of Chemistry
College of Charleston
Charleston, South Carolina

Ruth Hathaway, Ph.D.
Hathaway Consulting
Cape Girardeau, Missouri

Contents

Human Biology and Health

Check your compass— regularly assess student progress.

Self-assessment tools are built right into the student text and **on-going assessment** is woven throughout the Teacher's Edition. You'll find a wealth of **assessment technology** in the Resource Pro®, Interactive Student Tutorial, and Assessment Resources CD-ROMs.

Activities

Inquiry Activities

CHAPTER PROJECT

Opportunities for long-term inquiry

Sharpen your *Skills*

Practice of specific science inquiry skills

DISCOVER

Exploration and inquiry before reading

TRY THIS
Reinforcement of key concepts

Skills Lab
In-depth practice of inquiry skills

Real-World Lab
Everyday application of science concepts

Interdisciplinary Activities

Draw upon the world around you.
Interdisciplinary Activities connect to every discipline and give science a meaningful, real-world context.

Math Toolbox

Science and History

Science and Society

Connection

Finding a Balance in Nutrition

Focus on Nutrition

In this feature, students are introduced to the process of scientific inquiry by learning about a working scientist, nutritionist Alex Martinez. In an interview, Alex explains how nutrition is related to science. He also identifies some nutritional issues and considerations that are especially important for teenagers.

Nutrition is presented in detail in Chapter 3, Sections 3-1 and 3-2, of this book. However, students need not have any previous knowledge of that chapter's content to understand and appreciate this article.

Scientific Inquiry

◆ Have students preview the feature by reading the title, examining the photographs, and reading the questions. Then ask: **What questions came into your mind as you looked at these pictures?** *(Students might suggest questions such as these: What does a nutritionist do? Can you eat foods high in fat and still be healthy? Would it be healthy to never eat fat at all? How many Calories should you eat each day in order to stay healthy?)* **How might a scientist find the answer to one of these questions?** *(Answers may vary. Samples: He or she could use the question to form a hypothesis and then conduct an experiment to test the hypothesis. He or she could do research to see if another scientist had already found the answer to the question.)*

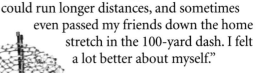

Finding a Balance in NUTRITION

Nutritionist Alex Martinez's first experiment in science was on himself. Alex says that when he was growing up, he was quite chubby. Then as a high school freshman he began to play football and run track.

"My weight really hindered my athletic performance," he says. "It was very hard to turn down good cooking. But I knew if I wanted to get in shape, my eating habits would have to change." So Alex decided to change his diet by cutting back on fried foods and eating more fruits and vegetables. He also tried eating rice and chicken instead of beef, and he exercised.

"I became the subject of my own lab test, experimenting with different foods," Alex says. "And I could see the results. I lost weight and had more energy and endurance. I could run longer distances, and sometimes even passed my friends down the home stretch in the 100-yard dash. I felt a lot better about myself."

Alex Martinez, a Mexican American, grew up in New Mexico. He has a degree in nutrition and food science from New Mexico State University. He works as a roving health instructor, traveling to different cities in New Mexico to teach people about nutrition. An outdoor enthusiast, Alex spends his free time in the mountains—hiking, bicycling, and rock climbing.

Background

A nutritionist studies how foods affect people. The nutritionist is knowledgeable about vitamins, minerals, and other nutrients in foods and helps people learn how to eat the right mixture of foods for them to have a healthy diet for their lifestyle.

In contrast, food scientists use science and technology to bring food from the source to the store shelves. Food scientists help to keep the food supply safe. They also design packaging to preserve food and create new kinds of foods. They perform testing and research on foods, they design new food processing systems, and they have other responsibilities relating to the food industry.

That experience inspired Alex to pursue a career in nutrition, studying how the body uses food to grow and produce energy. Today, Alex is a nutritionist and health educator in New Mexico.

"For me, food is a science," Alex says. "Most people don't think of it that way. But food causes chemical reactions in the body. And those reactions all have specific effects."

Alex plans nutritious diets for people. At a camp for diabetic children, he helped young people plan diets to keep their blood sugar levels balanced. Currently he speaks to parent and student groups about healthy eating habits. He believes that eating right is not hard.

"There's no such thing as good food and bad food," Alex says. "All foods are good. We just have to balance them in our lives."

Talking With Alex Martinez

Q *How did you become interested in nutrition?*

A When I was training for track and football as a teen, I did a lot of reading about the right things to eat. My coaches were always talking about proper nutrition for athletes. When I found out there were college programs in nutrition, I knew that's what I wanted to study.

Q *How much science is involved in nutrition?*

A Quite a lot. I studied chemistry, biology, and human physiology. I learned how the body works—what allows me to run down the street, and how my body converts food into energy. Good nutrition is the starting point for this energy.

Q *Why should young people be concerned about nutrition?*

A Two reasons: Around the age of 11 or 12, teens start to go through growth spurts. A good, balanced diet is critically important to meet the demands of a changing body. Also, the habits young people develop at an early age stay with them for the rest of their life. If they want to be healthy when they grow up, they should be developing healthy eating habits right now.

Exercising (top) and eating a variety of nutritious foods (left) are keys to good health.

◆ Point out that scientists investigate relationships between cause and effect—in other words, they try to determine what causes something to happen. Ask: **When Alex changed his diet by decreasing fatty foods and substituting fruits and vegetables, what was the effect of the change?** *(Alex lost weight and his athletic performance improved.)*

◆ Ask a volunteer to read the caption on page 10 aloud. Ask: **What is a roving instructor?** *(One who travels from place to place)* **Why does Alex travel so much?** *(So that he can teach more people.)*

◆ Have a volunteer use a dictionary or encyclopedia to find out what human physiology is. Have the student share the definition with the class. Then ask: **Why do you think a nutritionist needs to study physiology?** *(Because food affects the way the body functions.)* Use this as an opportunity to point out that different branches of science are interdependent.

◆ Point out that Alex's experience with exercise was positive and rewarding because he enjoyed the exercise he chose to participate in. Many exercise programs fail because people do not choose a form of exercise that they enjoy. In order for an exercise program to succeed, people must find a way of exercising that they find fun, whether it be a solo activity such as jogging, a partner activity such as tennis, or a group activity such as volleyball.

Background

Iron has an important role in the oxygen-carrying part of the blood. People who do not have enough iron in their diets can develop anemia. Anemia is a condition in which the blood cannot carry enough oxygen. As a result, people with anemia may feel dizzy, tired, and weak. They may get sick more often than normal. Treatment for anemia due to iron deficiency involves increasing the amount of iron-rich foods in the diet. Foods especially high in iron include liver, prune juice, and iron-fortified cereals. The amount of iron in the diet can also be increased by taking iron supplements. Cooking foods in pans made of iron can add small amounts of this mineral to the food. Vitamin C helps the body to take in and use iron. Therefore, people with anemia can benefit from foods such as orange juice that contain a large amount of this vitamin.

◆ As students discuss diet and nutrition, watch for students who make insensitive remarks about the weights of others. Steer students' conversations away from comparisons of each other's height, weight, or level of fitness. Also watch for students who seem overly concerned with weight loss. Emphasize that Alex changed his diet by substituting healthful foods for fried foods; he did not drastically reduce his food intake.

◆ Ask: **What do you think it means to have a balanced diet?** *(To eat a mix of different foods so that you obtain the right proportions of different nutrients.)*

◆ Alex recommends that students eat foods that are rich in calcium and iron. Refer students to Chapter 3, page 74, to learn good sources of these nutrients. In addition, if students seem particularly interested in nutrition, suggest that they consult library books to learn more. (See Further Reading, page 13.)

◆ To extend this activity, challenge students to write down ten foods they eat most often. Have students guess how many Calories and how much fat is in each food. Then have students use nutrition books to find out the number of Calories and the nutrient content of each food.

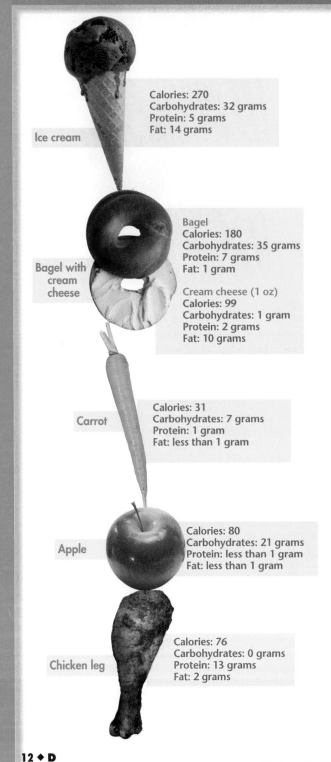

Ice cream
Calories: 270
Carbohydrates: 32 grams
Protein: 5 grams
Fat: 14 grams

Bagel with cream cheese
Bagel
Calories: 180
Carbohydrates: 35 grams
Protein: 7 grams
Fat: 1 gram

Cream cheese (1 oz)
Calories: 99
Carbohydrates: 1 gram
Protein: 2 grams
Fat: 10 grams

Carrot
Calories: 31
Carbohydrates: 7 grams
Protein: 1 gram
Fat: less than 1 gram

Apple
Calories: 80
Carbohydrates: 21 grams
Protein: less than 1 gram
Fat: less than 1 gram

Chicken leg
Calories: 76
Carbohydrates: 0 grams
Protein: 13 grams
Fat: 2 grams

Q *What ingredients in foods are important to teens?*

A Iron is very important for developing muscles and for helping to carry oxygen through the bloodstream. Without enough iron, people may feel overly tired. Calcium is also important. It plays a critical role in strong bone development. It's especially important for teenage girls to build strong bones. Later in life, women's bones tend to break more easily.

Q *What about fat?*

A Fat is very important. It helps regulate hormones and vitamin absorption. But there are good fats and bad fats. Too many saturated fats, like those found in steak or hamburger, aren't good for people. Monounsaturated fats, found in foods such as nuts, are much healthier.

Q *Is sugar important?*

A Yes, although like fat, people tend to eat too much of it. Sugar is a kind of carbohydrate. It's a person's primary energy source. But people shouldn't get sugar from candy bars and soda. Those are simple carbohydrates, low in nutrition. It's better to get sugar from foods such as fruits. They contain vitamins and minerals in addition to sugars.

Q *Are there specific foods that young people should avoid?*

A My philosophy is that people can eat almost anything they want, as long as they balance it out. If they're dying for a hamburger and french fries one day, there's nothing wrong with that. They just have to balance it the next day by eating fruits and vegetables, and by getting more exercise.

12 ◆ D

Background

It is especially important that teenagers obtain enough calcium, since this may help prevent them from developing osteoporosis later in life. Osteoporosis is a condition in which human bones lose mass and become fragile. All bones are affected, but fractures of the hip, wrist, and spine are the most common. All people can be affected by osteoporosis, though white women seem most susceptible.

Osteoporosis has many causes. Some of these causes, such as insufficient calcium in the diet, are preventable. Since bone mass develops slowly over time, one way to help prevent osteoporosis is to get plenty of calcium, especially during the years that the bones are growing. Throughout their lives, people can keep their bones in shape by performing exercises that put weight on the bones, such as running or lifting weights.

Fresh fruits are good sources of carbohydrates, vitamins, and minerals.

Q *What kinds of problems can an unbalanced diet create?*

A I'll give you an example. A patient of mine loves ice cream—she eats it all the time. Her diet was really high in fat and lacking in a lot of vitamins and minerals. She wasn't overweight. But she was always feeling tired.

Q *What did you recommend?*

A I suggested that she eat less ice cream and instead add more natural sources of carbohydrates, such as grains, cereal, and fruit. She could still eat the same number of Calories, but from different, healthier sources.

Q *How do you determine the proper diet for a person?*

A I use a formula based on age, weight, and a person's activity level to calculate the caloric intake—how much the person should eat every day. Then I try to get an idea about what he or she is already eating. Gradually I help the person convert to a healthy balance of about 60 percent carbohydrates and 30 percent fat.

Q *Why is exercise important?*

A Every Calorie we take in, we have to burn off—otherwise, it stays around our hips and waist, especially when we get older. Also, exercising releases endorphins, a substance in our body that makes us feel good. Exercise keeps us healthy and feeling good about ourselves.

Q *What goal should people set?*

A The goal is to be healthy. We can't all be professional athletes. But we can try to eat right and stay fit. And as long as we're trying, that makes a world of difference.

In Your Journal

Alex describes how his personal experiences influenced his career choice. Think about how experiences growing up can help a person choose a career many years later. Describe an experience in your life that might influence your career choice in the future.

D ◆ 13

◆ Focus students' attention on the question and answer in which Alex explains how he determines the proper diet for a person. Use this to point out that people's dietary needs vary, depending on factors such as age and activity level. Also note that Alex uses a mathematical formula to calculate a person's Calorie needs. Emphasize that scientists frequently use math in their investigations. Ask students to suggest some other ways in which scientists use math. *(Samples: measuring such things as temperature and mass; graphing the results of experiments; calculating such things as a person's breathing rate)*

In Your Journal Prompt students' thinking by asking questions such as these: **Did you ever meet a working professional who inspired you and made you want to follow in his or her footsteps? Did you ever think about a problem that affects many people and wish you could solve it? Do you have an interest or a hobby that you might use in a career?**

Introducing Human Biology and Health

Have students look through the table of contents and the book to find the parts that relate most closely to this article. *(Chapter 1, Healthy Body Systems, particularly Section 1-3, Integrating Health: Wellness; Chapter 3, Food and Digestion, particularly Section 3-1, Why You Need Food, and Section 3-2, Integrating Health: Healthy Eating)* Ask: **Which chapter will deal with blood and the circulatory system?** *(Chapter 4)* **What are some other body systems that you will learn about?** *(Accept all reasonable responses based on an examination of the table of contents.)*

READING STRATEGIES

Further Reading

◆ Coleman, Ellen, and Suzanne Nelson Steen. *The Ultimate Sports Nutrition Handbook.* Bull Publishing Company, 1996.
◆ Figtree, Dale, and John McDougall. *Eat Smart: A Guide to Good Health for Kids.* New Win Publishing, 1997.
◆ Gaman, P. M., and K. B. Sherrington. *The Science of Food : An Introduction to Food Science, Nutrition, and Microbiology.* Butterworth-Heinemann, 1990.
◆ Netzer, Corinne T. Corinne T. Netzer *Encyclopedia of Food Values.* Dell Books, 1992.

CHAPTER 1
Healthy Body Systems

Sections	Time	Student Edition Activities	Other Activities	
CHAPTER PROJECT 1 **Time for a Change** p. 15	Ongoing (1½ weeks)	Check Your Progress, pp. 21, 27 Wrap Up, p. 35	TE	Chapter 1 Project Notes, pp. 14–15
1 **How the Body Is Organized** pp. 16–22 ◆ Identify the levels of organization in the body. ◆ Identify and describe the four basic types of tissue in the human body.	3½ periods/ 1–2 blocks	**Discover** What Lets You Lift Books?, p. 16 **Try This** How Is a Book Organized?, p. 18 **Real-World Lab: How It Works** A Body of Knowledge, p. 22	TE TE	Building Inquiry Skills: Making Models, p. 17 Demonstration, p. 18
2 **Keeping the Body in Balance** pp. 23–27 ◆ Define homeostasis. ◆ Describe the physical responses to stress and ways to deal with stress.	2½ periods/ 1–2 blocks	**Discover** What Happens When You Are Startled?, p. 23 **Sharpen Your Skills** Interpreting Data, p. 24	TE IES	Integrating Chemistry, p. 25 "Soap From Concept to Consumer," pp. 9–10
3 *INTEGRATING HEALTH* **Wellness** pp. 28–32 ◆ Name and describe the three components of wellness. ◆ Explain how to evaluate wellness and list ways to improve personal health.	2½ periods/ 1–2 blocks	**Discover** How Well Do You Take Care of Your Health?, p. 28 **Try This** Wellness in the Balance, p. 30	TE IES	Building Inquiry Skills: Communicating, p. 29 "Soap From Concept to Consumer," pp. 27–30
Study Guide/Chapter Review pp. 33–35	1 period/ ½ block		ISAB	Provides teaching and review of all inquiry skills

For Standard or Block Schedule The Resource Pro® CD-ROM gives you maximum flexibility for planning your instruction for any type of schedule. Resource Pro® contains Planning Express®, an advanced scheduling program, as well as the entire contents of the Teaching Resources and the Computer Test Bank.

CHAPTER PLANNING GUIDE

Program Resources	Assessment Strategies	Media and Technology
TR Chapter 1 Project Teacher Notes, pp. 8–9 **TR** Chapter 1 Project Overview and Worksheets, pp. 10–13 **TR** Chapter 1 Project Scoring Rubric, p. 14	**SE** Performance Assessment: Chapter 1 Project Wrap Up, p. 35 **TE** Check Your Progress, pp. 21, 27 **TE** Performance Assessment: Chapter 1 Project Wrap Up, p. 35 **TR** Chapter 1 Project Scoring Rubric, p. 14	
TR 1-1 Lesson Plan, p. 15 **TR** 1-1 Section Summary, p. 16 **TR** 1-1 Review and Reinforce, p. 17 **TR** 1-1 Enrich, p. 18 **TR** Chapter 1 Real-World Lab, pp. 27–29	**SE** Section 1 Review, p. 21 **SE** Analyze and Conclude, p. 22 **TE** Ongoing Assessment, pp. 17, 19 **TE** Performance Assessment, p. 21 **TR** 1-1 Review and Reinforce, p. 17	Exploring Life Science Videodisc, Unit 1 Side 2, "Cell Specialization" Audiotapes: English-Spanish Summary 1-1 Transparency 1, "Exploring Levels of Organization in the Body" Interactive Student Tutorial CD-ROM, D-1
TR 1-2 Lesson Plan, p. 19 **TR** 1-2 Section Summary, p. 20 **TR** 1-2 Review and Reinforce, p. 21 **TR** 1-2 Enrich, p. 22 **SES** Book K, *Chemical Building Blocks*, Chapter 2	**SE** Section 2 Review, p. 27 **TE** Ongoing Assessment, p. 25 **TE** Performance Assessment, p. 27 **TR** 1-2 Review and Reinforce, p. 21	Audiotapes: English-Spanish Summary 1-2 Interactive Student Tutorial CD-ROM, D-1
TR 1-3 Lesson Plan, p. 23 **TR** 1-3 Section Summary, p. 24 **TR** 1-3 Review and Reinforce, p. 25 **TR** 1-3 Enrich, p. 26 **SES** Book E, *Environmental Science,* Chapter 4	**SE** Section 3 Review, p. 32 **TE** Ongoing Assessment, pp. 29, 31 **TE** Performance Assessment, p. 32 **TR** 1-3 Review and Reinforce, p. 25	Exploring Life Science Videodisc, Unit 4 Side 1, "Olympic Bound" Audiotapes: English-Spanish Summary 1-3 Interactive Student Tutorial CD-ROM, D-1
TR Chapter 1 Performance Assessment, pp. 236–238 **TR** Chapter 1 Test, pp. 239–242	**SE** Chapter Review, pp. 33–35 **TR** Chapter 1 Performance Assessment, pp. 236–238 **TR** Chapter 1 Test, pp. 239–242 **CTB** Test D–1	Computer Test Bank, Test D-1 Interactive Student Tutorial CD-ROM, D-1 Science Explorer Internet Site

Key: **SE** Student Edition   **TE** Teacher's Edition   **TR** Teaching Resources
       CTB Computer Test Bank   **SES** Science Explorer Series Text   **ISLM** Integrated Science Laboratory Manual
       ISAB Inquiry Skills Activity Book   **PTA** Product Testing Activities by *Consumer Reports*   **IES** Interdisciplinary Explorations Series

Meeting the National Science Education Standards and AAAS Benchmarks

National Science Education Standards	Benchmarks for Science Literacy	Unifying Themes
Science as Inquiry (Content Standard A) ◆ **Ask questions that can be answered by scientific investigations** Where are some important organs in the human body? *(Real-World Lab)* **Life Science** (Content Standard C) ◆ **Structure and function of living systems** Students learn that the bodies of humans are organized into cells, tissues, organs, and organ systems. The cell is the basis unit of structure and function in a living thing. Tissues have specialized jobs and the body has systems that interact with one another. *(Section 1)* ◆ **Science in Personal and Social Perspectives** Students learn about the components of wellness and the decision-making process to determine if something is good for their health. *(Section 3)* Students formulate and carry out a plan to change a health habit. *(Chapter Project)*	**5C Cells** Characteristics that describe cells, the basic unit of life, are presented in a general format. Characteristics of cells, tissues, organs, and organ systems are described. *(Sections 1, 3, 4)* **6C Basic Functions** The functions of organs and organ systems are described in general terms. *(Section 1; Real-World Lab)* **11C Constancy and Change** Homeostasis is the body's ability to maintain an internal balance. An organism's internal environment remains stable in spite of change in the external environment. *(Section 2)* **12D Communication Skills** Students interpret data in a table and describe the results. *(Sharpen Your Skills; Section 2)*	◆ **Energy** Energy in the form of food and oxygen is provided to the cells of the body. *(Section 1)* ◆ **Patterns of Change** The human body is organized into systems that enable it to maintain homeostasis despite changes in its internal and external environments. *(Sections 1, 2)* ◆ **Scale and Structure** The human body contains trillions of cells that are organized into tissues, organs, and organ systems. *(Sections 1, 2)* ◆ **Systems and interactions** Cells, tissues, organs, and organ systems interact in the human body enabling it to function and remain stable. *(Sections 1, 2)* ◆ **Unity and diversity** Although human organ systems contain many different organs with different tissues and different functions, the organ systems work together so that humans can survive. *(Sections 1, 2)* ◆ **Stability** The organ systems of the body work together to maintain homeostasis in a changing external environment. Decisions regarding wellness promote stability in the human body. *(Sections 2, 3)*

Media and Technology

Exploring Life Science Videodisc
◆ **Section 1** "Cell Specialization" describes the five levels of specialization in multicellar organisms.
◆ **Section 3** "Olympic Bound" features junior Olympian racquetball player, Rhonda Rajsich. The functions of all systems are modeled.

Interactive Student Tutorial CD-ROM
◆ **Chapter Review** Interactive questions help students to self-assess their mastery of key chapter concepts.

Student Edition Connection Strategies

◆ **Section 2** Integrating Chemistry, p. 25
Language Arts Connection, p. 26
◆ **Section 3** Integrating Health, p. 28
Integrating Environmental Health, p. 31

USING THE INTERNET

ACTIVITY

www.science-explorer.phschool.com

Visit the Science Explorer Internet site to find an up-to-date activity for Chapter 1 of *Human Biology and Health*.

ACTIVITY	Time (minutes)	Materials Quantities for one work group	Skills
Section 1			
Discover, p. 16	10	**Nonconsumable** two medium-sized books, clock or watch with second hand	Inferring
Try This, p. 18	15	**Nonconsumable** student textbook	Making Models
Real-World Lab, p. 22	30	**Nonconsumable** outline of the human body, colored pencils	Observing, Inferring, Posing Questions
Section 2			
Discover, p. 23	10	**Consumable** balloon **Nonconsumable** straight pin	Predicting
Sharpen your Skills, p. 24	15	**Consumable** No special materials are required.	Interpreting Data
Section 3			
Discover, p. 28	10	**Consumable** No special materials are required.	Making Judgments
Try This, p. 30	25	**Consumable** cardboard, string, tape, magazines **Nonconsumable** scissors, ruler, markers, glue	Making Models

A list of all materials required for the Student Edition activities can be found on pages T14–T15. You can order Materials Kits by calling 1-800-828-7777 or by accessing the Science Explorer Internet site at **www.science-explorer.phschool.com.**

CHAPTER PROJECT 1

Time for a Change

Students will learn from this project that wellness is achieved by maintaining healthy behavior and by making wise decisions in matters that impact physical, social, and mental well-being. Good health habits promote the stability of the systems in the body and help people react appropriately to stress.

Purpose In this project, students will identify and attempt to change a habit that negatively affects their health.

Skills Focus After completing the Chapter 1 project, students will be able to
- identify an unhealthy habit and design a plan to help change it;
- keep a daily log to record their progress;
- communicate their results by writing a summary of their experiences.

Project Time Line The project will take three or four weeks. Students should spend the first week collecting information about a habit that they would like to change. The next two to three weeks will be used to carry out a plan to change the habit. Set aside ten or fifteen minutes a few times each week to allow students to talk about the progress they are making. Students will need a few days at the end of the project to prepare summaries of their experiences. Before beginning the project, see Chapter 1 Project Teacher Notes on pages 8–9 in Teaching Resources for more details on carrying out the project. Also distribute the students' Chapter 1 Project Overview and Worksheets and Scoring Rubric on pages 10–14 in Teaching Resources.

Launching the Project To introduce the project, ask students to discuss when a behavior becomes a habit. Answers will vary, but students should realize that behaviors that have become part of their routine are difficult to change. Mention that some unhealthy habits, such as rushing out to school each day, involve neglecting important healthy behaviors such as eating breakfast.

CHAPTER 1 Healthy Body Systems

WHAT'S AHEAD

SECTION 1 How the Body Is Organized
Discover **How Do You Lift Books?**
Try This **How Is a Book Organized?**
Real-World Lab **A Body of Knowledge**

SECTION 2 Keeping the Body in Balance
Discover **What Happens When You Are Startled?**
Sharpen Your Skills **Interpreting Data**

SECTION 3 *Integrating Health* Wellness
Discover **How Well Do You Take Care of Your Health?**
Try This **Wellness in the Balance**

14 ◆ D

Allow time for students to read the description of the project in their text and the Chapter Project Overview on pages 10–11 in Teaching Resources. Then have the class make a list of examples of both good and bad habits.

Inform students that several factors can increase the likelihood that their plan will succeed, such as replacing their unhealthy habit with a new, positive habit; getting support from friends and family members; and including a system to reward themselves when they meet their goals.

Make sure students understand that their projects will not be evaluated on their success at changing their habits, but on their plans, daily logs, and summaries. Some students may be unwilling to share information on their plans with their classmates. Assure the class that all reports will be confidential.

Pass out copies of the Chapter 1 Project Worksheets on pages 12–13 in Teaching Resources for students to review.

Time for a Change

Surrounded by spectacular scenery, the hikers slowly climb to the top of the mountain. Hiking is good exercise—it helps keep your heart, lungs, bones, and muscles in good shape. Other healthful behaviors include eating a balanced diet and getting about eight hours of sleep each night. Behaviors such as these, if performed over and over, become good health habits.

Unfortunately, some habits can harm your health. But bad habits can be changed. One way to change a bad health habit is to replace it with a healthful behavior. For example, if you sit and watch television every day after school, try going for a bike ride with a friend instead.

Your Goal To identify a health habit you want to change, and to carry out a plan to change that habit.

To complete this project successfully, you must
◆ choose an unhealthy habit you want to change
◆ design a plan to change the unwanted habit—a plan that is realistic and has step-by-step goals
◆ keep a daily log to record your progress
◆ follow the safety guidelines in Appendix A

Get Started Preview the chapter to identify some habits that can harm your health. Choose one and identify a positive health behavior you could substitute. Begin to think about an overall goal and a realistic plan to achieve your goal.

Check Your Progress You'll be working on this project as you study this chapter. To keep your project on track, look for Check Your Progress boxes at the following points.
Section 1 Review, page 21: Choose the behavior that you want to change, and make a plan.
Section 2 Review, page 27: Keep a log of your progress.

Wrap Up At the end of the chapter (page 35), you will reflect on your successes and setbacks, and identify your next steps.

Hiking is a fun activity that is good for your health.

Program Resources

◆ Teaching Resources Chapter 1 Project Teacher Notes, pp. 8–9; Chapter 1 Project Overview and Worksheets, pp. 10–13; Chapter 1 Project Scoring Rubric, p. 14

Performance Assessment

The Chapter 1 Project Scoring Rubric on page 14 of Teaching Resources will help you evaluate how well students complete the Chapter 1 Project. Students will be assessed on
◆ the identification and clear definition of an unhealthy habit;
◆ the completeness of their plans and how well the plans are designed to replace the identified habit;
◆ the thoroughness and organization of their entries in the daily logs;
◆ the clarity and completeness of their summaries.

By sharing the Chapter 1 Scoring Rubric with students at the beginning of the project, you will make it clear to them what they are expected to do.

How the Body Is Organized

Objectives

After completing the lesson, students will be able to

◆ identify the levels of organization in the body;

◆ identify and describe the four basic types of tissue in the human body.

Key Terms cell, cell membrane, nucleus, cytoplasm, tissue, muscle tissue, nerve tissue, connective tissue, epithelial tissue, organ, organ system

1 Engage/Explore

Activating Prior Knowledge

Pose to students that a marching band is organized on several levels from bandleader to individual members to sections, and that each part at each level performs a different function in the band. Ask: **How is the organization of the human body similar to that of a marching band?** *(Different parts, such as the heart or the muscles, perform different functions.)* Tell students that in this section they learn how the organization of the human body on different levels helps the body to work together as a whole.

········· DISCOVER ·········

Skills Focus inferring
Materials *two medium-sized books, clock or watch with second hand*
Time 10 minutes
Tips Make sure the books are heavy enough so that students will tire holding them, but not so heavy that students will not be able to hold them level with their shoulders.
Expected Outcome Most students' arms will feel tired after 30 seconds.
Think It Over Most students will include arms, shoulders, hands, brain, head, and muscles.

How the Body Is Organized

DISCOVER ··· ACTIVITY

How Do You Lift Books?

1. Stack one book on top of another one.

2. Lift the two stacked books in front of you so the lowest book is about level with your shoulders. Hold the books in this position for 30 seconds. While you are performing this activity, note how your body responds. For example, how do your arms feel at the beginning and toward the end of the 30 seconds?

3. Balance one book on the top of your head. Walk a few steps with the book on your head.

Think It Over
Inferring List all the parts of your body that worked together as you performed the activities in Steps 1 through 3.

GUIDE FOR READING

◆ What are the levels of organization in the body?

◆ What are the four basic types of tissue in the human body?

Reading Tip Before you read, preview *Exploring Levels of Organization in the Body.* Write down any unfamiliar words. Then, as you read, write their definitions.

T he bell rings—lunchtime at last! You hurry down the noisy halls toward the cafeteria. The unmistakable aroma of hot pizza makes your mouth water. At last, after waiting in line, you pick up a plate with a slice of pizza and some salad. When you get to the cashier, you dig in your pocket for lunch money. Then, carefully balancing your tray, you scan the crowded cafeteria for your friends. You spot them, walk to their table, sit down, and begin to eat.

Think for a minute about how many parts of your body were involved in the simple act of getting and eating your lunch. You heard the bell with your ears and smelled the pizza with your nose. Bones and muscles worked together as you walked to the cafeteria, picked up your food, and sat down at the table. Without your brain, you couldn't have remembered where you put your lunch money. Once you began to eat, your teeth chewed the food and your throat muscles swallowed it. Then other parts of your digestive system, such as your stomach, began to process the food for your body to use.

Levels of Organization

Every minute of the day, whether you are eating, studying, playing basketball, or even sleeping, your body is busily at work. Each part of the body has a specific job to do, and all the different parts work together. This smooth functioning is due partly to the way in which the

---

READING STRATEGIES

Reading Tip As students preview the Exploring feature and list unfamiliar words, encourage them to list questions they have about cells, tissues, organs, and organ systems of the body. Have them leave several lines of space beneath each question. As students read the section, they can write answers to the questions.

Study and Comprehension Have students work alone or with partners to outline the information in the section. Suggest that students use the four levels of organization as main topics in their outlines. Encourage students to include specific examples in their outlines.

human body is organized. **The levels of organization in the human body consist of cells, tissues, organs, and organ systems.** The smallest unit is the cell, and the largest is the organ system. As you read about each level of organization, refer to *Exploring Levels of Organization in the Body*, which shows how your skeletal system is organized.

☑ *Checkpoint* *What is the largest level of organization in the human body?*

EXPLORING Levels of Organization in the Body

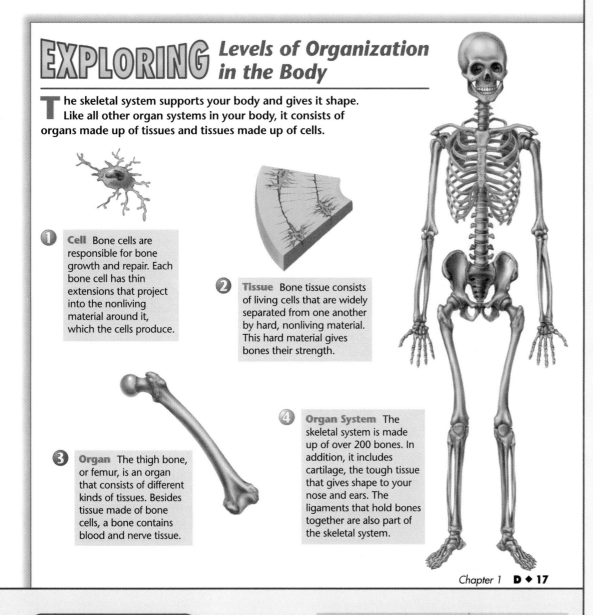

The skeletal system supports your body and gives it shape. Like all other organ systems in your body, it consists of organs made up of tissues and tissues made up of cells.

1 Cell Bone cells are responsible for bone growth and repair. Each bone cell has thin extensions that project into the nonliving material around it, which the cells produce.

2 Tissue Bone tissue consists of living cells that are widely separated from one another by hard, nonliving material. This hard material gives bones their strength.

3 Organ The thigh bone, or femur, is an organ that consists of different kinds of tissues. Besides tissue made of bone cells, a bone contains blood and nerve tissue.

4 Organ System The skeletal system is made up of over 200 bones. In addition, it includes cartilage, the tough tissue that gives shape to your nose and ears. The ligaments that hold bones together are also part of the skeletal system.

Answers to Self-Assessment

☑ *Checkpoint*
The largest level of organization in the human body is the organ system.

2 Facilitate

Levels of Organization

Building Inquiry Skills: Making Models

Materials *toothpicks, craft sticks, modeling clay, colored paper, scissors, glue, tape* **ACTIVITY**
Time 25 minutes

To help students understand that all the levels of organization work together, have them work in groups to build models of organized objects in which each level is composed of the levels below it. Students should discuss their ideas for a model within the group before attempting to build the model. Provide an example of a model by suggesting that students might decide to use geometric shapes to form a larger shape, such as toothpicks glued into triangles to form squares, squares glued together to form cubes, cubes glued together to form a tall tower. Each student in the group should help to plan and build the model. **cooperative learning**

EXPLORING

Levels of Organization in the Body

Point out to students that the skeletal system is only one system in the human body, but that all systems follow the same general organization. Have students describe the relationships between the levels of organization. Ask: **What does an organ system consist of?** *(An organ system is made up of organs.)* **What are organs made of?** *(Different kinds of tissues)* Have students find the individual bones cells in the illustration of bone tissue. Make sure that students can differentiate between the cells and the hard material that surrounds them. **learning modality: visual**

Ongoing Assessment

Writing Ask students to list the four levels of organization in the human body and rank them in order from smallest to largest.

Cells

Skills Focus making models

Materials *student textbook*

Time 15 minutes

Tips To help students make their concept maps, suggest they study the table of contents. Also refer students to the section on concept mapping in the Skills Handbook, p. 268.

Expected Outcome Sample answer: sentences—cells; subsections—tissues; sections—organs; chapters—organ systems

Extend Ask students: **What level in the human body might the whole book correspond to?** *(The whole body)*

learning modality: logical/ mathematical

Demonstration

Materials *flat toothpick, microscope slide, cover slip, dropper, methylene blue, light microscope*

Time 20 minutes

Tips To show students the structures of a human cell, use the flat end of the toothpick to *gently* scrape the inside of your cheek. (The toothpick will remove cheek cells just by touching the inside of the cheek; it isn't necessary to use force.) Then stir the scrapings into a drop of water on a microscope slide, place a cover slip over the drop, and add a drop of methylene blue to the edge of the cover slip. You can use a piece of paper towel to absorb the excess water from the other side of the cover slip. Make up several slides and set up the microscopes at stations around the room. Small groups of students can observe the slides under high and low powers. Encourage them to make labeled sketches of their observations, including the nucleus, cytoplasm, and cell membrane.

learning modality: visual

Portfolio Students can save their sketches in their portfolios.

How Is a Book Organized?

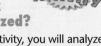

In this activity, you will analyze the levels of organization in a book.

1. Examine this textbook to see how it is subdivided— into chapters, sections, and so on.

2. Make a concept map that shows this pattern of organization. Place the largest subdivision at the top of the map and the smallest at the bottom.

3. Compare the levels of organization in this book to those in the human body.

Making Models Which level of organization in the book represents cells? Which represent tissues, organs, and organ systems?

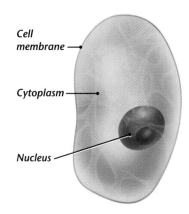

Figure 1 The cells in your body are surrounded by a cell membrane, and most have a nucleus. The cytoplasm is the area between the cell membrane and the nucleus.

Cell membrane

Cytoplasm

Nucleus

Cells

A **cell** is the basic unit of structure and function in a living thing. Complex organisms are composed of many cells in the same way a building is composed of many bricks. The human body contains about 100 trillion cells. Cells are quite tiny, and most cannot be seen without a microscope.

Most animal cells, including those in the human body, have a structure similar to the cell in Figure 1. The **cell membrane** forms the outside boundary of the cell. Inside the cell membrane is a large structure called the **nucleus.** The nucleus is the control center that directs the cell's activities and contains information that determines the cell's characteristics. When the cell divides, or reproduces, this information is passed onto the newly formed cells. The area between the cell membrane and the nucleus is called the **cytoplasm.** The cytoplasm contains a clear, jellylike substance in which many important cell structures are found.

Cells carry on the processes that keep organisms alive. Inside cells, for example, molecules from digested food undergo chemical reactions that provide energy for the body's activities.

✓ Checkpoint *What is the function of the nucleus?*

Tissues

The cell is the smallest unit of organization in your body; the next level is a tissue. A **tissue** is a group of similar cells that perform the same function. **The human body contains four basic types of tissue: muscle tissue, nerve tissue, connective tissue, and epithelial tissue.** To see examples of each of these tissues, look at Figure 2.

Like the muscle cells that form it, **muscle tissue** can contract, or shorten. By doing this, muscle tissue makes parts of your body move. When you turn the pages of this book or focus your eyes on this page, you are using muscle tissue.

While muscle tissue carries out movement, nerve tissue directs and controls it. **Nerve tissue** carries messages back and forth between the brain and every other part of the body. Your brain is made up mostly of nerve tissue.

Connective tissue provides support for your body and connects all its parts. Bone is one kind of connective tissue; its strength and hardness support your body and protect its delicate structures. Fat, which pads parts of your body, provides insulation from cold, and stores energy, is also a connective tissue. So is blood, which travels to all parts of your body.

Epithelial tissue (ep uh THEE lee ul) covers the surfaces of your body, inside and out. Some epithelial tissue, such as the outermost layer of your skin, protects the delicate structures that lie

Connective tissue
Parts of the body are connected and supported by connective tissue, such as the blood cells shown here. Blood carries substances throughout your body. Fat, cartilage, bones, and the tendons that attach muscles to bones are all connective tissues.

Epithelial tissue
Epithelial tissue covers the surfaces of your body and the outside of your internal organs. This tissue also lines the inside of organs such as the small intestine. The skin cells shown here form a protective barrier against the environment outside the body.

Nerve tissue
Nerve tissue, such as the brain cells shown here, enables you to see, hear, and think. Your brain, spinal cord, and nerves consist of nerve tissue.

Muscle tissue
Every movement you make depends on muscle tissue. One kind of muscle tissue allows the body to move—as when a skater glides across the ice. Other kinds of muscle tissue move blood through the heart and move food through the digestive system.

Figure 2 Your body contains four different kinds of tissues. An example of each kind is shown here. *Comparing and Contrasting* How is the function of nerve tissue different from that of epithelial tissue?

Chapter 1 **D ◆ 19**

Media and Technology

 Exploring Life Science Videodisc
Unit 1, Side 2,
"Cell Specialization"

Chapter 6

Answers to Self-Assessment

Caption Question

Figure 2 Nerve tissue transports messages. Epithelial tissue covers the surfaces and lines the organs of the body.

 Checkpoint

The nucleus directs the cell's activities and contains information that determines the cell's characteristics.

Tissues

Language Arts
CONNECTION

Challenge students to compare the different meanings of the word *tissue* in the following terms: facial tissue, connective tissue, and "tissue of lies." Students can work in pairs to look up and discuss the definitions of the terms. **limited English proficiency**

Using the Visuals: Figure 2

Ask students to compare and contrast the shapes of the cells shown in the different tissues. Ask: **Are all body tissues made of the same type of cell?** *(No, there are different types of cells.)* Have students describe the shapes of the cells shown in the illustration. Point out that the types of cells shown are representative of only one kind of cell. All skin cells, for example, do not have the same shape. *(Red blood cells—circular; skin cells—flat; brain cells—a central body with radiating projections; muscle cells—narrow, striped)* **learning modality: visual**

Ongoing Assessment

Writing Have students list the tissue types involved in the function of one body part, such as the mouth or hand. *(Sample: The hand has nerve tissue, connective tissue like bone and blood, muscle tissue, and epithelial tissue such as skin.)*

D ◆ 19

Organs and Organ Systems

Building Inquiry Skills: Communicating

Let students work with partners to formulate questions they have about the organ systems shown in Figure 4. Point out that they will not know enough to answer the questions at this time, but they will be able to as they read later chapters. Suggest students include questions that might help them clarify the relationship between two or more organ systems. For example, after reading the descriptions of organ systems they might ask: How do the digestive and muscular systems work together to digest food? Students should save the questions in their portfolios and then answer them as they study subsequent chapters.

learning modality: verbal

 Students can save their questions in their portfolios.

Including All Students

Some students may have difficulty understanding the relationship between *organ* and *organ system.* Explain to these students that the word *system* refers to an organized whole made up of individual parts that relate to and depend upon one another. In an organ system, a group of individual organs work together as a unit to some particular end. Ask: **What is the function of the circulatory organ system?** *(It carries materials to and removes wastes from the cells, and helps fight disease.)* Ask: **What is the relationship between the heart, the blood vessels, and the circulatory system?** *(The heart and blood vessels are individual organs; they also work together to form the circulatory organ system.)* Refer students to Figure 4, then ask students to name the organ systems to which the stomach, the brain, and the lungs belong. *(Stomach—digestive; brain—nervous; lungs—respiratory)*

limited English proficiency

---

beneath it. Other kinds of epithelial tissue absorb or release substances. The lining of your digestive system consists of epithelial tissue. Some of the cells in this tissue release chemicals used in digestion, while others absorb digested food.

Organs and Organ Systems

Your stomach, heart, brain, and lungs are all organs. An **organ** is a structure that is composed of different kinds of tissue. Like a tissue, an organ performs a specific job. The job of an organ, however, is generally more complex than that of a tissue. The heart, for example, pumps blood throughout your body, over and over again. The heart contains all four kinds of tissue— muscle, nerve, connective, and epithelial. Each tissue type contributes to the overall job of pumping blood.

Each organ in your body is part of an **organ system,** a group of organs that work together to perform a major function. Your heart is part of your circulatory system, which carries oxygen and other materials throughout the body. Besides the heart, blood vessels are organs in the circulatory system. Figure 4 describes the major organ systems in the human body.

The different organ systems work together and depend on one another. You can compare the functioning of the human body to the work it takes to put on a school play. A play needs actors, of course, but it also needs a director, someone to make the costumes, and people to sell tickets. Similarly, when you ride a bike, you use your muscular and skeletal systems to steer and push the pedals. But you also need your nervous system to direct your arms and legs to move. Your respiratory, digestive, and circulatory systems work together to fuel your muscles with the energy they need. And your excretory system removes the wastes produced while your muscles are hard at work.

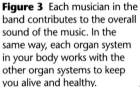

Figure 3 Each musician in the band contributes to the overall sound of the music. In the same way, each organ system in your body works with the other organ systems to keep you alive and healthy.

Background

Facts and Figures Epithelial tissues cover the body and internal organs, and form the lining of cavities and passageways.

Epithelial cells in cavities and passageways secrete a mucus that lubricates the surfaces. Glands, which are clusters of epithelial cells, synthesize and secrete substances such as perspiration, saliva, and hormones.

Epithelial tissues that provide protection, such as the epidermis, are strengthened and reinforced by cell junctions that bind cells together. Tight junctions form seals around individual cells in internal organs to prevent leakage between cells.

Epithelial tissues are classified by cell shape. Squamous or flat cells are found in the outer layer of skin, in the lining of the mouth, and in mucous membranes. Cuboidal and columnar cells are found in glands and lining of passageways.

Organ Systems in the Human Body

Endocrine Controls many body processes—such as intake of sugar by cells—by means of chemicals.

Excretory Removes wastes.

Immune Fights disease.

Muscular Enables the body to move; moves food through the digestive system; keeps the heart beating.

Nervous Detects and interprets information from the environment outside the body and from within the body; controls most body functions.

Skeletal Supports the body, protects it, and works with muscles to allow movement; makes blood cells and stores some materials.

Skin Protects the body, keeps water inside the body, and helps regulate body temperature.

▲ **Circulatory** Carries needed materials to the body cells; carries wastes away from body cells; helps fight disease.

Digestive Takes food into the body, breaks food down, and absorbs the digested materials.

Reproductive Produces sex cells that can unite with other sex cells to create offspring; controls male and female characteristics.

Respiratory Takes oxygen into ▶ the body and eliminates carbon dioxide.

Figure 4 The human body is made up of eleven organ systems. *Interpreting Charts* Which two systems work together to get oxygen to your cells?

Section 1 Review

1. List the four levels of organization in the human body. Give an example of each level.
2. What are the four types of tissue found in the human body? What is the general function of each type?
3. Describe the structure of an animal cell.
4. **Thinking Critically** **Applying Concepts** What systems of the body are involved when you prepare a sandwich and then eat it?

Check Your Progress

CHAPTER PROJECT 1

Once you have chosen a behavior that you want to change, make a day-by-day plan. Get your teacher's approval for the plan. Then set up a log in which you will record your progress. Start now to work toward your first goal. *(Hint:* Your plan will be more successful if you set realistic intermediate goals along the way. For example, if you want to get more exercise, begin by exercising three times a week for a short period. Over time, you can gradually increase your exercise time and frequency.)

Program Resources

◆ **Teaching Resources** 1-1 Review and Reinforce, p. 17; Enrich, p. 18

Media and Technology

 Interactive Student Tutorial CD-ROM D-1

Answers to Self-Assessment

Caption Question

Figure 4 The respiratory and the circulatory systems

---

3 Assess

Section 1 Review Answers

1. Sample: cell—bone cell; tissue—muscle tissue; organ—heart; organ system—nervous system
2. Muscle tissue—movement; nerve tissue—carries messages between the brain and other parts of the body; connective tissue—provides support and connects all parts of the body; epithelial tissue—covers surfaces of the body, absorbs and releases substances
3. A cell membrane forms the outside boundary of the cell. Inside the cell membrane is a large nucleus. The area between the nucleus and cell membrane is the cytoplasm, which contains important cell structures.
4. Skeletal, nervous, muscular, circulatory, and digestive systems

Check Your Progress

CHAPTER PROJECT 1

Students' plans should specifically state what new behaviors will be performed and have reasonable final goals. Make sure their plans are consistent with students' medical and other requirements. Encourage students as they try to implement their plans. Suggest they recruit friends and family members to help them follow their plans. Students who want to change their plans after a few days should check with you before making changes.

Performance Assessment

Writing Have students describe the types of cells and/or tissues that make up the organs of the skeletal system, then describe that system's function.

A Body of Knowledge

Preparing for Inquiry

Key Concept Students draw organs in the human body and compare their initial drawing to the one they make after researching these organs.

Skills Objective Students will be able to
- make a model showing the size, shape, and location of several organs on an outline of the human body;
- pose questions about the organs.

Time 30 minutes

Advance Planning Prepare the necessary number of outlines. If floor space is limited, use outlines of the torso and head.

Guiding Inquiry

Invitation

Ask students who have seen some organs of other animals to compare the size of those organs to the size of the animal.

Introducing the Procedure

Suggest students use regular pencils to make light outlines of the organs so they can be erased if students do not like their first sketches.

Troubleshooting the Experiment

Drawings might get messy if students redraw an organ repeatedly. Try to have students, working in groups, agree on each organ before they draw it on the outline.

Expected Outcome

Initial drawings may show misconceptions or lack of knowledge. Revised drawings should show the brain filling about half the head; two lungs filling the upper third of the chest; a slightly left-of-center heart (fist-sized) in front of the lungs; and the stomach in the middle of the body, bigger than the heart.

Analyze and Conclude

1. Students' charts should show that the heart pumps blood; the brain processes information; the lungs exchange gas between blood and air; and the stomach begins the breakdown of food.

A Body of Knowledge

In this lab, you will discover how much you already know about the human body.

Problem

Where are some important organs in the human body located?

Skills Focus

observing, inferring, posing questions

Materials

outline of the human body   colored pencils

Procedure

1. Obtain an outline of the human body and five colored pencils. Notice that the outline shows a front view of the body, and that the right and left sides of the body are labeled.
2. Use one color to draw in the heart at the size and shape that you think it is. Draw the heart in the approximate place in the body where you think it is located. Label the heart on your drawing.
3. Select three different colors to represent the brain, lungs, and stomach. Draw each of these organs, showing its general size and shape and where you think it is located. Label each organ.
4. Choose one of the organs you just drew, and think of other organs that may be part of the same organ system. Draw those organs and label them. If the organs are part of a pathway, draw arrows to show the path.

Analyze and Conclude

1. Create a chart that lists the brain, heart, lungs, and stomach in the first column. In the second column, describe your understanding of the function of each of those organs.
2. Describe the role of the organ system you drew. How does it function in the body?
3. **Apply** For each organ in your chart, write one question you would like to have answered. Then write one question about the organ system you drew.

More to Explore

Find illustrations in this book that show the correct location of the organs you drew. Use a new body outline to make more accurate drawings of the organs and organ system.

2. Sample: Digestive system—responsible for the breakdown of food and absorption of water and nutrients.

3. Students may want to know the function, size, color, or shape of the organ or system. Sample: Does the stomach change in size after a meal?

Extending the Inquiry

More to Explore Encourage students to answer their questions as they research the organs.

Program Resources

- **Teaching Resources** Chapter 1 Real-World Lab, pp. 27–29

SECTION 2 Keeping the Body in Balance

DISCOVER ⋯⋯⋯⋯⋯⋯⋯⋯⋯⋯⋯⋯⋯ ACTIVITY ⋯⋯

What Happens When You Are Startled?

1. Read this activity, and then close your eyes.

2. Your teacher is behind you and will pop a balloon at any moment.

3. Pay attention to how your body reacts when you hear the balloon pop. Observe whether you jump and whether your heartbeat rate and breathing rate change.

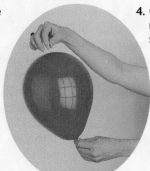

4. Observe how your body returns to normal after it responds to the sound.

Think It Over

Predicting How might your body respond if you suddenly saw a huge, threatening animal rushing toward you? How might your response be an advantage to you?

Imagine that you are trapped in a damp, dark dungeon. Somewhere near you is a deep, water-filled pit into which you could fall. Overhead swings a pendulum with a razor-sharp edge. With each swing, the pendulum lowers closer and closer to your body.

The main character in Edgar Allan Poe's story "The Pit and the Pendulum" finds himself in that very situation. Here's his reaction: "A fearful idea now suddenly drove the blood in torrents upon my heart. . . . I at once started to my feet, trembling convulsively in every fibre. . . . Perspiration burst from every pore, and stood in cold, big beads upon my forehead."

> ### GUIDE FOR READING
>
> ◆ What is homeostasis?
> ◆ What happens during the alarm stage of stress?
>
> *Reading Tip* **Before you read, write the headings in this section on a piece of paper, leaving a space after each. As you read, write a summary of the information under each heading.**

D ◆ 23

READING STRATEGIES

Reading Tip As students write section headings on a sheet of paper, instruct them to include subheadings as well as major headings. Remind students that summarizing means identifying the main ideas of a passage and restating them accurately, concisely, and in their own words. Students can use their summaries as study guides.

Program Resources

◆ **Teaching Resources** 1-2 Lesson Plan, p. 19; 1-2 Section Summary, p. 20

Media and Technology

Audiotapes English-Spanish Summary 1-2

Objectives

After completing the lesson, students will be able to
◆ define homeostasis;
◆ describe the physical responses to stress and ways to deal with stress.

Key Terms homeostasis, stress, adrenaline

1 Engage/Explore

Activating Prior Knowledge

Ask students to describe how they feel when they are suddenly worried or upset. *(Sample: Mind starts racing, heart beats faster, feel nervous)* Ask students to think about how long this feeling usually lasts. *(Most students will say that it doesn't last very long, and soon they feel normal again.)* Tell students that they will now learn how the body reacts to an upsetting situation.

⋯⋯⋯ DISCOVER ⋯⋯⋯

Skills Focus predicting
Materials *balloon, straight pin*
Time 10 minutes

Tips If possible, stand out of students' field of vision, and then wait several seconds before you pop the balloon. Make sure that all students have their eyes closed before you pop the balloon.
Expected Outcome Students will probably jump when the balloon is popped, and some may feel a slight increase in their heart rate.
Think It Over If you see a large animal, your heartbeat and breathing rates might increase. You might jump away. This response could be an advantage because it prepares the body to take action against the threat.

Homeostasis

Language Arts
CONNECTION

Write the term *homeostasis* on the chalkboard. Have students repeat the word until they are comfortable pronouncing it correctly. Then ask students to look it up in the dictionary and find definitions for *homeo-* (the same) and *-stasis* (state of balance). Ask: **How are the meanings of *homeo-* and *-stasis* related to the definition of homeostasis?** (*Homeostasis is the body's tendency to maintain an internal balance.*) **learning modality: verbal**

Sharpen your Skills

Interpreting Data

Time 15 minutes
Tips Ask students how  often the blood sugar level was checked during the experiment. (*Every 30 minutes*) Then ask: **How long did it take for the animal's body to reach homeostasis?** (*2 hours*)
Expected Results Students should infer that the last three readings were the same because the sugar level in the body had returned to its original value due to homeostasis.
Extend Challenge students to make a line graph of the data. **learning modality: logical/mathematical**

Addressing Naive Conceptions

Students may think that their temperature will always be 37°C unless they are ill. In fact, 37°C is an average temperature for healthy adults. Many people have normal temperatures that are slightly above or slightly below 37°C, and temperature changes slightly throughout the day. In general, internal body temperature is lowest in the morning and as much as a degree higher in the evening. **learning modality: logical/mathematical**

Sharpen your Skills

Interpreting Data

A scientist fed a strong sugar solution to an animal. The scientist then checked the concentration of sugar in the animal's blood during the next three hours. The table below shows the results of the experiment.

Time After Eating Sugar (minutes)	Sugar Concentration (milligrams/ 100 milliliters)
0	75
30	125
60	110
90	90
120	75
150	75
180	75

Explain how the data show homeostasis at work. (*Hint:* Think about what happened to the blood-sugar level during the first hour and then during the next two hours.)

Homeostasis

Poe's character is reacting to danger. Your body, too, responds to threatening or startling events in specific ways. For example, your heart and breathing rates increase. Once you are no longer in danger or startled, your heart slows down. As the saying goes, you "breathe more easily."

The body's return to normal after a scare is one example of **homeostasis** (hoh mee oh STAY sis), the body's tendency to maintain an internal balance. **Homeostasis is the process by which an organism's internal environment is kept stable in spite of changes in the external environment.**

To see homeostasis in action, all you have to do is take your temperature when the air is chilly. Then take it again in an overheated room. No matter what the temperature of the air around you, your internal body temperature will be close to 37 degrees Celsius, as long as you are healthy. If you get sick, your body temperature may rise. But when you get well again, it returns to 37 degrees.

Your body has various ways of maintaining homeostasis. For example, you need food and water to stay alive. When your body is low on either of these substances, your brain sends signals that result in your feeling hungry or thirsty. When you eat or drink, you maintain homeostasis by providing your body with substances that it needs.

Figure 5 The wind is icy and the ground is covered with snow. In spite of the chill, the body temperatures of these sledders remain fairly constant at about 37° Celsius.
Applying Concepts What is the term for the body's tendency to maintain a stable internal environment?

When you perspire on a hot day, your body is maintaining its internal balance. When perspiration evaporates, the liquid water becomes water vapor, which is a gas. In order for a liquid to become a gas, heat must be added to it. As the water in perspiration evaporates, it absorbs heat from your body and carries it away. This removal of heat helps cool you down and enables your body to maintain a constant temperature on a hot day.

☑ *Checkpoint* *How do feelings of thirst help your body maintain homeostasis?*

Stress and Homeostasis

The rapid heartbeat and trembling of the character in "The Pit and the Pendulum" are both signs of stress. **Stress** is the reaction of your body and mind to threatening, challenging, or disturbing events. Many things can act as stressors, or events that cause stress. A snarling dog, an argument with a friend, or an upcoming oral report can all be stressors. Stress upsets homeostasis, and your body reacts in specific ways.

Physical Responses to Stress Figure 6 shows what happens in your body within seconds after you experience stress. During this stage, which is called the alarm stage, your body releases a

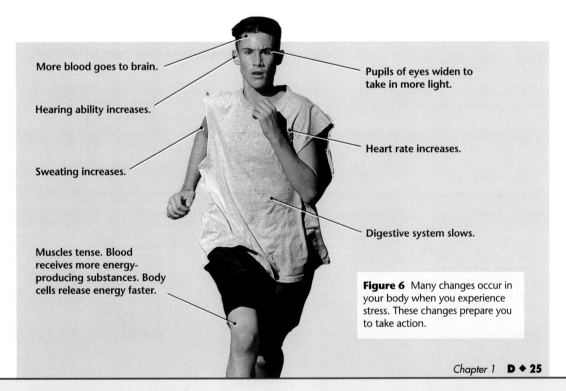

More blood goes to brain.

Hearing ability increases.

Sweating increases.

Muscles tense. Blood receives more energy-producing substances. Body cells release energy faster.

Pupils of eyes widen to take in more light.

Heart rate increases.

Digestive system slows.

Figure 6 Many changes occur in your body when you experience stress. These changes prepare you to take action.

Chapter 1 **D ◆ 25**

Integrating Chemistry

ACTIVITY

To allow students to feel how the temperature changes when liquid water becomes water vapor, have them dip one index finger into a cup of room-temperature water, then hold the finger in the air. Ask: **How does your index finger feel?** *(The finger feels cool.)* Have students explain how this is like what happens when people sweat. *(When sweat evaporates, it removes heat from your skin and makes you feel cooler.)* **limited English proficiency**

Stress and Homeostasis

Using the Visuals: Figure 6

As students examine the visual, ask: **What is the advantage of increasing heart rate?** *(The heart pumps blood to the body faster.)* **What is the advantage of widened pupils?** *(You can see better with more light.)* Ask students to infer the advantages of increased hearing ability. *(Increased hearing ability allows you to hear things that you might not be attuned to under normal circumstances, such as a person or animal approaching you outside your field of vision.)* **learning modality: visual**

Program Resources

● **Science Explorer Series** *Chemical Building Blocks,* Chapter 2
◆ **Interdisciplinary Exploration Series** "Soap From Concept to Consumer," pp. 9–10

Answers to Self-Assessment

Caption Question

Figure 5 homeostasis

☑ *Checkpoint*

Thirst prompts people to drink the water their bodies need to maintain homeostasis.

Ongoing Assessment

Writing Have students write brief explanations of two ways in which the body maintains homeostasis.

 Students can save their explanations in their portfolios.

Stress and Homeostasis, continued

Building Inquiry Skills: Communicating

Have students work in small groups to describe how adrenaline and the fight-or-flight response affect various body systems. Students should take on specific roles in preparing and presenting the information. For example, one student might pantomime a stress response while another student describes which organ systems are involved. After each group makes its presentation, ask: **What are some of the body systems involved in the fight-or-flight response?** (Sample: respiratory, muscular, skeletal, and circulatory systems) **cooperative learning**

Language Arts
CONNECTION

Invite students to read more of "The Pit and the Pendulum." Ask students to note other passages in the story that indicate the main character's physical and emotional responses to stress.

In Your Journal Students can work in groups to brainstorm stressful situations that they might describe. Suggest that before students begin to write, they make a list of the descriptive details they want to include. **learning modality: verbal**

Long-Term Stress

Addressing Naive Conceptions

Some students might believe that stressful events are always negative. Point out that stressors can include positive experiences, such as being elected class president, acting in a school play, or making a new friend. Suggest students consider positive stressors in their own lives. Call on students to share some of these experiences. **learning modality: verbal**

Language Arts
CONNECTION

The quotation from "The Pit and the Pendulum" that you read at the beginning of this section (page 23) describes a character's reaction to extreme stress. Notice how the author, Edgar Allan Poe, uses detailed descriptions of the character's physical reactions, such as his rapid heartbeat and sweating, to convey the character's fear.

In Your Journal

Create a situation in which a character faces an extremely stressful situation. Describe the character's physical reactions and feelings. Make sure to use vivid and precise descriptive words that clearly convey the character's reactions.

chemical called **adrenaline** into your bloodstream. **Adrenaline gives you a burst of energy and causes many other changes in your body. These changes prepare you to take quick action.**

The effects of adrenaline, which take only a few seconds, are dramatic. Your breathing quickens, sending more oxygen to your body cells to provide energy for your muscles. That extra oxygen gets to your cells rapidly because your heart begins to beat faster. The faster heartbeat increases the flow of blood to your muscles and some other organs. In contrast, less blood flows to your skin and digestive system, so that more is available for your arms and legs. The pupils of your eyes become wider, allowing you to see better.

Fight or Flight The reactions caused by adrenaline are sometimes called the "fight-or-flight" response, because they prepare you either to fight the stressor or to take flight and escape. Scientists think that the fight-or-flight response was important for primitive people who faced wild-animal attacks and similar dangers. Today, the same reactions still occur with any stressor, whether it is a snarling dog or a social studies test.

During the fight-or-flight response, your body systems work together to respond to the stressor. For example, your respiratory system provides you with extra oxygen, which your circulatory system delivers to the parts of your body that need it. Your muscular system, in turn, works with your skeletal system to help you move—fast.

☑ *Checkpoint* During the alarm stage, how do your eyes respond?

Figure 7 Oops! One sure way to cause stress is to do too many things at once. *Relating Cause and Effect How does stress affect a person's heartbeat and breathing rates?*

26 ◆ D

Background

Integrating Science Behavioral scientists categorize behavior into two types, based on a person's reaction to stress. Type A behaviors include aggressiveness, competitiveness, and self-imposed pressure. Type B behavior is characteristic of people who deal with stress in a patient and relaxed manner.

The Homes-Rahe Social Readjustment Rating Scale ranks life events in order of their estimated level of stress on a scale of 0 to 100, with 100 as the most stressful. The list includes the following:

Divorce: 73
Death of a close family member: 63
Personal injury or illness: 53
Death of a close friend: 37
Beginning or finishing school: 26
Change in residence: 20
Change in school: 20
Vacation: 13

Long-Term Stress

The alarm stage of stress only lasts for a short time. If the stress is over quickly, your body soon returns to its normal state. Some kinds of stressors, however, continue for a long time. Suppose, for example, you are stressed because you are moving to a new community. You cannot fight the stressor, and you cannot run away from it either. When a stressful situation does not go away quickly, your body cannot restore homeostasis. If you do not deal with the stress, you may become tired, irritable, and have trouble getting along with others. In addition, you may be more likely to become ill.

Dealing With Stress

Stress is a normal part of life. No one can avoid stress entirely. When you are in a stressful situation, it is important that you recognize it and take action to deal with it, rather than pretending that the stressor doesn't exist. For example, suppose you aren't doing well in math class. If you accept the problem and deal with it—perhaps by asking your teacher for help—your stress will probably decrease.

In addition, when you are experiencing long-term stress, physical activity can help you feel better. Riding a bike, skating, or even raking leaves can take your mind off the stress. It is also important to talk about the situation and your feelings with friends and family members.

Figure 8 When you are under stress, it is important to find ways to relax.

 Section 2 Review

1. What is homeostasis?
2. Describe what happens during the alarm stage of stress.
3. Explain how your body temperature is an example of homeostasis.
4. What problems may result if a stressful situation does not go away quickly?
5. **Thinking Critically** **Making Judgments** What are three helpful ways of dealing with stress?

Check Your Progress

CHAPTER PROJECT 1

By now you should be carrying out your behavior-change plan. Keep a daily log to monitor your successes and setbacks. Don't be discouraged if things do not go exactly as you planned—just make adjustments to get yourself back on track. (*Hint:* Enlist your family and friends to support your effort. In addition, give yourself rewards, such as a trip to the movies, for reaching each intermediate goal you set.)

Program Resources

◆ **Teaching Resources** 1-2 Review and Reinforce, p. 21; 1-2 Enrich, p. 22

Media and Technology

Interactive Student Tutorial CD-ROM D-1

Answers to Self-Assessment

Caption Question

Figure 7 Heartbeat and breathing rates increase.

☑ *Checkpoint*

During the alarm stage, your pupils widen to take in more light.

Dealing with Stress

Including All Students

Students with disabilities may have difficulty identifying physical exercise they can do to help them manage stress. Encourage these students to identify activities that they enjoy and to include them in their plans for dealing with stress. **learning modality: verbal**

3 Assess

Section 2 Review Answers

1. Homeostasis is the process by which an organism's internal environment is kept stable in spite of changes in the external environment.
2. The body releases adrenaline, which provides a burst of energy and causes physical changes that prepare the body for quick action. These include widened pupils, faster breathing and heartbeat, an increase in blood flow to the muscles, and a decreased blood flow to the skin and digestive system.
3. Body temperature remains somewhat constant, about 37°C, regardless of the outside environment.
4. A person may become tired, irritable, or ill.
5. Accept any three: taking action, exercising, relaxing, or talking about the situation with family or friends.

Check Your Progress

CHAPTER PROJECT 1

Encourage students to stay with their plans even if they suffer frustrating set-backs. Check students' logs and make sure they include details about students' progress. If students are having difficulty meeting their goals, help them set more reasonable intermediate goals.

Performance Assessment

Oral Presentation Ask students to explain how the alarm stage of stress can affect homeostasis.

SECTION 3 Wellness

Objectives

After completing the lesson, students will be able to
- name and describe the three components of wellness;
- explain how to evaluate wellness and list ways to improve personal health.

Key Terms wellness, physical health, mental health, social health, peer pressure, continuum

1 Engage/Explore

Activating Prior Knowledge

Ask students to describe decisions they make every day that can affect their overall health. Prompt students with examples, such as: **What if you have to decide whether to eat an apple or a candy bar for a snack?** or **Do you always buckle your seatbelt when you ride in a motor vehicle?** Guide students to realize that they make many health-related decisions every day.

 **DISCOVER**

Skills Focus making judgments
Time 10 minutes
Tips Encourage students to evaluate each question and to answer honestly. Point out that all answers are confidential.
Think It Over Students' answers will depend on their assessments of the healthiness of their lifestyles.

SECTION 3 Wellness

DISCOVER •••••••••••••••••••••••••••••• **ACTIVITY**

How Well Do You Take Care of Your Health?

Answer *yes* or *no* to each question.

1. Do you engage in vigorous exercise, such as sports or brisk walking, several times a week?
2. Do you eat at least three servings of vegetables, two servings of fruit, and six servings of grain foods, such as bread, rice, and pasta, every day?
3. Do you get about eight hours of sleep each night?
4. Do you face and deal with stressful situations rather than ignore them?
5. Are you happy with yourself most of the time?
6. Do you have friends and family members you can turn to for help with a problem?

Think It Over
Making Judgments Add up the number of *yes* answers you gave. The more *yes* answers, the healthier the lifestyle you lead.

GUIDE FOR READING

- What are the three components of wellness?
- How can you think through a decision to make sure it is good for your health?

Reading Tip As you read, write a definition, in your own words, of each boldfaced term.

Tension is high as the soccer ball whizzes toward you. You aim your kick, and the ball soars into the net. You have scored the winning goal!

Playing soccer can be a great experience. The exercise is good for your body. But soccer does more than just keep your body healthy. It's fun to be part of a team and to share the thrill of competition. When your team plays well, you feel good about yourself and gain confidence in your abilities.

Components of Wellness

Everything you do, from playing soccer to going to the movies with friends, affects your overall level of health. **Wellness** is being at your best possible level of health—in your body, in your mind, and in your relationships with others. **Wellness has three components—physical health, mental health, and social health.**

Physical Health Your **physical health** consists of how well your body functions. When you are physically healthy, you have energy to carry out your daily tasks. To ensure your physical health, you need to eat healthy foods, exercise regularly, get enough sleep, and wear protective gear when you play sports. You also need to avoid harmful activities, such as smoking.

READING STRATEGIES

Reading Tip Have students write each boldfaced term on one side of a note card and the definition on the other side of the card as they read. Suggest students include specific examples along with the definitions. Partners can use the note cards to quiz each other on definitions of the terms.

Study and Comprehension Have students organize information from the section into a concept map. For information on concept maps, refer students to the *Skills Handbook*, p. 268. Instruct students to write *Wellness* in an oval in the center of the map. Then have them write the components of wellness—physical health, mental health, and social health—in separate ovals branching out from the center oval. Next, direct students to add to each of these components information that answers these questions:
- What does the component involve?
- How do you ensure wellness in this area?

Mental Health Your **mental health** involves your feel-ings, or emotions—how you feel about yourself and how you handle the day-to-day demands of your life. When you are mentally healthy, you recognize your achievements and learn from your mistakes. Mentally healthy people handle stress well—by changing the stressful situation when they can, and by engaging in stress-relieving activities. In addition, people who are mentally healthy generally feel good about themselves.

Social Health **Social health** refers to how well you get along with others. When you are socially healthy, you have loving relationships, respect the rights of others, and give and accept help. Building healthy relationships with family members, making and keeping friends, and communicating your needs to others are all important for social health.

For teenagers especially, peer pressure can have an impact on social health. **Peer pressure** consists of pressure from your friends and classmates to behave in certain ways. Peer pressure can be good, if your friends encourage you to work hard in school and participate in sports and other healthy activities. Sometimes, however, you may experience peer pressure to do harmful things, such as drinking alcohol. Socially healthy people understand that it is okay to say no when they are asked to do things that can harm themselves or others.

Figure 9 Wellness means being at your best possible level of health. Having fun with friends (top) is part of social health. Physical health (middle) is important for demanding sports such as soccer. The feeling of accomplishment that comes from playing an instrument (bottom) helps develop mental health.

Components of Wellness

Addressing Naive Conceptions

Students may believe that being healthy means they will never experience illness or have bad moods. Point out that the real test of wellness is how people respond to these things when they happen. Students should realize that wellness is not a permanent state but is dependent on a continuous series of decisions and actions. Describe situations and have students describe a healthy response and an unhealthy response. For example, ask: **Suppose Carla is a goalie and she wakes up on the morning of a big soccer game with a high fever. What is a healthy response and what is an unhealthy response?** *(Sample: A healthy response is to stay in bed until she feels better. An unhealthy response is to pretend nothing is wrong and play the game anyway.)* **learning modality: verbal**

Building Inquiry Skills: Communicating

Invite students to take part in a role-playing activity in which they practice ways to refuse participation in harmful activities with peers. First, have students identify several activities that could be harmful to their mental, physical, or social health. Then they should create a list of possible responses such as "Smoking does not interest me because it stains your teeth." Have students state simple reasons for their refusal. Students can work together to develop various scenarios. **cooperative learning**

Program Resources

◆ **Teaching Resources** 1-3 Lesson Plan, p. 23; 1-3 Section Summary, p. 24

Media and Technology

 Audiotapes English-Spanish Summary 1-3

Ongoing Assessment

Writing Have students write a definition of physical, mental, and social health, and a behavior that illustrates each.

 Students can save their definitions in their portfolios.

Components of Wellness, continued

Skills Focus making models

Materials *cardboard, string, scissors, tape, ruler, markers, magazines, glue*

Time 25 minutes

Tips Students' mobiles may not balance due to the size of the pictures they paste on them. If necessary, allow them to add more photos until their mobiles balance.

Expected Outcome The mobile will not balance properly unless there are representatives of all three components of health. Ask: **How does your mobile model the three components of wellness?** *(A balance of all three components is necessary for wellness.)*

Extend Have students make unbalanced mobiles using pictures of bad health habits, then use pictures of good health habits to bring the mobile into balance.

learning modality: kinesthetic

Evaluating Your Wellness

Using the Visuals: Figure 10

Students who are learning English may have difficulty understanding the meaning of *continuum*. To help make the definition concrete, ask students to place a finger on the center of the continuum. Call out several behaviors and have students move their finger right or left along the continuum based on how they think the behaviors would affect a person's health. Possible behaviors include: using a seat belt, chewing tobacco, borrowing prescription medication from a friend, joining a volunteer organization, joining a gang, flossing your teeth, getting eight hours of sleep every night. Ask students: **Why is a continuum a better way to measure health than simply deciding whether someone is healthy or unhealthy?** *(Sample: There are many factors that affect health, and it is the balance of these factors that determines a person's wellness.)*

limited English proficiency

Wellness in the Balance

In this activity, you will make a mobile showing the three aspects of wellness.

1. Cut out a cardboard triangle about 20 cm on each side. Label the sides of the triangle "Physical Health," "Mental Health," and "Social Health." Tape a string to the center of the triangle.

2. Cut pictures from magazines showing activities that contribute to each of the three components of wellness.

3. Glue each picture onto a separate piece of cardboard. Tape one end of a string to each picture. Tape the other end to the appropriate side of the triangle. Hang the mobile from the center string.

Making Models How does your mobile show that all three components of wellness are important?

Overall Wellness Like three pieces in a jigsaw puzzle, your physical health, mental health, and social health are linked together. You can understand this if you think about what happens when a soccer team wins a game. To make the kick to score a goal, your body needs to be in good physical health. If you play well, you feel good about yourself—excited, happy, and proud. When you celebrate with your teammates, you enjoy good social relationships.

☑ *Checkpoint* How is social health different from mental health? How are they related?

Evaluating Your Wellness

Think for a minute about your overall level of health—physical, mental, and social. How healthy are you? You could think of your overall level of health as a point on a **continuum,** which is a gradual progression through many stages between one extreme and another. The illness-wellness continuum is shown in Figure 10. The far right end of the continuum represents perfect wellness, and the far left end represents very poor health, or even early death. The point in the middle is neutral—neither ill nor well. Your level of wellness is represented by a point somewhere between the two ends. For the most part, it is the behaviors that you choose that determine where on the continuum your level of health falls.

Figure 10 A person's level of health can be represented by a point on the illness-wellness continuum.
Making Judgments How can you improve your health and move closer to the wellness end of the continuum?

Loss of health   Improving health
Very poor health   *Neither sick nor well*   *Excellent health*

Background

History of Science The Greek physician Hippocrates (c. 460–377 B.C.) is known as the "Father of Medicine." Today, new physicians pay tribute to Hippocrates in the ethical oath they take when they graduate from medical school. The original Hippocratic oath includes the following:

"I will give no deadly medicine to any one if asked, nor suggest any such counsel. . . . With purity and with holiness I will pass my life and practice my Art . . ."

Program Resources

- **Science Explorer Series** *Environmental Science*, Chapter 4
- ◆ **Interdisciplinary Exploration Series** "Soap From Concept to Consumer," pp. 27–30

Improving Your Health

Your health doesn't have to stay in the same place on the illness-wellness continuum. Working on wellness is a lot like keeping your room clean. You can't clean your room just once. After a few days, dirty clothes pile up, your trash basket overflows, and dust settles on everything. Like keeping your room tidy, you must work to improve your wellness every day.

Factors You Cannot Change Before you plan how to improve your wellness, you need to recognize that there are some health-related factors that you cannot change. Some of these may be traits that you inherited from your parents, such as skin that sunburns easily. However, you can still work toward wellness. You can use a sunscreen and limit your exposure to sunlight.

 INTEGRATING ENVIRONMENTAL SCIENCE You probably cannot change the environment in which you live, even though it affects your health. Polluted air can damage the lungs and make the circulatory system struggle to get oxygen to the cells. Polluted water can carry chemicals and microorganisms that harm the body. Although you by yourself may not be able to change your environment, you can avoid some environmental risks. You can, for example, refuse to swim or fish in polluted water.

Making Wise Decisions Every day you make many decisions that affect your health. Some of these decisions, such as whether to wear a jacket on a cold day, are fairly simple. Others, such as how to deal with a friend who is pressuring you to use tobacco, may be a lot more complicated. For help with very important decisions, talk to a parent, teacher, or other trusted adult.

Figure 11 Snowboarding can affect your health in positive or negative ways. By taking proper precautions and being careful, snowboarding can be a positive experience.

Integrating Environmental Science

Ask students to brainstorm ways people in their community can avoid environmental health risks. *(Sample: Exercise indoors when the air is polluted; wash fruits and vegetables carefully.)* Interested students may want to research the levels of pollutants in local water supplies. **learning modality: verbal**

Real-Life Learning

Students may be confused by conflicting information about health issues offered by television or newspapers. Students may be interested in a particular issue, such as how much fat their diet should contain or whether it is healthy to exercise in hot weather. Based on student interests, use the library or search the Internet to find articles that offer different advice on this issue. Distribute appropriate articles to students. After students have read the articles, discuss them with the class and guide students to decide how to make wise decisions about the issue. Ask: **How can you tell whether an article gives good advice?** *(To be reliable, an article's recommendations should be based on facts, rather than emotional appeal.)* Encourage students to seek help with important health decisions. **learning modality: verbal**

Answers to Self-Assessment

Caption Question

Figure 10 Sample: Eat properly, get enough rest and exercise, avoid smoking.

✓ *Checkpoint*

Social health refers to a person's ability to get along with others. Mental health involves feelings and emotions. Social factors may affect a person's mental health, and vice versa.

Ongoing Assessment

Oral Presentation Ask students to describe how to use the idea of a continuum to evaluate and improve their health. *(Students should realize that they can identify their current overall health as a point on the continuum, and that they must continue to improve their wellness.)*

Improving Your Health,
continued

Building Inquiry Skills:
Applying Concepts

Challenge students to create a list of scenarios such as the one shown in Figure 12. Then have students create flowcharts listing all aspects of the decision-making process. Students should be encouraged to make judgments and evaluate the soundness of their decisions. **learning modality: visual**

3 Assess

Section 3 Review Answers

1. Physical health—how well the body functions; mental health—how you feel about yourself and how you handle stress; social health—your relationships and how well you get along with others

2. The steps are the following: identifying the problem, outlining the benefits and the risks, making a decision, and evaluating the decision.

3. Sample: Getting more exercise would move a person toward the wellness end of the continuum.

4. The friend could exert positive peer pressure to encourage you to adopt a healthful lifestyle.

Science at Home

Encourage students to have each family member make a suggestion towards improving wellness. Suggestions could include activities that a family could do together such as preparing meals, getting involved in their neighborhood or community, hiking and biking, playing games, and building things together.

Performance Assessment

Drawing Have students make posters describing the three components of wellness, including pictures and examples of ways to improve health in each area.

32 ◆ D

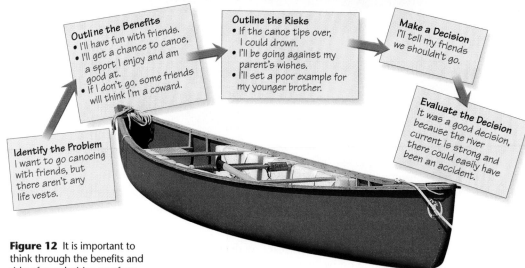

Decision: Whether or Not to Go Canoeing

Identify the Problem
I want to go canoeing with friends, but there aren't any life vests.

Outline the Benefits
• I'll have fun with friends.
• I'll get a chance to canoe, a sport I enjoy and am good at.
• If I don't go, some friends will think I'm a coward.

Outline the Risks
• If the canoe tips over, I could drown.
• I'll be going against my parent's wishes.
• I'll set a poor example for my younger brother.

Make a Decision
I'll tell my friends we shouldn't go.

Evaluate the Decision
It was a good decision, because the river current is strong and there could easily have been an accident.

Figure 12 It is important to think through the benefits and risks of any decision you face. *Problem Solving What decision would you reach if you were faced with this problem?*

To make a healthy decision, it is important to think through the benefits and risks of an action you might take. You increase the likelihood of making a healthy decision if you think about it carefully beforehand. Evaluate the advantages and disadvantages of each choice you might make. Figure 12 shows how decision making can work in a real situation.

In this textbook, you will learn many ways to improve your health. You will discover that this textbook is something like an owner's manual. It will explain how your body works, and give you some suggestions for keeping your body healthy. The decision to do that is up to you.

Section 3 Review

 1. Identify the three components of wellness. Briefly explain each one.

2. Explain the process involved in making a healthy decision.

3. Give an example of something that might change a person's position on the illness-wellness continuum. In which direction would the person move?

4. Thinking Critically Inferring How might having a friend who is very wellness-conscious affect your own level of wellness? Explain.

32 ◆ D

Science at Home

Explain to your family what the concept of wellness means. Then work with family members to identify four or five changes that you, as a family, could make to improve family wellness. Make sure to include changes that would improve mental and social health as well as physical health.

Program Resources

◆ **Teaching Resources** 1-3 Review and Reinforce, p. 25; 1-3 Enrich, p. 26

Media and Technology

Interactive Student Tutorial CD-ROM D-1

Answers to Self-Assessment

Caption Question

Figure 12 Answers may vary. Encourage students not to choose the canoe trip because it would endanger their physical health.

32 ◆ D

SECTION

① How the Body Is Organized

Key Ideas

◆ The levels of organization in the human body consist of cells, tissues, organs, and organ systems.

◆ The cell is the basic unit of structure and function in living things. The human body contains about 100 trillion cells.

◆ A tissue is a group of cells that perform the same function. The human body contains four basic types of tissue—muscle, nerve, connective, and epithelial.

◆ Organs, which are composed of different kinds of tissue, perform complex functions. An organ system is a group of organs that work together to perform a major function.

Key Terms

cell	nerve tissue
cell membrane	connective tissue
nucleus	epithelial tissue
cytoplasm	organ
tissue	organ system
muscle tissue	

 SECTION

② Keeping the Body in Balance

Key Ideas

◆ Homeostasis is the process by which an organism's internal environment is kept stable in spite of changes in the external environment.

◆ Stress disturbs homeostasis. When under stress, the body releases adrenaline, which causes many changes in the body. The changes prepare the body to take quick action.

◆ Exercise and relaxing activities can help relieve stress.

Key Terms

homeostasis   stress   adrenaline

SECTION

③ Wellness

 INTEGRATING **HEALTH**

Key Ideas

◆ Wellness is being at the best possible level of health. The three components of wellness are physical health, mental health, and social health.

◆ Physical health consists of how well the body functions. Mental health consists of how you feel about yourself and how well you handle the demands of your life. Social health is how well you get along with other people.

◆ A person's overall level of wellness can range from very poor health to excellent health. Most people fall somewhere between those two points. Behavior can affect wellness, either by harming it or improving it.

◆ To make a health-related decision, you should consider both the benefits and the risks of any action.

Key Terms

wellness	social health
physical health	peer pressure
mental health	continuum

USING THE INTERNET

www.science-explorer.phschool.com

CHAPTER 1 REVIEW

Program Resources

◆ **Teaching Resources** Chapter 1 Project Scoring Rubric, p. 14; Chapter 1 Performance Assessment Teacher Notes, p. 236–237; Chapter 1 Performance Assessment Student Worksheet, p. 238; Chapter 1 Test, pp. 239–242

CHAPTER 1 REVIEW

Reviewing Content:

Multiple Choice

1. c **2.** d **3.** c **4.** b **5.** a

True or False

6. muscle **7.** true **8.** true **9.** stress
10. mental

Checking Concepts

11. An organ system is a group of organs that perform a major function; an organ is made up of different tissues that together perform a specific function within the organ system; tissues are made up of similar cells that perform a specific function which is more limited than the function of an organ.

12. The respiratory system takes oxygen into the body and gets rid of carbon dioxide.

13. Your body needs materials from food in order to function. Hunger prompts you to eat, thus supplying your body with the food it needs and maintaining your body's stability.

14. Sample: You are moving to a new community. Actions you can take to relieve stress: get involved with school activities to make new friends; keep in touch with your friends from the old community; engage in sports or other strenuous activities to relieve stress.

15. Sample: Polluted air and polluted water. To protect yourself from polluted air, it is best to exercise indoors. Do not swim in or drink polluted water.

16. Sample: Dear Aspiring Actor, To deal with the stress, read the play carefully ahead of time, so that you are familiar with it and the part you are trying out for. Get a good night's sleep before the tryout. Ride your bike or rake leaves to relieve tension. Talk with your best friend and family about the tryout.

Thinking Visually

17. a. Mental health **b.** Social health
c. Eat healthy foods, exercise regularly, get enough sleep, or wear protective gear when playing sports. **d.** Build healthy relationships, respect the rights of others, accept help, or communicate your needs.

C H A P T E R 1 R E V I E W

Reviewing Content

 For more review of key concepts, see the Interactive Student Tutorial CD-ROM.

Multiple Choice

Choose the letter of the best answer.

1. A group of similar cells that perform a similar function is called a(n)
   a. cell.
   b. organ.
   c. tissue.
   d. organ system.
2. The control center of the cell is the
   a. cell membrane.
   b. cell fluid.
   c. cytoplasm.
   d. nucleus.
3. Which type of tissue is blood?
   a. muscle tissue
   b. epithelial tissue
   c. connective tissue
   d. nerve tissue
4. The term most closely associated with homeostasis is
   a. growth.
   b. stability.
   c. temperature.
   d. energy.
5. Which of the following is *not* a way to protect your social health?
   a. getting enough sleep
   b. making friends
   c. respecting the rights of others
   d. accepting help

True or False

If the statement is true, write true. If it is false, change the underlined word or words to make the statement true.

6. <u>Epithelial</u> tissue makes parts of your body move.
7. The <u>circulatory</u> system carries needed materials to the body cells.
8. The brain is an example of <u>an organ</u>.
9. The fight-or-flight response is part of the body's reaction to <u>peer pressure</u>.
10. Feeling good about yourself is one aspect of <u>social</u> health.

34 ◆ D

Checking Concepts

11. Explain the relationship between cells, tissues, organs, and organ systems.
12. What is the function of the respiratory system?
13. How does hunger help your body maintain homeostasis?
14. Think of a situation that might cause long-term stress. Identify some ways in which a person might deal with that stress.
15. List two possible health hazards in the environment, and explain how you might protect yourself from them.
16. **Writing to Learn** Imagine that you write a newspaper advice column called Ask Dr. Wellness. You receive the following letter:
    Dear Dr. Wellness: I am under a great deal of stress because I will soon be trying out for a major part in the school play. I want the part badly. How can I deal with this stress?
    Aspiring Actor
    Write an answer to this letter that gives Aspiring Actor some specific suggestions.

Thinking Visually

17. **Concept Map** The concept map below diagrams the three components of wellness. Copy the map and complete it. (For more on concept maps, see the Skills Handbook.)

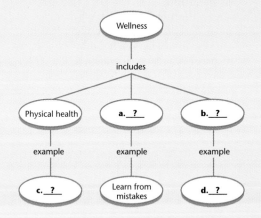

Applying Skills

18. The girl's internal temperature stays constant as the environmental temperature rises. This demonstrates stability of her internal temperature despite changes in the external temperature.

19. Her skin temperature rises as the external temperature increases. Her skin is in direct contact with the external environment (the air) and thus warms as the external temperature increases.

20. Most students will hypothesize that her internal temperature would remain constant due to homeostasis while her skin temperature would decline.

21. Sample experiment: Measure internal temperature using an oral thermometer when the girl is inside and then ten minutes after she steps outside. Measure skin temperature at the same times by holding a thermometer next to her cheek.

Applying Skills

The graph below shows the effects of the temperature of the environment on a girl's skin temperature and on the temperature inside her body. Use the graph to answer Questions 18–21.

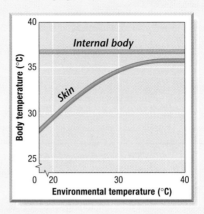

18. Interpreting Data As the temperature of the environment rises, what happens to the girl's internal temperature? How does this demonstrate homeostasis?

19. Inferring What happens to the temperature of the girl's skin? Why is this pattern different from the pattern shown by the girl's internal temperature?

20. Developing Hypotheses Suppose the girl went outdoors on a chilly fall morning. Write a hypothesis that predicts what would happen to her internal body temperature and skin temperature.

21. Designing Experiments Design an experiment to test your hypothesis from Question 20.

Thinking Critically

22. Making Judgments Suppose some friends were pressuring you to go skateboarding on a road with heavy traffic. Identify the benefits and risks of the choices you have. Then make a decision and explain your reasons.

23. Inferring Why do you think scientists classify blood as a connective tissue?

24. Making Generalizations How is homeostasis important to the survival of living things?

Performance Assessment

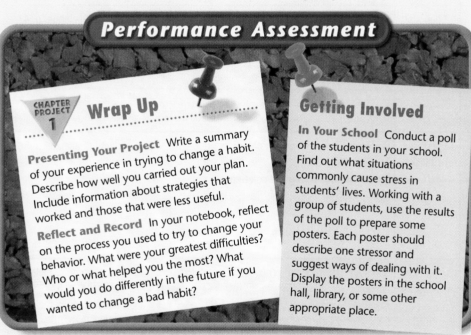

CHAPTER PROJECT 1 **Wrap Up**

Presenting Your Project Write a summary of your experience in trying to change a habit. Describe how well you carried out your plan. Include information about strategies that worked and those that were less useful.

Reflect and Record In your notebook, reflect on the process you used to try to change your behavior. What were your greatest difficulties? Who or what helped you the most? What would you do differently in the future if you wanted to change a bad habit?

Getting Involved

In Your School Conduct a poll of the students in your school. Find out what situations commonly cause stress in students' lives. Working with a group of students, use the results of the poll to prepare some posters. Each poster should describe one stressor and suggest ways of dealing with it. Display the posters in the school hall, library, or some other appropriate place.

Thinking Critically

22. Sample: Risks of skateboarding on a busy road include injury, angering drivers and police, and breaking parents' rules. Benefits include making friends happy and having fun doing an enjoyable activity. Students' final decisions should be well supported and should indicate a concern for wellness.

23. Blood flows through the whole body, connecting all parts of the body.

24. If living things could not maintain a stable internal environment, body functions could not take place. For example, if the body did not have a steady supply of food, the cells would not obtain the materials they need.

Performance Assessment

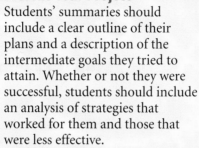

CHAPTER PROJECT 1

Wrap Up

Present Your Project Students' summaries should include a clear outline of their plans and a description of the intermediate goals they tried to attain. Whether or not they were successful, students should include an analysis of strategies that worked for them and those that were less effective.

Reflect and Record If students' plans were unsuccessful, encourage them to re-evaluate the behavior they wanted to change. Some students may have realized that they were not ready to change this habit, or that they could make other changes that would affect their health more directly. Encourage students to remember that wellness requires constant attention, and that they can use what they learned in this project to attempt to change or implement habits throughout their lives.

Program Resources

◆ **Inquiry Skills Handbook** Provides teaching and review of all inquiry skills

Getting Involved

In Your School Help students develop an anonymous method of polling students. Read the questions before allowing students to give the poll, and have groups of students practice answering the questions to make sure the questionnaire elicits the desired information. Students should ask permission to hang posters in their chosen location.

Bones, Muscles, and Skin

Sections	Time	Student Edition Activities	Other Activities	
CHAPTER PROJECT 2 **On the Move** p. 37	Ongoing (2–3 weeks)	Check Your Progress, pp. 45, 54 Wrap Up, p. 65	TE	Chapter 2 Project Notes, pp. 36–37
1 The Skeletal System pp. 38–45 ◆ Identify the functions of the skeleton. ◆ Explain the role that moveable joints play in the body. ◆ List ways that individuals can keep their bones strong and healthy ◆ Describe the structure of bones and how they grow and form.	4 periods/ 2 blocks	**Discover** Hard as a Rock?, p. 38 **Try This** Soft Bones?, p. 40 **Sharpen Your Skills** Classifying, p. 42	TE TE TE TE PTA	Including All Students, p. 40 Using the Visuals: Figure 3, p. 42 Including All Students, p. 43 Integrating Health, p. 44 "Testing Yogurt," pp.1–8
2 *INTEGRATING TECHNOLOGY* **Diagnosing Bone and Joint Injuries** pp. 46–49 ◆ List common skeletal system injuries and describe methods for their diagnosis. ◆ List ways that bone and joint injuries can be prevented.	2 periods/ 1 block	**Discover** What Do X-Ray Images Show?, p. 46	TE TE PTA	Inquiry Challenge, p. 47 Integrating Health, p. 49 "Testing Jeans," pp. 1–8
3 The Muscular System pp. 50–55 ◆ Identify the three types of muscles found in the body and describe the function of each. ◆ Explain how skeletal muscles work in pairs. ◆ List ways in which people can keep their muscles healthy.	3 periods/ 1½ blocks	**Discover** How Do Muscles Work?, p. 50 **Try This** Get a Grip, p. 52 **Skills Lab: Observing** A Look Beneath the Skin, p. 55	TE	Inquiry Challenge, p. 53
4 The Skin pp. 56–62 ◆ Describe the functions of skin. ◆ List ways that individuals can keep skin healthy. ◆ Identify and describe the layers of the skin.	3½ periods/ 1–2 blocks	**Discover** What Can You Observe About Skin?, p. 56 **Try This** Sweaty Skin, p. 59 **Real-World Lab: You and Your Environment** Sun Safety, pp. 60–61	TE TE PTA PTA	Building Inquiry Skills: Observing, p. 57 Building Inquiry Skills: Observing, p. 59 "Testing Bandages," pp. 1–8 "Testing Lip Balms," pp. 1–8
Study Guide/Chapter Review pp. 63–65	1 period/ ½ block		ISAB	Provides teaching and review of all inquiry skills

For Standard or Block Schedule The Resource Pro® CD-ROM gives you maximum flexibility for planning your instruction for any type of schedule. Resource Pro® contains Planning Express®, an advanced scheduling program, as well as the entire contents of the Teaching Resources and the Computer Test Bank.

CHAPTER PLANNING GUIDE

Program Resources	Assessment Strategies	Media and Technology
TR Chapter 2 Project Teacher Notes, pp. 30–31 **TR** Chapter 2 Project Overview and Worksheets, pp. 32–35 **TR** Chapter 2 Project Scoring Rubric, p. 36	**SE** Performance Assessment: Chapter 2 Project Wrap Up, p. 65 **TE** Check Your Progress, pp. 45, 54 **TE** Performance Assessment: Chapter 2 Project Wrap Up, p. 65 **TR** Chapter 2 Project Scoring Rubric, p. 36	
TR 2-1 Lesson Plan, p. 37 **TR** 2-1 Section Summary, p. 38 **TR** 2-1 Review and Reinforce, p. 39 **TR** 2-1 Enrich, p. 40	**SE** Section 1 Review, p. 45 **TE** Ongoing Assessment, pp. 39, 41, 43 **TE** Performance Assessment, p. 45 **TR** 2-1 Review and Reinforce, p. 39	🎧 Audiotapes: English-Spanish Summary 2-1 📽 Transparency 2, "The Human Skeleton" 📽 Transparency 3, "The Structure of a Bone" 📽 Transparency 4, "Exploring Movable Joints" 💿 Interactive Student Tutorial CD-ROM, D-2
TR 2-2 Lesson Plan, p. 41 **TR** 2-2 Section Summary, p. 42 **TR** 2-2 Review and Reinforce, p. 43 **TR** 2-2 Enrich, p. 44 **SES** Book O, *Sound and Light,* Chapter 1	**SE** Section 2 Review, p. 49 **TE** Ongoing Assessment, p. 47 **TE** Performance Assessment, p. 49 **TR** 2-2 Review and Reinforce, p. 43	📀 Exploring Physical Science Videodisc, Unit 6 Side 2, "The Electromagnetic Spectrum" 🎧 Audiotapes: English-Spanish Summary 2-2 💿 Interactive Student Tutorial CD-ROM, D-2
TR 2-3 Lesson Plan, p. 45 **TR** 2-3 Section Summary, p. 46 **TR** 2-3 Review and Reinforce, p. 47 **TR** 2-3 Enrich, p. 48 **TR** Chapter 2 Skills Lab, pp. 53–54	**SE** Section 3 Review, p. 54 **SE** Analyze and Conclude, p. 55 **TE** Ongoing Assessment, pp. 51, 53 **TE** Performance Assessment, p. 54 **TR** 2-3 Review and Reinforce, p. 47	📀 Exploring Life Science Videodisc, Unit 4 Side 1, "Muscles and Bones" 🎧 Audiotapes: English-Spanish Summary 2-3 💿 Interactive Student Tutorial CD-ROM, D-2
TR 2-4 Lesson Plan, p. 49 **TR** 2-4 Section Summary, p. 50 **TR** 2-4 Review and Reinforce, p. 51 **TR** 2-4 Enrich, p. 52 **TR** Chapter 2 Real-World Lab, pp. 55–57	**SE** Section 4 Review, p. 62 **SE** Analyze and Conclude, p. 61 **TE** Ongoing Assessment, pp. 57, 59 **TE** Performance Assessment, p. 62 **TR** 2-4 Review and Reinforce, p. 51	🎧 Audiotapes: English-Spanish Summary 2-4 📽 Transparency 5, "The Skin" 💿 Interactive Student Tutorial CD-ROM, D-2
TR Chapter 2 Performance Assessment, pp. 243–245 **TR** Chapter 2 Test, pp. 246–249	**SE** Chapter Review, pp. 63–65 **TR** Chapter 2 Performance Assessment, pp. 243–245 **TR** Chapter 2 Test, pp. 246–249 **CTB** Test D-2	💾 Computer Test Bank, Test D-2 🌐 Science Explorer Internet Site

Key:
SE Student Edition
CTB Computer Test Bank
ISAB Inquiry Skills Activity Book
TE Teacher's Edition
SES Science Explorer Series Text
PTA Product Testing Activities by *Consumer Reports*
TR Teaching Resources
ISLM Integrated Science Laboratory Manual
IES Interdisciplinary Explorations Series

Meeting the National Science Education Standards and AAAS Benchmarks

National Science Education Standards	Benchmarks for Science Literacy	Unifying Themes
Science as Inquiry (Content Standard A) ◆ **Ask questions that can be answered by scientific investigations** What are some characteristics of skeletal muscles? How do skeletal muscles work? *(Skills Lab)* How well do different materials protect the skin from the sun? *(Real-World Lab)* **Life Science** (Content Standard C) ◆ **Structure and function of living systems** The skeleton has five major functions: shape, support, movement, protection, and production of blood cells. Joints allows the body to move in different ways. *(Section 1)* The human body has three types of muscle tissue—skeletal, smooth, and cardiac. Muscles work in pairs to move the bones of the body. *(Section 3)* The skin covers the body, prevents loss of water, protects the body from injury and infection, regulates body temperature, eliminates wastes, and produces Vitamin D. *(Section 4)* **Science and Technology** (Content Standard E) ◆ **Understandings about science and technology** X-rays and MRI technology help identify injuries of the skeletal system. *(Section 3)* **Science in Personal and Social Perspectives** (Content Standard F) ◆ **Personal health** Bone and joint injuries can be prevented through regular exercise and a balanced diet. *(Section 3)*	**3C Issues in Technology** Advances in medical technology such as X-ray, MRI, and arthroscopic surgery have influenced the diagnosis and treatment of injuries to the skeletal and muscular systems. *(Section 2)* **6B Human Development** Bones lose mass with age. This may result in a condition called osteoporosis. *(Section 1)* **6C Basic Functions** The skin, skeletal, and muscular systems provide essential functions that are integral parts of the overall function of the human body. *(Section 2)* **6E Physical Health** Regular exercise and a balanced diet are important for maintaining muscle tone and bone strength. *(Section 1)*	◆ **Energy** The muscular system obtains, stores, and uses energy to perform its functions. Energy is required to grow new bone and muscle tissue. *(Sections 1, 3)* ◆ **Patterns of Change** Some bone tissue develops from cartilage tissue. Different types of muscle tissue are specialized to perform specific voluntary and involuntary functions. *(Sections 1, 3)* ◆ **Scale and Structure** The skeletal system is made up of bones, ligaments, tendons, and cartilage. The muscular system is made up of voluntary and involuntary muscles. *(Sections 1, 3)* ◆ **Unity and Diversity** The structure of bones and muscles differ, but both systems work together to enable the body to move. *(Sections 1, 3, 4)* ◆ **Systems and Interactions** There are three types of muscles in the human body: cardiac, which are involuntary muscles found in the heart; smooth, which are involuntary muscles found in other body systems such as the digestive system and circulatory system; and skeletal muscles, which permit voluntary movement. *(Sections 1, 3)*

Media and Technology

Exploring Physical Science Videodisc

◆ **Section 2** "The Electromagnetic Spectrum" defines visible and invisible electromagnetic waves and describes how we rely on all waves in this spectrum.

Exploring Life Science Videodisc

◆ **Section 3** "Muscles and Bones" details the interdependence of the skeletal and muscular systems as they function for an athlete in training.

Interactive Student Tutorial CD-ROM

◆ **Chapter Review** Interactive questions help students to self-assess their mastery of key chapter concepts.

Student Edition Connection Strategies

◆ **Section 1** Integrating Health, p. 44
  Visual Arts Connection, p. 44

◆ **Section 2** Integrating Technology, p. 46
  Integrating Physics, p. 47
  Integrating Health, p. 48

◆ **Section 3** Integrating Health, p. 54

USING THE INTERNET

www.science-explorer.phschool.com

Visit the Science Explorer Internet site to find an up-to-date activity for Chapter 2 of *Human Biology and Health*.

ACTIVITY	Time (minutes)	Materials *Quantities for one work group*	Skills
Section 1			
Discover, p. 38	10	**Consumable** leg bone from a cooked chicken or turkey **Nonconsumable** rock of similar size to bone, hand lens	Observing
Try This, p. 40	15 min set up,15 min obser-vation 1 wk later	**Consumable** 2 plastic jars or other containers, vinegar, water, 2 clean chicken bones, gloves	Drawing Conclusions
Sharpen Your Skills, p. 42	15	**Consumable** No special materials are required.	Classifying
Section 2			
Discover, p. 46	15	**Consumable** No special materials are required.	Observing
Section 3			
Discover, p. 50	15	**Nonconsumable** spring-type clothespin	Predicting
Try This, p. 52	10	**Nonconsumable** wooden stirrer or other item that is very thin and smooth on its edges, hairpin	Inferring
Skills Lab, p. 55	30	**Consumable** protective gloves; paper towels; water; uncooked chicken wing, treated with bleach **Nonconsumable** scissors, dissecting tray	Observing
Section 4			
Discover, p. 56	15	**Nonconsumable** hand lens, plastic gloves	Inferring
Try This, p. 59	15	**Consumable** wet cotton ball, piece of cardboard **Nonconsumable** 2 thermometers	Measuring
Real-World Lab, pp. 60–61	45 min, plus 2 to 4 hr of sun exposure, and 20 min to analyze the results	**Consumable** 3 different fabrics, plastic knife, photosensitive paper, white construction paper, resealable plastic bag **Nonconsumable** scissors, pencil, metric ruler, stapler, staple remover, 2 sunscreens with SPF ratings of 4 and 30	Predicting, Observing, Drawing Conclusions

A list of all materials required for the Student Edition activities can be found on pages T14–T15. You can order Materials Kits by calling 1-800-828-7777 or by accessing the Science Explorer Internet site at **www.science-explorer.phschool.com.**

Bones, movable joints, and skeletal muscles interact in the human body to allow a wide range of movement, from the simple act of holding a spoon to a dramatic gymnastic floor routine.

Purpose In this project, students will apply the chapter's concepts and terms to make working models of a specific simple movement. To demonstrate this movement, students must include the main bones, muscles, and joints involved. Students will then present their models to the class and describe how the movement is produced by the contraction of muscles.

Skills Focus After completing the Chapter 2 Project, students will be able to
- identify the main bones, joints, and muscles involved in a simple movement;
- create a working model that accurately describes a simple movement;
- explain how skeletal muscles contract to produce movement;
- describe how skeletal muscles work in pairs.

Project Time Line This project requires at least two weeks for completion. Allow at least three days for students to choose a movement to model. Planning and building the model will require about one week. Students should complete their models at least one day before they will present them. This will give students time to test their models and practice their presentations. Before beginning the project, see Chapter 2 Project Teacher Notes on pages 31–32 in Teaching Resources for more details on carrying out the project. Also distribute the Chapter 2 Project Student Materials and Scoring Rubric on pages 33–37 in Teaching Resources.

Suggested Shortcuts You may choose to have students work in small groups as a cooperative learning task. To ensure that every student will have ample opportunity to participate in planning and building the model, each group should consist of no more than four students.

CHAPTER 2 Bones, Muscles, and Skin

WHAT'S AHEAD

SECTION 1 The Skeletal System

Discover **Hard as a Rock?**
Try This **Soft Bones?**
Sharpen Your Skills **Classifying**

Integrating Technology
SECTION 2 Diagnosing Bone and Joint Injuries

Discover **What Do X-Ray Images Show?**

SECTION 3 The Muscular System

Discover **How Do Muscles Work?**
Try This **Get a Grip**
Skills Lab **A Look Beneath the Skin**

Possible Materials Provide a wide variety of materials from which students can choose. Some possibilities are listed below. Encourage students to suggest and use other materials as well.
- *To model bones:* pieces of wood, cardboard, plastic foam, or papier-mâché
- *To model muscles:* rubber bands, springs, wire, or string
- *To model ligaments and tendons:* paper fasteners, screws, springs, wire, glue, or staples

- Another option is to allow students to construct their models using computer animation.

On the Move

People are able to perform an amazing variety of movements. For example, a baseball player can swing a bat, a chef can twirl pizza dough, and an artist can mold clay into a sculpture. Behind every human movement, there's a complex interaction of bones, muscles, and other parts of the body.

In this chapter, you'll find out how bones and muscles work. And in this project, you'll take a close look at a simple movement, such as stretching a leg, bending an arm at the elbow, or another movement you choose.

Your Goal To make a working model that shows how bones and muscles interact to move the body in a specific way.

To complete this project you will
◆ select a specific movement, and identify all of the major bones, joints, and muscles that are involved
◆ design an accurate physical model of the movement
◆ explain how the bones and muscles make the movement possible
◆ follow the safety guidelines in Appendix A

Get Started Let all group members name a motion from a sport or other familiar activity that they'd like to investigate. If the motion is long or complicated, discuss how to simplify it for the project. Also consider what kind of model you'll make, such as a wood or cardboard cutout, clay structure, or computer animation. Then write up a plan for your teacher's approval.

Check Your Progress You'll be working on this project as you study this chapter. To keep your project on track, look for Check Your Progress boxes at the following points.
Section 1 Review, page 45: Choose a simple motion to analyze and sketch.
Section 3 Review, page 54: Create your working model.

Wrap Up At the end of the chapter (page 65), you'll demonstrate your working model.

For this baseball player to hit the ball, his bones and muscles must work together in a coordinated manner.

SECTION 4 The Skin

Discover **What Can You Observe About Skin?**
Try This **Sweaty Skin**
Real-World Lab **Sun Safety**

Program Resources

◆ **Teaching Resources** Chapter 2 Project Teacher Notes, pp. 31–32; Chapter 2 Project Overview and Worksheets, pp. 33–36; Chapter 2 Project Scoring Rubric, p. 37

Launching the Project To introduce the project and to stimulate student interest, ask: **What are some of the movements you make every day?** *(Samples: Walking, chewing, running, breathing)* Write students' responses on the board. Then ask: **What parts of your body are involved in each of these movements?** *(Sample for walking: Your legs and feet move your body forward, and your arms swing back and forth.)*

Allow time for students to read the description of the project in their text and the Chapter 2 Project Overview on pages 33–34 in Teaching Resources. Then encourage discussions on how a movement could be modeled, what types of materials could be used, and any initial questions students may have. Pass out copies of the Chapter 2 Project Worksheets on pages 35–36 in Teaching Resources for students to review.

If students select complex motions such as pitching a ball, help them narrow their focus to a simple portion of that action.

Because the muscular system is not covered until later in the chapter, you may wish to preview a few of the concepts relating to skeletal muscles that students will be using in planning their models.

Performance Assessment

The Chapter 2 Project Scoring Rubric on page 37 of Teaching Resources will help you evaluate how well students complete the Chapter 2 Project. Students will be assessed on
◆ how well they plan their models, including identification of the main muscles, bones, and joints involved, and a list of materials;
◆ the accuracy of their explanation of how muscles work;
◆ the organization and thoroughness of their presentations;
◆ their participation in their groups (if applicable).
By sharing the Chapter 2 Scoring Rubric with students at the beginning of the project, you will make it clear to them what they are expected to do.

Objectives

After completing the lesson, students will be able to
- identify the functions of the skeleton;
- explain the role that movable joints play in the body;
- list ways that individuals can keep their bones strong and healthy;
- describe the structure of bones and how they grow and form.

Key Terms vertebra, marrow, cartilage, joint, ligament, osteoporosis

1 Engage/Explore

Activating Prior Knowledge

Ask students to hold out one hand and feel the bones beneath the skin. Then have them draw a picture of what they think the bones look like. They can keep their drawings for later reference.

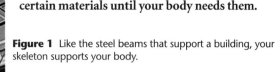

DISCOVER

Skills Focus observing
Materials *leg bone from a cooked chicken or turkey, rock of similar size, hand lens*
Time 10 minutes
Tips Remind students to observe as many characteristics as possible, such as size, shape, color, texture, composition, and strength. Make sure the chicken or turkey bone has been thoroughly cooked and washed.
Think It Over Students will probably say that bones are sometimes compared to rocks because they are both hard. A bone has a definite shape and a rock does not. Bone is not as dense as rock and has a definite structure.

DISCOVER • **ACTIVITY**

Hard as a Rock?

1. Your teacher will give you a leg bone from a cooked turkey or chicken and a rock.
2. Use a hand lens to examine both the rock and the bone.
3. Gently tap both the rock and the bone on a hard surface.
4. Pick up each object to feel how heavy it is.
5. Wash your hands. Then make notes of your observations.

Think It Over
Observing Based on your observations, why do you think bones are sometimes compared to rocks? List some ways in which bones and rocks are similar and different.

GUIDE FOR READING

- What are the functions of the skeleton?
- What role do movable joints play in the body?
- How can you keep your bones strong and healthy?

Reading Tip Before you read, rewrite the headings in the section as *how, why,* or *what* questions. As you read, write answers to the questions.

A construction site is a busy place. After workers have prepared the building's foundation, they begin to assemble thousands of steel pieces into a frame for the building. People watch as the steel pieces are joined to create a rigid frame that climbs toward the sky. By the time the building is finished, however, the building's framework will no longer be visible.

Like a building, you too have an inner framework, but it is made up of bones instead of steel. Your framework, or skeleton, is shown in Figure 2. The number of bones in your skeleton depends on your age. A newborn baby has about 275 bones. An adult, however, has about 206 bones. As a baby grows, some of the bones fuse together. For example, as a baby, you had many more individual bones in your skull than you do now. As you grew, some of your bones grew together to form the larger bones of your skull.

What the Skeletal System Does

Just as a building could not stand without its frame, you too would collapse without your skeleton. **Your skeleton has five major functions. It provides shape and support, enables you to move, protects your internal organs, produces blood cells, and stores certain materials until your body needs them.**

Figure 1 Like the steel beams that support a building, your skeleton supports your body.

READING STRATEGIES

Reading Tip After students write answers to the questions they created from the section headings, have them use the information to write question-and-answer flashcards. Instruct students to write a question on one side of a note card and the answer on the other side of the card. Then have partners use the flashcards to review the information in the section.

Concept Mapping As students read, have them create concept maps about movable joints. Students' concept maps should include the main types of movable joints, a description of how each type works, and an example of each.

Your skeleton determines the shape of your body, much as a steel frame determines the shape of a building. The backbone, or vertebral column, is the center of the skeleton. Locate the backbone in Figure 2. Notice that all the bones of the body are in some way connected to this column. If you move your fingers down the center of your back, you can feel the 26 small bones, or **vertebrae** (VUR tuh bray)(singular **vertebra**), that make up your backbone. Bend forward at the waist and feel the bones adjust as you move. You can think of each individual vertebra as a bead on a string. Just as a beaded necklace is flexible and able to bend, so too is your vertebral column. If your backbone were just one bone, you would not be able to bend or twist.

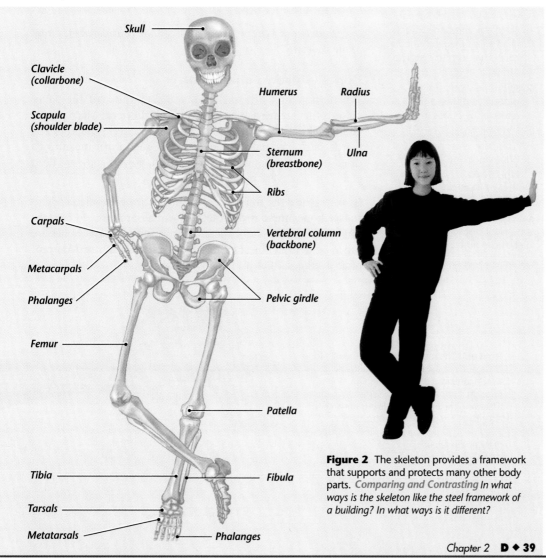

Figure 2 The skeleton provides a framework that supports and protects many other body parts. *Comparing and Contrasting In what ways is the skeleton like the steel framework of a building? In what ways is it different?*

---

2 Facilitate

What the Skeletal System Does

Using the Visuals: Figure 2

Help students pronounce the names of all the bones shown in Figure 2. Call attention to the bones that make up the arms and the legs. Point out that the lower portion of each limb is made up of two bones, and the upper portion is made up of one bone. Then explain that the skull is made of hard, thick bone. Ask: **How does the skull's structure relate to one of its functions?** (*The skull's hardness and thickness enable it to form a protective covering for the brain.*) Point out that the two sides of the human skeleton are symmetrical. **limited English proficiency**

Building Inquiry Skills: Compare and Contrast

Ask students to list the parts of the body where many small bones are connected together. (*Sample: hand, foot, spine*) Ask: **How is the motion of these body parts similar?** (*These regions can undergo a wide range of motion and are very flexible.*) **learning modality: logical/mathematical**

Language Arts
CONNECTION

Ask students to look in a dictionary to find the origins of some names of bones. For example, the word *femur* is the Latin term for thigh. *Tibia* comes from the Latin word meaning "tubelike or hollow." Challenge students to find the derivation of as many words as possible. **learning modality: verbal**

Ongoing Assessment

Writing Ask students to list the five main functions of the skeletal system.

D ◆ 39

Program Resources

◆ **Teaching Resources** 2-1 Lesson Plan, p. 38; 2-1 Section Summary, p. 39

Media and Technology

 Audiotapes English-Spanish Summary 2-1

 Transparencies "The Human Skeleton," Transparency 2

Answers to Self-Assessment

Caption Question

Figure 2 Like the steel framework, the skeleton shapes and supports the body. Unlike the framework, the skeleton is living, produces necessary materials, and is flexible.

What the Skeletal System Does, continued

Skills Focus drawing conclusions **ACTIVITY**

Materials *2 plastic jars or other containers, vinegar, water, 2 clean chicken bones, gloves*

Time 15 minutes for set up; 15 minutes for observation one week later

Tips After students examine the chicken bones, make sure they wash their hands before and after they remove the gloves.

Drawing Conclusions After the bones have soaked in vinegar, they lose their calcium and become soft and rubbery. Students should conclude that a diet high in calcium is important to keep bones hard.

Extend Ask students to examine food labels at home to find food sources rich in calcium, then report their findings to the class. **learning modality: kinesthetic**

Bones—Strong and Living

Including All Students

Have volunteers act out various sports in front of the class. Encourage other students to guess the activity that is being demonstrated. Ask the student who supplies the correct answer whether or not the activity requires the body to absorb the force of weight. Use these answers to create a list of weight-bearing activities and a list of non-weight-bearing activities on the board. Some examples of weight-bearing activities include jogging, aerobics, walking, softball, jumping rope, weight lifting, skating, soccer, and basketball. Non-weight-bearing activities include cycling and swimming. **learning modality: kinesthetic** **ACTIVITY**

Soft Bones?

In this activity, you will explore the role that calcium plays in bones. **ACTIVITY**

1. Put on protective gloves. Soak one clean chicken bone in a jar filled with water. Soak a second clean chicken bone in a jar filled with vinegar. (Vinegar causes calcium to dissolve out of bone.)

2. After one week, put on protective gloves and remove the bones from the jars.

3. Compare how the two bones look and feel. Note any differences between the two bones.

Drawing Conclusions Based on your results, explain why it is important to consume a diet that is high in calcium.

Your skeleton also allows you to move. Most of the body's bones are associated with muscles. The muscles pull on the bones to make the body move. Bones also protect many of the organs in your body. For example, your skull protects your brain, and your breastbone and ribs form a protective cage around your heart and lungs.

Some of the bones in your body produce substances that your body needs. You can think of the long bones of your arms and legs as factories that make blood cells. Bones also store minerals such as calcium and phosphorus. Calcium and phosphorus make bones strong and hard. When the body needs these minerals, the bones release small amounts of them into the blood for use elsewhere.

☑ *Checkpoint* *Why is the vertebral column considered the center of the skeleton?*

Bones—Strong and Living

When you think of a skeleton, you may think of the paper cutouts that are used as decorations at Halloween. Many people connect skeletons with death. The ancient Greeks did, too. The word *skeleton* actually comes from a Greek word meaning "a dried body." The bones of your skeleton, however, are not dead at all. They are very much alive.

Bone Strength Your bones are both strong and lightweight. In fact, bones are so strong that they can absorb more force without breaking than can concrete or granite rock. Yet, bones are much lighter than these materials. In fact, only about 20 percent of an average adult's body weight is bone.

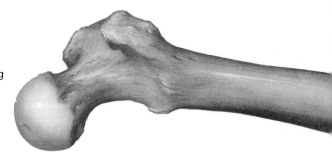

Figure 3 The most obvious feature of a long bone, such as the femur, is its long shaft, which contains compact bone. Running through compact bone is a system of canals that bring materials to the living bone cells. One canal is seen in the photograph. *Interpreting Diagrams* *What different tissues make up the femur?*

Background

Facts and Figures The strength and structure of fish and animal bones have allowed them to serve many purposes throughout human history.

◆ Bone sewing needles have been used for 20,000 years or longer.

◆ Buttons used to fasten clothes became popular in Europe during the 1200s, when fashion began to favor fitted clothes instead of loose robes. Buttons were made of many materials, from precious gems to animal bones.

◆ Animal bones are a good source of phosphorus. The bones are ground into meal and used for plant fertilizer. Although calcium phosphate—the chemical compound found in bones and bone ash—can also be mined from mineral deposits, that source also originated in bones of animals that lived millions of years ago.

Have you ever heard the phrase "as hard as a rock"? Most rock is hard because it is made up of minerals that are packed tightly together. In a similar way, bones are hard because they are made up of two minerals—phosphorus and calcium.

Bone Growth Bones also contain cells and tissues, such as blood and nerves. And, because your bone cells are alive, they form new bone tissue as you grow. But even after you are grown, bone tissue continues to form within your bones. For example, every time you play soccer or basketball, your bones absorb the force of your weight. They respond by making new bone tissue.

Sometimes, new bone tissue forms after an accident. If you break a bone, for example, new bone tissue forms to fill the gap between the broken ends of the bone. The healed region of new bone may be stronger than the original bone.

The Structure of Bones

Figure 3 shows the structure of the femur, or thighbone. The femur, which is the body's longest bone, connects the pelvic bones to the lower leg bones. Notice that a thin, tough membrane covers all of the bone except the ends. Blood vessels and nerves enter and leave the bone through the membrane. Beneath the membrane is a layer of compact bone, which is hard and dense, but not solid. As you can see in Figure 3, small canals run through the compact bone. These canals carry blood vessels and nerves from the bone's surface to the living cells within the bone.

Just inside the compact bone is a layer of spongy bone. Spongy bone is also found at the ends of the bone. Like a sponge, spongy bone has many small spaces within it. This structure makes spongy bone lightweight but strong.

CANAL

COMPACT BONE

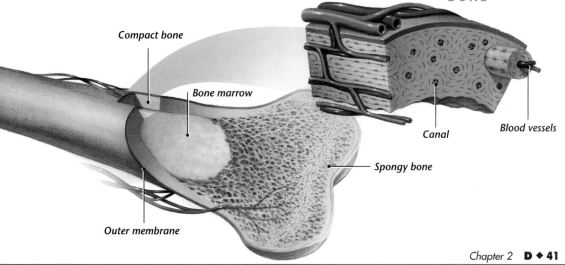

Compact bone

Bone marrow

Outer membrane

Canal

Blood vessels

Spongy bone

Chapter 2 **D ◆ 41**

Program Resources

◆ **Product Testing Activities by** *Consumer Reports,* "Testing Yogurt," pp. 1–8

Media and Technology

 Transparencies "The Structure of a Bone," Transparency 3

Answers to Self-Assessment

Caption Question

Figure 3 Compact bone, bone marrow, spongy bone, and blood vessels

✓ *Checkpoint*

The vertebral column is the center of the skeleton because it is in the center of the body and all the bones in the body are connected to it in some way.

Physical Education
CONNECTION

Tell students that weight-bearing exercise has been found to promote bone growth and prevent bone loss. Astronauts who live for extended periods away from the gravity of Earth often experience serious bone loss. Ask students to infer why this happens. *(Without Earth's gravity, the astronauts' bodies do not weigh enough to benefit their bones when they exercise.)* Explain that astronauts use specially designed exercise equipment to help combat this problem, and scientists are working on the development of artificial gravity in order to prevent this problem for people who live or work in space for extended periods of time. **learning modality: verbal**

The Structure of Bones

Using the Visuals: Figure 3

Remind students that a tissue is a group of similar cells that all have the same function. Point out the photo of the canal system and explain that this is an enlarged cross-section of the compact bone shown in the visual. Ask: **How do blood and other materials get to the living cells inside the bone?** *(Blood vessels run through the canals.)* **learning modality: visual**

Ongoing Assessment

Writing Have students describe how the structure of bones allows the bones to grow and makes them strong. *(Samples: The membrane allows blood vessels and nerves to enter the bone. Blood vessels run through canals in the compact bone to deliver nutrients to the bones. Spongy bone has spaces within it that allow it to absorb large amounts of force.)*

 Students can save their descriptions in their portfolios.

D ◆ 41

The Structure of Bones, continued

Using the Visuals: Figure 3

Materials *leg bones from* **ACTIVITY** *thoroughly cooked chickens or turkeys, dissecting trays, hand lens*
Time 15 minutes

Before class, use a small kitchen saw to slice one leg bone crosswise and one lengthwise for each group. Place the bones in dissecting trays. Encourage small groups of students to compare the chicken bone to the femur in Figure 3, and identify the various parts of the bone. **learning modality: visual**

How Bones Form

Using the Visuals: Figure 4

Have students look at the photos in sequence starting with the X-rays of the 1-year-old. Ask: **How does the X-ray image change as a child ages?** *(The image shows more white places.)* Ask students to identify the cartilage in the images. *(The dark places are cartilage.)* **learning modality: visual**

Joints of the Skeleton

Sharpen your Skills

Classifying

Time 15 minutes
Tips Students can work **ACTIVITY** in pairs. One student can perform the activity while the other student observes the movement; then partners can switch roles.
Expected Outcome Arm—ball and socket joint (shoulder); door—hinge joint (elbow), pivot joint (wrist); book—hinge joint (elbow), pivot joint (wrist); kneeling—hinge joint (knee); hand—pivot joint (wrist); head—pivot joint (neck)
Extend Ask students to describe the type of joint found in the hip *(ball-and-socket)* and the ankle *(pivot)*. **learning modality: kinesthetic**

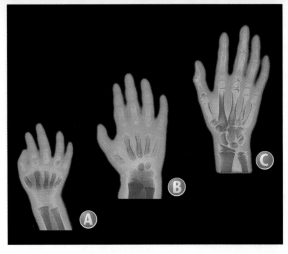

Figure 4 X-rays of the hands of a 1-year-old (**A**) and a 3-year-old (**B**) show that the cartilage in the wrist has not yet been replaced by bone. In the X-ray of the 13-year-old's hand (**C**), the replacement of cartilage by bone is almost complete.

Sharpen your Skills

Classifying

Perform each of the activities **ACTIVITY** listed below:

◆ move your arm in a circle
◆ push open a door
◆ lift a book from a desk
◆ kneel down
◆ wave your hand
◆ twist your head from side to side.

Determine which type of joint or joints is involved in performing each activity. Give a reason to support your classifications.

The spaces in bone contain a soft connective tissue called **marrow.** There are two types of marrow—red and yellow. Red bone marrow produces the body's blood cells. As a child, most of your bones contained red bone marrow. As a teenager, only the ends of your femur, your hip bones, and your sternum (breastbone) contain red marrow. Your other bones contain yellow marrow. This marrow stores fat that serves as an energy reserve.

How Bones Form

Try this activity: Move the tip of your nose from side to side between your fingers. Notice that the tip of your nose is not stiff. That is because it contains cartilage. **Cartilage** (KAHR tuh lij) is a connective tissue that is more flexible than bone. As an infant, much of your skeleton was cartilage. Over time, most of the cartilage has been replaced with hard bone tissue.

The replacement of cartilage by bone tissue usually is complete by the time you stop growing. But not all of your body's cartilage is replaced by bone. Even in adulthood, cartilage covers the ends of many bones. For example, in the knee, cartilage acts like a cushion that keeps your femur from rubbing against the bones of your lower leg.

✓ *Checkpoint* **What happens to cartilage as you grow?**

Joints of the Skeleton

Imagine what life would be like if your femur ran the length of your leg. How would you get out of bed in the morning? How would you run for the school bus? Luckily, your body contains many small bones rather than fewer large ones. A place in the body where two bones come together is a **joint.** Joints allow bones to move in different ways. There are two kinds of joints in the body—immovable joints and movable joints.

Immovable Joints Some joints in the body connect bones in a way that allows little or no movement. These joints are called immovable joints. The bones of the skull are held together by immovable joints. The joints that attach the ribs to the sternum are also immovable.

Movable Joints Most of the joints in the body are movable joints. **Movable joints allow the body to make a wide range of movements.** Look at *Exploring Movable Joints* to see the variety of movements that these joints make possible.

Background

Integrating Science Since 1987, people who injure the cartilage in the knee can be treated with autologous chondrocyte implantation (ACI). Chondrocytes are cartilage cells. In ACI, chondrocytes are "harvested" from the patient's thighbone, then cultured for 4–5 weeks until there are 5–10 million chondrocytes. Then, using arthroscopy (see p. 48, Section 2), the surgeon prepares a watertight patch over the damaged area. The patch is made from a piece of periosteum, a fibrous membrane that covers the surfaces of bones, and sealed with a glue made from fibrin, a protein formed when blood clots. After the patch is made and sealed, the surgeon injects the cartilage cells under the patch, closes the wound, and applies an elastic bandage. Tissue produced by ACI closely resembles normal cartilage, and is durable and long lasting.

EXPLORING *Movable Joints*

Without movable joints, your body would be as stiff as a board. The four types of movable joints shown here allow your body to move in a variety of ways.

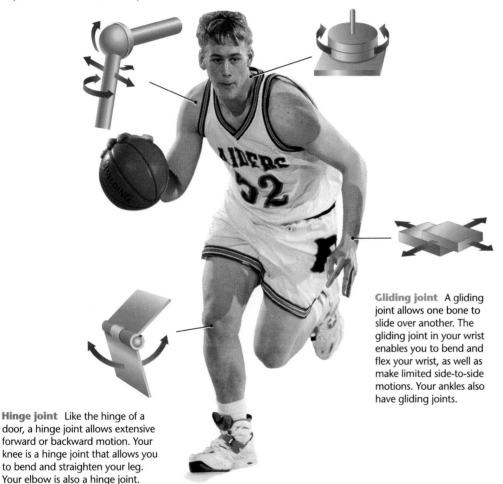

Ball-and-socket joint Ball-and-socket joints allow the greatest range of motion. In your shoulder, the top of the arm bone fits into the deep, bowl-like socket of the scapula (shoulder blade). The joint allows you to swing your arm freely in a circle. Your hips also have ball-and-socket joints.

Pivot joint A pivot joint allows one bone to rotate around another. The pivot joint in the top of your neck gives you limited ability to turn your head from side to side.

Gliding joint A gliding joint allows one bone to slide over another. The gliding joint in your wrist enables you to bend and flex your wrist, as well as make limited side-to-side motions. Your ankles also have gliding joints.

Hinge joint Like the hinge of a door, a hinge joint allows extensive forward or backward motion. Your knee is a hinge joint that allows you to bend and straighten your leg. Your elbow is also a hinge joint.

Chapter 2 **D ◆ 43**

EXPLORING
Movable Joints

Have volunteers read aloud the annotations for each kind of joint. Ask: **What types of movements does the ball-and-socket joint in the shoulder allow the arm to make?** *(Samples: Up and down, backward and forward, shrugging, in a circle)* Give each student a diagram of the human skeleton. Have students compare the skeleton to the photo of the basketball player and use the information in the visual to label where each type of joint is on the skeleton. **Extend** Have students invent a creature whose joints are in the same places as a human's but are of different kinds. Students should sketch the creature and write a description of its movements. **learning modality: visual**

Including All Students

Materials *model of a human skeleton*
Time 15 minutes

Students who need additional help or those who are visually impaired may benefit from examining a model of a human skeleton. (You may be able to borrow one from a local high school or college.) Supervise students as they examine the model closely. Have them manipulate the bones to see how the joints of the skeleton move. Ask: **How does the human skeleton enable you move?** *(Bones are connected at joints and can rotate, pivot, and bend back and forth)* **learning modality: kinesthetic**

Media and Technology

 Transparencies "Exploring Movable Joints," Transparency 4

Answers to Self-Assessment

☑ *Checkpoint*
As a person grows, most cartilage is replaced by bone.

Ongoing Assessment

Skills Check Have students create charts comparing the four basic types of joints. Have them describe how each joint moves and give an example of each kind of joint.

Joints of the Skeleton, continued

Taking Care of Your Bones

 Integrating Health

Materials *nutritional analyses of different foods* **Time** 20 minutes

Have students look ahead to the diagram of the Food Guide Pyramid in Chapter 3, page 79. Consult the Science Explorer website for current references or supply nutrition labels from a variety of foods. Challenge students to use the Food Guide Pyramid and nutritional analyses to create a healthy diet that is rich in calcium. Tell students that the recommended daily intake of calcium for growing teens is 1,200 mg. Interested students may want to do additional research to find out how well calcium from different sources is absorbed by the body. **learning modality: verbal**

Visual Arts
CONNECTION

Leonardo da Vinci (1452–1519), was an Italian artist, inventor, and scientist. Although he is well known for his paintings, including the Mona Lisa, Leonardo also made accurate sketches of the human body. As a scientist, Leonardo used dissections and took precise measurements to create accurate drawings of bones, ligaments, tendons, and other body parts. His sketches are considered to be the first accurate drawings of the human body.

In Your Journal

Leonardo da Vinci relied on measurements and visual observations to make his drawings. Use a metric ruler to measure the lengths of the bones in your arm or leg. Then try to make an accurate drawing of your arm or leg.

Figure 5 Leonardo da Vinci drew these sketches of the human chest, hip, and leg bones in 1510.

The bones in movable joints are held together by a strong connective tissue called a **ligament**. Cartilage that covers the ends of the bones keeps them from rubbing against each other. In addition, a fluid lubricates the ends of the bones, allowing them to move smoothly over each other.

Taking Care of Your Bones

INTEGRATING HEALTH Because your skeleton performs so many necessary functions, it is important to keep it healthy. This is especially true while you are still growing. **A combination of a balanced diet and regular exercise can start you on the way to a lifetime of healthy bones.**

One way to ensure healthy bones is to eat a well-balanced diet. A well-balanced diet includes enough calcium and phosphorus to keep your bones strong while they are growing. Meats, whole grains, and leafy green vegetables are all excellent sources of both calcium and phosphorus. Dairy products, including milk, are excellent sources of calcium.

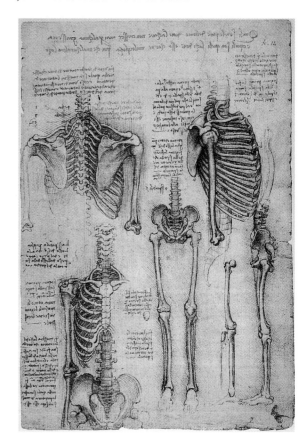

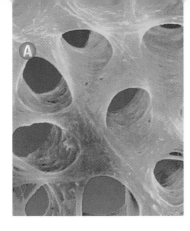
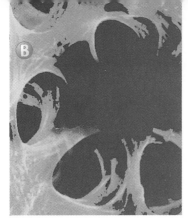

Figure 6 Without enough calcium in the diet, a person's bones weaken. **A.** This magnified view of healthy bone shows a continuous framework. **B.** Notice the large empty space in this bone from a person with osteoporosis. *Relating Cause and Effect What can you do to prevent osteoporosis?*

Another way to build and maintain strong bones is to get plenty of exercise. During activities such as walking, soccer, or basketball, your bones support the weight of your entire body. This helps your bones grow stronger and denser. Running, skating, and aerobics are other activities that help keep your bones healthy and strong.

As people become older, their bones begin to lose some of the minerals they contain. Mineral loss can lead to **osteoporosis** (ahs tee oh puh ROH sis), a condition in which the body's bones become weak and break easily. You can see the effect of osteoporosis in Figure 6B. Osteoporosis is more common in women than in men. Evidence indicates that regular exercise throughout life can help prevent osteoporosis. A diet with enough calcium can also help prevent osteoporosis. If you eat enough calcium-rich foods now, during your teenage years, you may help prevent osteoporosis later in life.

Section 1 Review

1. List five important functions that the skeleton performs in the body.
2. What is the role of movable joints in the body?
3. What behaviors are important for keeping your bones healthy?
4. Compare the motion of a hinge joint to that of a pivot joint.
5. **Thinking Critically** **Predicting** How would your life be different if your backbone consisted of just one bone?

Check Your Progress CHAPTER PROJECT 2

By now, you should have your teacher's approval for modeling the movement you chose. Ask a classmate or friend to perform the movement. Make drawings to study the motion. Find out what bones are involved, and determine their sizes and shapes. (*Hint:* Notice the direction of bone movement and the kinds of joints that are involved.)

Section 1 Review Answers

1. The skeleton gives the body shape, protects internal organs, and enables movement. Bones also produce blood cells and store minerals.
2. Movable joints allow the body to make a wide range of movements.
3. Eating a balanced diet rich in calcium and phosphorus; exercising regularly
4. Hinge joints allow for forward and backward movement. Pivot joints not only allow forward and backward movements but also side-to-side motions.
5. If the backbone consisted of one bone, people could not bend at the waist or curl their backs; this would affect almost every activity people do.

Check Your Progress CHAPTER PROJECT 2

Show students how to model movements. They should move very slowly and stop in different positions throughout the movement to allow other students to study and sketch the motion. Help students realize that they can make simple line drawings at this stage, rather than elaborate drawings.

Answers to Self-Assessment

Caption Question

Figure 6 Exercise regularly and eat a diet with enough calcium.

Performance Assessment

Writing Ask students to describe one of the major functions of the human skeleton and explain how the skeleton carries out that function.

 Students can save their descriptions in their portfolios.

SECTION 2 Diagnosing Bone and Joint Injuries

Objectives

After completing the lesson, students will be able to
◆ list common skeletal system injuries and describe methods for their diagnosis;
◆ list ways that bone and joint injuries can be prevented.

Key Terms fracture, sprain, dislocation, X-ray, magnetic resonance imaging

1 Engage/Explore

Activating Prior Knowledge

Ask students if they have ever had a broken bone or a joint injury. Have them describe their experiences with having X-rays or MRI images taken. Ask them to describe what features of the skeletal system appear in an X-ray or an MRI.

DISCOVER

Skills Focus observing
Time 15 minutes
Tips When students identify the part of the body shown in the X-ray image, have them compare the image to their own hands to help them identify the types of structures that are not visible in the image.
Expected Outcome Students should identify the part of the body as the arm, wrist, hand, and fingers, and should state that the broken bone is in the arm. Some students may identify the broken bone as the radius.
Think It Over The bones can be seen clearly. The surrounding skin, muscles, blood vessels, and other soft tissues are not visible.

SECTION 2 Diagnosing Bone and Joint Injuries

DISCOVER .... ACTIVITY

What Do X-Ray Images Show?

1. Examine the photo below of an X-ray image.
2. Try to identify what part of the human body the X-ray shows.
3. Look at the X-ray to find the break in a bone.

Think It Over
Observing What types of structures are seen clearly in the X-ray? What types of structures cannot be seen?

GUIDE FOR READING

◆ How do X-rays help identify injuries of the skeletal system?
◆ How can bone and joint injuries be prevented?

Reading Tip As you read, create a table comparing X-rays and MRI. Include columns for the procedure involved, effect on body cells, cost, and types of injuries shown.

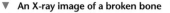
▼ An X-ray image of a broken bone

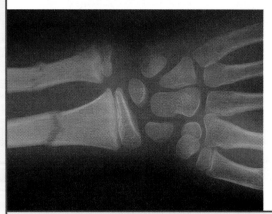

You call out, "Wait for me," as you run across an icy sidewalk to catch up to a friend. Suddenly, you slip. As you lose your balance, you put out your arms to break your fall. The next thing you know, you're on the ground. Your hands sting, and you notice they are scraped. One wrist is starting to swell, and it hurts! If you try to move your wrist, it hurts even more. You need to get to a doctor—and fast.

Common Skeletal System Injuries

On the way to the doctor, you'd probably be wondering, "Is my wrist broken, or is it just bruised?" Your swollen wrist could be injured in one of three common ways: it could be fractured, sprained, or dislocated.

A **fracture,** or a break in a bone, can occur when you fall so that all of your weight is placed on only a few bones. A **sprain** occurs when ligaments are stretched too far and tear in places. If you have ever stumbled and turned an ankle, you may have felt a sharp pain. The pain probably occurred because the ligaments on the outside of your ankle stretched too far and tore. Sprains, especially of the ankle, are the most common joint injuries. Both sprains and fractures can cause swelling around the injured area.

A third injury of the skeletal system is a dislocation. A **dislocation** occurs when a bone comes out of its joint. For example, have you ever caught a ball with the tips of your fingers? You may have knocked a finger bone out of its joint. Sometimes a doctor can put back a dislocated bone without surgery. Other times surgery is needed.

READING STRATEGIES

Reading Tip Have students make a table like this one to compare X-rays and MRI:

	X-Rays	MRI
Procedure	Film placed under area to be viewed; beam of X-rays is emitted.	Patient placed in cylinder exposed to magnetic energy.
Effect on Cells	can cause damage	causes no damage
Cost	low cost	high cost
Injury Type	bone or bone	soft tissue

Study and Comprehension Before students begin reading, have them preview the section by reading the headings, captions, and boldfaced terms and looking at the pictures. Suggest that students write questions they have about skeletal system injuries, X-rays, magnetic resonance imaging, arthroscopy, and prevention of skeletal system injuries. Then have students write answers to the questions as they read.

X-Rays—A Look Inside the Body

 INTEGRATING PHYSICS X-ray images can determine whether bones have been broken. **X-rays,** like the light that your eyes can see, are a form of energy that travels in waves. Although the energy in the waves passes through some living tissue, it does not pass through bone.

Before an X-ray image is taken, a lead apron is placed on your body to protect you from unnecessary exposure to X-rays. Lead is a dense metal that absorbs X-rays. Photographic film is placed under the area to be viewed. Then a machine that emits a beam of X-rays is aimed at the area.

Because most X-rays pass through the skin and other body tissues, the X-rays strike the photographic film beneath the area. Unlike other body tissues, bone absorbs X-rays. Absorbed X-rays do not reach the film. After the film is developed, it shows bones as clearly defined white areas.

X-ray imaging has drawbacks. One limitation is that X-rays cannot be used to view injuries to soft tissues, such as the skin, muscle, connective tissue, and internal organs. In addition, the energy in X-rays can damage your body cells. This is why you should not have unnecessary X-ray images taken.

Magnetic Resonance Imaging

In 1970, a new method for taking clear images of both the bones and soft tissues of the body was developed. This method is called **magnetic resonance imaging,** or MRI. An MRI scanner is a large

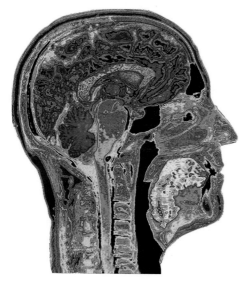

Figure 7 Magnetic resonance imaging can produce images of muscles and other soft tissues in the body.

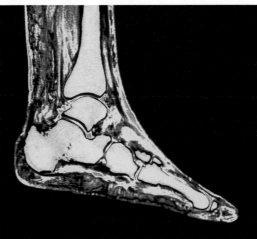

Program Resources

◆ **Teaching Resources** 2-2 Lesson Plan, p. 50; 2-2 Section Summary, p. 51
◆ **Product Testing Activities by *Consumer Reports,*** "Testing Jeans," pp. 1–8

Media and Technology

 Audiotapes English-Spanish Summary 2-2

 Exploring Physical Science Videodisc Unit 6, Side 2, "The Electromagnetic Spectrum" Chapter 7

---

2 Facilitate

Common Skeletal System Injuries

Inquiry Challenge

Materials *pipe cleaners, clothespins, pencils, cardboard, poster board, rubber bands, scissors, tape, craft sticks, and other common materials* **ACTIVITY**
Time 25 minutes

Have small groups of students create models of each kind of common skeletal system injury and then present their models to the class, explaining how each model shows the specific type of injury. *(Sample: Fracture—broken craft stick)* Encourage students to identify the types of injuries in each other's models. **cooperative learning**

X-Rays—A Look Inside the Body

 Integrating Physics

Point out that the X-ray image shown on page 46 is like a shadow image of the bones, because the bones absorb the X-rays while the other tissues allow them to pass through. Students may be confused because shadows are dark but the image of the bone is white. Explain that the photographic film turns dark when exposed to X-rays, so the dark places are actually the parts of the film that received radiation. **learning modality: verbal**

Ongoing Assessment

Writing Ask students to describe the three types of common skeletal system injuries and explain which injuries are easily diagnosed with X-rays. *(Fractures and dislocations)*
 Portfolio Students can save their descriptions in their portfolios.

Magnetic Resonance Imaging

Arthroscopy

cylinder that contains electromagnets. The person is placed on a platform that slides into the center of the cylinder. The person is then exposed to short bursts of magnetic energy. This magnetic energy causes atoms within the body to vibrate, or resonate. A computer then analyzes the vibration patterns and produces an image of the area.

MRI images are amazingly sharp and clear. MRI can produce images of body tissues at any angle. In addition, it can show a clear image of muscles and other soft tissues that an X-ray image cannot show. Another advantage of MRI is that it does not damage cells. Because MRI machines are very expensive to buy and use, this technique is not used to examine broken bones.

☑ *Checkpoint* **What is one advantage that X-rays have over MRI?**

Arthroscopy

Before 1970, if you had a pain in a movable joint, a surgeon had to make a large incision into the joint to see what was causing the

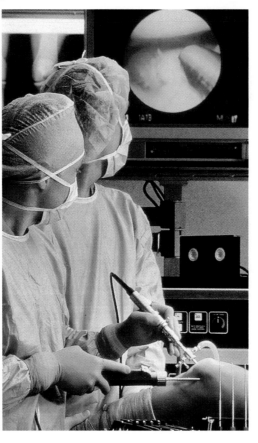

Figure 8 To diagnose and treat a knee injury, this surgeon has inserted an arthroscope into the patient's knee.

pain. Today, doctors make a small incision and insert a slim, tubelike instrument called an arthroscope (AHR thruh skohp) into the joint. The arthroscope allows doctors to look inside the joint to see what is wrong. After the problem is diagnosed, tiny instruments are inserted through a second small incision to make the necessary repairs. The arthroscope has helped to diagnose and repair many joint problems. Sometimes, however, a joint may be too damaged to repair. The damaged joint may then be replaced with an artificial joint.

Preventing Skeletal System Injuries

INTEGRATING HEALTH Although injuries such as fractures, sprains, and dislocations are fairly common, they can be prevented. **Simple preventive measures include warming up before exercising, wearing appropriate protective equipment, and exercising in safe places.**

When you warm up before exercising, your joints become more flexible. This may help prevent a sprain or dislocation. In addition, it is important to wear the appropriate safety equipment for the activity you are doing. Helmets,

Figure 9 By wearing safety equipment, these hockey players can avoid bone and joint injuries. *Observing* List all the safety equipment that these athletes are wearing.

knee pads, shoulder pads, and padded gloves can help prevent injuries. You should also always wear shoes that are appropriate for your activity. Lastly, be aware of your surroundings. If you skate, run, or bike on a path or track, you are much less likely to be involved in an accident with a car or with another person.

If you do get injured, be sure to apply proper first aid. Placing ice on an injured area and elevating it can minimize pain and swelling. Make sure you tell a parent, coach, or other adult if you get hurt. If a trainer, doctor, or nurse gives you medical instructions, be sure you understand them, and then follow them exactly. Finally, don't return to regular activity until your injury has healed. By giving your bones or joints time to heal, you can help prevent further injury to the area.

Section 2 Review

1. What property of X-rays makes them useful for identifying injuries to the skeletal system?
2. What can you do to decrease the chances of injuring your skeletal system?
3. Describe three common bone and joint injuries.
4. List the advantages of MRI over X-rays.
5. **Thinking Critically Applying Concepts** Suppose that an X-ray image of your injured wrist did not show a fracture. But, after a month, your wrist is still painful and stiff. Why might your doctor order an MRI?

Science at Home

List the types of exercise you and your family members do. With your family, brainstorm a list of safety gear and precautions to use for each activity. (For example, for bicycling, you might list wearing a helmet, stretching before riding, and avoiding busy streets and nighttime riding.) How can you put these safety measures into practice?

Chapter 2 **D ◆ 49**

Program Resources

 Science Explorer Series *Sound and Light*, Chapter 1
◆ **Teaching Resources** 2-2 Review and Reinforce, p. 44; 2-2 Enrich, p. 45

Media and Technology

 Interactive Student Tutorial CD-ROM D-2

Answers to Self-Assessment

Caption Question
Figure 9 Helmet, face guard, knee pads, shoulder pads, padded gloves

☑ *Checkpoint*
X-rays are less expensive.

Preventing Skeletal System Injuries

 Integrating Health

Materials *magazines, poster board, scissors, glue, markers*
Time 15 minutes
Have groups of students find pictures in magazines of people exercising or playing sports. Encourage students to identify safe and unsafe situations. Have students work together to create posters showing exercise safety "Do" and "Don't." *(Samples: Do—wearing safety gear; Don't—inline skating in traffic)*
limited English proficiency

3 Assess

Section 2 Review Answers

1. X-rays pass through the skin and other soft tissues, but are absorbed by bones.
2. Wear protective equipment; warm up before exercising; exercise in safe places.
3. Fracture—broken bone; sprain—stretched ligament; dislocation—bone out of joint
4. Does not damage cells; produces images of soft tissues and organs.
5. An MRI image is sharper and clearer than an X-ray. It can also show damage to muscles and other soft tissues.

Science at Home

Suggest students create charts to show each kind of exercise, listing safety measures in one column and safety equipment in another column.

Performance Assessment

Oral Presentation Ask students to name a common injury and to tell whether the injury can best be diagnosed with X-rays or MRI. Then have students describe safety measures that might have prevented the injury.

D ◆ 49

SECTION 3 The Muscular System

Objectives

After completing the lesson, students will be able to

◆ identify the three types of muscles found in the body and describe the function of each;

◆ explain how skeletal muscles work in pairs;

◆ list ways in which people can keep their muscles healthy.

Key Terms involuntary muscle, voluntary muscle, skeletal muscle, tendon, smooth muscle, cardiac muscle

1 Engage/Explore

Activating Prior Knowledge

Ask each student to hold a science book in one hand. Have students stand and hold the books down at their sides. Have them lift the books while feeling their arm muscles with the opposite hand. Ask: **What muscles did you feel contract? What else did you notice?** Record their observations on the board.

DISCOVER

Skills Focus predicting
Materials *spring-type clothespin*
Time 15 minutes
Tips Caution students not to move so fast that they lose their grip; otherwise they might pinch their fingers in the spring.
Expected Outcome The muscles can respond repetitively but tire easily. Most students will find that the number of times they are able to squeeze the clothespin decreases in Step 2.
Think It Over Students might predict that repeating the steps with the other hand would produce the same pattern, but that they will not be able to squeeze the clothespin as many times as in the first trial because the writing hand is stronger.

50 ◆ D

DISCOVER ·ACTIVITY

How Do Muscles Work?

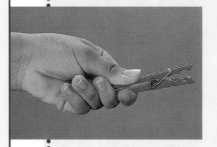

1. Grip a spring-type clothespin with the thumb and index finger of your writing hand. Squeeze the clothespin open and shut as quickly as possible for two minutes. Count how many times you can squeeze the clothespin before your muscles tire.

2. Rest for one minute. Then repeat Step 1.

Think It Over
Predicting What do you think would happen if you repeated Steps 1 and 2 with your other hand? Give a reason for your prediction. Then test your prediction.

GUIDE FOR READING

◆ What three types of muscles are found in the body?

◆ Why do muscles work in pairs?

Reading Tip Before you read, preview Figure 10. Predict how skeletal, smooth, and cardiac muscles function.

A rabbit becomes still when it senses danger. The rabbit sits so still that it doesn't seem to move a muscle. Could you sit without moving any muscles? If you tried to, you'd find that it is impossible to sit still for very long. Saliva builds up in your mouth. You swallow. You need to breathe. Your chest expands to let air in. All of these actions involve muscles.

There are about 600 muscles in your body. Muscles have many functions. For example, they keep your heart beating, pull your mouth into a smile, and move the bones of your skeleton.

Muscle Action

Some of your body's movements, such as smiling, are easy to control. Other movements, such as the beating of your heart, are impossible to control completely. That is because some muscles are not under your conscious control. Those muscles are called **involuntary muscles.** Involuntary muscles are responsible for activities such as breathing and digesting food.

The muscles that are under your control are called **voluntary muscles.** Smiling, turning a page in a book, and getting out of your chair when the bell rings are all actions controlled by voluntary muscles.

◀ A rabbit "frozen" in place

50 ◆ D

READING STRATEGIES

Reading Tip After students preview Figure 10, have them divide a sheet of paper into two columns. Direct students to write their predictions in the first column. After students read the section, have them write in the second column whether their predictions were correct and note additional information they learned from their reading.

Study and Comprehension After students read the section, have them write ten questions about the muscular system. Suggest they write a mixture of short-answer, fill-in-the-blank, and matching questions. Remind them to create answer keys. Then have partners exchange questions and answer them. Instruct students to use the answer keys to check their answers.

Types of Muscles

Your body has three types of muscle tissue—skeletal muscle, smooth muscle, and cardiac muscle. In Figure 10, you see a magnified view of each type of muscle in the body. Both skeletal and smooth muscles are found in many places in the body. Cardiac muscle is found only in the heart. Each muscle type performs specific functions in the body.

Skeletal Muscle Every time you type on a computer keyboard, shoot a basketball, or walk across a room, you are using skeletal muscles. As their name suggests, **skeletal muscles** are attached

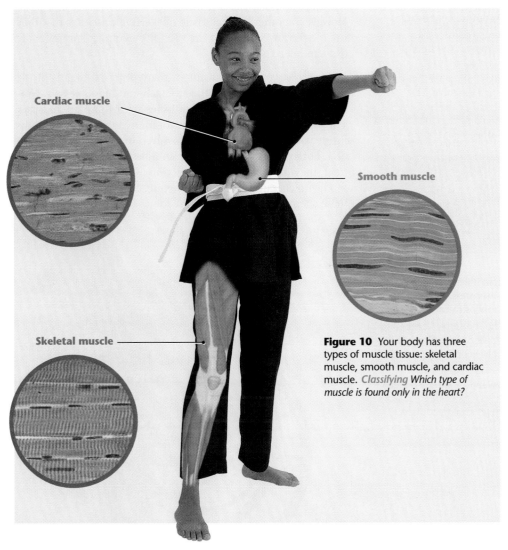

Cardiac muscle

Smooth muscle

Skeletal muscle

Figure 10 Your body has three types of muscle tissue: skeletal muscle, smooth muscle, and cardiac muscle. *Classifying* Which type of muscle is found only in the heart?

Program Resources

◆ **Teaching Resources** 2-3 Lesson Plan, p. 46; 2-3 Section Summary, p. 47

Answers to Self-Assessment
Caption Question
Figure 10 Cardiac muscle

Media and Technology

 Audiotapes English-Spanish Summary 2-3

---

2 Facilitate

Muscle Action

Building Inquiry Skills: Inferring

Ask students to infer where in the body they might find involuntary muscles. *(Samples: Heart, stomach, lungs)* Then ask: **Where in the body would you find voluntary muscles?** *(Samples: Arms, legs, abdomen)* **learning modality: verbal**

Types of Muscles

Using the Visuals: Figure 10

For students who are having difficulty understanding the written text, use Figure 10 to clarify the anatomical differences among the three kinds of muscles. Ask students to compare the appearance of the different types of muscles shown in the figure. Ask: **How are skeletal and cardiac muscles alike?** *(Both have a striped appearance.)* **Where is the smooth muscle located in the figure?** *(In the stomach)* **limited English proficiency**

Ongoing Assessment

Writing Have students describe the difference between voluntary and involuntary muscles. Then have them list the three types of muscle tissues.

Types of Muscles, continued

Building Inquiry Skills: Observing

Materials *prepared slides of skeletal, smooth, and cardiac muscle; microscope*
Time 20 minutes

Have students observe the slides with a low power lens before switching to high power. Have students observe and sketch each type of muscle, noting whether the cells contain striations, or stripes. Challenge students to label the nucleus, cell membrane, and cytoplasm of each cell. **learning modality: visual**

Portfolio Students can save their sketches in their portfolios.

Skills Focus inferring
Materials *wooden stirrer or other item that is very thin and smooth on its edges; hairpin*
Time 10 minutes
Tips Ask students to predict what may happen to the hairpin as they hold the stirrer out in front of them.
Inferring Students should find that even when they hold their hands still, some of the muscles are at work as evidenced by the movement, or "walking," of the hairpin.
Extend Have students rest a hand on their desks, make a fist, and then extend the index finger. They should try to hold the index finger still. If students watch carefully, they can probably see the finger trembling slightly, even when they are trying not to move it. **learning modality: kinesthetic**

Get a Grip

Are skeletal muscles at work when you're not moving? Try this activity and see.

1. Hold a stirrer in front of you, parallel to a table top. Do not touch the table.
2. Have a partner place a hairpin on the stirrer.
3. Raise the stirrer until the "legs" of the hairpin just touch the table. The "head" of the hairpin should rest on the stirrer, as you see in the photo.

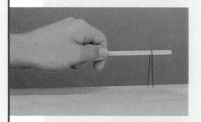

4. Hold the stirrer steady for 20 seconds. Observe what happens to the hairpin.
5. Grip the stirrer tighter and repeat Step 4. Observe what happens.

Inferring Based on your observations, are the skeletal muscles in your hand at work when you hold your hand still? Explain.

to the bones of your skeleton. These muscles provide the force that moves your bones. At each end of a skeletal muscle is a tendon. A **tendon** is a strong connective tissue that attaches muscle to bone. As you can see in Figure 10, skeletal muscle cells appear banded, or striated (STRY ay tid). For this reason, skeletal muscle is sometimes called striated muscle.

Because you have conscious control of skeletal muscles, they are classified as voluntary muscles. One characteristic of skeletal muscles is that they react very quickly. You can see an example of just how quickly skeletal muscle reacts by watching a swim meet. Immediately after the starting gun sounds, a swimmer's leg muscles quickly push the swimmer off the block into the pool. However, another characteristic of skeletal muscles is that they tire quickly. By the end of the race, the swimmer's muscles are tired and need a rest.

Smooth Muscle The inside of many internal organs of the body, such as the walls of the stomach and blood vessels, contain smooth muscles. **Smooth muscles** are involuntary muscles. They work automatically to control many types of movements inside your body, such as those involved in the process of digestion. For example, as the smooth muscles of your stomach contract, they produce a churning action. The churning mixes the food with chemicals produced by your stomach. This action and these chemicals help to digest the food.

Background

Facts and Figures What are some other benefits of aerobic exercise—exercise that makes the body use more oxygen? Regular aerobic training

◆ increases the mass of the muscle in the left ventricle of the heart. This means the heart can pump more blood with each beat, making the heart bigger, stronger, and more efficient.

◆ increases the number of red blood cells and blood volume. This allows more oxygen and fuel to be transported to the muscles.

◆ strengthens the muscles involved in respiration so that more air moves through the lungs in a given time.

Aerobic exercise also releases endorphins, chemicals that cause a person to feel relaxed and happy. This can help adolescents overcome the mood swings caused by puberty.

Unlike skeletal muscles, smooth muscle cells are not striated. Smooth muscles behave differently than skeletal muscles, too. Smooth muscles react more slowly and tire more slowly.

Cardiac Muscle The tissue called **cardiac muscle** has characteristics in common with both smooth and skeletal muscles. Like smooth muscle, cardiac muscle is involuntary. Like skeletal muscle, cardiac muscle cells are striated. However, unlike skeletal muscle, cardiac muscle does not get tired. It can contract repeatedly. You call those repeated contractions heartbeats.

☑ *Checkpoint* *Which type of muscle reacts and tires quickly?*

Muscles at Work

Has anyone ever asked you to "make a muscle"? If so, you probably tightened your fist, bent your arm at the elbow, and made the muscles in your upper arm bulge. Like other skeletal muscles, the muscles in your arm do their work by contracting, or becoming shorter and thicker. Muscle cells contract when they receive messages from the nervous system. **Because muscle cells can only contract, not extend, skeletal muscles must work in pairs. While one muscle contracts, the other muscle in the pair returns to its original length.**

Figure 11 shows the muscle action involved in moving the lower arm. First, the biceps muscle on the front of the upper arm contracts to bend the elbow, lifting the forearm and hand. As the biceps contracts, the triceps on the back of the upper arm returns to its original length. Then to straighten the elbow, the triceps muscle contracts. As the triceps contracts to extend the arm, the biceps returns to its original length. Another example of muscles that work in pairs are those in your thigh that bend and straighten the knee joint.

Figure 11 Because muscles can only contract, or shorten, they must work in pairs. To bend the arm at the elbow, the biceps contracts while the triceps returns to its original length.
Interpreting Diagrams What happens to each muscle to straighten the arm?

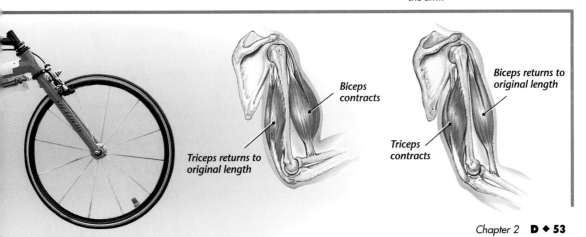

Biceps contracts

Triceps returns to original length

Biceps returns to original length

Triceps contracts

Chapter 2 **D ◆ 53**

Answers to Self-Assessment

Caption Question

Figure 11 To straighten the arm, the triceps contracts and the biceps returns to its original length.

☑ *Checkpoint*
Skeletal muscle

Muscles at Work

Using the Visual: Figure 11

Have students bend their elbows so they can feel their muscles contract and relax as shown in the figure. Ask: **How does the biceps change as it contracts?** (*It gets shorter and thicker and feels firmer.*) Then ask: **What happens to your arm when your triceps contracts?** (*The arm straightens and the biceps lengthens.*) **Extend** Have students demonstrate the position of the man's hand on the wheel in the first diagram, which shows the contracted biceps. (*The man's hand would be near the top of the wheel, as if it were pointing to 1 on a clock.*) Ask: **What position of the man's hand would be represented by the second diagram?** (*The man's hand would be near the bottom of the wheel, as if it were pointing to 4 on a clock.*) **learning modality: visual**

Inquiry Challenge

Materials *strips of cardboard, long elastic bands, brass fasteners*
Time 25 minutes

Have students build models to show how muscle pairs work together. Students may work in small groups. They may construct a model using strips of cardboard fastened together to show the two parts of the arm or leg. They can attach rubber bands to the pieces of cardboard to show the action of the muscle pairs. Have a reporter from each group demonstrate the group's model to the class and explain how the muscles work in pairs. You may want to allow students to use their models for the Chapter 2 Chapter Project.
cooperative learning

Ongoing Assessment

Drawing Have students observe which muscles alternately contract and lengthen as they bend and straighten their legs. Then have them sketch the bones and muscles of the leg in each position and indicate which muscle is contracted.

Taking Care of
Your Skeletal Muscles

3 Assess

Figure 12 When you warm up before exercising, you increase the flexibility of your muscles.

Taking Care of Your Skeletal Muscles

INTEGRATING HEALTH Exercise is important for maintaining both muscular strength and flexibility. Exercise makes individual muscle cells grow wider. This, in turn, causes the whole muscle to become thicker. The thicker a muscle is, the stronger the muscle is. When you stretch and warm up thoroughly, your muscles become more flexible. This helps prepare your muscles for the work involved in exercising or playing.

Like your bones and joints, your skeletal muscles are subject to injuries. Some of the same precautions that help prevent bone and joint injuries can also help prevent muscle injuries. For example, warming up increases the flexibility of joints as well as muscles. In addition, using proper safety equipment can protect all of your tissues, including muscles and tendons.

Sometimes, despite taking proper precautions, muscles can become injured. A muscle strain, or a pulled muscle, can occur when muscles are overworked or overstretched. Tendons can also be overstretched or partially torn. After a long period of exercise, a skeletal muscle can cramp. When a muscle cramps, the entire muscle contracts strongly and stays contracted. If you injure a muscle or tendon, it is important to follow medical instructions and to rest the injured area until it heals.

Section 3 Review

1. Name the three types of muscle tissue. Where is each type found?
2. Describe how the muscles in your upper arm work together to bend and straighten your lower arm.
3. How do voluntary and involuntary muscles differ? Give an example of each type of muscle.
4. **Thinking Critically** **Predicting** The muscles that move your fingers are attached to the bones in your fingers by long tendons. Suppose one of the tendons in a person's index finger were cut all the way through. How would this injury affect the person's ability to move his or her index finger? Explain.

Check Your Progress CHAPTER PROJECT 2

You should now be assembling your working model. Be sure that you include the muscles involved in the movement you are modeling. Also, remember that your model must show how muscle contractions produce the chosen movement. (*Hint*: After you have assembled your model, do a final check to be sure it functions the way it should.)

A Look Beneath the Skin

In this lab, you will learn about your own skeletal muscles by observing the "arm" muscles of a chicken.

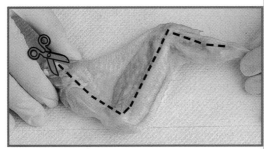

Problem

What are some characteristics of skeletal muscles? How do skeletal muscles work?

Materials

protective gloves	water
paper towels	dissection tray
scissors	uncooked chicken wing, treated with bleach

Procedure

1. Put on protective gloves. **CAUTION:** *Wear gloves whenever you handle the chicken.*
2. Your teacher will give you a chicken wing. Rinse it well with water, dry it with paper towels, and place it in a dissecting tray.
3. Carefully extend the wing to find out how many major parts it has. Draw a diagram of the external structure. Label the upper arm, elbow, lower arm, and hand (wing tip).
4. Use scissors to remove the skin. Cut along the cut line as shown in the photo. Only cut through the skin. **CAUTION:** *Cut away from your body and your classmates.*
5. Examine the muscles, the bundles of pink tissue around the bones. Find the two groups of muscles in the upper arm. Hold the arm down at the shoulder, and alternately pull on each muscle group. Observe what happens.
6. Find the two groups of muscles in the lower arm. Hold down the arm at the elbow, and alternately pull on each muscle group. Then make a diagram of the wing's muscles.
7. Find the tendons—shiny white tissue at the ends of the muscles. Notice what parts the tendons connect. Add the tendons to your diagram.
8. Remove the muscles and tendons. Find the ligaments, the whitish ribbonlike structures between bones. Add them to your diagram.
9. Dispose of the chicken parts according to your teacher's instructions. Wash your hands.

Analyze and Conclude

1. How does a chicken wing move at the elbow? How does the motion compare to how your elbow moves? What type of joint is involved?
2. What happened when you pulled on one of the arm muscles? What muscle action does the pulling represent?
3. Classify the muscles you observed as smooth, cardiac, or skeletal.
4. **Think About It** Why is it valuable to record your observations with accurate diagrams?

More to Explore

Use the procedures from this lab to examine an uncooked chicken thigh and leg. Compare how the chicken leg and a human leg move.

Safety

After students dispose of the wings, have them wash their hands with gloves on, remove the gloves and dispose of them, then wash their hands a second time. Remind students to cut away from themselves and others at all times. Review the safety guidelines in Appendix A.

Extending the Inquiry

More to Explore Students should use chicken leg quarters with the thighs and legs attached, and repeat all safety procedures.

Program Resources

◆ **Teaching Resources** Chapter 2 Skills Lab, pp. 62–63
◆ **Inquiry Skills Activity Book** Provides teaching and review of all inquiry skills

---

A Look Beneath the Skin

Preparing for Inquiry

Key Concept Skeletal muscles work in pairs to allow animals to move their limbs.

Skills Objective Students will be able to
◆ observe the structure and function of the muscles in a chicken wing;
◆ classify the muscles based on their observations.

Time 30 minutes

Advance Planning
◆ Use only fresh chicken wings. Wings should be used within 24 hours of purchase and must be stored in a refrigerator.
◆ Soak all wings in a solution of 2 parts household bleach and 8 parts water for 2 hours before the lab. Rinse thoroughly with clear water to remove the bleach.
◆ Use disposable latex or nitrile gloves, or food-handling gloves.
◆ Make sure students wear protective gloves throughout the lab.

Guiding Inquiry

Invitation

Show students a human skeleton or a drawing of the bones in the human arm. Have students compare their arms to the arm of the skeleton and visualize how the muscles move the arm.

Troubleshooting the Experiment

Remind students to work slowly so they do not destroy parts of the wing before they have completely examined it.

Analyze and Conclude

1. Up and down at the elbow, like a human elbow; hinge joint
2. If students pull on the biceps, they bend the arm at the elbow. If they pull on the triceps, the arm straightens. The pulling represents muscle contraction.
3. skeletal
4. Sample: Diagrams allow you to compare structures of the arm even though they are not visible at the same time.

SECTION 4 The Skin

Objectives

After completing the lesson, students will be able to
◆ describe the functions of skin;
◆ list ways that individuals can keep skin healthy;
◆ identify and describe the layers of the skin.

Key Terms epidermis, melanin, dermis, pore, follicle, cancer, acne

1 Engage/Explore

Activating Prior Knowledge

Have students look at the skin on their arms and hands. Ask them to speculate about what they think their skin does. *(Samples: It protects the body tissues, keeps bacteria out of the body, provides feeling through the sense of touch, perspires.)*

DISCOVER

Skills Focus inferring
Materials *hand lens, plastic gloves*
Time 15 minutes
Tips Ask students to predict what they will observe through the hand lens. Ask: **What structures would you expect to see on the surface of your skin?**
Expected Outcome Students should observe hairs on the back of their hands. Students should be able to observe the ridges of the skin as well as the openings to the pores.
Think It Over After students have had the plastic glove on, there will be moisture covering the skin's surface. Students should infer that perspiration is one of the functions of the skin.

SECTION 4 The Skin

DISCOVER ·········· ACTIVITY

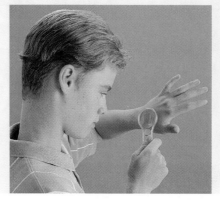

What Can You Observe About Skin?

1. Using a hand lens, examine the skin on your hand. Look for pores and hairs on both the palm and back of your hand.

2. Place a plastic glove on your hand. After five minutes, remove the glove. Then examine the skin on your hand with the hand lens.

Think It Over
Inferring Compare your hand before and after wearing the glove. What happened to the skin when you wore the glove? Why did this happen?

GUIDE FOR READING

◆ What are the functions of skin?

◆ What habits can help keep your skin healthy?

Reading Tip As you read, create a table that shows the two major layers of skin. Include columns to record the location, structures, and functions of each layer.

Figure 13 The skin forms a barrier that protects the inside of the body from substances such as the chlorine in pool water.

Here's a question for you: What's the largest organ in the human body? If your answer is the skin, you are right! If an adult's skin were stretched out flat, it would cover an area larger than 1.5 square meters—about the size of a mattress on a twin bed. You may think of the skin as nothing more than a covering that separates the inside of the body from the outside environment. You may be surprised to learn about the many important roles that the skin plays.

The Body's Tough Covering

The skin performs several major functions in the body. **The skin covers the body and prevents the loss of water. It protects the body from injury and infection. The skin also helps to regulate body temperature, eliminate wastes, gather information about the environment, and produce vitamin D.**

The skin protects the body by forming a barrier that keeps disease-causing microorganisms and harmful substances outside the body. In addition, the skin helps keep important substances inside the body. Like plastic wrap that keeps food from drying out, the skin prevents the loss of important fluids such as water.

READING STRATEGIES

Reading Tip Have students create a table like the one shown in which to list facts about the two major skin layers.

	Location	Structures	Function
Epidermis	outermost layer		
Dermis	lower layer		

Study and Comprehension Before students read the section, have them work in small groups to discuss whether they agree or disagree with the statements below. After students read the section, have them discuss reasons for their initial opinions and reasons for any changes in their opinions.

1. A well-balanced diet is important in the care of the skin.
2. The dermis is the outer layer of the skin.
3. The skin helps regulate body temperature.
4. Dead cells of the outermost layer of the skin are valuable to the body.

Figure 14 When you exercise, your body becomes warmer. Sweat glands in the skin produce perspiration, which leaves the body through pores like the one you see here. *Relating Cause and Effect* How does perspiration help cool your body?

Another function of the skin is to help the body maintain a steady temperature. Many blood vessels run through skin. When you become too warm, these blood vessels enlarge to increase the amount of blood that flows through them. This allows heat to move from your body into the outside environment. In addition, sweat glands in the skin respond to excess heat by producing perspiration. As perspiration evaporates from your skin, heat moves into the air. Because perspiration contains some dissolved waste materials, your skin also helps to eliminate wastes.

The skin also gathers information about the environment. To understand how the skin does this, place your fingertips on the skin of your arm and press down firmly. Then lightly pinch yourself. You have just tested some of the nerves in your skin. The nerves in skin provide information about such things as pressure, pain, and temperature. Pain messages are important because they warn you that something in your surroundings may have injured you.

Lastly, some skin cells produce vitamin D in the presence of sunlight. Vitamin D is important for healthy bones. This is because Vitamin D helps the cells in your digestive system to absorb the calcium in your food. Your skin cells need only a few minutes of sunlight to produce all the vitamin D you need in a day.

✓ *Checkpoint* How does your skin help eliminate waste materials from your body?

Program Resources

◆ **Teaching Resources** 2-4 Lesson Plan, p. 50; 2-4 Section Summary, p. 51

Media and Technology

 Audiotapes English-Spanish Summary 2-4

Answers to Self-Assessment

Caption Question

Figure 14 As perspiration evaporates from the skin, heat moves into the air.

✓ *Checkpoint*

Perspiration contains dissolved waste materials.

2 Facilitate

The Body's Tough Covering

Building Inquiry Skills: Applying Concepts

Have pairs of students make lists of the skin's major functions and identify how each function helps the body maintain homeostasis. For each function, ask: **What would happen if the skin could not perform this function?** (*Sample: If the skin could not help regulate temperature, the kinds of environments in which people live would be restricted.*) **learning modality: verbal**

Building Inquiry Skills: Observing

Materials *rubbing alcohol, cotton ball, dishwashing liquid, dropper*
Time 10 minutes

ACTIVITY

Prepare a dilute solution of dishwashing liquid in advance by mixing one drop of dishwashing liquid and 200 mL of water. Students will work in pairs to investigate the waterproof nature of the skin. Have a member of each pair clean one of their partner's palms with a cotton ball dipped in rubbing alcohol, then use the dropper to put two or three separate drops of the dilute dishwashing liquid on both of their partner's palms. Ask students to describe what they observe. (*The drops on one palm spread out. The drops on the other palm remain rounded.*) Ask: **What caused the drops on one hand to spread out while the drops on the other hand did not?** (*The rubbing alcohol removed the oil from the skin, so that palm was no longer waterproof.*) **learning modality: visual**

Ongoing Assessment

Organizing Information Have students create concept maps that describe the skin and its functions.

The Epidermis

Call students' attention to the epidermis, and ask students to identify the openings found in that layer. *(Pores and openings of hair follicle)* Ask students to infer the function of the pores. *(They allow sweat to reach the surface of the skin.)* Point out that some nerves are located near the hair follicles. Ask students to infer the relationship between the hair and the nerves. *(Sample: When something touches or blows against the hairs, the nerves pick up the sensation.)* **learning modality: visual**

Real-Life Learning

Tell students that researchers have found that most household dust—up to 80 percent—is mostly composed of dead human skin cells. However, it is not the dead skin cells that so many people are allergic to. Dust allergies are caused by dust mites, tiny spider-like creatures that live off dead skin cells and the water vapor that people produce by breathing and perspiring. Ask students: **Where are dust mites most likely to be found in your home? Why?** *(The bedroom; most people spend about one third of their day there.)* Then ask: **How could you reduce your exposure to dust mites?** *(Samples: Use special covers for mattresses and pillows; wash linens regularly; decrease the humidity in your home.)* **learning modality: verbal**

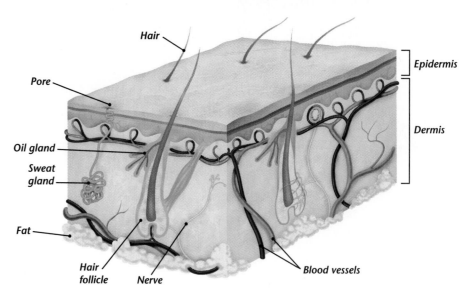

Figure 15 The skin is made of two main layers. The top layer is called the epidermis. The bottom layer is called the dermis. *Interpreting Diagrams In which layer of the skin do you find blood vessels?*

The Epidermis

The skin is organized into two main layers, the epidermis and the dermis. You can see these layers in Figure 15. The **epidermis** is the outermost layer of the skin. In most places, the epidermis is thinner than the dermis. The epidermis does not have nerves or blood vessels. This is why you usually don't feel pain from very shallow scratches and why shallow scratches do not bleed.

Dead or Alive? The cells in the epidermis have a definite life cycle. Each epidermal cell begins life deep in the epidermis, where cells divide to form new cells. The new cells gradually mature and move upward in the epidermis as new cells form beneath them. After about two weeks, the cells die and become part of the surface layer of the epidermis. Under a microscope, this surface layer of dead cells resembles flat bags laid on top of each other. Cells remain in this layer for about two weeks. Then they are shed and replaced by the dead cells below.

Protecting the Body In some ways, the cells of the epidermis are more valuable to the body dead than alive. Most of the protection provided by the skin is due to the layer of dead cells on the surface. The thick layer of dead cells on your fingertips, for example, protects and cushions your fingertips. The shedding of dead cells also helps to protect the body. As the cells fall away, they carry with them bacteria and other substances that settle on the skin. Every time you rub your hands together, you lose hundreds, even thousands, of dead skin cells.

Background

Integrating Science Forensic scientists can use friction ridge patterns, the ridges on the ends of a person's fingers, to identify people. If a suspect is at the scene of a crime, oil or perspiration around the friction ridges will transfer to objects he or she handles. Forensic scientists can develop recent fingerprints by treating them with special chemicals. Prints up to several years old can be recorded by shining lasers at them, then photographing them with time-lapse photography. After the prints are taken, they can be entered into a computer network and compared with prints on file

Fingerprints can also be taken for medical purposes, because some genetic conditions are associated with certain print patterns.

Some cells in the inner layer of the epidermis help to protect the body, too. On your fingers, for example, some cells produce hard nails, which protect the fingertips from injury and help you scratch and pick up objects.

Other cells deep in the epidermis produce **melanin,** a pigment, or colored substance, that gives skin its color. The more melanin in your skin, the darker it is. Exposure to sunlight stimulates the skin to make more melanin. Melanin production helps to protect the skin from burning.

☑ *Checkpoint* *How do dead skin cells help to protect the body?*

The Dermis

The **dermis** is the lower layer of the skin. Find the dermis in Figure 15. Notice that it is located below the epidermis and above a layer of fat. This fat layer pads the internal organs and helps keep heat in the body.

The dermis contains nerves and blood vessels. The dermis also contains other structures as well—sweat glands, hairs, and oil glands. Sweat glands produce perspiration, which reaches the surface through openings called **pores.** Strands of hair grow within the dermis in structures called **follicles** (FAHL ih kulz). The hair that you see above the skin's surface is made up of dead cells. Oil produced in glands around the hair follicles waterproofs the hair. In addition, oil that reaches the surface helps to keep the skin moist.

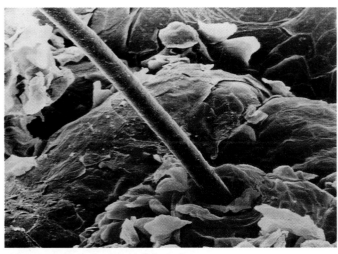

Figure 16 Hairs grow from follicles in the dermis of the skin. Hair is made of dead cells.

Sweaty Skin

This activity illustrates one of the skin's important functions.

1. 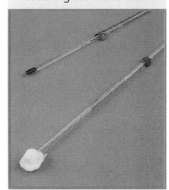 Wrap a wet cotton ball around the bulb of one thermometer. Place a second thermometer next to the first one, but not touching the cotton ball.

2. After two minutes, record the temperature reading on each thermometer.

3. Using a piece of cardboard, fan both thermometers for several minutes. The cardboard should be at least 10 cm from the thermometers. Then record the temperatures.

Measuring Which of the two thermometers had a lower temperature after Step 3? How does this activity relate to the role of skin in regulating body temperature?

Program Resources

◆ **Product Testing Activities** by *Consumer Reports,* "Testing Bandages," pp. 1–8

Media and Technology

 Transparencies "The Skin," Transparency 5

Answers to Self-Assessment

Caption Question

Figure 15 The dermis

☑ *Checkpoint*

Dead cells protect and cushion the living cells beneath them. They also carry away bacteria and other substances that settle on the skin.

The Dermis

TRY THIS

Skills Focus measuring
Materials 2 *thermometers, wet cotton ball, piece of cardboard*
Time 15 minutes
Tips Have students note the temperatures on both thermometers before beginning the activity. Ask students to predict what the temperatures will be at the conclusion of the activity.
Measuring Students should note that the thermometer wrapped in wet cotton has a lower temperature after it is fanned. They should conclude that when skin is moist, sweat evaporates into the air, removing body heat and lowering the temperature of the body.
Extend Ask students why an athlete might put on a jacket after a workout, even though the air is warm. *(The jacket will keep the athlete from getting chilled when sweat evaporates.)* **learning modality: logical/mathematical**

Building Inquiry Skills: Observing

Materials *microscope, prepared slides of hair cells, human hair, hand lens*
Time 15 minutes

Invite students to provide strands of hair that have been carefully removed from their heads. Have students use a hand lens to observe the hair, noting the structure, texture, thickness, and coloration. Have students look at slides of hair cells under the microscope. Have students use their observations and the images in Figure 15 and Figure 16 to make a detailed diagram of how the hair grows out of the dermis. Students should label their diagrams with their observations. **learning modality: visual**

Ongoing Assessment

Writing Have students write paragraphs that compare and contrast the structure and function of the dermis and epidermis.

Sun Safety

Preparing for Inquiry

Key Concept Students have probably used commercial lotions, oils, and creams containing sunscreens to protect themselves from sunburn. However, they may not understand the relationship between a product's SPF (sun protection factor) rating and its effectiveness in protecting the skin from burning.

Skills Objective Students will be able to
- predict the outcome of an experiment that compares the sun-blocking ability of different sunscreens;
- make observations during an experiment;
- draw conclusions based on their observations.

Time 45 minutes, plus 2 to 4 hours of sun exposure, and 20 minutes to analyze the results

Advance Planning
- Obtain photosensitive paper from science supply houses or some toy or craft stores.
- Collect fabric or have students bring in scraps of fabric. Try to choose fabrics used in clothing commonly worn by students, such as T-shirt material and denim.

Guiding Inquiry

Invitation
Engage the class in a brief discussion of how sunscreens protect the skin. Point out that sunscreens have an SPF number, and ask: **What does this number mean? Would you be less likely to get a sunburn if you used a sunscreen product with a higher SPF?**

Introducing the Procedure
- Have students work in small groups so each team member can be responsible for a strip of photosensitive paper.
- Demonstrate how to cut the photosensitive and construction paper strips and staple them in place in the plastic bag. Demonstrate the technique for coating the bag with sunscreen.

Caring for Your Skin

Because your skin has so many important functions, it is important to take care of it. **Four simple habits can help you keep your skin healthy. Eat properly. Drink enough water. Limit your exposure to the sun. Keep your skin clean and dry.**

Eating Properly Your skin is always active. The cells in the epidermis are replaced, hair strands and nails grow, and oil is produced. These activities require energy—and a well-balanced diet provides the energy needed for these processes. You will learn more about healthy diets in Chapter 3.

Real-World Lab

You and Your Environment

Sun Safety

In this lab, you'll investigate how sunscreen products and various fabrics protect your skin from the sun.

Problem

How well do different materials protect the skin from the sun?

Skills Focus

predicting, observing, drawing conclusions

Materials

scissors
3 different fabrics
photosensitive paper
white construction paper
resealable plastic bag
2 sunscreens with SPF ratings of 4 and 30

pencil
plastic knife
metric ruler
stapler
staple remover

Procedure

1. Read over the procedure. Then write a prediction about how well each of the sunscreens and fabrics will protect against the sun.

2. Use scissors to cut five strips of photosensitive paper that measure 5 cm by 15 cm.
3. Divide each strip into thirds by drawing lines across the strips as shown in the photo.
4. Cover one third of each strip with a square of white construction paper. Staple each square down.

Part 1 Investigating Sunscreens
5. Use a pencil to write the lower SPF (sun protection factor) rating on the back of the first strip. Write the other SPF rating on the back of a second strip.
6. Place the two strips side by side in a plastic bag. Seal the bag, then staple through the white squares to hold the strips in place.

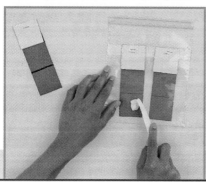

- Make sure students understand that the white construction paper allows them to control the experiment and compare their results. Students should be able to identify other controls, such as using the same amount of sunscreen and making sure the strips are exposed to direct sunlight.
- Place the strips where they will receive direct sunlight, but not in a sunny window, because UV rays cannot penetrate glass. You could use an artificial source of ultraviolet light such as a sun lamp. Make sure no one looks at the light source; it can seriously damage the retina.

Analyze and Conclude
1. Yes. Sections not covered by sunscreen changed color drastically. The covered sections changed color slightly or not at all.
2. The sunscreen with a higher SPF provided more protection. Students' predictions will be correct if they predicted this result.
3. Yes. The sections covered by fabric did not change color as much as the uncovered areas.

Drinking Water To keep your skin healthy, it is also important to drink plenty of water. When you participate in strenuous activities, such as playing soccer, you can perspire up to 10 liters of liquid a day. You need to replace the water lost in perspiration by drinking water or other beverages and by eating foods, such as fruits, that contain water.

Limiting Sun Exposure You can also take actions to protect your skin from cancer and early aging. **Cancer** is a disease in which some body cells divide uncontrollably. Repeated exposure to sunlight can damage skin cells and cause them to become

7. With a plastic knife, spread a thin layer of each sunscreen on the bag over the last square of each strip. Make certain each layer has the same depth. Be sure not to spread sunscreen over the middle squares.

8. Place the bag in direct sunlight with the sunscreen side up. Leave it there until the middle squares turn white.

9. Remove the strips from the bag, and take off the construction paper. Rinse the strips for one minute in cold water. Then dry them flat.

10. Observe all the squares. Record your observations.

Part 2 Investigating Fabrics

11. Obtain three fabrics of different thicknesses. Staple a square of each fabric over the last square of a photosensitive strip. Write a description of the fabric on the back of the strip.

12. Expose the strips to the sun, fabric-side up, until the middle square turns white. Then follow Steps 9 and 10.

Analyze and Conclude

1. Did the sunscreens protect against sun exposure? How do you know?

2. Which sunscreen provided more protection? Was your prediction correct?

3. Did the fabrics protect against sun exposure? How do you know?

4. Which fabric provided the most protection? The least protection? How did your results compare with your predictions?

5. **Apply** What advice would you give people about protecting their skin from the sun?

Design an Experiment

Design an experiment to find out whether ordinary window glass protects skin against sun exposure. Obtain your teacher's approval before carrying out this experiment.

4. The heaviest or most tightly woven fabric, such as denim, provided the most protection. Thin fabrics such as t-shirt material or light gauze provided less protection.

5. Samples: Choose a sunscreen with a high SPF rating, wear clothing that blocks the sun.

Extending the Inquiry

Design an Experiment Students' designs should include placing one strip of photosensitive paper in direct sunlight and one on an inside window sill or under a piece of window glass. Make sure students control variables such as the angle and amount of sunlight received.

Caring for Your Skin

Real-Life Learning

Provide a list of the Recommended Daily Allowances for different vitamins and minerals as well as resources that describe the functions performed by each. Have students identify vitamins and minerals that are important for healthy skin. Encourage students to find food sources that contain these vitamins and minerals. **learning modality: verbal**

Program Resources

◆ **Teaching Resources** Chapter 2 Real-World Lab, pp. 56–57

Safety

Remind students to be careful when using scissors. Caution them not to get any sunscreen into their eyes or mouths. They should wash their hands thoroughly after the lab. If sunlamps are used, be sure students observe safety precautions. Review the safety guidelines in Appendix A.

3 Assess

Section 4 Review Answers

1. Skin covers the body and protects it from injury and infection. It also helps regulate body temperature, eliminate wastes, gather information about the environment, and produce Vitamin D.

2. Accept any three: eat properly, drink enough water, limit exposure to the sun, and keep the skin clean and dry.

3. The epidermis contains some dead cells and some living cells, but no blood vessels or nerves. Some of the deepest cells of the epidermis produce melanin. The dermis is located beneath the epidermis and contains blood vessels, nerves, sweat glands, oil glands, and hair follicles.

4. Sample: Washing the skin too much may cause dryness and remove dead skin cells that are necessary to protect the skin.

Science at Home

Before students perform this activity, have them identify ways that people protect themselves from the sun. Encourage students to include items such as hats, parasols, and beach umbrellas. Students may want to ask older family members about items they may have used when they were young to avoid too much exposure to the sun.

Performance Assessment

Oral Presentation Group students into five teams. Assign each team one of the following functions of skin: prevents loss of water, protects body from injury and infection, regulates body temperature, eliminates wastes, and gathers information about the environment. Mention that the skin also produces vitamin D. Encourage each group to integrate material throughout the section to explain the importance of their assigned function and how it is accomplished by the skin.

Figure 17 This person is taking precautions to protect her skin from the sun. *Applying Concepts What other behaviors can provide protection from the sun?*

cancerous. In addition, exposure to the sun can cause the skin to become leathery and wrinkled.

There are many things you can do to protect your skin from damage by the sun. When you are outdoors, wear a hat and sunglasses and use a sunscreen on exposed skin. The clothing you wear can also protect you. Choose clothing made of tightly woven fabrics for the greatest protection. In addition, avoid exposure to the sun between the hours of 10 A.M. and 2 P.M. That is the time when sunlight is the strongest.

Keeping Skin Clean When you wash your skin with mild soap, you get rid of dirt and harmful bacteria. Good washing habits are particularly important during the teenage years when oil glands are more active. When oil glands become clogged with oil, bacterial infections can occur.

One bacterial infection of the skin that can be difficult to control is known as **acne.** If you develop acne, your doctor may prescribe an antibiotic to help control the infection. When you wash, you help to control oiliness and keep your skin from becoming infected with more bacteria.

Other organisms, called fungi, can also live on and infect the skin. Fungi grow best in warm, moist surroundings. Athlete's foot is a very common fungal infection that occurs on the feet, especially between the toes. You can prevent athlete's foot by keeping your feet, especially the spaces between your toes, clean and dry.

Section 4 Review

1. Describe the functions of the skin.
2. List three things you can do to keep your skin healthy.
3. Describe the structure of the two layers of skin.
4. **Thinking Critically** **Making Judgments** Do you think it is possible to wash your skin too much and damage it as a result? Why or why not?

Science at Home

With a family member, look for products in your home that provide protection from the sun. You may also want to visit a store that sells these products. Make a list of the products and place them in categories such as sunblocks, clothing, eye protectors, and other products. Explain to your family member why it is important to use such products.

Answers to Self-Assessment

Caption Question

Figure 17 Wearing a hat and sunglasses, wearing protective clothing, and avoiding exposure to the sun between 10 A.M. and 2 P.M.

Program Resources

◆ **Teaching Resources** 2-4 Review and Reinforce, p. 52; 2-4 Enrich, p. 53
◆ **Product Testing Activities by** *Consumer Reports,* "Testing Lip Balms," pp. 1–8

Media and Technology

 Interactive Student Tutorial CD-ROM D-2

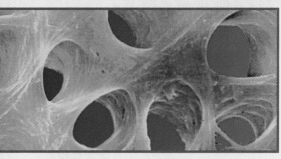

SECTION 1 The Skeletal System

Key Ideas

◆ The skeleton provides shape and support, enables movement, protects internal organs, produces blood cells, and stores materials.

◆ Movable joints allow the body to make a wide range of motions. Movable joints include gliding joints, hinge joints, pivot joints, and ball-and-socket joints.

◆ A combination of a balanced diet and regular exercise helps keep bones healthy.

Key Terms

vertebra	cartilage	ligament
marrow	joint	osteoporosis

SECTION 2 Diagnosing Bone and Joint Injuries

INTEGRATING TECHNOLOGY

Key Ideas

◆ X-rays are used to take images of bones. The waves of energy pass through the skin and other tissues and strike the photographic film underneath the area being observed.

◆ In magnetic resonance imaging (MRI), magnetic energy is used to produce an image of soft tissues.

◆ Skeletal injuries can be prevented by warming up, wearing protective equipment, and exercising in safe places.

Key Terms

fracture	X-ray
sprain	magnetic resonance
dislocation	imaging

SECTION 3 The Muscular System

Key Ideas

◆ Skeletal muscles are voluntary muscles that are attached to the bones of the skeleton. Smooth muscles, which are involuntary muscles, line the walls of many internal organs and blood vessels. Cardiac muscles are involuntary muscles found only in the heart.

◆ Because muscles can only contract and not expand, skeletal muscles work in pairs. When one muscle contracts, the other muscle in the pair returns to its original length.

Key Terms
involuntary muscle
tendon
voluntary muscle
smooth muscle
skeletal muscle
cardiac muscle

SECTION 4 The Skin

Key Ideas

◆ Skin covers and protects the body from injury and infection. It also helps to regulate body temperature, get rid of wastes, gather information about the environment, and produce vitamin D.

◆ The epidermis is the top layer of the skin. The dermis is the lower layer of the skin.

◆ For healthy skin, eat a well-balanced diet and drink enough water. Also limit your exposure to the sun and keep your skin clean.

Key Terms

epidermis	pore	cancer
melanin	follicle	acne
dermis		

USING THE INTERNET   ACTIVITY

www.science-explorer.phschool.com

Program Resources

◆ **Teaching Resources** Chapter 2 Project Scoring Rubric, p. 37; Chapter 2 Performance Assessment Teacher Notes, p. 242; Chapter 2 Performance Assessment Student Worksheet, p. 244; Chapter 2 Test, pp. 245–248

Reviewing Content:
Multiple Choice
1. b 2. c 3. b 4. c 5. c

True or False
6. marrow 7. ligament 8. skeletal or bone 9. true 10. dermis

Checking Concepts
11. Bone is covered by a thin, tough membrane except at its ends. Blood vessels and nerves enter and leave the bone through the membrane. Compact bone, which contains canals that have blood vessels and nerves, is directly under the membrane. Spongy bone is found under compact bone and also at the ends of the bone. Marrow fills the spaces in bone.

12. Ball-and-socket—allows range of motion through a complete circle; pivot—allows one bone to rotate around another; gliding—allows one bone to slide over another; hinge—allows forward and backward motion

13. The energy in X-rays passes through soft tissue, but is absorbed by bone. If a photographic film is placed under an injured area and X-rays are taken of the area, the X-rays develop the film beneath the soft tissues. The shadow of the bone is seen on the film.

14. Smooth muscle is not striated.

15. Because skeletal muscles can only contract and thereby pull a bone in one direction, there must be another muscle attached to the bone that can contract and pull the bone in the opposite direction.

16. They control functions that are performed automatically, without conscious control.

17. An epidermal cell forms deep in the epidermis. As it matures, it is pushed upward as other cells are produced beneath it. Within two weeks, the cell dies and becomes part of the surface layer. After about two weeks, the dead cell is exposed to the environment and washed away or shed.

18. Sunlight can injure skin cells, which may eventually become cancerous.

19. Students' articles should discuss proper exercise techniques such as stretching and wearing appropriate safety gear.

Reviewing Content
 For more review of key concepts, see the Interactive Student Tutorial CD-ROM.

Multiple Choice
Choose the letter of the best answer.

1. Blood cells are produced in
   a. compact bone.
   b. marrow.
   c. cartilage.
   d. ligaments.
2. Joints that allow only forward or backward movement are
   a. pivot joints.
   b. ball and socket joints.
   c. hinge joints.
   d. gliding joints.
3. An injury in which the ligaments are overstretched and tear is called
   a. a fracture.
   b. a sprain.
   c. a dislocation.
   d. tendinitis.
4. Muscles that help the skeleton move are
   a. cardiac muscles.
   b. smooth muscles.
   c. skeletal muscles.
   d. involuntary muscles.
5. Which structures help to maintain body temperature?
   a. oil glands
   b. follicles
   c. sweat glands
   d. nerves

True or False
If the statement is true, write true. If it is false, change the underlined word or words to make the statement true.

6. Spongy bone is filled with <u>cartilage</u>.
7. The connective tissue that connects the bones in a movable joint is called a <u>tendon</u>.
8. An X-ray is commonly used to diagnose <u>soft tissue</u> injuries.
9. <u>Skeletal</u> muscle is sometimes called striated muscle.
10. The <u>epidermis</u> contains nerve endings and blood vessels.

Checking Concepts
11. Describe the structure of a bone.
12. List the four kinds of movable joints. Describe how each kind of joint functions.
13. Why do X-ray images show bones but not muscles or other soft tissues?
14. How does the appearance of smooth muscle differ from that of skeletal muscle when viewed with a microscope?
15. Explain how skeletal muscles work in pairs to move a body part.
16. Why are smooth muscles called involuntary muscles?
17. Describe the life cycle of an epidermal cell.
18. Why is it important to limit your exposure to the sun?
19. **Writing to Learn** Write an article for your school newspaper about preventing skeletal and muscular injuries. The article should focus on ways in which athletes can decrease the risk of injuries during sports.

Thinking Visually
20. **Concept Map** Copy the concept map about muscles onto a separate sheet of paper. Then complete it and add a title. (For more information on concept maps, see the Skills Handbook.)

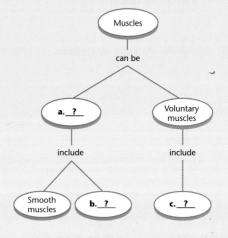

Thinking Visually
20. a. Involuntary muscles **b.** Cardiac muscles **c.** Skeletal muscles

Applying Skills
21. Strength—gymnastics, weight training; flexibility—gymnastics, karate

22. Sample: Ballet would probably increase both strength and flexibility, because it has movements that are similar to gymnastics.

23. Answers will vary. Students should provide specific ways to measure improvements in strength. Experiments should be controlled, with clearly defined manipulated variables and responding variables. A sample experiment: See how many push-ups you can do. Then, every day for a week, practice doing push-ups. Then test again to see how many push-ups you can do. (Caution students not to perform their experiments without your approval.)

Applying Skills

The table below rates different activities as to how well they improve muscular strength and flexibility. Use the table to answer Questions 21–23.

Fitness Ratings of Physical Activities

Activity	Builds Muscular Strength	Improves Flexibility
Baseball/Softball	Low	Moderate
Gymnastics	Very High	Very High
Karate	Moderate	High
Soccer	Moderate	Moderate
Weight Training	Very High	Moderate

21. **Interpreting Data** Which activities rate highest for strength? For flexibility?
22. **Inferring** Would ballet improve muscular strength or flexibility? Why?
23. **Designing Experiments** Design an experiment to determine if an activity that you do increases muscular strength. How would you measure improvements in your strength?

Thinking Critically

24. **Inferring** Disks of rubbery cartilage are found between the vertebrae. What function do you think these disks serve?
25. **Applying Concepts** At birth, the joints in an infant's skull are flexible and not yet fixed. As the child develops, the bones become more rigid and grow together. Why is it important that the bones of an infant's skull not grow together too rapidly?
26. **Comparing and Contrasting** How are ligaments and tendons similar? How are they different?
27. **Predicting** If smooth muscle had to be consciously controlled, what problems could you foresee in day-to-day living?
28. **Relating Cause and Effect** A person who is exposed to excessive heat may suffer from a condition known as heat stroke. The first sign of heat stroke is that the person stops sweating. Why is this condition a life-threatening emergency?

27. Sample: People would have to spend a lot of time consciously controlling processes that normally happen automatically, such as digestion. People would not be able to sleep, since life processes would not happen automatically.
28. Without being able to sweat, a person cannot get rid of excess body heat to maintain homeostasis.

Performance Assessment

Wrap Up
CHAPTER PROJECT 2

Present Your Project
Encourage students to ask questions after other students make their presentations. Students may want to share their sketches or have another student demonstrate the motion before they show their models. Make sure students' models and explanations include paired muscles.
Reflect and Record For new information, students will probably indicate the names, locations, and functions of the muscles involved in their models. Encourage students to consider other students' projects as they assess their own work. For example, some materials may work better than others to model bones and muscles.

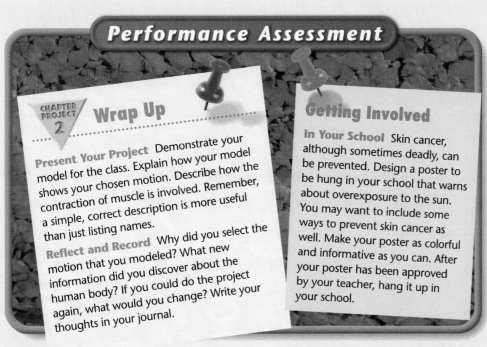

Performance Assessment

CHAPTER PROJECT 2 Wrap Up

Present Your Project Demonstrate your model for the class. Explain how your model shows your chosen motion. Describe how the contraction of muscle is involved. Remember, a simple, correct description is more useful than just listing names.

Reflect and Record Why did you select the motion that you modeled? What new information did you discover about the human body? If you could do the project again, what would you change? Write your thoughts in your journal.

Getting Involved

In Your School Skin cancer, although sometimes deadly, can be prevented. Design a poster to be hung in your school that warns about overexposure to the sun. You may want to include some ways to prevent skin cancer as well. Make your poster as colorful and informative as you can. After your poster has been approved by your teacher, hang it up in your school.

Thinking Critically

24. They act as cushions and reduce friction between the bone material that could rub together during movement.
25. If the bones grew together too rapidly, there would not be enough space for the brain to grow.
26. Both ligaments and tendons connect bones to other structures. Ligaments connect bones to other bones, and tendons connect muscles to bones.

Program Resources

◆ **Inquiry Skills Handbook** Provides teaching and review of all inquiry skills

Getting Involved

In Your School Students' posters should be creative and clear. Students may want to draw pictures or use pictures of people from magazines or newspapers. Provide resources for students who have questions about skin cancer. If possible, hang posters in a common area in your school or allow students to present their information to another class.

CHAPTER 3 Food and Digestion

Sections	Time	Student Edition Activities	Other Activities	
CHAPTER PROJECT 3 **What's for Lunch?** p. 67	Ongoing (2–3 weeks)	Check Your Progress, pp. 75, 81, 93 Wrap Up, p. 97	TE	Chapter 3 Project Notes, pp. 66–67
1 Food and Energy pp. 68–76 ◆ List and describe each of the six nutrients needed by the body. ◆ Describe the function of water in the body.	4½ periods/ 2–3 blocks	**Discover** Food Claims—Fact or Fiction?, p. 68 **Sharpen Your Skills** Predicting, p. 70 **Real-World Lab: You, the Consumer** Iron for Breakfast, p. 76	TE TE TE	Building Inquiry Skills: Calculating, p. 69 Including All Students, p. 70 Inquiry Challenge, p. 74
2 INTEGRATING HEALTH **Healthy Eating** pp. 77–81 ◆ Describe the Food Guide Pyramid and state how it can be used to plan a healthy diet. ◆ List and describe the information that is included on nutrition labels.	2½ periods/ 1–2 blocks	**Discover** Do Snack Foods Contain Fat?, p. 77	TE TE TE PTA	Building Inquiry Skills: Classifying, p. 78 Including All Students, p. 78 Real-Life Learning, p. 80 "Testing Cereals," pp. 1–8
3 The Digestive Process Begins pp. 82–89 ◆ Describe the general functions carried out by the digestive system and the specific functions of the mouth, esophagus, and stomach.	4 periods/ 2 blocks	**Discover** How Can You Speed up Digestion?, p. 82 **Try This** Modeling Peristalsis, p. 85 **Skills Lab: Drawing Conclusions** As the Stomach Churns, pp. 88–89	PTA ISLM	"Testing Antacids," pp. 1–8 D-3, "Nutrient Identification"
4 Final Digestion and Absorption pp. 90–94 ◆ Explain the role of the small intestine and large intestine in digestion.	2½ periods/ 1–2 blocks	**Discover** Which Surface Is Larger?, p. 90 **Try This** Break Up!, p. 91	TE TE PTA PTA	Demonstration, p. 91 Including All Students, p. 92 "Testing Yogurt," pp. 1–8 "Testing Sports Drinks," pp. 1–8
Study Guide/Chapter Review pp. 95–97	1 period/ ½ block		ISAB	Provides teaching and review of all inquiry skills

 For Standard or Block Schedule The Resource Pro® CD-ROM gives you maximum flexibility for planning your instruction for any type of schedule. Resource Pro® contains Planning Express®, an advanced scheduling program, as well as the entire contents of the Teaching Resources and the Computer Test Bank.

66a

CHAPTER PLANNING GUIDE

Program Resources	Assessment Strategies	Media and Technology
TR Chapter 3 Project Teacher Notes, pp. 58–59 **TR** Chapter 3 Project Overview and Worksheets, pp. 60–63 **TR** Chapter 3 Project Scoring Rubric, p. 64	**SE** Performance Assessment: Chapter 3 Project Wrap Up, p. 97 **TE** Check Your Progress, pp. 75, 81, 93 **TE** Performance Assessment: Chapter 3 Project Wrap Up, p. 97 **TR** Chapter 3 Project Scoring Rubric, p. 64	
TR 3-1 Lesson Plan, p. 65 **TR** 3-1 Section Summary, p. 66 **TR** 3-1 Review and Reinforce, p. 67 **TR** 3-1 Enrich, p. 68 **TR** Chapter 3 Real-World Lab, pp. 81–82 **SES** Book M, *Motion, Forces, and Energy,* Chapter 6 **SES** Book L, *Chemical Interactions,* Chapter 2	**SE** Section 1 Review, p. 75 **SE** Analyze and Conclude, p. 76 **TE** Ongoing Assessment, pp. 69, 71, 73 **TE** Performance Assessment, p. 75 **TR** 3-1 Review and Reinforce, p. 67	Exploring Physical Science Videodisc, Unit 4 Side 1, "Balancing Act" Audiotapes: English-Spanish Summary 3-1 Interactive Student Tutorial CD-ROM, D-3
TR 3-2 Lesson Plan, p. 69 **TR** 3-2 Section Summary, p. 70 **TR** 3-2 Review and Reinforce, p. 71 **TR** 3-2 Enrich, p. 72	**SE** Section 2 Review, p. 81 **TE** Ongoing Assessment, p. 79 **TE** Performance Assessment, p. 81 **TR** 3-2 Review and Reinforce, p. 71	Exploring Life Science Videodisc, Unit 4 Side 1, "You Are What You Eat" Audiotapes: English-Spanish Summary 3-2 Transparency 6, "The Food Guide Pyramid" Interactive Student Tutorial CD-ROM, D-3
TR 3-3 Lesson Plan, p. 73 **TR** 3-3 Section Summary, p. 74 **TR** 3-3 Review and Reinforce, p. 75 **TR** 3-3 Enrich, p. 76 **TR** Chapter 3 Skills Lab, pp. 83–85 **SES** Book L, *Chemical Interactions,* Chapter 2	**SE** Section 3 Review, p. 87 **SE** Analyze and Conclude, p. 89 **TE** Ongoing Assessment, pp. 83, 85 **TE** Performance Assessment, p. 87 **TR** 3-3 Review and Reinforce, p. 75	Exploring Life Science Videodisc, Unit 4 Side 1, "Digestion and Absorption" Audiotapes: English-Spanish Summary 3-3 Transparency 7, "The Digestive System" Interactive Student Tutorial CD-ROM, D-3
TR 3-4 Lesson Plan, p. 77 **TR** 3-4 Section Summary, p. 78 **TR** 3-4 Review and Reinforce, p. 79 **TR** 3-4 Enrich, p. 80	**SE** Section 4 Review, p. 93 **TE** Ongoing Assessment, p. 91 **TE** Performance Assessment, p. 93 **TR** 3-4 Review and Reinforce, p. 79	Exploring Life Science Videodisc, Unit 4 Side 1, "Digestion and Absorption" Audiotapes: English-Spanish Summary 3-4 Interactive Student Tutorial CD-ROM, D-3
TR Chapter 3 Performance Assessment, pp. 250–252 **TR** Chapter 3 Test, pp. 253–256	**SE** Chapter Review, pp. 95–97 **TR** Chapter 3 Performance Assessment, pp. 250–252 **TR** Chapter 3 Test, pp. 253–256 **CTB** Test D-3	Computer Test Bank, Test D-3 Interactive Student Tutorial CD-ROM, D-3 Science Explorer Internet Site

Key: **SE** Student Edition **TE** Teacher's Edition **TR** Teaching Resources
  CTB Computer Test Bank **SES** Science Explorer Series Text **ISLM** Integrated Science Laboratory Manual
  ISAB Inquiry Skills Activity Book **PTA** Product Testing Activities by *Consumer Reports* **IES** Interdisciplinary Explorations Series

Meeting the National Science Education Standards and AAAS Benchmarks

National Science Education Standards	Benchmarks for Science Literacy	Unifying Themes
Science as Inquiry (Content Standard A) ◆ **Ask questions that can be answered by scientific investigations** How can you test whether iron has been added to cereals? *(Real-World Lab)* What conditions are needed for the digestion of proteins in the stomach? *(Skills Lab)* **Life Science** (Content Standard C) ◆ **Structure and function in living systems** The digestive system breaks down food into molecules the body can use. These molecules are absorbed into the blood carried throughout the body. Wastes are eliminated from the body. Most of the chemical digestion takes place in the small intestine. Most of the absorption of water takes place in the large intestine. *(Sections 3, 4)* **Science in Personal and Social Perspectives** (Content Standard F) ◆ **Personal health** Food provides energy and nutrients for growth and development. The six kinds of nutrients are carbohydrates, fats, proteins, vitamins, minerals, and water. *(Section 1)* Nutrition requirements vary. The Food Guide Pyramid and food nutritional labels can help a person plan a healthy diet.	**1A The Scientific World View** Students learn about observations that led to the understanding of how the digestive system works. *(Section 3, Skills Lab)* **5E Flow of Matter and Energy** Food provides molecules that serve as fuel and building material for the human body. *(Sections 1, 2)* Food can be used immediately or stored. *(Sections 3, 4)* **6C Basic Functions** The digestive system is composed of organs that enable all cells in the body to be provided with nutrients for energy and building materials. Food is digested into molecules that are absorbed and transported to the cells of the body. *(Sections 3, 4)* **6E Physical Health** The amount of calories a person requires varies with body weight and age. *(Section 1)* **12D Communication Skills** Organize information from experimental data into tables and identify the relationships revealed. *(Skills Lab)*	◆ **Energy** Energy comes from the six kinds of nutrients necessary for human health. These include carbohydrates, fats, proteins, vitamins, minerals, and water. A balanced diet can be obtained by following the guidelines of the Food Guide Pyramid. A balanced diet will help keep the digestive system functioning properly. *(Sections 1, 2, 3, 4)* ◆ **Scale and Structure** As food moves through the digestive system, organs work together to help digest food into molecules that can be absorbed and transported to other areas of the body. This is done by mechanical and chemical digestion. *(Sections 3, 4)* ◆ **Unity and Diversity** Different nutrients are essential for proper health. Food labels give necessary information that tell the nutrient content of foods. *(Sections 1, 3, 4)* ◆ **Systems and Interactions** Organs in the digestive system secrete various enzymes that enable the digestive process. Each enzyme has a different function, but all work together to help in the breakdown of foods. *(Skills Lab)*

Media and Technology

Exploring Physical Science Videodisc
◆ **Section 1** "Balancing Act" defines spirometry and models the relationship between heat, food, energy, exercise, and calories.

Exploring Life Science Videodisc
◆ **Section 2** "You Are What You Eat" allows an athlete to share the details of her training diet. The relationship between the nutrients in food and the resulting energy, growth, maintenance, and development of the body are discussed.
◆ **Section 3** "Digestion and Absorption" exemplifies the workings of the digestive system and contains X-ray footage of a meal being processed.

Interactive Student Tutorial CD-ROM
◆ **Chapter Review** Interactive questions help students to self-assess their mastery of key chapter concepts.

Student Edition Connection Strategies

◆ **Section 1** Integrating Physics, p. 69
   Math Toolbox, p. 71
   Social Studies Connection, p. 72
   Integrating Chemistry, p. 72

◆ **Section 2** Integrating Health, p. 77

◆ **Section 3** Integrating Chemistry, p. 84
   Integrating Chemistry, p. 86

USING THE INTERNET

www.science-explorer.phschool.com

Visit the Science Explorer Internet site to find an up-to-date activity for Chapter 2 of *Human Biology and Health.*

ACTIVITY	Time (minutes)	Materials Quantities for one work group	Skills
Section 1			
Discover, p. 68	15	**Consumable** No special materials are required.	Posing Questions
Sharpen Your Skills, p. 70	20	**Consumable** fruits and vegetables, including potatoes, rice, bread, breakfast cereals; soft drinks (diet and regular); iodine solution **Nonconsumable** plastic dropper, test tubes, notebook	Predicting
Real-World Lab, p. 76	55	**Consumable** white paper towels, plastic spoon, instant oatmeal, warm water, 2 dry breakfast cereals, 3 sealable plastic freezer bags **Nonconsumable** long bar magnet, balance, watch or clock, wooden dowel, plastic jar with sealable cover	Observing, Predicting, Interpreting Data
Section 2			
Discover, p. 77	25	**Consumable** 4 squares of brown paper, each about 8 cm by 8 cm; crushed potato chips; crushed pretzels; piece of chocolate; slice of apple; paper towel	Classifying
Section 3			
Discover, p. 82	15	**Consumable** water, sugar cubes **Nonconsumable** 2 jars with lids	Predicting
Try This, p. 85	15	**Consumable** 20-cm clear flexible plastic straw (about 6 mm in diameter) **Nonconsumable** round bead (5–6 mm in diameter)	Making Models
Skills Lab, pp. 88–89	60–80	**Consumable** pepsin, dilute hydrochloric acid, water, plastic stirrers, litmus paper, cubes of boiled egg white **Nonconsumable** test tube rack, marking pencil, 10-mL plastic graduated cylinder, 4 test tubes with stoppers	Drawing Conclusions
Section 4			
Discover, p. 90	10	**Nonconsumable** 1 m string, metric ruler	Predicting
Try This, p. 91	15	**Consumable** oil, baking soda **Nonconsumable** 2 jars, stirring rod or spoon	Observing

A list of all materials required for the Student Edition activities can be found on pages T14–T15. You can order Materials Kits by calling 1-800-828-7777 or by accessing the Science Explorer Internet site at **www.science-explorer.phschool.com.**

What's for Lunch?

Nutritionists claim that many people who maintain healthy lifestyles do so, in part, by keeping track of their diets. In this project, students will have the opportunity to find out how their eating habits correspond to the diets that are recommended for optimum health.

Purpose In this project, students will keep track of the food they eat for three days. They will learn how to estimate portions and will compare their diets to the Food Guide Pyramid recommendations. Students will be able to use what they learn to improve their eating habits.

Skills Focus After completing the Chapter 3 Project, students will be able to
♦ observe and maintain records of their eating habits;
♦ measure or estimate the size of food servings;
♦ graph data from their data tables;
♦ compare and contrast their data with the recommendations;
♦ interpret their diagrams and make judgments about how to improve their own diets.

Project Time Line The project should take approximately two weeks—three days to record food intake, three or four days to analyze their data, and three more days to implement a diet based on the Food Guide Pyramid. Before beginning the project, see Chapter 3 Project Teacher Notes on pages 58–59 in Teaching Resources for more details on carrying out the project. Also distribute to students the Chapter 3 Project Overview, Worksheets, and Scoring Rubric on pages 60–64 in Teaching Resources.

Possible Materials Students need graph paper, paper, and pencils. You may want to create a chart for students to record foods or you may allow the layout of the chart to grow out of a class discussion on recordkeeping.

Launching the Project To introduce the project and to stimulate student interest, ask students to write down what they have eaten so far today. Explain to students that their notes and lab reports

WHAT'S AHEAD

Integrating Health

SECTION 1 Food and Energy

Discover **Food Claims—Fact or Fiction?**
Sharpen Your Skills **Predicting**
Real-World Lab **Iron for Breakfast**

SECTION 2 Healthy Eating

Discover **Do Snack Foods Contain Fat?**

SECTION 3 The Digestive Process Begins

Discover **How Can You Speed up Digestion?**
Try This **Modeling Peristalsis**
Skills Lab **As the Stomach Churns**

66 ♦ D

will be kept confidential, so no one else will know what they have eaten. Using the illustration of the Food Guide Pyramid as a guide, ask the students to try to sort their food items into the appropriate groups.

Allow time for students to read the description of the project in their text and the Chapter Project Overview on pages 60–61 in Teaching Resources. Then discuss the Food Guide Pyramid and talk about the kind of diet it describes as ideal.

Describe the project by explaining that each

student will record all the foods they eat each day for three days. To help students see the importance of daily record keeping, ask them to try to remember what they ate for supper two days ago. Point out that it is difficult to remember things even a few hours later, so they should be sure to write down every meal and snack as soon as possible.

Review Student Worksheet Number 1 as an example of a way to record foods. Write a sample of a food record on the board, including spaces to record three meals and snacks.

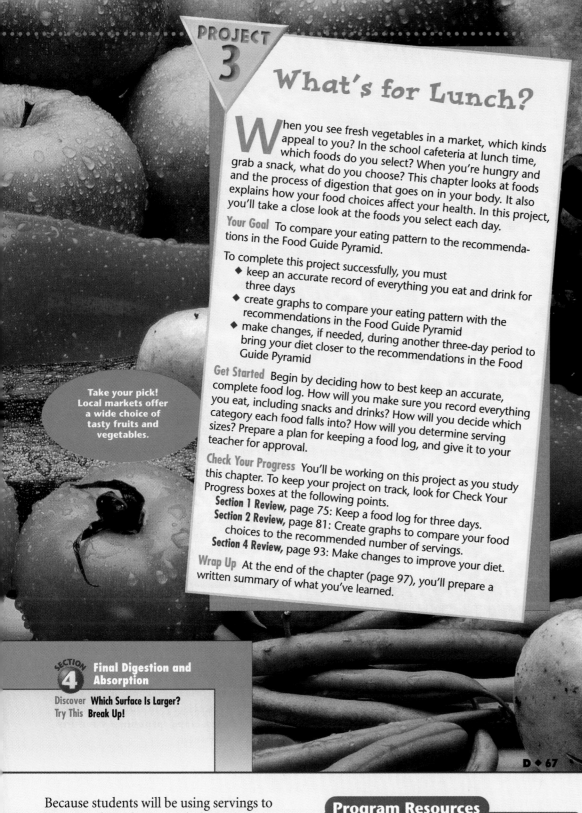

What's for Lunch?

When you see fresh vegetables in a market, which kinds appeal to you? In the school cafeteria at lunch time, which foods do you select? When you're hungry and grab a snack, what do you choose? This chapter looks at foods and the process of digestion that goes on in your body. It also explains how your food choices affect your health. In this project, you'll take a close look at the foods you select each day.

Your Goal To compare your eating pattern to the recommendations in the Food Guide Pyramid.

To complete this project successfully, you must
- keep an accurate record of everything you eat and drink for three days
- create graphs to compare your eating pattern with the recommendations in the Food Guide Pyramid
- make changes, if needed, during another three-day period to bring your diet closer to the recommendations in the Food Guide Pyramid

Get Started Begin by deciding how to best keep an accurate, complete food log. How will you make sure you record everything you eat, including snacks and drinks? How will you decide which category each food falls into? How will you determine serving sizes? Prepare a plan for keeping a food log, and give it to your teacher for approval.

Check Your Progress You'll be working on this project as you study this chapter. To keep your project on track, look for Check Your Progress boxes at the following points.

Section 1 Review, page 75: Keep a food log for three days.
Section 2 Review, page 81: Create graphs to compare your food choices to the recommended number of servings.
Section 4 Review, page 93: Make changes to improve your diet.

Wrap Up At the end of the chapter (page 97), you'll prepare a written summary of what you've learned.

Take your pick! Local markets offer a wide choice of tasty fruits and vegetables.

SECTION 4 Final Digestion and Absorption

Discover Which Surface Is Larger?
Try This Break Up!

Because students will be using servings to compare their choices with the USDA recommendations, have them brainstorm ways they can record the amounts of food they eat so they can easily convert food listings into servings.

Program Resources

- **Teaching Resources** Chapter 3 Project Teacher Notes, pp. 58–59; Chapter 3 Project Overview and Worksheets, pp. 60–63; Chapter 3 Project Scoring Rubric, p. 64

Performance Assessment

The Chapter 3 Project Scoring Rubric on page 64 of Teaching Resources will help you evaluate how well students complete the Chapter 3 Project. Students will be assessed on
- how thoroughly they keep records of the types and amounts of food they eat;
- the completeness of their graphs, including the conversion of servings into totals;
- how well they analyze their diets based on the Food Guide Pyramid;
- the thoroughness and organization of their written presentations and how well they show an understanding of food choices and healthy and unhealthy diets.

By sharing the Chapter 3 Scoring Rubric with students at the beginning of the project, you will make it clear to them what they are expected to do.

Objectives

After completing the lesson, students will be able to
- ◆ list and describe each of the six nutrients needed by the body;
- ◆ describe the function of water in the body.

Key Terms nutrient, calorie, carbohydrate, glucose, fiber, fat, unsaturated fat, saturated fat, cholesterol, protein, amino acid, vitamin, mineral

1 Engage/Explore

Activating Prior Knowledge

Ask students to name foods that they think supply them with energy. Write their responses on the board. Then ask them what they think a calorie is and write these responses on the board. Revisit the responses once students have read the section.

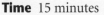

DISCOVER

Skills Focus posing questions
Time 15 minutes
Tips Write the statements on the board or use an overhead projector to project the statements on a screen.
Expected Outcome All the statements are false. At this stage, you may wish to collect students' opinions and look for misconceptions, then address specific issues later as you teach the chapter.
Think It Over Students should volunteer additional statements about nutrition and discuss whether or not the statements are true. Encourage students to identify reliable sources of information about nutrition.

SECTION
1 Food and Energy

DISCOVER
····················· ACTIVITY ····

Food Claims—Fact or Fiction?

1. Examine the list of statements at the right. Copy the list onto a separate sheet of paper.

2. Next to each statement, write *agree* or *disagree*. Give a reason for your response.

3. Discuss your responses with a small group of classmates. Compare the reasons you gave for agreeing or disagreeing with each statement.

Think It Over
Posing Questions List some other statements about nutrition that you have heard. How could you find out whether the statements are true?

Fact or Fiction?

a. Athletes need more protein in their diets than other people do.

b. The only salt that a food contains is the salt that you have added to it.

c. As part of a healthy diet, everyone should take vitamin supplements.

d. You can go without water for longer than you can go without food.

GUIDE FOR READING

- ◆ What are the six nutrients needed by the body?
- ◆ What is the function of water in the body?

Reading Tip As you read, create a table that includes the function and sources of each nutrient group.

68 ◆ D

Imagine a Thanksgiving dinner—roast turkey on a platter, delicious stuffing, and lots of vegetables—an abundance of colors and aromas. Food is an important part of many happy occasions, of times shared with friends and family. Food is also essential. Every living thing needs food to stay alive.

Why You Need Food

Foods provide your body with materials for growing and for repairing tissues. Food also provides energy for everything you do—running, playing a musical instrument, reading, and even sleeping. By filling those needs, food enables your body to maintain homeostasis. Recall that homeostasis is the body's ability to keep a steady internal state in spite of changing external conditions. Suppose, for example, that you cut your finger. Food provides both the raw materials necessary to grow new skin and the energy that powers this growth.

Your body converts the foods you eat into nutrients. **Nutrients** (NOO tre unts) are the substances in food that provide the raw materials and energy the body needs to carry out all the essential processes. **There are six kinds of nutrients necessary for human health— carbohydrates, fats, proteins, vitamins, minerals, and water.**

READING STRATEGIES

Reading Tip Help students get started by creating the framework for a three-column table on the board. Label the columns *Nutrient, Function,* and *Source.* Then have a volunteer read aloud the boldfaced sentence under *Why You Need Food* that names the six nutrients necessary for human health. List these nutrients in the first column of the table. Students can copy the table and fill in the remaining columns as they read.

Study and Comprehension Before students begin reading, discuss what they already know about the nutrients essential for human health. Then have students preview the section by reading the headings and captions and looking at the pictures. Invite students to dictate questions suggested by this information. Write these on the board. When students finish reading, have them answer the questions.

Carbohydrates, fats, and proteins all provide the body with energy. When nutrients are used by the body for energy, the amount of energy they release can be measured in units called calories. One **calorie** is the amount of energy needed to raise the temperature of one gram of water by one Celsius degree. Most foods contain many thousands of calories of energy. Scientists usually use the term *Calorie*, with a capital *C*, to measure the energy in foods. One Calorie is the same as 1,000 calories. For example, one serving of popcorn may contain 60 Calories, or 60,000 calories, of energy. The more Calories a food has, the more energy it contains.

You need to eat a certain number of Calories each day to meet your body's energy needs. This daily energy requirement depends on a person's level of physical activity. It also changes as a person grows and ages. Infants and small children grow very rapidly, so they generally have the highest energy needs. Your current growth and level of physical activity affect the number of Calories you need. The more active you are, the higher your energy needs are.

Carbohydrates

The nutrients called **carbohydrates** (kar boh HY drayts), which are nutrients composed of carbon, oxygen, and hydrogen, are a major source of energy. One gram of carbohydrate provides your body with four Calories of energy. Carbohydrates also provide the raw materials to make parts of cells. Based on their chemical structure, carbohydrates are divided into two groups, simple carbohydrates and complex carbohydrates.

Figure 1 Your body obtains energy from carbohydrates. The sugars in fruits are simple carbohydrates. Starch is a complex carbohydrate found in grains and other plant products.

Chapter 3 **D ◆ 69**

Program Resources

◆ **Teaching Resources** 3-1 Lesson Plan, p. 65; 3-1 Section Summary, p. 66

Media and Technology

Audiotapes English-Spanish Summary 3-1

Why You Need Food

Integrating Physics

Describe how the amount of energy supplied by each food is determined. The food is placed into a strong metal container that is surrounded by a container of water. The whole device is insulated from temperature changes and heat loss. The food is burned inside the metal container, and the heat released raises the temperature of the water. By measuring the change in the temperature of the water, the scientists can determine the calorie content of the food. Ask students: **What measurements would scientists have to take before performing the experiment?** *(The mass of the food and of the water, and the initial temperature of the water)* **learning modality: verbal**

Building Inquiry Skills: Calculating

ACTIVITY

Materials *calorie requirement charts for different age groups, calorie content charts for foods*
Time 20 minutes

Have students use the information to determine their recommended daily calorie intake. Then have them use nutrition textbooks or calorie-counting references to find the calorie content of their favorite foods. They can use the information to calculate the calorie content of a meal that they might have for breakfast, lunch, or dinner.
learning modality: logical/ mathematical

Ongoing Assessment

Writing Have students explain why they need food and list the six main types of nutrients.

Carbohydrates

Sharpen your Skills

Predicting

Obtain food samples from your teacher. Write a prediction stating whether each food contains starch. Then test your predictions. First, put on your apron. Then use a plastic dropper to add three drops of iodine to each food sample. **CAUTION:** *Iodine can stain skin and clothing. Handle it carefully.* If the iodine turns blue-black, starch is present. Which foods contain starch?

Figure 2 Fiber is found in fruits, whole-grain foods, and the other foods shown here. *Applying Concepts Why is fiber important in the diet?*

Simple Carbohydrates Simple carbohydrates are also known as sugars. There are many types of sugars. They are found naturally in fruits, milk, and some vegetables. Sugars are also added to foods such as cookies, candies, and soft drinks. One sugar, **glucose** (GLOO kohs), is the major source of energy for your body's cells. However, most foods do not contain large amounts of glucose. The body converts other types of sugars into glucose, the form of sugar the body can use.

Complex Carbohydrates Complex carbohydrates are made up of many sugar molecules linked together in a chain. Starch is a complex carbohydrate found in plant foods such as potatoes, rice, corn, and grain products, such as pasta, cereals, and bread. To use starch as an energy source, your body first breaks it down into smaller, individual sugar molecules. Only then can your body release the molecules' energy.

Like starch, **fiber** is a complex carbohydrate found in plant foods. However, unlike starch, fiber cannot be broken down into sugar molecules by your body. Instead, the fiber passes through the body and is eliminated. Because your body cannot digest it, fiber is not considered a nutrient. Fiber is an important part of the diet, however, because it helps keep the digestive system functioning properly. Fruits, vegetables, and nuts contain fiber. So do products made with whole grains, such as some breads and cereals.

Nutritionists recommend that 50 to 60 percent of the Calories in a diet come from carbohydrates. When choosing foods containing carbohydrates, it is better to eat more complex carbohydrates than simple carbohydrates. Sugars can give a quick burst of energy, but starches provide a more even, long-term energy source. In addition, foods that are high in starch usually contain a variety of other nutrients. Foods made with a lot of sugar, such as candy, cookies, and soft drinks, usually have few valuable nutrients.

☑ *Checkpoint* *What are the two types of carbohydrates? Give an example of each.*

Figure 3 You obtain fats from foods such as steak, ice cream, and cooking oils.
Classifying Which of these foods contain saturated fats?

Fats

Like carbohydrates, **fats** are high-energy nutrients that are composed of carbon, oxygen, and hydrogen. However, fats contain more than twice as much energy as an equal amount of carbohydrates. In addition, fats perform other important functions. For example, they form part of the structure of cells. Fatty tissue also protects and supports your internal organs and acts as insulation to keep heat inside your body.

Fats are classified as either unsaturated fats or saturated fats, based on their chemical structure. **Unsaturated fats** are usually liquid at room temperature. Most oils, such as olive oil and canola oil, are unsaturated fats. Unsaturated fat is also found in some types of seafood, such as salmon. **Saturated fats** are usually solid at room temperature. Animal products, such as meat, dairy products, and egg yolks, contain relatively large amounts of saturated fat. Some oils, such as palm oil and coconut oil, are also high in saturated fat.

Foods that contain saturated fat often contain cholesterol as well. **Cholesterol** (kuh LES tur awl) is a waxy, fatlike substance found only in animal products. Like fats, cholesterol is an important part of your body's cells. But your liver makes all of the cholesterol your body needs. Therefore, cholesterol is not a necessary part of the diet.

Although people need some fats in their diet, they only need a small amount. Nutritionists recommend that no more than 30 percent of the Calories eaten each day come from fats. In particular, people should limit their intake of saturated fats and cholesterol. Extra fats and cholesterol in the diet can lead to a buildup of a fatty material in the blood vessels. This fatty buildup can cause heart disease. You will learn about the connections among fats, cholesterol, and heart disease in Chapter 4.

Math TOOLBOX

Calculating Percent

A percent (%) is a number compared to 100. For example, 30% means 30 out of 100.

Here is how to calculate the percent of Calories from fat in a person's diet. Suppose that a person eats a total of 2,000 Calories in one day. Of those Calories, 500 come from fats.

1. Write the comparison as a fraction:

$$\frac{500}{2,000}$$

2. Multiply the fraction by 100% to express it as a percent:

$$\frac{500}{2,000} \times \frac{100\%}{1} = 25\%$$

Calories from fat made up 25% of the person's diet that day.

Fats

Real-Life Learning

Students may think that eating 30 percent of Calories each day from fat (65 grams from a 2,000 Calorie diet) sounds like too much. Explain that when a person's fat intake is lower, he or she runs the risk of developing a deficiency in chemicals called essential fatty acids, which are building blocks for molecules that help regulate blood pressure, blood clotting, and the immune response. The symptoms of a deficiency are red, irritated skin, infections, and dehydration. Other fats help in the absorption of fat-soluble vitamins, such as A, D, E, and K. In addition, when the fat content of the diet goes below 25 percent, a person feels less satisfied after a meal and may actually eat more. Allow interested students to conduct additional research on diet and nutrition.
learning modality: verbal

Math TOOLBOX

Remind students that when they set up their fractions, they should use the number of Calories in one day as the denominator and the number of Calories from fat as the numerator. To multiply the fraction by 100%, they must multiply the numerators, then divide by the product of the denominators.
Extend Have students find the percent of Calories from carbohydrates in the diet of a person who eats 2,000 Calories per day, of which 1,100 are from carbohydrates. **learning modality: logical/mathematical**

Answers to Self-Assessment

Caption Question

Figure 2 Fiber helps keep the digestive tract functioning properly.
Figure 3 Steak, ice cream, and butter

☑ *Checkpoint*

Simple carbohydrates—sugars; complex carbohydrates—starch

Ongoing Assessment

Skills Check Have students make compare/contrast tables for simple and complex carbohydrates and saturated and unsaturated fats, giving an example of each.

Proteins

Integrating Chemistry

Explain to students that amino acids are organic compounds containing carbon, hydrogen, and oxygen. Amino acids also contain nitrogen, which makes them different from most other kinds of organic compounds that living organisms need. Different types of proteins are made up of different amino acids, and their arrangement in each kind of protein varies. Ask: **Why is it important to eat foods that contain the essential amino acids?** *(The body cannot make these amino acids; they must come from food.)* **learning modality: verbal**

Cultural Diversity

Point out that people in many cultures rely primarily on plant foods and do not use animal products to provide the necessary proteins. Tell students that incomplete proteins, when eaten in combination over the course of a day, provide the essential amino acids the body needs. In many Latin cultures, people eat rice and beans together. Many Indian vegetarian dishes also have the plant food combinations that provide these essential amino acids. Encourage interested students to find recipes for some of these foods. **learning modality: verbal**

Vitamins

Including All Students

This activity will benefit students who are learning English. Have students work in pairs to create a vitamin chart similar to the one in Figure 5. Students should list the food sources for each of the vitamins in both English and in their native languages. Encourage pairs to practice saying the food names aloud in both languages. **limited English proficiency**

Figure 4 Meats and these other foods are sources of protein.

Social Studies CONNECTION

Industry grew rapidly in the 1800s. During that time, many children of factory workers developed rickets, a condition in which the bones become soft. Rickets is caused by a lack of vitamin D. The main source of vitamin D is sunlight, which acts on skin cells to produce the vitamin.

Factory workers in the 1800s often lived in cities with dark, narrow streets. Air pollution from factories also blocked some sunlight. One researcher, Theobald A. Palm, wrote this statement in 1890: "It is in the narrow alleys, the haunts and playgrounds of the children of the poor, that this exclusion of sunlight is at its worst, and it is there that the victims of rickets are to be found in abundance."

In Your Journal

Write several questions that a newspaper reporter might have asked Dr. Palm about rickets among poor city residents. Then write the answers he might have given.

Proteins

Proteins are nutrients that contain nitrogen as well as carbon, hydrogen, and oxygen. Proteins are needed for tissue growth and repair. They also play a part in chemical reactions within cells. Proteins can serve as a source of energy, but they are a less important source of energy than carbohydrates or fats. Foods that contain high amounts of protein include meat, poultry, fish, dairy products, nuts, beans, and lentils. About 12 percent of your daily Calorie intake should come from proteins.

Amino Acids Proteins are made up of small units called **amino acids** (uh MEE noh), which are linked together chemically to form large protein molecules. Thousands of different proteins are built from only about 20 different amino acids. Your body can make about half of the amino acids it needs. The others, called essential amino acids, must come from the foods you eat.

Complete and Incomplete Proteins Proteins from animal sources, such as meat and eggs, are called complete proteins because they contain all the essential amino acids. Proteins from plant sources, such as beans, grains, and nuts, are called incomplete proteins because they are missing one or more essential amino acids. Different plant foods lack different amino acids. Therefore, to obtain all the essential amino acids from plant sources alone, people need to eat a variety of plant foods.

✓ *Checkpoint* *What is meant by the term* incomplete protein?

Vitamins

The life of a sailor in the 1700s could be difficult indeed. For one thing, sailors on long voyages ate hard, dry biscuits, salted meat, and not much else. In addition, many sailors developed a serious disease called scurvy. People with scurvy suffer from bleeding gums, stiff joints, and sores that do not heal.

Background

Facts and Figures Because eggs and milk are complete-protein foods, vegetarians who eat eggs and milk products will be able to get all the essential amino acids. However, because the body breaks down proteins and redistributes them, eating a combination of foods that have incomplete proteins in the same meal has the same effect as eating complete proteins. Recommended combinations include tofu and rice, and beans and corn. Vegetarians who do not eat eggs and milk products can get enough protein by eating tofu, lentils, nuts, and peas—in the right combinations.

Athletes often consume more protein in an effort to build muscle. However, as most Americans eat more protein than recommended, it is likely that an athlete's diet already includes enough to build muscle.

A Scottish doctor, James Lind, hypothesized that scurvy was the result of the sailors' poor diet. Lind divided sailors with scurvy into groups and fed different foods to each group. The sailors who were fed citrus fruits—oranges and lemons—quickly recovered from the disease. In 1754, Lind recommended that all sailors eat citrus fruits. When Lind's recommendations were finally carried out by the British Navy in 1795, scurvy disappeared from the navy.

Scurvy is caused by the lack of a nutrient called vitamin C. **Vitamins** act as helper molecules in a variety of chemical reactions within the body. The body needs only small amounts of vitamins. Figure 5 lists the vitamins necessary for health. The body can make a few of these vitamins. For example, bacteria that live in your intestines make small amounts of vitamin K.

Figure 5 Both fat-soluble vitamins and water-soluble vitamins are necessary to maintain health. *Interpreting Charts What foods provide a supply of both vitamins A and B$_6$?*

Essential Vitamins		
Vitamin	**Sources**	**Function**
Fat-soluble		
A	Dairy products; eggs; liver; yellow, orange, and dark green vegetables; fruits	Maintains healthy skin, bones, teeth, and hair; aids vision in dim light
D	Fortified dairy products; fish; eggs; liver; made by skin cells in presence of sunlight	Maintains bones and teeth; helps in the use of calcium and phosphorus
E	Vegetable oils; margarine; green, leafy vegetables; whole-grain foods; seeds; nuts	Aids in maintenance of red blood cells
K	Green, leafy vegetables; milk; liver; made by bacteria in the intestines	Aids in blood clotting
Water-soluble		
B$_1$ (thiamin)	Pork; liver; whole-grain foods; legumes; nuts	Needed for breakdown of carbohydrates
B$_2$ (riboflavin)	Dairy products; eggs; leafy, green vegetables; whole-grain breads and cereals	Needed for normal growth
B$_3$ (niacin)	Many protein-rich foods; milk; eggs; meat; fish; whole-grain foods; nuts; peanut butter	Needed for release of energy
B$_6$ (pyridoxine)	Green and leafy vegetables; meats; fish; legumes; fruits; whole-grain foods	Helps in the breakdown of proteins, fats, and carbohydrates
B$_{12}$	Meats; fish; poultry; dairy products; eggs	Maintains healthy nervous system; needed for red blood cell formation
Biotin	Liver; meat; fish; eggs; legumes; bananas; melons	Aids in the release of energy
Folic acid	Leafy, green vegetables; legumes; seeds; liver	Needed for red blood cell formation
Pantothenic acid	Liver; meats; fish; eggs; whole-grain foods	Needed for the release of energy
C	Citrus fruits; tomatoes; potatoes; dark green vegetables; mangoes	Needed to form connective tissue and fight infection

Answers to Self-Assessment

Caption Question

Figure 5 Fruits and green vegetables

☑ *Checkpoint*

Proteins from plant sources that are missing one or more of the essential amino acids.

Social Studies CONNECTION

Explain to students that vitamin D deficiency results in a failure to absorb calcium and phosphorus, causing faulty bone formation. Children with rickets often have deformities of the rib cage and skull, and they also can be bow-legged. Tell students that because milk sold in stores has been fortified with vitamin D, rickets is a rare condition in the United States today. Ask: **Why do you think that vitamin D deficiency used to have a greater incidence in North America or Europe than in tropical countries?** *(Exposure to sunlight is greater in tropical countries, and sunlight is the main source of vitamin D.)*
Extend Allow students to research more about the causes and treatment of rickets.

In Your Journal Sample questions: What can be done to decrease the number of rickets cases? *(Reduce air pollution; build playgrounds where children can be exposed to sunlight.)* What can parents do to keep their children from getting rickets? *(Make sure that their children are exposed to direct sunlight every day.)* **learning modality: verbal**

Using the Visuals: Figure 5

Ask students to identify the water-soluble vitamins. *(B$_1$, B$_2$, B$_3$, B$_6$, B$_{12}$, C, biotin, folic acid, pantothenic acid)* Ask: **Why is it important to include the water-soluble vitamins in your daily diet?** *(These vitamins dissolve in water and are not stored in the body.)* **learning modality: verbal**

Ongoing Assessment

Writing Have students explain why the proper amounts of proteins and vitamins are important in their daily diets.

Minerals

Using the Visuals: Figure 6

Have students review the minerals in the chart. Ask: **To obtain enough calcium, what foods should people eat if they do not drink milk?** *(Cheese, dark-green leafy vegetables, tofu, legumes, meat, eggs, poultry, fish)* **What does the body use calcium for?** *(Sample: Building healthy bones and teeth)* **How can vegetarians get enough iron in their diets?** *(By eating green, leafy vegetables and dried fruits)* **learning modality: visual**

Inquiry Challenge

Materials *silver nitrate solution from a chemical supply company, test tubes, processed and canned foods and condiments*
Time 20 minutes

Tell students that foods containing salt will react to silver nitrate solution by turning a cloudy white. Ask students to plan experiments to test certain foods for salt. Experiments should include a list of foods to be tested, a control, and a list of materials. Students should predict which foods contain salt, then test each food in a test tube by adding 1 mL of silver nitrate solution. CAUTION: *Silver nitrate solution can cause dark brown stains on skin and clothing. Students should wear aprons, safety goggles, and gloves.* After you review the plans for safety, allow students to carry out their investigations.
cooperative learning

Water

Addressing Naive Conceptions

Students may believe they are in no danger of dehydration unless they feel thirsty. Explain that thirst is not an accurate signal of water deficiency. A better indication is a decrease in the production of urine and saliva. By the time the brain signals a feeling of thirst, the water levels in the body may already be too low. **learning modality: verbal**

However, people must obtain most vitamins from foods. If people eat a wide variety of foods, they will probably get enough of each vitamin. Most people do not need to take vitamin supplements.

Vitamins are classified as either fat-soluble or water-soluble. Fat-soluble vitamins dissolve in fat, and they are stored in fatty tissues in the body. Vitamins A, D, E, and K are all fat-soluble vitamins. Water-soluble vitamins dissolve in water and are not stored in the body. This fact makes it especially important to include sources of water-soluble vitamins—vitamin C and all the B vitamins—in your diet every day.

✓ Checkpoint **List the fat-soluble vitamins.**

Minerals

Like vitamins, minerals are needed by your body in small amounts. **Minerals** are nutrients that are not made by living things. They are present in soil and are absorbed by plants through their roots. You obtain minerals by eating plant foods or animals that have eaten plants. Figure 6 lists some minerals you

Figure 6 Eating a variety of foods each day provides your body with the minerals it needs.
Interpreting Charts Which minerals play a role in regulating water levels in the body?

◄ **Source of calcium**

▼ **Source of potassium**

Essential Minerals		
Mineral	**Sources**	**Function**
Calcium	Milk; cheese; dark green, leafy vegetables; tofu; legumes	Helps build bones and teeth; important for blood-clotting, nerve and muscle function
Chlorine	Table salt; soy sauce; processed foods	Helps maintain water balance; aids in digestion
Fluorine	Fluoridated drinking water; fish	Helps form bones and teeth
Iodine	Seafood; iodized salt	Makes up part of hormones that regulate the release of energy
Iron	Red meats; seafood; green, leafy vegetables; legumes; dried fruits	Forms an important part of red blood cells
Magnesium	Green, leafy vegetables; legumes; nuts; whole-grain foods	Needed for normal muscle and nerve function; helps in the release of energy
Phosphorus	Meat; poultry; eggs; fish; dairy products	Needed for healthy bones and teeth; helps in the release of energy
Potassium	Grains; fruits; vegetables; meat; fish	Helps maintain water balance; needed for normal muscle and nerve function
Sodium	Table salt; soy sauce; processed foods	Helps maintain water balance; needed for normal nerve function

Source of sodium ►

Background

Facts and Figures Nutritionists, including those at the American Heart Association and the American Dietetic Association, do not recommend that people take vitamin and mineral supplements under normal circumstances. The vitamins and minerals in food are cheaper and absorbed better than supplements. In addition, some vitamins and minerals can be toxic when taken in large amounts over a long period of time. The few people who need to take vitamin and mineral supplements include those on weight-loss diets of less than 1,600 calories per day and strict vegetarians who eat no animal products.

need. As you know from Chapter 2, calcium is needed for strong bones and teeth. Iron is needed for the proper function of red blood cells.

Water

Imagine that a boat is sinking. The people are getting into a lifeboat. They have room for one of the following: a bag of fruit, a can of meat, a loaf of bread, or a jug of water. Which item should they choose?

You might be surprised to learn that the lifeboat passengers should choose the water. Although people can probably survive for weeks without food, they will die within days without fresh water. Water is the most abundant substance in the body. It accounts for about 65 percent of the average person's body weight.

Water is the most important nutrient because the body's vital processes—including chemical reactions such as the breakdown of nutrients—take place in water. Water makes up most of the body's fluids, including blood. Nutrients and other important substances are carried throughout the body dissolved in the watery part of the blood. Your body also needs water to produce perspiration.

Under normal conditions, you need to take in about 2 liters of water every day. You can do this by drinking water and other beverages, and by eating foods with lots of water, such as fruits and vegetables. If the weather is hot or you are exercising, you need to drink even more to replace the water that you lose in sweat.

Figure 7 Like all living things, you need water. Without regular water intake, your body cannot carry out the processes that keep you alive.

Section 1 Review

1. List the six nutrients that are needed by the body.
2. Give three reasons why water is necessary for the body to function.
3. Why should you eat more complex carbohydrates than simple carbohydrates?
4. What is the difference between fat-soluble vitamins and water-soluble vitamins?
5. **Thinking Critically   Applying Concepts** Why is it especially important that vegetarians eat a varied diet?

Check Your Progress

CHAPTER PROJECT 3

By now, you should have given your teacher your plan for keeping your food log. Adjust the plan as your teacher suggests. Then start your three days of record-keeping. If possible, your record-keeping should span two weekdays and one weekend day. Be sure to keep an accurate record of all the foods and beverages you consume. (*Hint:* Either make your log portable, or plan a method for recording your food intake when you're away from home.)

Chapter 3 **D ◆ 75**

Section 1 Review Answers

1. Carbohydrates, fats, proteins, vitamins, minerals, water
2. Any three: Water makes up about 65 percent of the average person's weight. It makes up most of the body's fluids, including blood. The body's chemical reactions take place in water. Nutrients are carried throughout the body in the watery part of blood. Water is needed to regulate body temperature.
3. Complex carbohydrates provide more even, long-term energy than do simple carbohydrates. Foods high in complex carbohydrates usually provide more nutrients than simple carbohydrate foods.
4. Fat-soluble—dissolve in fat, stored in the body's fatty tissue; water-soluble—dissolve in water, not stored in the body
5. Proteins in plant foods are incomplete proteins. Therefore, no plant food by itself supplies all the essential amino acids. To obtain all the essential amino acids, vegetarians need to eat a variety of foods.

Check Your Progress

CHAPTER PROJECT 3

Remind students to record foods soon after they eat, as it can be difficult to remember later. Encourage students not to modify their diets during the project. Recording what they actually eat will help them better understand how their habits affect their health.

Program Resources

◆ **Teaching Resources** 3-1 Review and Reinforce, p. 67; 3-1 Enrich, p. 68

Media and Technology

Interactive Student Tutorial CD-ROM D-3

Answers to Self-Assessment

Caption Question

Figure 6 Chlorine, potassium, and sodium

☑ *Checkpoint*

A, D, E, and K

Performance Assessment

Drawing Have small groups of students prepare posters showing one nutrient needed by the body. Posters should explain why the nutrient is essential and name foods that provide that nutrient.

D ◆ 75

Iron for Breakfast

Preparing for Inquiry

Key Concept Students will use the properties of elemental iron to test whether iron has been added to cereals.

Skills Objective Students will be able to
- observe how breakfast cereals react when a magnet is used to test for the presence of iron;
- predict the results of the test based on the information contained in the food label for the cereal;
- interpret data to determine whether the cereals are fortified with iron.

Time 55 minutes

Advance Planning You can purchase bar magnets from a supply company or hardware store. Make sure at least one cereal has 100 percent of the recommended daily requirement (RDA) of iron.

Guiding Inquiry

Invitation Ask students: **When you see cereals that are fortified with essential vitamins and minerals, what do you think some of the minerals are?** *(Samples: iron, calcium, zinc)* Show students a periodic table and have them find these minerals.

Introducing the Procedure

Ask students how they are going to separate the iron from the cereal in this activity. *(Iron can be mechanically separated because it will be strongly attracted to the magnet.)*

Troubleshooting the Experiment

Make sure students shake the cereal-water mixture for 15 minutes. Have partners take turns to avoid injury or muscle fatigue.

Analyze and Conclude

1. Students should describe small gray filings. This material was attracted to the magnet.
2. Answers will vary; fortified cereals usually have the most iron. Students should compare their observations with the labels.
3. The plant products from which cereal

Iron for Breakfast

Have you ever looked at the nutrition facts on a cereal box? Some of the listed nutrients occur naturally in the cereal. Others are added as it is processed. In this lab, you will look for evidence that extra iron has been added to some cereals.

Problem

How can you test whether iron has been added to cereals?

Skills Focus

observing, predicting, interpreting data

Materials

long bar magnet	balance
white paper towels	plastic spoon
instant oatmeal	warm water
watch or clock	
wooden dowel	
2 dry breakfast cereals	
3 sealable plastic freezer bags	
plastic jar with sealable cover	

Procedure

1. Read the nutrition facts listed on the packages of the cereals that you'll be testing. Record the percent of iron listed for each of the cereals.
2. Put a paper towel on the pan of a balance. Use a spoon to measure out 50 grams of instant oatmeal. **CAUTION:** *Do not eat any of the cereals in this lab.*
3. Place the oatmeal in a plastic bag. Push down gently on the bag to remove most of the air, then seal the bag. Roll a dowel over the cereal repeatedly to crush it into a fine powder.
4. Pour the powdered cereal into a plastic jar. Cover the cereal with warm water. Cover the jar tightly and shake it for about 15 minutes.
5. Move a bar magnet along the outside of the jar. Observe the results.
6. Repeat Steps 2 through 5 with your other cereal samples.

Analyze and Conclude

1. Describe the material you saw inside the jar near the magnet. What evidence do you have that this material is iron?
2. Which sample appeared to have the most added iron? The least? Were those results consistent with the listed amounts?
3. Why is it likely that any iron metal present in the cereal was added during the processing?
4. What roles does iron play in the body?
5. **Apply** Why might adding iron to breakfast cereal be a good way to ensure that children receive an adequate amount of that mineral?

More to Explore

Read the labels on five snack foods. Make a bar graph showing their iron content.

---

is made usually do not contain any metals.
4. Sample: Iron becomes part of the hemoglobin, the molecule that makes blood red.
5. Sample: Children can sometimes be picky eaters, but they often eat breakfast cereal.

Extending the Inquiry

More to Explore Make sure students choose a variety of foods and compare similar serving sizes.

Safety

Remind students not to eat any of the cereals. Review the safety guidelines in Appendix A.

Program Resources

◆ **Teaching Resources** Chapter 3 Real-World Lab, pp. 81–82

SECTION 2 Healthy Eating

DISCOVER ··················· ACTIVITY ···

Do Snack Foods Contain Fat?

1. Cut four small squares from a brown paper bag. Label them *A, B, C,* and *D.*
2. Rub some crushed potato chips on square A.
   CAUTION: *Do not eat any of the foods in this activity.*
3. Repeat Step 2 using crushed pretzels (on square B), a piece of chocolate (on square C), and an apple slice (on square D).
4. Remove any food. Allow the paper squares to dry.
5. Note which squares have spots of oil on them.

Think It Over
Classifying If a food contains fat, it will leave oily spots on the brown paper. What does this tell you about the foods you tested?

W hat does healthy eating mean to you? Eating more fresh fruits and vegetables? Not skipping breakfast? Cutting down on soft drinks and chips? You have just learned about the six types of nutrients—carbohydrates, fats, proteins, vitamins, minerals, and water—that are part of a healthy diet. You may now be wondering how you can use this information to make healthful changes in your diet.

With so many foods available, it may seem more difficult, not easier, to establish a healthful diet. Luckily, nutritionists have developed some aids—the Food Guide Pyramid and food labels.

GUIDE FOR READING

◆ How can the Food Guide Pyramid help you plan a healthy diet?

◆ What kind of information is included on food labels?

Reading Tip Before you read, preview *Exploring the Food Guide Pyramid* on page 79. Write a list of questions about the pyramid. As you read, try to answer your questions.

Figure 8 Fruits and vegetables are essential parts of a healthy diet. Some people enjoy picking these foods right off the plant.

READING STRATEGIES

Reading Tip While students preview *Exploring the Food Guide Pyramid,* point out that the foods within each group of the pyramid supply similar nutrients. Point out and discuss the relationship between the shape of the Food Guide Pyramid and the number of recommended servings of foods in each group. Then have students list questions, which they will try to answer as they read.

Program Resources

◆ **Teaching Resources** 3-2 Lesson Plan, p. 65; 3-2 Section Summary, p. 66

Media and Technology

 Audiotapes English-Spanish Summary 3-2

SECTION 2 Healthy Eating

Objectives
After completing the lesson, students will be able to
◆ describe the Food Guide Pyramid and state how it can be used to plan a healthy diet;
◆ list and describe the information that is included on nutrition labels.

Key Terms Food Guide Pyramid, Percent Daily Value

1 Engage/Explore

Activating Prior Knowledge
Ask students to describe what they look for when they're shopping for food. Students will probably mention flavor and price. Ask students whether they ever look at the nutrition labels on food, and what kinds of information they think a nutrition label contains.

········· DISCOVER ·········

Skills Focus inferring
Materials *4 squares of brown paper, each about 8 cm by 8 cm; crushed potato chips; crushed pretzels; piece of chocolate; slice of apple; paper towel*
Time 25 minutes
Tips Caution students not to eat any of the foods. They can hold the food in a paper towel to rub it onto the squares of brown paper. If there is not enough time to wait for the spots to dry, students can distinguish wet spots from oily spots by holding the papers up to a light. Oily stains are translucent.
Expected Outcome Chocolate and potato chips will leave oily spots.
Think It Over Chocolate and potato chips contain fat; apples and pretzels do not.

2 Facilitate

The Food Guide Pyramid

Building Inquiry Skills: Classifying

Materials *note cards*
Time 15 minutes

Give each student ten note cards and have them list a favorite food on each card. Place students in groups of three or four and have them work together to classify the foods according to the categories in the Food Guide Pyramid. Students can write the classifications on the backs of the cards. Explain that some foods, such as pasta with sauce or pizza, fall into more than one category. Then have groups use their cards to plan nutritious meals. Ask: **Where do most of your favorite foods fall on the Food Guide Pyramid?** (*Answers will vary according to preference.*) Ask students if they need to include more of any food groups in their daily diets. Students can add foods from these food groups to their stack of cards and to their meal plans. **cooperative learning**

Building Inquiry Skills: Comparing and Contrasting

Challenge students to identify sources of fat and sugar in the food groups shown in the three bottom levels of the pyramid. Ask: **What foods are naturally high in sugar?** (*Sample: fruits*) **What foods are naturally high in fat?** (*Eggs, nuts, and some meats*) **learning modality: verbal**

Including All Students

Materials *heavy cardboard*
Time 20 minutes

For the benefit of visually impaired students, copy the Food Guide Pyramid onto heavy cardboard, cut it out with scissors, and then cut the food groups apart. Reassemble the pyramid. Have students use their sense of touch to learn the relative sizes of the groups as you orally identify the food in each group. **learning modality: kinesthetic**

Figure 9 If you are very active, you need to eat more servings within the ranges specified for each food group in the Food Guide Pyramid.

The Food Guide Pyramid

The **Food Guide Pyramid** was developed by nutritionists to help people plan a healthy diet. **The Food Guide Pyramid classifies foods into six groups. It also indicates how many servings from each group should be eaten every day to maintain a healthy diet.** You can combine the advice within the pyramid with knowledge of your own food preferences. By doing this, you can have a healthy diet containing foods you like.

You can see the six food groups in *Exploring the Food Guide Pyramid.* Notice that the food group at the base of the pyramid includes foods made from grains, such as bread, cereal, rice, and pasta. This bottom level is the widest part of the pyramid. The large size indicates that these foods should make up the largest part of the diet.

The second level in the pyramid is made of two food groups, the Fruit group and the Vegetable group. Notice that this level is not as wide as the bottom level. This size difference indicates that people need fewer servings of these foods than of foods from the bottom level. The third level of the pyramid contains the Milk, Yogurt, and Cheese group, and the Meat, Poultry, Fish, Dry Beans, Eggs, and Nuts group. People need still smaller amounts of food from the third level.

At the top of the pyramid are foods containing large amounts of fat, sugar, or both. Notice that this is the smallest part of the pyramid. The small size indicates that intake of these foods should be limited. There is a good reason for this advice. Foods in the other groups already contain fats and sugars. Limiting intake of *additional* fats and sugars can help you prevent heart disease and other problems.

☑ *Checkpoint* *What types of foods should make up the largest portion of a person's diet?*

Food Labels

After a long day, you and your friends stop into a store on your way home from school. What snack should you buy? How can you make a wise choice? One thing you can do is to read the information provided on food labels. The United States Food and Drug Administration (FDA) requires that all food items except meat, poultry, fresh vegetables, and fresh fruit must be labeled with specific nutritional information.

Background

Facts and Figures In the early 1990s, the traditional four food groups, consisting of meats, dairy products, grains, and fruits and vegetables were reorganized into the six groups now found in the USDA Food Guide Pyramid. Serving sizes vary according to the foods in the pyramid. For example, in the grain group, one serving may be one slice of bread, $\frac{1}{4}$ to $1\frac{1}{4}$ cup of cereal, or $\frac{1}{2}$ cup of cooked pasta. A serving size in the fruit group may be $\frac{1}{2}$ of a banana or one small apple or orange, in the vegetable group, $\frac{1}{2}$ cup cooked vegetables or 1 cup raw leafy vegetables. In the dairy group, 1 cup of milk or a 2.5 cm square of cheese counts as a serving. For the meat, dry beans, eggs, and nut food group, 2 to 3 ounces of cooked meat is a serving; 1 cup of cooked dry beans, 1 egg, or 2 tablespoons of peanut butter count as 1 ounce of meat.

EXPLORING *the Food Guide Pyramid*

The Food Guide Pyramid recommends the number of servings that a person should eat each day from six food groups. Note that each number of servings is listed as a range. Active, growing teenagers may need to eat the larger number of servings for each group.

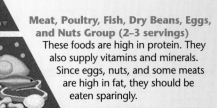

Fats, Oils, and Sweets (Use sparingly.)
Soft drinks, candy, ice cream, mayonnaise, and other foods in this group have few valuable nutrients. In addition, these foods are high in Calories. They should be eaten only in small quantities.

Milk, Yogurt, and Cheese Group (2–3 servings) Milk and other dairy products are rich in proteins, carbohydrates, vitamins, and minerals. Try to select low-fat dairy foods, such as low-fat milk.

Meat, Poultry, Fish, Dry Beans, Eggs, and Nuts Group (2–3 servings)
These foods are high in protein. They also supply vitamins and minerals. Since eggs, nuts, and some meats are high in fat, they should be eaten sparingly.

Vegetable Group (3–5 servings)
Vegetables are low-fat sources of carbohydrates, fiber, vitamins, and minerals.

Fruit Group (2–4 servings)
Fruits are good sources of carbohydrates, fiber, vitamins, and water.

Bread, Cereal, Rice, and Pasta Group (6–11 servings)
The foods at the base of the pyramid are rich in complex carbohydrates and also provide proteins, fiber, vitamins, and some minerals.

● *Fat (naturally occurring and added)*
▲ *Sugars (naturally occurring and added)*

Have students read aloud each of the annotations for the six food groups on the Food Guide Pyramid. Ask: **From which food group should most of your servings come?** *(The bread, cereal, rice, and pasta group)* Have students choose one food that they like from each category. For each food group, ask: **Would you be healthy if you ate only one food from this group, as long as you ate the right number of servings each day? Explain.** *(Probably not. Although the foods in a given category are similar, they do not provide exactly the same nutrients. A variety of each type of food should be eaten from each category.)*
Extend Have students create charts that list the six food groups, then fill in the charts by adding foods that are not listed in the pyramid. **learning modality: visual**

Food Labels

Building Inquiry Skills: Making Generalizations

Ask students to explain why they think foods such as meat, poultry, and fresh fruits and vegetables are not required to have food labels. *(Because these are unprocessed foods. All apples, for example, have basically the same contents and nutritional value. Also, since the size of fresh items varies, it would be difficult to standardize serving sizes.)* **learning modality: verbal**

Program Resources

◆ **Product Testing Activities by** *Consumer Reports,* "Testing Cereals," pp. 1–8

Media and Technology

 Transparencies "The Food Guide Pyramid," Transparency 6

Answers to Self-Assessment

☑ *Checkpoint*
Foods made from grains, such as bread, cereal, rice, and pasta

Ongoing Assessment

Drawing Have students draw the Food Guide Pyramid, then label the six food groups and the number of servings for each group.
 Students can save their drawings in their portfolios.

Food Labels, continued

Real-Life Learning

ACTIVITY

Bring—or have students bring—a wide variety of food labels to class. Group students who are less proficient in English with those who are more proficient. Divide the food labels among the groups and have group members work together to read and interpret the labels. Ask students questions such as these: **Which of these cereals is higher in fiber? Which food is a good source of vitamin C? If you were on a low-sodium diet, which of these foods should you avoid?** limited English proficiency

Building Inquiry Skills: Calculating

Give students the following examples or have them use labels from snacks to practice finding the percent of Calories that come from fat.

Example: 30 potato chips
Calories 340
Calories from Fat 200

$$\frac{200}{340} \times \frac{100\%}{1} = 58.8\%$$

Example: 8 wheat crackers
Calories 130
Calories from Fat 25

$$\frac{25}{130} \times \frac{100\%}{1} = 19.2\%$$

Ask: **In order to follow the Food Guide Pyramid, do the Calories from fat in every single food you eat have to be less than 30%?** (*No. Some foods can be higher in fat as long as others are lower. No more than 30% of the entire day's Calories should come from fat.*) learning modality: logical/mathematical

---

Figure 10 shows a food label that might appear on a box of cereal. Refer to that label as you read about some of the important nutritional information it contains.

Serving Size Notice that the serving size and the number of servings in the container are listed at the top of the label. The FDA has established standard serving sizes for all types of foods. This means that all containers of ice cream, for example, use the same serving size on their labels. The information on the rest of the label, including Calorie counts and nutrient content, is based on the serving size. Therefore, if you eat a portion that's twice as large as the serving size, you'll consume twice the number of Calories and nutrients listed on the label.

Calories from Fat The next item on the food label is the number of Calories in a serving and the number of Calories that come from fat. Notice that a single serving of this cereal supplies the body with 110 Calories of energy.

Recall that no more than 30 percent of the Calories you consume should come from fats. To calculate whether a specific food falls within this guideline, divide the number of Calories from fat by the total number of Calories, then multiply by 100%. For this cereal,

$$\frac{15}{110} \times \frac{100\%}{1} = 13.6\%.$$

That number shows you that a serving of this cereal is well within the recommended limits for fat intake.

Daily Values Locate the % Daily Value column on the label. The **Percent Daily Value** indicates how the nutritional content of one serving fits into the diet of a person who consumes a total of 2,000 Calories a day. One serving of this cereal contains 280 milligrams of sodium. That's 12 percent of the total amount of sodium a person should consume in one day.

As you have learned, the number of Calories you need daily depends on your age, size, and level of activity. An active teenager may require 2,500 Calories or more each day. If your needs exceed 2,000 Calories, you should take in more of each nutrient in your daily diet. Some food labels include a list of the nutrient needs for both a 2,000-Calorie and a 2,500-Calorie diet.

Figure 10 By law, specific nutritional information must be listed on food labels. *Calculating How many servings of this product would you have to eat to get 90 percent of the Daily Value for iron?*

Nutrition Facts

Serving Size	1 cup (30g)
Servings Per Container	About 10

Amount Per Serving

Calories 110	Calories from Fat 15

	% Daily Value*
Total Fat 2g	3%
Saturated Fat 0g	0%
Cholesterol 0mg	0%
Sodium 280mg	12%
Total Carbohydrate 22g	7%
Dietary Fiber 3g	12%
Sugars 1g	
Protein 3g	

Vitamin A	10%	•	Vitamin C	20%
Calcium	4%	•	Iron	45%

* Percent Daily Values are based on a 2,000 Calorie diet. Your daily values may be higher or lower depending on your caloric needs:

		Calories	2,000	2,500
Total Fat	Less than		65g	80g
Sat. Fat	Less than		20g	25g
Cholesterol	Less than		300mg	300mg
Sodium	Less than		2,400mg	2,400mg
Total Carbohydrate			300g	375g
Fiber			25g	30g

Calories per gram:
Fat 9 • Carbohydrate 4 • Protein 4

Ingredients: Whole grain oats, sugar, salt, milled corn, oat fiber, dried whey, hon~~ ~~ almonds ~~...~~

Background

Facts and Figures Students may be interested to learn that the FDA developed the present format for food labels in 1994 based on guidelines in the Nutrition Labeling and Education Act of 1990 (NLEA). Before NLEA, manufacturers were able to define a serving as any amount they wished. NLEA requires the servings to reflect the amount that people usually eat at one time, and similar food items must use the same serving size. There is one exception to this rule—packages that contain less than two full servings may be labeled as one or two servings. Canned soup is one example; some 15-ounce (420g) cans of soup list the contents as one serving while others list two.

Ingredients Packaged foods, such as crackers and soup mixes, usually contain a mixture of ingredients. The food label lists those ingredients in order by weight, starting with the main ingredient. In a breakfast cereal, for example, that may be corn, oats, rice, or wheat. Often, sugar and salt are added for flavor. The list can alert you to substances that have been added to a food to improve its flavor or color, or to keep it from spoiling. In addition, some people can become sick or break out in a rash if they eat certain substances. By reading ingredients lists, people can avoid foods that contain those substances.

Using Food Labels You can use food labels to help you make healthful food choices. **Food labels allow you to evaluate a single food as well as to compare the nutritional value of two foods.** Suppose you are shopping for breakfast cereals. By reading the labels, you might find that one cereal contains little fat and a high percentage of the Daily Value for valuable nutrients such as complex carbohydrates and several vitamins. Another cereal might have fewer complex carbohydrates and vitamins and contain significant amounts of fat. You can see that the first cereal would be a better choice as a regular breakfast food. If you really enjoy the other cereal, however, you might make it an occasional treat rather than an everyday choice.

Figure 11 Food labels allow you to compare the nutritional content of similar kinds of foods.

Section 2 Review

1. What information does the Food Guide Pyramid provide? Into how many groups are foods classified?
2. Explain how food labels can help a person make healthy food choices.
3. Why are foods in the Bread, Cereal, Rice, and Pasta group placed at the bottom of the Food Guide Pyramid?
4. **Thinking Critically** **Applying Concepts** Why might a runner need more servings from the Bread, Cereal, Rice, and Pasta group than a less active person?

Check Your Progress

CHAPTER PROJECT 3

By this point, you should have completed three full days of record keeping. Now create bar graphs to compare your food intake to the recommended numbers of servings in the Food Guide Pyramid. Analyze your graphs to identify changes you could make in your diet.

Chapter 3 **D ◆ 81**

Answers to Self-Assessment

Caption Question

Figure 10 Two

Program Resources

◆ **Teaching Resources** 3-2 Review and Reinforce, p. 71; 3-2 Enrich, p. 72

3 Assess

Section 2 Review Answers

1. The Food Guide Pyramid classifies food into six groups. It indicates how many servings from each group should be eaten on a daily basis to maintain a healthy diet.
2. Nutrition fact labels include information about the ingredients and quantities of different nutrients in foods. This information allows a person to evaluate the nutritional contents of a single food and to compare foods.
3. Because this is the largest part of the pyramid, and people should eat more servings of this group each day than of any of the other food groups.
4. A runner is more active and uses more energy than the average person. The cereals and grains food group is the best source of Calories for energy because complex carbohydrates provide an even and long-term energy source.

Check Your Progress

CHAPTER PROJECT 3

Students should identify the categories on the Food Guide Pyramid for each food they list. Provide resources for students to find the established serving sizes for a variety of foods. As students analyze their graphs, remind them that they may need to eat more than 2,000 Calories if they are very active or experiencing growth.

Performance Assessment

Writing Provide students with food labels and have them write captions describing the information given on different parts of the labels.

 Students can save their labels in their portfolios.

SECTION 3 The Digestive Process Begins

Objective

After completing the lesson, students will be able to
- describe the general functions carried out by the digestive system and the specific functions of the mouth, esophagus, and stomach.

Key Terms digestion, absorption, saliva, enzyme, epiglottis, esophagus, mucus, peristalsis, stomach

1 Engage/Explore

Activating Prior Knowledge

Ask students to describe what they think happens after they eat a food. Ask: **How does your body obtain nutrients from the food?** Give students a specific example, such as a baked potato, and have them discuss what they know about the processes that change it from a potato to nutrients and energy.

DISCOVER

Materials *2 jars with lids, water, sugar cubes*
Time 15 minutes
Tips Pair students; each student can shake one jar. Make sure students understand that the jars must receive equal shaking. Have students synchronize their shaking techniques. Have students predict what will happen to the sugar in each jar.
Expected Outcome The crushed sugar cube will dissolve more quickly than the whole cube.
Think It Over Students should predict that a large piece of food would take longer to digest than one that has been cut up into many small pieces.

82 ◆ D

SECTION 3 **The Digestive Process Begins**

DISCOVER .... ACTIVITY....

How Can You Speed up Digestion?

1. Obtain two jars with lids. Fill the jars with equal amounts of water.

2. At the same time, place a whole sugar cube into one jar. Place a crushed sugar cube into the other jar.

3. Fasten the lids on the jars. Holding one jar in each hand, shake the two jars gently and equally.

4. Place the jars on a flat surface. Observe whether the whole cube or the crushed cube dissolves faster.

Think It Over
Predicting Use the results of this activity to predict which would take longer to digest: a large piece of food or one that has been cut up into many small pieces. Explain your answer.

GUIDE FOR READING

- What general functions are carried out in the digestive system?

Reading Tip Before you read, preview the headings in this section. Predict the functions of the mouth, the esophagus, and the stomach.

Dr. William Beaumont ▼

In June of 1822, nineteen-year-old Alexis St. Martin was wounded in the stomach while hunting. William Beaumont, a doctor with the United States Army, saved St. Martin's life. However, the wound left an opening in St. Martin's stomach that never closed completely. Beaumont realized that by looking through the opening, he could observe what was happening inside St. Martin's stomach.

Beaumont observed that milk changed chemically inside the stomach. He hypothesized that chemical reactions inside the stomach broke down foods into smaller particles. To test his hypothesis, Beaumont removed liquid from St. Martin's stomach. He had the liquid analyzed to determine what materials it contained. The stomach liquid contained an acid that could break down foods into simpler substances.

Functions of the Digestive System

Beaumont's observations helped scientists understand the role of the stomach in the digestive system. The digestive system has three main functions. **First, it breaks down food into molecules the body can use. Then, the molecules are absorbed into the blood and carried throughout the body. Finally, wastes are eliminated from the body.**

The process by which your body breaks down food into small nutrient molecules is called **digestion.** There are two kinds of digestion—mechanical and chemical. In mechanical digestion, foods are physically broken down into smaller pieces. Mechanical digestion occurs when you bite into

---

READING STRATEGIES

Reading Tip Have volunteers offer predictions about the functions of the mouth, esophagus, and stomach. Write these on the board. After students read the section, work as a class to confirm or revise the predictions.

Vocabulary Have students list boldfaced vocabulary words from the section on a sheet of paper and write a definition for each term using their own words. Students can use their lists as study guides.

82 ◆ D

a sandwich and chew it into small pieces. In chemical digestion, chemicals produced by the body break foods into their smaller chemical building blocks. For example, the starch in bread is broken down into individual sugar molecules.

After your food is digested, the molecules are ready to be transported throughout your body. **Absorption** (ab SAWRP shun) is the process by which nutrient molecules pass through the wall of your digestive system into your blood. Materials that are not absorbed, such as fiber, are eliminated from the body as wastes.

Figure 12 shows the organs of the digestive system, which is about nine meters long from beginning to end. As food moves through the digestive system, the processes of digestion, absorption, and elimination occur one after the other in an efficient, continuous process.

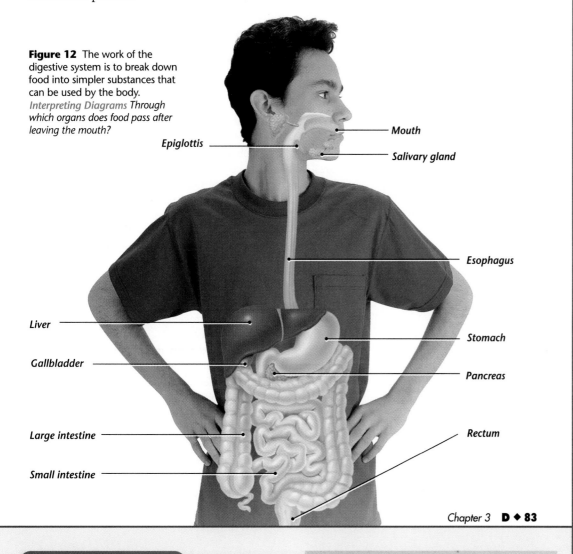

Figure 12 The work of the digestive system is to break down food into simpler substances that can be used by the body. *Interpreting Diagrams Through which organs does food pass after leaving the mouth?*

Mouth
Epiglottis
Salivary gland
Esophagus
Liver
Stomach
Gallbladder
Pancreas
Large intestine
Rectum
Small intestine

Functions of the Digestive System

Including All Students

This activity will benefit students who are still mastering English. Have students make a diagram of the human digestive system. Students should label each of the organs in their native languages and in English. Have students practice saying the names of the organs aloud in each language. As they study, students can refer to their diagrams to help them learn the names for each organ. **limited English proficiency**

Using the Visuals: Figure 12

Have students trace the path of food through the digestive system, beginning with the mouth and ending with the rectum. Make certain that students realize that food does not pass through the liver or pancreas. Have students compare the relative lengths and diameters of the small and large intestines. Note that the twists and turns in the small intestine enable it to fit compactly into the abdomen. **learning modality: visual**

Ongoing Assessment

Writing Have students write a short description of the digestive process, explaining what happens to a food when it is digested and absorbed. *(Students should state that mechanical and chemical digestion break the food down first into small pieces and then into individual molecules. These molecules are transported through the body and absorbed into cells.)*

Portfolio Students can save their descriptions in their portfolios.

Program Resources

◆ **Teaching Resources** 3-3 Lesson Plan, p. 73; 3-3 Section Summary, p. 74

Media and Technology

 Audiotapes English-Spanish Summary 3-3

 Transparencies "The Digestive System," Transparency 7

Answers to Self-Assessment

Caption Question

Figure 12 The esophagus, the stomach, the small intestine, and the large intestine

History
CONNECTION

Tell students that in the early part of the twentieth century, a Russian scientist named Ivan Pavlov studied the phenomenon of salivation at the smell or thought of food. Pavlov found that a dog would begin to salivate at the smell of food, or even at the appearance of the person who fed the dog. Pavlov realized that the dog was able to remember and associate related events. In his experiments, he discovered that if he rang a bell and fed the dog at the same time, over and over, the dog would eventually salivate when the bell rang, even if no food were present. These experiments led to a new understanding of the way animals and people learn.
learning modality: verbal

Integrating Chemistry

Tell students that the chemical reactions that fuel all living things depend on enzymes. Without enzymes, these chemical reactions either would not occur at all or would occur too slowly to support life. Explain that enzymes speed up chemical reactions thousands and even millions of times. Most enzymes are protein molecules. Each enzyme performs one specific function and can perform this function as many as a million times a minute. The human body alone has thousands of kinds of enzymes, and it is because of enzymes that humans have the ability to see, breathe, and move. Most enzymes break down complex substances into simpler ones, such as in digestion. Some enzymes require trace elements such as copper, iron, or magnesium in order to function, while others require vitamins, particularly the B vitamins. Enzyme deficiencies can lead to deformities, mental retardation, and death.
learning modality: verbal

Figure 13 Mechanical digestion begins in the mouth, where the teeth cut and tear food into smaller pieces. *Observing Which teeth are specialized for biting into a juicy apple?*

Incisor  Canine  Premolar  Molar

The Mouth

Have you ever walked past a bakery or restaurant and noticed your mouth watering? Smelling or even just thinking about food when you're hungry is enough to start your mouth watering. This response isn't accidental. Your body is responding to hunger and thoughts of food by preparing for the delicious meal it expects. The fluid released when your mouth waters is called **saliva** (suh LY vuh). Saliva plays an important role in both the mechanical and chemical digestive processes that take place in the mouth.

Mechanical Digestion   The process of mechanical digestion begins as you take your first bite of food. Your teeth carry out the first stage of mechanical digestion. Your center teeth, or incisors (in SY zurz), cut the food into bite-sized pieces. On either side of the incisors are sharp, pointy teeth called canines (KAY nynz). These teeth tear and slash the food in your mouth into smaller pieces. Behind the canines are the premolars and molars, which crush and grind the food. As the teeth do their work, saliva mixes with the pieces of food, moistening them into one slippery mass.

Chemical Digestion   Like mechanical digestion, chemical digestion begins in the mouth. If you take a bite of a cracker and roll it around your mouth, the cracker begins to taste sweet. It tastes sweet because a chemical in the saliva has broken down the starch in the cracker into sugar molecules. Chemical digestion—the breakdown of complex molecules into simpler ones—has taken place. Chemical digestion is accomplished by enzymes. An **enzyme** is a protein that speeds up chemical reactions in the body. The chemical in saliva that digests starch is an enzyme. Your body produces many different enzymes. Each enzyme has a specific chemical shape. Its shape enables it to take part in only one kind of chemical reaction. For example, the enzyme that breaks down starch into sugars cannot break down proteins into amino acids.

INTEGRATING CHEMISTRY

Background

Facts and Figures   The enamel covering teeth is the hardest material in the human body. However, because it is a form of calcium phosphate, it can be dissolved by acid, resulting in dental cavities, or *caries.* Sugars in foods are converted to lactic acid by bacteria in the mouth called *Streptococcus mutans.*

Streptococcus mutans are normally present in the mouth. Although the bacteria can be controlled by saliva, which washes them out

of the mouth, medications and other conditions can lead to a reduction in the amount of saliva, allowing the bacteria population to grow.

The bacteria also change sugars in food to sticky polymers called plaque. Plaque shields the bacteria from saliva, especially in the "valleys" of the teeth and between the teeth. These areas are particularly vulnerable to cavities.

The Esophagus

If you've ever choked on food, someone may have said that your food "went down the wrong way." That's because there are two openings at the back of your mouth. One opening leads to your windpipe, which carries air into your lungs. Usually, your body keeps food out of your windpipe. As you swallow, muscles in your throat move the food downward. While this happens, a flap of tissue called the **epiglottis** (ep uh GLAHT is) seals off your windpipe, preventing the food from entering. As you swallow, food goes into the **esophagus** (ih SAHF uh gus), a muscular tube that connects the mouth to the stomach. The esophagus is lined with mucus. **Mucus** is a thick, slippery substance produced by the body. In the digestive system, mucus makes food easier to swallow and to be moved along.

Food remains in the esophagus for only about 10 seconds. After food enters the esophagus, contractions of smooth muscles push the food toward the stomach. These involuntary waves of muscle contraction are called **peristalsis** (pehr ih STAWL sis). The action of peristalsis is shown in Figure 14. Peristalsis also occurs in the stomach and farther down the digestive system. These muscular waves keep food moving in one direction.

☑ *Checkpoint* *How is food prevented from entering the windpipe?*

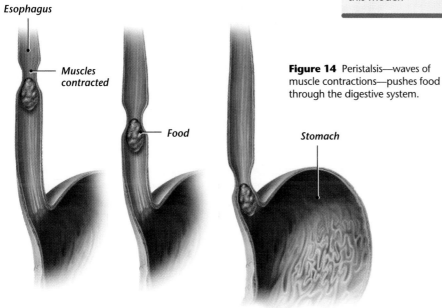

Esophagus

Muscles contracted

Food

Stomach

Figure 14 Peristalsis—waves of muscle contractions—pushes food through the digestive system.

Modeling Peristalsis

ACTIVITY

1. Obtain a clear, flexible plastic straw.
2. Put on your goggles. Hold the straw vertically and insert a small bead into the top of the straw. The bead should fit snugly into the straw. Do not blow into the straw.
3. Pinch the straw above the bead so that the bead begins to move down the length of the tubing.
4. Repeat Step 3 until the bead exits the straw.

Making Models How does this action compare with peristalsis? What do the bead and the straw represent in this model?

Skills Focus making models **ACTIVITY**

Materials *20-cm clear flexible plastic straw (about 6 mm in diameter); round bead (5–6 mm in diameter)*

Time 15 minutes

Tips You may substitute a seed, pebble, or other object of similar size for the bead.

Making Models The pinching motion models the muscular contractions of the muscles around the esophagus. The straw models the esophagus. The bead represents food.

Extend Challenge students to modify their models to show how food is prevented from entering the windpipe. *(Students can tape their straw to another straw that represents the windpipe and cut a flap at the top to show the action of the epiglottis.)* **learning modality: kinesthetic**

Program Resources

Science Explorer Series *Chemical Interactions*, Chapter 2

Media and Technology

Exploring Life Science Videodisc
Unit 4, Side 1, "Digestion and Absorption"

Chapter 4

Answers to Self-Assessment

Caption Question

Figure 13 Incisors

☑ *Checkpoint*
The epiglottis seals off the windpipe as you swallow.

Ongoing Assessment

Skills Check Have students compare and contrast mechanical and chemical digestion.

D ◆ 85

The Stomach

Integrating Chemistry

Ask students: **Why do you think people take antacids?** *(People take antacids when they suffer from indigestion.)* Explain that indigestion can be caused by excess hydrochloric acid in the stomach. Antacids react chemically with hydrochloric acid in such a way that stomach acidity is reduced. One antacid is magnesium hydroxide, or $Mg(OH)_2$. A suspension of magnesium hydroxide in water is called milk of magnesia because of its milky color. **learning modality: verbal**

Building Inquiry Skills: Interpreting Diagrams

Have students work in pairs to draw diagrams of the digestive system as shown in Figure 12. Students should use the information in Figure 15 to label each organ with its name and a description of its role in digestion, including the enzymes and secretions that it produces and what types of nutrients it digests. Then have each student write five questions about the digestive system. Pairs of students can quiz each other, using the diagrams to answer the questions. **learning modality: visual**

 Students can save their diagrams in their portfolios.

The Stomach

When food leaves the esophagus, it enters the **stomach,** a J-shaped, muscular pouch located in the abdomen. As you eat, your stomach expands to hold all of the food that you swallow. An average adult's stomach holds about 2 liters of food.

Most mechanical digestion occurs in the stomach. Three strong layers of muscle contract to produce a churning motion. This action squeezes the food, mixing it with fluids in somewhat the same way that clothes and soapy water are mixed in a washing machine.

INTEGRATING CHEMISTRY While mechanical digestion is taking place, so too is chemical digestion. The churning of the stomach mixes food with digestive juice, a fluid produced by cells in the lining of the stomach.

Digestive juice contains the enzyme pepsin. Pepsin chemically digests the proteins in your food, breaking them down into amino acids. Digestive juice also contains hydrochloric acid, a very strong acid. This acid would burn a hole in clothes if it were spilled on them. Without this strong acid, however, your stomach could not function properly. First, pepsin works best in an acid environment. Second, the acid kills many bacteria that you swallow along with your food.

Since the acid is so strong, you may wonder why it doesn't burn a hole in your stomach. The reason is that digestive juice

Figure 15 As food passes through the digestive system, the digestive juices gradually break down large food molecules into smaller molecules. *Interpreting Charts In which organs are proteins digested?*

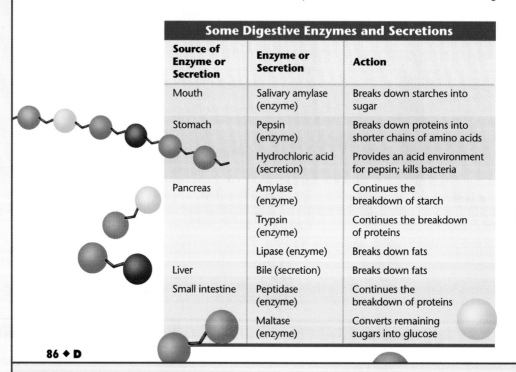

Some Digestive Enzymes and Secretions		
Source of Enzyme or Secretion	Enzyme or Secretion	Action
Mouth	Salivary amylase (enzyme)	Breaks down starches into sugar
Stomach	Pepsin (enzyme)	Breaks down proteins into shorter chains of amino acids
	Hydrochloric acid (secretion)	Provides an acid environment for pepsin; kills bacteria
Pancreas	Amylase (enzyme)	Continues the breakdown of starch
	Trypsin (enzyme)	Continues the breakdown of proteins
	Lipase (enzyme)	Breaks down fats
Liver	Bile (secretion)	Breaks down fats
Small intestine	Peptidase (enzyme)	Continues the breakdown of proteins
	Maltase (enzyme)	Converts remaining sugars into glucose

Background

Integrating Science Ulcers are sores in the lining of the stomach. Most ulcers are caused by bacteria called *Heliobacter pylori—H. pylori* for short. These bacteria can live in the acid environment of the stomach because they produce an enzyme that neutralizes the acid. *H. pylori* are spiral-shaped. They embed themselves into the lining of the stomach, and produce substances that decrease the amount of mucus, making the stomach lining more vulnerable to stomach acid and pepsin. *H. pylori* can attach to stomach cells, producing inflammation and stimulating the stomach to make more acid.

Ulcers caused by *H. pylori* can be treated with antibiotics. Researchers do not know why some people infected with *H. pylori* get ulcers and some do not. People seem to be infected as children, and the infection lasts for life, even without visible symptoms.

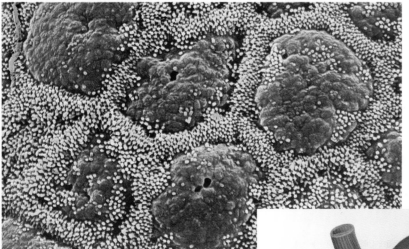

Figure 16 The stomach walls (left) produce mucus, shown here in yellow. Mucus protects the stomach from its own acid and enzymes. The stomach has powerful muscles (below) that help grind up food.

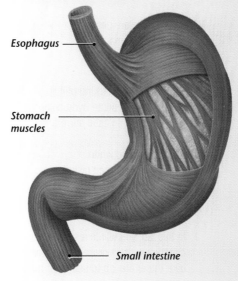

Esophagus

Stomach muscles

Small intestine

also contains mucus, which coats and protects the lining of your stomach. In addition, the cells that line the stomach are quickly replaced when they are damaged or worn out.

Food remains in the stomach until all of the solid material has been digested into liquid form. A few hours after you finish eating, the stomach completes mechanical digestion of the food. By that time, most of the proteins have been chemically digested into shorter chains of amino acids. The food, now a thick liquid, is released into the next part of the digestive system. That is where final chemical digestion and absorption will take place.

Section 3 Review

1. List the functions of the digestive system.
2. What role does saliva play in digestion?
3. Describe peristalsis and explain its function in the digestive system.
4. What is the function of pepsin?
5. **Thinking Critically** Predicting If your stomach could no longer produce acid, how do you think that would affect digestion?

Science at Home

Explain to your family what happens when people choke on food. With your family, find out how to recognize when a person is choking and what to do to help the person. Learn about the Heimlich maneuver and how it is used to help someone who is choking.

3 Assess

Section 3 Review Answers

1. To break down food into molecules that can be used by the body; to absorb the food molecules into the blood; to eliminate wastes from the body
2. Saliva helps with the mechanical digestion of food by moistening the food so it can be easily swallowed. Enzymes in the saliva begin the breakdown of starches into simple sugars as part of chemical digestion.
3. Peristalsis consists of involuntary waves of muscle contractions that help push food through the digestive system.
4. Pepsin is an enzyme in the digestive juice produced in the stomach; it breaks down proteins into shorter chains of amino acids.
5. Without acid, pepsin cannot function properly, and therefore protein digestion couldn't take place in the stomach.

Science at Home

Make sure students can explain the causes of choking. Suggest that they and their parents consult first-aid manuals or a health-care professional to learn the symptoms of choking and how to use the Heimlich maneuver. Students and their families should be able to distinguish between situations in which the person can breathe (shown by the ability to talk and to cough) and situations in which the Heimlich maneuver is required.

Program Resources

◆ **Product Testing Activities** by *Consumer Reports*, "Testing Antacids," pp. 1–8
◆ **Teaching Resources** 3-3 Review and Reinforce, p. 75; 3-3 Enrich, p. 76

Media and Technology

 Interactive Student Tutorial CD-ROM D-3

Answers to Self-Assessment

Caption Question
Figure 15 Pepsin, trypsin, and peptidase

Performance Assessment

Organizing Information Have students prepare flowcharts that show the process of digestion, from the mouth through mechanical digestion of food in the stomach.

Portfolio Students can save their flowcharts in their portfolios.

Drawing Conclusions

As The Stomach Churns

Preparing for Inquiry

Key Concept In the stomach, proteins are digested by the chemicals in the digestive juices and by the mechanical processes as the stomach churns.

Skills Objectives Students will be able to
◆ predict the conditions necessary for protein to be digested in the stomach;
◆ conduct controlled experiments to test their predictions;
◆ observe the reactions that occur and identify the relationship between the manipulated variable and the responding variable;
◆ interpret data and draw conclusions.

Time 60–80 minutes

Advance Planning Obtain blue litmus paper and a 0.2% solution of hydrochloric acid. Boil eggs and cut whites into 1-cm cubes, Prepare enough eggs for students to have 3 cubes per test tube.

Guiding Inquiry

Invitation Ask students to name some foods that contain protein. *(Sample: Meat, poultry, fish, dairy, nuts, beans, and lentils)* Ask: **What role does protein play in nutrition?** *(It aids in tissue growth and repair.)* Have students think about the environment in the stomach. Ask: **How does it feel when stomach fluids enter the esophagus, as in heartburn?** *(It burns.)* Ask: **Why might it be important for the stomach to be so acidic?** *(To dissolve needed nutrients like proteins)*

Introducing the Procedure

◆ Discuss safety issues. Hydrochloric acid can cause burns. Make sure all students, teachers, and visitors wear goggles throughout the lab.
◆ Review the litmus test procedure. Discuss ways to prevent cross-contamination of the test tubes by using a clean stirrer for each litmus test, and by using clean graduated cylinders when adding fluids to a new test tube.

Skills Lab

Drawing Conclusions

AS THE STOMACH CHURNS

The proteins you eat are constructed of large, complex molecules. Your body begins to break down those complex molecules in the stomach. In this lab, you will draw conclusions about the process by which proteins are digested.

Problem

What conditions are needed for the digestion of proteins in the stomach?

Materials

test tube rack marking pencil
pepsin dilute hydrochloric acid
water plastic stirrers
litmus paper
cubes of boiled egg white
10-mL plastic graduated cylinder
4 test tubes with stoppers

Procedure

1. In this lab, you will investigate how acidic conditions affect protein digestion. Read over the entire lab to see what materials you will be testing. Write a prediction stating which conditions you think will speed up protein digestion. Then copy the data table into your notebook.

2. Label four test tubes A, B, C, and D and place them in a test tube rack.

3. In this lab, the protein you will test is boiled egg white, which has been cut into cubes about 1 cm on each side. Add 3 cubes to each test tube. Note and record the size and overall appearance of the cubes in each test tube. **CAUTION:** *Do not put any egg white into your mouth.*

4. Use a graduated cylinder to add 10 mL of the enzyme pepsin to test tube A. Observe the egg white cubes to determine whether an immediate reaction takes place. Record your observations under *Day 1* in your data table. If no changes occur, write "no immediate reaction."

5. Use a clean graduated cylinder to add 5 mL of pepsin to test tube B. Then rinse the graduated cylinder and add 5 mL of water to test tube B. Observe whether or not an immediate reaction takes place.

6. Use a clean graduated cylinder to add 10 mL of hydrochloric acid to test tube C. Observe whether or not an immediate reaction takes place. **CAUTION:** *Hydrochloric acid can burn skin and clothing. Avoid direct contact with it. Wash any splashes or spills with plenty of water, and notify your teacher.*

DATA TABLE

Test Tube	Egg White Appearance		Litmus Color	
	Day 1	Day 2	Day 1	Day 2
A				
B				
C				
D				

Troubleshooting the Experiment

Students' results may be unconvincing if the egg white cubes are too large or if the hydrochloric acid solution is too weak.

Expected Outcome

◆ Students will not observe changes in egg white appearance in test tubes A, B, or C. After one day, the egg white in test tube D will begin to dissolve, then disappear.
◆ The solution of pepsin and hydrochloric acid will digest protein. Pepsin is only effective in an acid environment such as the stomach.

Sample Data Table

Test Tube	Egg White Appearance		Litmus Color	
	Day 1	Day 2	Day 1	Day 2
A	White cubes	Unchanged	Blue	Blue
B	White cubes	Unchanged	Blue	Blue
C	White cubes	Unchanged	Pink	Pink
D	White cubes	Cloudy liquid (digested)	Pink	Pink

7. Use a clean graduated cylinder to add 5 mL of pepsin to test tube D. Then rinse the graduated cylinder and add 5 mL of hydrochloric acid to test tube D. Observe whether or not an immediate reaction takes place. Record your observations.

8. Obtain four strips of blue litmus paper. (Blue litmus paper turns pink in the presence of an acid.) Dip a clean plastic stirrer into the solution in each test tube, and then touch the stirrer to a piece of litmus paper. Observe what happens to the litmus paper. Record your observations.

9. Insert stoppers in the four test tubes and store the test tube rack as directed by your teacher.

10. The next day, examine the contents of each test tube. Note any changes in the size and overall appearance of the egg white cubes. Then test each solution with litmus paper. Record your observations in your data table.

Analyze and Conclude

1. Which material(s) were the best at digesting the egg white? What observations enabled you to determine this?
2. Do you think that the chemical digestion of protein in food is a fast reaction or a slow one? Explain.
3. What did this lab demonstrate about the ability of pepsin to digest protein?
4. Why was it important that the cubes of egg white all be about the same size?
5. **Think About It** How did test tubes A and C help you draw conclusions about protein digestion in this investigation?

Design an Experiment

Design a way to test whether protein digestion is affected by the size of the food pieces. Write down the hypothesis that you will test. Then create a data table for recording your observations. Obtain your teacher's permission before carrying out your plan.

Analyze and Conclude

1. The combination of pepsin and hydrochloric acid digested the egg white best. After one day, the solid egg whites in test tube D begins to dissolve. The egg whites in the other solutions remained undigested.
2. The reaction did not occur immediately after the materials were put into test tube D, so it was not a quick reaction. However, students should recognize that they cannot be sure exactly how long the reaction took. The time range is from the moment of their last observation on Day 1 to the time just before their observation on Day 2.
3. Pepsin alone (or with water) cannot digest protein. It requires the presence of hydrochloric acid.
4. In a controlled experiment, it is important to keep all variables the same except the one being tested. Egg pieces of different sizes may have reacted at different rates and affected the results.
5. Test tube A had only pepsin. Test tube C had only hydrochloric acid. Neither one of these two substances could digest the egg white by itself. However, when they were combined in test tube D, they could.

Extending the Inquiry

Design an Experiment Students' experiments should involve placing large egg white pieces and small egg white pieces in a pepsin and hydrochloric acid solution to test their hypothesis. If students set up this experiment correctly, they should learn that small pieces of food are digested faster than large pieces.

Safety

Caution students to wear their lab aprons and safety goggles throughout the lab. Hydrochloric acid can burn skin and clothing. Caution students to wash splashes or spills with plenty of water and to contact you immediately. Review the safety guidelines in Appendix A.

Program Resources

◆ **Teaching Resources** Chapter 3 Skills Lab, pp. 83–84
◆ **Inquiry Skills Activity Book** Provides teaching and review of all inquiry skills

SECTION 4 Final Digestion and Absorption

Objective

After completing the lesson, students will be able to
◆ explain the role of the small intestine and large intestine in digestion.

Key Terms small intestine, liver, bile, gallbladder, pancreas, villi, large intestine, rectum, anus

1 Engage/Explore

Activating Prior Knowledge

Challenge students to describe how small they think nutrients from food would have to become to be carried in the blood. Ask: **What are some ways that particles can become that small?** *(Samples: Particles can become small by being dissolved in liquid or broken down chemically.)*

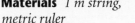
DISCOVER

Skills Focus predicting
Materials *1 m string, metric ruler*
Time 10 minutes
Tips Make sure students clearly mark the end of the string by holding it with their fingers and tying a knot, or by marking it with a marker. Students should realize that they cannot measure the outline directly with a ruler but must measure the length of string.
Think It Over Students' predictions will vary. The length of string needed to outline the hand with outspread fingers should be about twice as long as the length needed to outline the hand when the fingers are held tightly together.

DISCOVER .... ACTIVITY

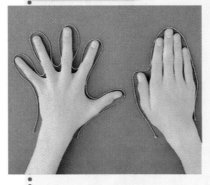

Which Surface Is Larger?

1. Work with a partner to carry out this investigation.
2. Begin by placing your hand palm-side down on a table. Keep your thumb and fingers tightly together. Lay string along the outline of your hand. Have your partner help you determine how long a string you need to outline your hand.
3. Use a metric ruler to measure the length of that string.

Think It Over
Predicting How long would you expect your hand outline to be if you spread out your thumb and fingers? Use string to test your prediction. Compare the two string lengths.

GUIDE FOR READING

◆ What roles do the small intestine and large intestine play in digestion?

Reading Tip As you read, create a table with the headings *Small Intestine, Liver, Pancreas,* and *Large Intestine.* Under each heading, list that organ's digestive function.

Have you ever been part of a huge crowd attending a concert or sports event? Barriers and passageways often guide people in the right direction. Ticket takers make sure that only those with tickets get in, and that they enter in an orderly fashion.

In some ways, the stomach can be thought of as the "ticket taker" of the digestive system. Once the food has been changed into a thick liquid, the stomach releases a little liquid at a time into the next part of the digestive system. This slow, smooth passage of food through the digestive system ensures that digestion and absorption take place smoothly.

The Small Intestine

After the thick liquid leaves the stomach, it enters the small intestine. The **small intestine** is the part of the digestive system where most of the chemical digestion takes place. If you look back at Figure 12, you may wonder how the small intestine got its name. After all, at about 6 meters—longer than some full-sized cars—it makes up two thirds of the digestive system. The small intestine was named for its small diameter. It is about two to three centimeters wide, about half the diameter of the large intestine.

When food reaches the small intestine, it has already been mechanically digested into a thick

READING STRATEGIES

Reading Tip Before students begin reading, have them preview the section by reading the headings and captions and looking at the pictures. Then have them create tables to list the digestive functions of the small intestine, liver, pancreas, and large intestine. After students read the section, invite volunteers to show their tables to the class and explain each function.

Study and Comprehension After students finish reading, have them review the section and write summaries of the information under each heading. Remind students that summarizing involves writing main points and key details. If any information under a heading is unclear, suggest students discuss the information with a partner before summarizing it.

liquid. But chemical digestion has just begun. Although starches and proteins have been partially broken down, fats haven't been digested at all. **Almost all chemical digestion and absorption of nutrients takes place in the small intestine.**

The small intestine is bustling with chemical activity. As the liquid moves into the small intestine, it mixes with enzymes and secretions. The enzymes and secretions are produced in three different organs—the small intestine, the liver, and the pancreas. The liver and the pancreas deliver their substances to the small intestine through small tubes.

The Role of the Liver The **liver** is located in the upper portion of the abdomen. It is the largest and heaviest organ in the body. You can think of the liver as an extremely busy chemical factory that plays a role in many body processes. For example, the liver breaks down medicines and other substances, and it helps eliminate nitrogen from the body. As part of the digestive system, the liver produces **bile**, a substance that breaks up fat particles. Bile flows from the liver into the **gallbladder,** the organ that stores bile. After you eat, bile passes through a tube from the gallbladder into the small intestine.

Bile is not an enzyme. It does not chemically digest foods. It does, however, break up large fat particles into smaller fat droplets. You can compare the action of bile on fats with the action of soap on oily skin. Soap physically breaks up the oil into small droplets that can mix with the soapy water and be washed away. Bile mixes with the fats in food to form small fat droplets. The droplets can then be chemically broken down by enzymes produced in the pancreas.

Break Up!
In this activity, you will model the breakup of fat particles in the small intestine.

1. Fill two jars half full of water. Add a few drops of oil to each jar.
2. Add $\frac{1}{4}$ teaspoon baking soda to one of the jars.
3. Stir the contents of both jars. Record your observations.

Observing In which jar did the oil begin to break up? What substance does the baking soda represent?

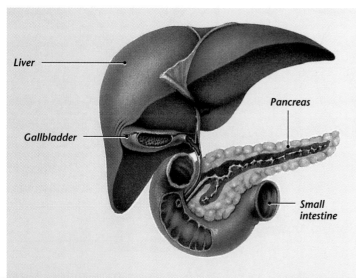

Figure 17 Substances produced by the liver and pancreas aid in the digestion of food.
Applying Concepts Where is bile produced? Where is it stored before it is released into the small intestine?

Liver
Pancreas
Gallbladder
Small intestine

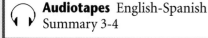
Answers to Self-Assessment
Caption Question
Figure 17 liver; gallbladder.

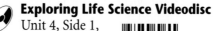

---

2 Facilitate

The Small Intestine

Demonstration
Materials *rope 6 m long*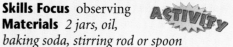
Time 5 minutes

Show students the length of rope to demonstrate the average length of the small intestine. Ask: **How is it possible for the body to accommodate such a long organ?** *(The small intestine is tightly coiled in the lower abdomen.)* **learning modality: visual**

TRY THIS

Skills Focus observing
Materials *2 jars, oil, baking soda, stirring rod or spoon*
Time 15 minutes
Tips You may want to have students use jars with lids so they can shake the liquid instead of stirring.
Observing The oil begins to break apart in the jar with the baking soda. The baking soda represents bile.
Extend Ask: **What do the jars represent?** *(The small intestine)* **learning modality: visual**

Ongoing Assessment

Writing Ask students to explain the roles of the liver and gallbladder in the digestive process that takes place in the small intestine.

The Small Intestine, continued

Using the Visuals: Figure 18

Make sure students understand that each diagram is a closer view of the part of the small intestine shown in the previous diagram. Ask students: **How do nutrients from the small intestine get to the rest of the body?** *(They pass from the cells on the villi into blood vessels.)* Have students explain how the structure of the villi allows this to happen. *(The villi contain blood vessels covered by a single layer of cells, so nutrients can pass through the cells into the blood.)* **learning modality: visual**

Including All Students

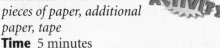

Materials *2 identical pieces of paper, additional paper, tape*
Time 5 minutes

Students who need additional help or students who are mastering English will benefit from this activity. Have students compare the two pieces of paper. Ask: **Do they have the same surface area?** *(yes)* Then have students make folds in one of the pieces of paper. Students should recognize that the two pieces still have the same surface area. Challenge students to fold another piece of paper and tape it to the folded paper to make it cover the same area on the desk as the unfolded piece. Ask: **Now which has the greater surface area?** *(The folded paper)* Ask students to describe how this models the villi in the small intestine. *(The villi allow the organ to have a greater surface area, yet take up the same space in the body.)* **limited English proficiency**

Figure 18 Tiny finger-shaped projections called villi line the inside of the small intestine. In the diagram, you can see that the blood vessels in the villi are covered by a single layer of cells. The photograph shows a closeup view of villi. *Interpreting Diagrams How does the structure of the villi help them carry out their function?*

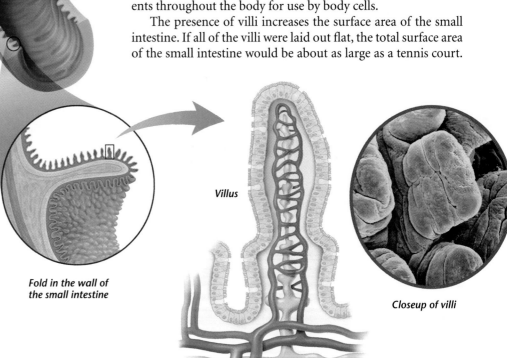

Small intestine

Fold in the wall of the small intestine

Villus

Closeup of villi

Help From the Pancreas The **pancreas** is a triangular organ that lies between the stomach and the first part of the small intestine. Like the liver, the pancreas plays a role in many body processes. As part of the digestive system, the pancreas produces enzymes that flow into the small intestine. These enzymes help break down starches, proteins, and fats.

The digestive enzymes produced by the pancreas and other organs do not break down all food substances, however. Recall that the fiber in food isn't broken down. Instead, fiber thickens the liquid material in the intestine. This makes it easier for peristalsis to push the material forward.

✓ *Checkpoint* **How does the pancreas aid in digestion?**

Absorption in the Small Intestine After chemical digestion takes place, the small nutrient molecules are ready to be absorbed by the body. The structure of the small intestine makes it well suited for absorption. As you can see in Figure 18, the inner surface, or lining, of the small intestine looks bumpy. Millions of tiny finger-shaped structures called **villi** (VIL eye) (singular *villus*) cover the surface. Notice that tiny blood vessels run through the center of each villus. Nutrient molecules pass from cells on the surface of a villus into blood vessels. The blood carries the nutrients throughout the body for use by body cells.

The presence of villi increases the surface area of the small intestine. If all of the villi were laid out flat, the total surface area of the small intestine would be about as large as a tennis court.

Background

Facts and Figures People who are more than 100 pounds overweight can undergo an operation called a gastric bypass (GB). In a GB, surgeons make a small pouch in the stomach and attach the lower end of the small intestine to an opening in the pouch. People who have had a GP lose weight, because less of the stomach and small intestine is available to absorb nutrients. Because there is less absorption, the side effects include:

◆ Excessive reaction to carbohydrates and sugar. The remainder of the small intestine processes these very quickly, causing an increase in insulin and a drop in blood sugar. This results in dizziness, nausea, and excessive perspiration.
◆ Vitamin B_{12} deficiency, anemia, and protein deficiency
◆ Formation of ulcers at the stomach opening

This greatly increased surface enables digested food to be absorbed faster than if the walls of the small intestine were smooth.

The Large Intestine

By the time material reaches the end of the small intestine, most nutrients have been absorbed. The remaining material moves from the small intestine into the large intestine. The **large intestine** is the last section of the digestive system. It is about one and a half meters long—about as long as the average bathtub. As you can see in Figure 19, the large intestine is shaped somewhat like a horseshoe. It runs up the right-hand side of the abdomen, across the upper abdomen, and then down the left-hand side. The large intestine contains bacteria that feed on the material passing through. These bacteria normally do not cause disease. In fact, they are helpful because they make certain vitamins, including vitamin K.

The material entering the large intestine contains water and undigested food such as fiber. **As the material moves through the large intestine, water is absorbed into the bloodstream. The remaining material is readied for elimination from the body.**

The large intestine ends in a short tube called the **rectum.** Here waste material is compressed into a solid form. This waste material is eliminated from the body through the **anus,** a muscular opening at the end of the rectum.

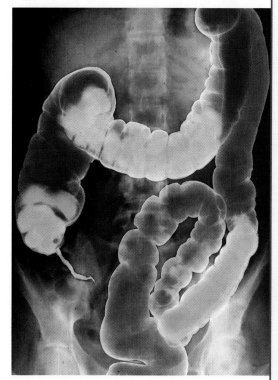

Figure 19 Notice the shape of the large intestine. As material passes through this structure, most of the water is absorbed by the body.

Section 4 Review

1. What two digestive processes occur in the small intestine? Briefly describe each process.
2. Which nutrient is absorbed in the large intestine?
3. How do the liver and pancreas function in the digestive process?
4. **Thinking Critically Relating Cause and Effect** Some people are allergic to a protein in wheat. When these people eat foods made with wheat, a reaction destroys the villi in the small intestine. What problems would you expect these people to experience?

> **Check Your Progress** CHAPTER PROJECT 3
> You should now be trying to eat a more healthful diet. Be sure you keep an accurate log of your food intake during this three-day period. Then graph the results. (*Hint:* You might find it helpful to focus on one food category when trying to improve your eating habits.)

Chapter 3 **D ◆ 93**

Program Resources

◆ **Product Testing Activities by *Consumer Reports,*** "Testing Sports Drinks," pp. 1–8
◆ **Teaching Resources** 3-4 Review and Reinforce, p. 79; 3-4 Enrich, p. 80

Media and Technology

 Interactive Student Tutorial CD-ROM D-3

Answers to Self-Assessment

Caption Question

Figure 18 Villi are composed of blood vessels surrounded by single layers of cells, so they can easily absorb nutrients and pass them to the blood vessels; also, villi present a large surface for absorption.

☑ *Checkpoint*

The pancreas produces enzymes that help break down starches, proteins, and fats.

The Large Intestine

Addressing Naive Conceptions

Students may think the waste material leaving a healthy body is made up entirely of undigested fiber. Explain that it also includes mucus, digestive juices, cellular waste materials, and bacterial waste. In fact, up to one third of the waste material is composed of bacteria and waste products produced by bacteria such as those in the large intestine.
learning modality: verbal

3 Assess

Section 4 Review Answers

1. Chemical digestion—liquefied food mixes with digestive juices and is broken down into the building blocks of starches, proteins, and fats. Absorption—villi absorb nutrients and pass them into blood vessels.
2. water
3. The liver produces bile, a substance that breaks up fat particles. The pancreas produces enzymes that help break down starches, proteins, and fats.
4. Without villi, the body cannot absorb nutrients. A person with this condition may eat large amounts of food and yet not obtain sufficient nutrients.

> **Check Your Progress** CHAPTER PROJECT 3
> Encourage students to develop plans for improving their diets by identifying specific areas that should be changed. Make sure students do not try to make drastic changes. Remind them they will only be keeping track of their new eating plan for three days, but they should try to implement a plan that they can maintain on a long-term basis.

Performance Assessment

Drawing Have students summarize the digestive process that occurs in the small intestine and the large intestine in a series of drawings and captions.

D ◆ 93

Advertising and Nutrition

Purpose

To provide students with an opportunity to investigate opinions about food advertising aimed at children.

Panel Discussion

Time 40 minutes

◆ Organize the class into small groups. Explain that each group shall argue for a particular point of view on whether unhealthy foods should be advertised on children's television programs. Possible viewpoints could include those of parents, children, advertising firms, nutritionists, snack food manufacturers, television executives, and manufacturers of health foods. Each group can brainstorm the benefits and drawbacks of advertising sugary and high-fat snacks and cereals. Students should consider whether changes in advertising should be made, what these changes might be, and how any changes might affect children and advertisers.

◆ Follow with a panel discussion.

◆ After the panel discussion, discuss whether any students have changed their opinions about foods advertised to children.

Extend

Ask students to compare and contrast the nutrition labels of cereals advertised on television with the information given in advertisements for the cereals.

You Decide

◆ Students can complete the first two steps to raise issues and possible solutions for class discussion. After the panel discussion, students can complete the last step, using what they have learned to design suggestions for improvement or public awareness.

Advertising and Nutrition

Millions of children enjoy Saturday morning television programs. As they watch, they see advertisements for high-sugar cereals, candy, soft drinks, and fat-filled foods. Such foods are not healthy choices. For example, in some cereals marketed to children, added sugar makes up almost half the cereal's weight. How greatly are children's eating habits influenced by food ads? Should these ads be allowed on children's television programs?

The Issues

Does Advertising Influence Children?
Advertising products to children between the ages of four and twelve works. Overall, companies spend more than $300 million a year advertising to that age group. In turn, children influence adults to spend more than 500 times that amount—at least $165 billion a year.

Should Food Companies Advertise on Children's Television? Some people want to regulate food ads on children's shows. Evidence indicates that children choose particular foods based on ads. The foods children eat can affect their health not just during childhood but for the rest of their lives.

Other people point out that children don't try to buy every food they see advertised. It is usually parents, not children, who decide what foods to buy. In addition, companies pay for advertisements. Without this money, television producers might not be able to afford to make good programs.

What Responsibilities Do Families and Schools Have? Many people believe that parents and teachers should teach children about nutrition. These people argue that adults should teach children to read food labels and to recognize misleading advertisements. For the rest of children's lives, they will be surrounded by advertising. If they learn to analyze ads critically, children will become wise consumers as adults.

You Decide

1. Describe the Issue
Summarize the debate about food advertisements on children's television.

2. Analyze the Options
List some possible solutions to the problem of food advertisements on children's television. How would each solution affect children and advertisers?

3. Find a Solution
Prepare a leaflet proposing one solution to the problem. Use persuasive arguments to support your proposal.

Background

The children's advertising industry regulates itself based on several principles: (**1**) Advertisers have a special responsibility to protect young children from their own susceptibilities. (**2**) Advertisers should be careful not to exploit children's imaginative qualities, creating unrealistic expectations for their products. (**3**) Advertisers should realize that children may try to imitate what they see in ads, which may affect their health and well-being. (**4**) Advertisers should provide examples of positive and beneficial social behavior. (**5**) Advertisers should avoid social stereotyping and appeals to prejudice.

You could have students research the complete guidelines, then review ads to evaluate whether advertisers are following their own guidelines.

SECTION 1 Food and Energy

Key Ideas

◆ Nutrients in food provide the body with energy and materials needed for growth, repair, and other life processes. The energy in foods is measured in Calories.

◆ The six nutrients necessary for human health are carbohydrates, fats, proteins, vitamins, minerals, and water.

◆ Water is the most important nutrient because it is necessary for all body processes.

Key Terms

nutrient	fiber	protein
calorie	fat	amino acid
carbohydrate	unsaturated fat	vitamin
glucose	cholesterol	mineral

SECTION 2 Healthy Eating

 INTEGRATING HEALTH

Key Ideas

◆ The Food Guide Pyramid classifies foods into six major groups and tells how many servings from each group to eat.

◆ Food labels list the nutrients in foods and shows how the foods fit into your daily diet.

Key Terms

Food Guide Pyramid   Percent Daily Value

SECTION 3 The Digestive Process Begins

Key Ideas

◆ The functions of the digestive system are to break down food, absorb food molecules into the blood, and eliminate wastes.

◆ During mechanical digestion, food is ground into small pieces. During chemical digestion, large food molecules are broken into small molecules by enzymes.

◆ Food first passes from the mouth into the esophagus, and then into the stomach. Waves of muscle contractions, known as peristalsis, keep the food moving in one direction.

Key Terms

digestion	enzyme	mucus
absorption	epiglottis	peristalsis
saliva	esophagus	stomach

SECTION 4 Final Digestion and Absorption

Key Ideas

◆ Almost all chemical digestion and absorption of nutrients takes place in the small intestine.

◆ Nutrients are absorbed into the bloodstream through the villi of the small intestine.

◆ As material moves through the large intestine, water is absorbed. The remaining material is readied for elimination.

Key Terms

small intestine	gallbladder	large intestine
liver	pancreas	rectum
bile	villus	anus

USING THE INTERNET

www.science-explorer.phschool.com

Chapter 3 **D ◆ 95**

CHAPTER 3 REVIEW

Program Resources

◆ **Teaching Resources** Chapter 3 Project Scoring Rubric, p. 64; Chapter 3 Performance Assessment Teacher Notes, p. 250; Chapter 3 Performance Assessment Student Worksheet, p. 252; Chapter 3 Test, pp. 253–256

Reviewing Content:
Multiple Choice
1. c 2. d 3. c 4. d 5. a

True or False
6. complete 7. fat-soluble 8. true 9. true
10. small

Checking Concepts
11. The more physical activity a person does, the higher his or her daily energy needs.
12. Fiber helps keep the digestive system functioning properly.
13. The Food Guide Pyramid gives information about recommended daily servings as a range instead of a single number because different people may need different amounts. For example, an active growing teenager may need to eat more servings than an adult.
14. The epiglottis prevents food from going down the windpipe instead of the esophagus.
15. Peristalsis is the wavelike motion of the muscles that pushes food and undigested matter through the digestive system.
16. The villi are finger-shaped structures that line the small intestine. They are specialized for absorbing and transferring nutrients from the small intestine to the blood stream.
17. Students' descriptions should include mechanical and chemical digestion, beginning in the mouth. They should describe the food's journey down the esophagus, into the stomach, the small intestine, and the large intestine. Students should describe the chemical action of different juices and enzymes, and the absorption of nutrients in the small intestine and water in the large intestine.

Reviewing Content

 For more review of key concepts, see the Interactive Student Tutorial CD-ROM.

Multiple Choice
Choose the letter of the best answer.

1. Which nutrient makes up about 65 percent of the body's weight?
   a. carbohydrate
   b. protein
   c. water
   d. fat
2. According to the Food Guide Pyramid, from which group should you eat the most servings?
   a. Milk, Yogurt, and Cheese
   b. Meat, Poultry, Fish, Beans, Eggs, and Nuts
   c. Vegetables
   d. Bread, Cereal, Rice, and Pasta
3. Most mechanical digestion takes place in the
   a. mouth.   b. esophagus.
   c. stomach.   d. small intestine.
4. The enzyme in saliva chemically breaks down
   a. fats.   b. proteins.
   c. sugars.   d. starches.
5. Bile is produced by the
   a. liver.   b. pancreas.
   c. small intestine. d. large intestine.

True or False

If the statement is true, write true. If it is false, change the underlined word or words to make the statement true.

6. Proteins that come from animal sources are <u>incomplete</u> proteins.
7. Vitamins that are stored in the fatty tissue of the body are <u>water-soluble</u>.
8. To determine which of two cereals supplies more iron, you can check the <u>Percent Daily Value</u> on the food label.
9. The physical breakdown of food is called <u>mechanical</u> digestion.
10. Most materials are absorbed into the bloodstream in the <u>large</u> intestine.

Checking Concepts
11. How does a person's level of physical activity affect his or her daily energy needs?
12. Why is fiber necessary in a diet even though it's not considered a nutrient?
13. Why does the Food Guide Pyramid give the recommended daily servings as a range instead of a single number?
14. Describe the function of the epiglottis.
15. Explain the role of peristalsis in the digestive system.
16. What is the function of villi? Where are villi located?
17. **Writing to Learn** Imagine that you are a bacon, lettuce, and tomato sandwich. Describe your journey through a person's digestive system, ending with absorption.

Thinking Visually
18. **Flowchart** Copy the incomplete flowchart onto a separate sheet of paper. Complete the flowchart with the names and functions of the missing organs. (For more on flowcharts, see the Skills Handbook.)

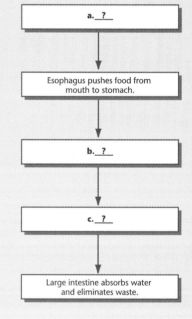

Thinking Visually
18. **a.** In the mouth, the teeth break food into smaller pieces and saliva begins to break down starches. **b.** In the stomach, food is churned and mixed with digestive juices that break down protein. **c.** In the small intestine, almost all chemical digestion and absorption occurs.

Applying Skills
19. Milk, Yogurt, and Cheese Group; 2–3 servings
20. About three cups
21. Low-fat; $\frac{20}{110} \times \frac{100\%}{1} = 18\%$. The other foods get 32% (yogurt) and 35% (chocolate milk) of their calories from fat.

Thinking Critically
22. The fat will be stored as an energy source to be used when the animal is hibernating and not taking in food as energy.
23. Similarity: Both an assembly line and the digestive system perform specific jobs in a sequence of steps. Difference: In an assembly line, something is constructed from many small part in many steps, but in digestion, the process is reversed—something is broken down into smaller parts step by step.

Applying Skills

Use the chart below to answer Questions 19–21.

Food (1 cup)	Calcium (% Daily Value)	Calories	Calories from Fat (grams)
Chocolate milk	30	230	80
Low-fat milk	35	110	20
Plain Yogurt	35	110	35

19. Classifying To which group in the Food Guide Pyramid do the foods in the chart belong? What is the recommended range of daily servings for that group?

20. Interpreting Data How many cups of low-fat milk provide the daily recommended amount of calcium?

21. Calculating Which of the foods meet the recommendation that no more than 30 percent of a food's Calories come from fat? Explain.

Thinking Critically

22. Applying Concepts Before winter arrives, animals that hibernate often prepare by eating foods that contain a lot of fat. How is this behavior helpful?

23. Comparing and Contrasting The digestive system is sometimes said to be "an assembly line in reverse." Identify some similarities and some differences between your digestive system and an assembly line.

24. Relating Cause and Effect "Heartburn" occurs when stomach acid enters the esophagus. Use your knowledge of the digestive system to explain how this condition affects the esophagus and how "heartburn" got its name.

25. Inferring Why is it important to chew your food thoroughly before swallowing?

26. Relating Cause and Effect Suppose a medicine killed all the bacteria in your body. How might this affect vitamin production in your body? Explain.

Performance Assessment

Wrap Up
CHAPTER PROJECT 3

Present Your Project Write a summary of what you've learned from keeping a food log. Address these questions: How close were your eating patterns to those recommended in the Food Guide Pyramid? How did you attempt to change your diet during the second three days? How successful were you at making those changes?

Reflect and Record Did your eating patterns surprise you? What additional changes could help you improve your diet? How might others help you make those changes? If your eating patterns match those that are recommended, how can you be sure to continue those patterns?

Getting Involved

In Your School As a class, review your school's lunch menus for a week. How closely do those meals reflect the recommended diet in the Food Guide Pyramid? Try to meet with the school's food service director to find out what guidelines are used in planning meals. Use this information and what you learned in this chapter to plan school lunches for one week.

---

24. Since acid can burn most of human tissue, when it enters the esophagus it burns tissue, and people feel a burning sensation—heartburn.

25. Chewing thoroughly breaks food into smaller particles and therefore makes it easier for chemical digestion to occur. Chewing food thoroughly also reduces the risk of choking.

26. Bacteria in the large intestine produce vitamin K. If they were killed by the medicine, the production of vitamin K would stop.

Program Resources

◆ **Inquiry Skills Handbook** Provides teaching and review of all inquiry skills

---

Performance Assessment

Wrap Up
CHAPTER PROJECT 3

Present Your Project Students' summaries should document the changes they tried to implement in the second phase of the project. Students should describe how their analyses of their eating habits in the first part of the project led them to make specific changes. This project may involve issues that are sensitive for some students. Tell students that their summaries are for their own benefit and for serving as evidence that they completed the project. Make sure students know that their summaries will be held in confidence.

Reflect and Record Encourage students to write reasonable plans for maintaining healthy eating habits. Students' plans should include strategies for dealing with any habits that compromise their nutrition. Make sure students do not try to implement radical plans. Remind students that their diets can be healthful even if some meals or snacks do not meet the guidelines. Encourage them to think of the average effect of each day or even of a whole week instead of focusing on each individual food.

Getting Involved

In Your School Obtain copies of your school's lunch menus and allow students to study them to develop questions before meeting with the food service director. Students should use the information in the chapter and any additional resources to analyze the week's menu. Students may want to analyze the nutritional value of the foods actually selected and eaten, as opposed to the foods that are offered. If possible, have students submit their menus to the food service director to find out whether the menu can be implemented, and if not, what changes would have to be made to the menus.

CHAPTER 4 Circulation

	Sections	Time	Student Edition Activities	Other Activities	
CHAPTER PROJECT 4	**Travels of a Red Blood Cell** p. 99	Ongoing (2 weeks)	Check Your Progress, pp. 106, 111, 118 Wrap Up, p. 127	TE	Chapter 4 Project Notes, pp. 98–99
1	**The Body's Transportation System** pp. 100–106 ◆ Describe the function of the cardiovascular system. ◆ Describe the structure of the heart and explain its function. ◆ Trace the path taken by blood through the circulatory system.	3½ periods/ 1–2 blocks	**Discover** How Hard Does Your Heart Work?, p. 100	TE TE TE	Building Inquiry Skills: Observing, p. 102 Including All Students, p. 108 Building Inquiry Skills: Interpreting Data, p. 104
2	**A Closer Look at Blood Vessels** pp. 107–112 ◆ Describe the functions of the arteries, capillaries, and veins. ◆ Identify the cause of blood pressure.	3 periods/ 1½ blocks	**Discover** How Does Pressure Affect the Flow of Blood?, p. 107 **Sharpen Your Skills** Creating Data Tables, p. 110 **Skills Lab: Measuring** Heart Beat, Health Beat, p. 112	TE TE TE	Math Toolbox, p. 108 Building Inquiry Skills: Calculating, p. 108 Real-Life Learning, p. 111
3	**Blood and Lymph** pp. 113–119 ◆ Name and describe the four components of blood. ◆ Explain blood type and how it determines what blood a person can receive in a transfusion. ◆ Describe the lymphatic system.	3½ periods/ 1–2 blocks	**Discover** What Kinds of Cells Are in Blood?, p. 113 **Try This** Caught in the Web, p. 116 **Real-World Lab: You and Your Community** Do You Know Your A-B-O's?, p. 119	TE TE	Demonstration, p. 114 Real-Life Learning, p. 117
4	**INTEGRATING HEALTH** **Cardiovascular Health** pp. 120–124 ◆ Describe behaviors that maintain cardiovascular health. ◆ List and describe types of cardiovascular disease.	2½ periods/ 1–2 blocks	**Discover** Which Foods Are "Heart Healthy"?, p. 120 **Try This** Blocking the Flow, p. 121	TE TE TE	Building Inquiry Skills: Predicting, p. 123 Building Inquiry Skills: Making Models, p. 123 Building Inquiry Skills: Making Judgments, p. 124
	Study Guide/Chapter Review pp. 125–127	1 period/ ½ block		ISAB	Provides teaching and review of all inquiry skills

For Standard or Block Schedule The Resource Pro® CD-ROM gives you maximum flexibility for planning your instruction for any type of schedule. Resource Pro® contains Planning Express®, an advanced scheduling program, as well as the entire contents of the Teaching Resources and the Computer Test Bank.

CHAPTER PLANNING GUIDE

Program Resources	Assessment Strategies	Media and Technology
TR Chapter 4 Project Teacher Notes, pp. 86–87 **TR** Chapter 4 Project Overview and Worksheets, pp. 88–91 **TR** Chapter 4 Project Scoring Rubric, p. 92	**SE** Performance Assessment: Chapter 4 Project Wrap Up, p. 127 **TE** Performance Assessment: Chapter 4 Project Wrap Up, p. 127 **TE** Check Your Progress, pp. 106, 111, 118 **TR** Chapter 4 Project Scoring Rubric, p. 92	
TR 4-1 Lesson Plan, p. 93 **TR** 4-1 Section Summary, p. 94 **TR** 4-1 Review and Reinforce, p. 95 **TR** 4-1 Enrich, p. 96	**SE** Section 1 Review, p. 106 **TE** Ongoing Assessment, pp. 101, 103, 105 **TE** Performance Assessment, p. 106 **TR** 4-1 Review and Reinforce, p. 95	Audiotapes: English-Spanish Summary 4-1 Transparency 8, "Exploring the Heart" Interactive Student Tutorial CD-ROM, D-4
TR 4-2 Lesson Plan, p. 97 **TR** 4-2 Section Summary, p. 98 **TR** 4-2 Review and Reinforce, p. 99 **TR** 4-2 Enrich, p. 100 **TR** Chapter 4 Skills Lab, pp. 109–110	**SE** Section 2 Review, p. 111 **SE** Analyze and Conclude, p. 112 **TE** Ongoing Assessment, p. 109 **TE** Performance Assessment, p. 111 **TR** 4-2 Review and Reinforce, p. 99	Audiotapes: English-Spanish Summary 4-2 Transparency 9, "Artery, Capillary, and Vein" Interactive Student Tutorial CD-ROM, D-4
TR 4-3 Lesson Plan, p. 101 **TR** 4-3 Section Summary, p. 102 **TR** 4-3 Review and Reinforce, p. 103 **TR** 4-3 Enrich, p. 104 **TR** Chapter 4 Real-World Lab, pp. 111–113	**SE** Section 3 Review, p. 118 **SE** Analyze and Conclude, p. 119 **TE** Ongoing Assessment, pp. 115, 117 **TE** Performance Assessment, p. 118 **TR** 4-3 Review and Reinforce, p. 103	Exploring Life Science Videodisc, Unit 4 Side 1, "Blood!" Audiotapes: English-Spanish Summary 4-3 Interactive Student Tutorial CD-ROM, D-4
TR 4-4 Lesson Plan, p. 105 **TR** 4-4 Section Summary, p. 106 **TR** 4-4 Review and Reinforce, p. 107 **TR** 4-4 Enrich, p. 108	**SE** Section 4 Review, p. 124 **TE** Ongoing Assessment, pp. 121, 123 **TE** Performance Assessment, p. 124 **TR** 4-4 Review and Reinforce, p. 107	Exploring Life Science Videodisc, Unit 4 Side 1, "The Heart of the Matter" Audiotapes: English-Spanish Summary 4-4 Interactive Student Tutorial CD-ROM, D-4
TR Chapter 4 Performance Assessment, pp. 257–259 **TR** Chapter 4 Test, pp. 260–263	**SE** Chapter Review, pp. 125–127 **TR** Chapter 4 Performance Assessment, pp. 257–259 **TR** Chapter 4 Test, pp. 260–263 **CTB** Test D–4	Computer Test Bank, Test D-4 Interactive Student Tutorial CD-ROM, D-4 Science Explorer Internet Site

Key: **SE** Student Edition   **TE** Teacher's Edition   **TR** Teaching Resources
     CTB Computer Test Bank   **SES** Science Explorer Series Text   **ISLM** Integrated Science Laboratory Manual
     ISAB Inquiry Skills Activity Book   **PTA** Product Testing Activities by *Consumer Reports*   **IES** Interdisciplinary Explorations Series

Meeting the National Science Education Standards and AAAS Benchmarks

National Science Education Standards	Benchmarks for Science Literacy	Unifying Themes
Science as Inquiry (Content Standard A) ◆ **Ask questions that can be answered by scientific investigations** How does physical activity affect your pulse rate? *(Skills Lab)* Which blood types can safely receive transfusions of type A blood? Which can receive type O blood? *(Real-World Lab)* **Life Science** (Content Standard C) ◆ **Develop descriptions, explanations, predictions, and models using evidence** Students design and construct a display showing the path of a red blood cell through the human body. *(Chapter Project)* ◆ **Structure and Function of Living Systems** The cardiovascular system consists of the heart, blood vessels, and blood and functions as the transport system of the body. *(Section 1)* Arteries, capillaries, and veins transport blood to organs of the body. *(Section 2)* **Science in Personal and Social Perspectives** (Content Standard F) ◆ **Personal Health** Personal behaviors can help maintain cardiovascular health. *(Section 4)* **History and Nature of Science** (Content Standard G) ◆ **History of Science** Many people have contributed to cardiovascular advances in the twentieth century. *(Section 4)*	**1B Scientific Inquiry** Students infer which types of blood can be safely received in transfusions. *(Real-World Lab)* **2C The Nature of Mathematics** Students apply mathematics to determine how physical activity affects pulse rate. *(Skills Lab)* **3C Issues in Technology** Technology has been responsible for advances in cardiovascular medicine which have improved treatments and saved human lives. *(Section 4)* **6C Basic Functions** The circulatory system moves materials and wastes to or from cells where they are needed or produced, responding to changing demands. *(Sections 1, 2, 3)* **6E Physical Health** Regular exercise is important to maintain a healthy cardiovascular system. *(Section 4)* White blood cells engulf invaders or produce antibodies that attack them or mark them for killing other white cells. *(Section 3)* **11A Systems** The cardiovascular system is connected to other systems in the human body. *(Section 1)*	◆ **Energy** Red blood cells provide the body with oxygen that is needed for energy. The circulatory system delivers the raw materials needed for the production of energy to the cells and carries the waste products of energy production away from the cells. *(Sections 1, 3, Chapter Project)* ◆ **Scale and Structure** The primary components of the cardiovascular system include the heart, blood vessels, and blood. The heart pumps blood, blood carries materials and wastes, and blood vessels transport these materials to other parts of the body. *(Sections 1, 2)* ◆ **Unity and Diversity** Arteries, veins, and capillaries all provide the transport network through which blood travels, although their structure and functions differ. Arteries carry blood away from the heart and are large and tough; capillaries are tiny vessels in which the exchange of materials takes place; and veins are smaller than arteries and carry blood back to the heart. *(Section 2)* ◆ **Systems and Interactions** The components of blood work together as a system, each performing a specific duty. The interaction of these components with the rest of the body enables the body to stay healthy and to function normally. *(Section 3)*

Media and Technology

Exploring Life Science Videodisc

◆ **Section 3** "Blood!" describes the structure of blood and the mechanics of the first blood transfusions.

◆ **Section 4** "The Heart of the Matter" tells how an athlete shares the diet and exercise program she follows to maintain a healthy heart.

Interactive Student Tutorial CD-ROM

◆ **Chapter Review** Interactive questions help students to self-assess their mastery of key chapter concepts.

Student Edition Connection Strategies

◆ **Section 1** Integrating Technology, p. 104
Language Arts Connection, p. 104
Integrating Physics, p. 106

◆ **Section 2** Math Toolbox, p. 108
Integrating Chemistry, p. 109
Integrating Physics, p. 110

◆ **Section 4** Integrating Health, p. 120
Science and History, pp. 122–123

USING THE INTERNET

www.science-explorer.phschool.com

Visit the Science Explorer Internet site to find an up-to-date activity for Chapter 4 of *Human Biology and Health*.

ACTIVITY	Time (minutes)	Materials *Quantities for one work group*	Skills
Section 1			
Discover, p. 100	20	**Consumable** newspapers, paper towels **Nonconsumable** two large plastic containers, cup with capacity of about 60 mL, watch or clock with a second hand	Inferring
Section 2			
Discover, p. 107	10	**Consumable** newspapers, paper towels **Nonconsumable** plastic squeeze bottle, dishpan	Inferring
Sharpen your Skills, p. 110	15	**Consumable** No special materials are required.	Creating Data Tables
Skills Lab, p. 112	40	**Consumable** graph paper **Nonconsumable** watch or clock with second hand	Measuring
Section 3			
Discover, p. 113	15	**Nonconsumable** microscope, prepared slides of human blood	Observing
Try This, p. 116	15	**Consumable** water, newspapers, paper towels **Nonconsumable** two sturdy plastic cups, 20-cm square piece of cheesecloth, rubber band, paper clips, coins	Making Models
Real-World Lab, p. 119	40	**Consumable** 4 paper cups, white paper, four model "blood" types, toothpicks **Nonconsumable** 4 plastic droppers, marking pen, 8 plastic petri dishes	Making Models, Inferring
Section 4			
Discover, p. 120	20	**Nonconsumable** assortment of foods	Forming Operational Definitions
Try This, p. 121	20	**Consumable** water, peanut butter, toothpick, newspaper, paper towels **Nonconsumable** plastic funnel, plastic jar, graduated cylinder, stopwatch or clock, plastic knife	Predicting

A list of all materials required for the Student Edition activities can be found on pages T14–T15. You can order Materials Kits by calling 1-800-828-7777 or by accessing the Science Explorer Internet site at **www.science-explorer.phschool.com.**

CHAPTER PROJECT 4

Travels of a Red Blood Cell

Students may have a hard time visualizing the circulation of blood throughout the body. This project will give them the opportunity to describe the travels of a single blood cell through the circulatory system.

Purpose In this project, students will research what happens as blood moves throughout the body. The students must also design a display to communicate their findings visually.

Skills Focus After completing the Chapter 4 Project, students will be able to

♦ describe the two main circuits in the circulatory system of the human body;
♦ make a model in the form of visual displays showing the two circuits traveled by red blood cells;
♦ communicate information concerning the function of the two circuits.

Project Time Line The entire project will require approximately two to three weeks. On the first day, class time should be allowed for students to exchange ideas on ways to create visual displays. On the second day, have students work on ideas for their own displays and talk with you about their plans. Have students present detailed sketches of their plans to you during the next few days. When you have approved their plans, students should spend eight to ten days building their displays. Allow one or two class periods at the end of the project for students to present their displays. Before beginning the project, see Chapter 4 Project Teacher Notes on pages 86–87 in Teaching Resources for more details on carrying out the project. Also distribute the Students' Chapter 4 Project Overview and Worksheets and Scoring Rubric on pages 88–92 in Teaching Resources.

Suggested Shortcuts Consider organizing the class in groups to do some or all phases of the project. Students can research the heart and its circulation in groups, or they can brainstorm display ideas in a group. For more ambitious projects, consider allowing students to work in groups for the whole project.

CHAPTER 4 Circulation

WHAT'S AHEAD

SECTION 1 The Body's Transportation System

Discover **How Hard Does Your Heart Work?**

SECTION 2 A Closer Look at Blood Vessels

Discover **How Does Pressure Affect the Flow of Blood?**
Sharpen Your Skills **Creating Data Tables**
Skills Lab **Heart Beat, Health Beat**

SECTION 3 Blood and Lymph

Discover **What Kinds of Cells Are in Blood?**
Try This **Caught in the Web**
Real-World Lab **Do You Know Your A-B-O's?**

98 ◆ D

Possible Materials Provide a wide variety of materials from which students can choose. Encourage them to also use videos, computers, and art media.

♦ For posters, provide poster board, colored pens, string, foil, and an assortment of magazines and newspapers.
♦ For displays involving more elaborate construction, provide cardboard, cardboard rolls, straws, scrap wood, assorted plastic bottles, and other materials.

Launching the Project To introduce the project and to stimulate student interest, compare blood circulation to a rural mail route. Each morning a mail carrier goes to the post office and picks up the mail, much as blood picks up oxygen in the lungs. The carrier then drives to where the customers live, delivers the mail, picks up mail from the customer, and returns to the post office. Just as the mail carrier picks up customer mail to be returned to the post office, so is carbon dioxide picked up by the blood to be returned to the lungs.

PROJECT 4

Travels of a Red Blood Cell

Every day, you travel from home to school and then back home again. Your path makes a loop, or circuit, ending where it began. In this chapter, you'll learn how your blood also travels in circuits. You'll find out how your heart pumps your blood throughout your body, bringing that essential fluid to all your living cells. As you learn more about the heart and circulatory system, you'll create a display to show how blood circulates throughout the body.

Your Goal To design and construct a display showing a complete journey of a red blood cell through the human body.

To complete the project successfully, your display must
- show a red blood cell that leaves from the heart and returns to the same place
- show where the red blood cell picks up and delivers oxygen and carbon dioxide
- provide written descriptions of the circuits made by the red blood cell, either with captions or in a continuous story
- be designed following the safety guidelines in Appendix A

Get Started Look ahead at the diagrams in the chapter. Then discuss the kinds of displays you could use, including a three-dimensional model, posters, a series of drawings, a flip-book, or a video animation. Write down any content questions you'll need to answer.

Check Your Progress You'll be working on this project as you study this chapter. To keep your project on track, look for Check Your Progress boxes at the following points.
Section 1 Review, page 106: Make a sketch of your display.
Section 2 Review, page 111: Begin to construct your display.
Section 3 Review, page 118: Add a written description to your display.

Wrap Up At the end of the chapter (page 127), you will use your display to show how blood travels through the body.

Blood cells travel in blood vessels to all parts of the body.

SECTION 4
Integrating Health
Cardiovascular Health

Discover **Which Foods Are "Heart Healthy"?**
Try This **Blocking the Flow**

D ◆ 99

Help students brainstorm ideas by reviewing the words that can be used for the blood travels, such as "circuit" or "loop." Help students modify overly ambitious or expensive plans; approve creative ideas that can be completed within the time period and with the resources available.

Program Resources

- **Teaching Resources** Chapter 4 Project Teacher's Notes, pp. 86–87; Chapter 4 Project Overview and Worksheets, pp. 88–91; Chapter 4 Project Scoring Rubric, p. 92

Performance Assessment

The Chapter 4 Project Scoring Rubric on page 92 of Teaching Resources will help you evaluate how well students complete the Chapter 4 Project. Students will be assessed on
- the thoroughness of their research on the circulatory system and the thoroughness of their plans for creating the display;
- the accuracy and creativity of their display and whether it was completed on time;
- the thoroughness and organization of their presentation of the display to the rest of the class;
- how well students work with others and participate in class discussions.
By sharing the Chapter 4 Scoring Rubric with students at the beginning of the project, you will make it clear to them what they are expected to do.

Objectives

After completing the lesson, students will be able to
◆ describe the function of the cardiovascular system;
◆ describe the structure of the heart and explain its function;
◆ trace the path taken by blood through the circulatory system.

Key Terms cardiovascular system, heart, atrium, ventricle, valve, pacemaker, artery, capillary, vein, aorta

1 Engage/Explore

Activating Prior Knowledge

Display a map of a subway, bus, train, or local highway system. Ask students what the function of the transportation system is. Then ask them to compare it with the system for transporting materials through the human body.

DISCOVER

ACTIVITY

Skills Focus inferring
Materials *newspapers, paper towels, two large plastic containers, cup with capacity of about 60 mL, watch or clock with a second hand*
Time 20 minutes
Tips Because spillage will occur, set up with newspapers, towels, or other materials for quick cleanup. If possible, put large plastic containers in a larger container to catch spills. Water spilled on floor should be mopped immediately. Students should wear aprons. Consider doing this activity outdoors.
Expected Outcome Students probably cannot make 75 transfers of water.
Think It Over Results will indicate that the heart can work faster than the hand.

SECTION 1
The Body's Transportation System

DISCOVER · ACTIVITY

How Hard Does Your Heart Work?

1. Every minute, your heart beats about 75 to 85 times. With each beat, it pumps about 60 milliliters of blood. Can you work as hard and fast as your heart does?

2. Cover a table or desk with newspapers. Place two large plastic containers side by side on the newspapers. Fill one with 2.5 liters of water, which is about the volume of blood that your heart pumps in 30 seconds. Leave the other container empty.

3. 🖐 With a plastic cup that holds about 60 milliliters, transfer water as quickly as possible into the empty container without spilling any. Have a partner time you for 30 seconds. As you work, count how many transfers you make in 30 seconds.

4. Multiply your results by 2 to find the number of transfers for one minute.

Think It Over

Inferring Compare your performance with the number of times your heart beats every minute. What do your results tell you about the strength and speed of a heartbeat?

GUIDE FOR READING

◆ What is the function of the cardiovascular system?
◆ What role does the heart play in the cardiovascular system?
◆ What path does blood take through the circulatory system?

Reading Tip As you read, create a flowchart that shows the path that blood follows as it circulates through the body.

In the middle of the night, a truck rolls rapidly through the darkness. Loaded with fresh fruits and vegetables, the truck is headed for a city supermarket. The driver steers off the interstate and onto a smaller highway. Finally, after driving through narrow city streets, the truck reaches its destination. As dawn begins to break, store workers unload the cargo. They work quickly, because other trucks—carrying meats, canned goods, and freshly baked breads—are waiting to be unloaded. And while workers fill the store with products to be sold, a garbage truck removes yesterday's trash. All these trucks have traveled long distances over roads. Without a huge network of roads, big and small, the supermarket couldn't stay in business.

Movement of Materials

Like the roads that link all parts of the country, your body has a "highway" network, called the cardiovascular system, that links all parts of your body. The **cardiovascular system,** or circulatory system, consists of the heart, blood vessels, and blood. **The cardiovascular system carries needed substances to cells and carries waste products away from cells.** In addition, blood contains cells that fight disease.

READING STRATEGIES

Reading Tip Have students use note cards to write each step that they want to include on their flowcharts. Encourage them to rearrange the cards as they read until they are sure they have the steps in the correct order.

Study and Comprehension Have students write brief summaries of the information in this section. Remind students to include main ideas and key details in their summaries. Students can then use the summaries as study guides for the section.

Needed Materials Most substances that need to get from one part of the body to another are carried by blood. For example, blood carries oxygen from your lungs to your body cells. Blood also transports the glucose your cells use to produce energy.

Waste Products The cardiovascular system also picks up wastes from cells. For example, when cells use glucose, they produce carbon dioxide as a waste product. The carbon dioxide passes from the cells into the blood. The cardiovascular system then carries carbon dioxide to the lungs, where it is exhaled.

Disease Fighters The cardiovascular system also transports cells that attack disease-causing microorganisms. This process can keep you from becoming sick. If you do get sick, these disease-fighting blood cells will kill the microorganisms to help you get well.

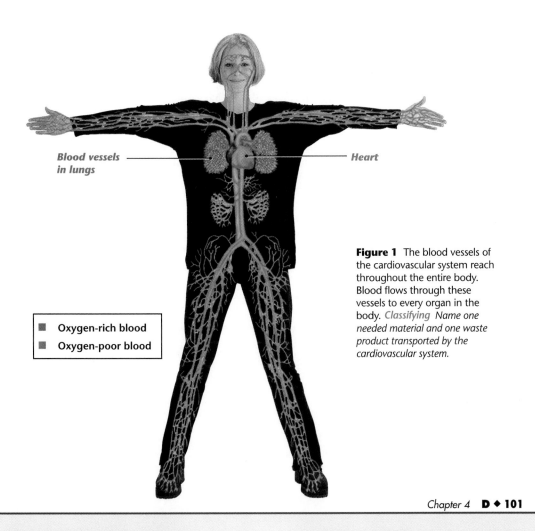

Blood vessels in lungs

Heart

■ Oxygen-rich blood
■ Oxygen-poor blood

Figure 1 The blood vessels of the cardiovascular system reach throughout the entire body. Blood flows through these vessels to every organ in the body. *Classifying Name one needed material and one waste product transported by the cardiovascular system.*

2 Facilitate

Movement of Materials

Including All Students

Some students may have difficulty in understanding how the parts of the cardiovascular system are interrelated. Ask: **What is the relationship between the heart, the blood vessels, and the blood?** *(The heart pumps the blood so that the blood can move throughout the body; the blood vessels link all parts of the body so that the blood can circulate; the blood transports glucose and oxygen to body cells and picks up carbon dioxide and other wastes that need to be removed; the blood also transports disease-fighting cells when necessary.)* **learning modality: logical/mathematical**

Building Inquiry Skills: Communicating

Tell students they will work in pairs to test each other on their knowledge of the circulatory system. Students should first read the section and study Figure 1. Then, each student should write down three questions to ask the other. Instruct students to ask questions that can be answered by reading the section. Provide an example: Which part of the circulatory system picks up carbon dioxide from the cells? *(The blood)* After students have tested each other, invite each pair of students to choose one of their questions to present to the class. **limited English proficiency**

Program Resources

◆ **Teaching Resources** 4-1 Lesson Plan, p. 93; 4-1 Section Summary, p. 94

Media and Technology

🎧 **Audiotapes** English-Spanish Summary 4-1

Answers to Self-Assessment

Caption Question

Figure 1 Needed materials—oxygen, glucose; waste products—carbon dioxide

Ongoing Assessment

Writing Have students describe the parts of the cardiovascular system and the materials it transports.

The Heart

Building Inquiry Skills: Observing

Materials *stethoscope*
Time 15 minutes

Have students use the stethoscope to listen to their own heartbeats. After each use, use rubbing alcohol to clean the parts of the stethoscope that are inserted into the ears. Then have students describe the sound of the beating heart. *(Students should describe a deeper sound, the "lub," and a higher sound, the "dup.")*
learning modality: kinesthetic

Using the Visuals: Figure 3

Have students identify the valve in the photograph. Ask: **Which way does the blood move through the valve?** *(Up from the left through the valve.)* Ask students to predict what would happen if the blood began to flow backward. *(The valve would remain closed and would prevent backward flow.)* **learning modality: visual**

Including All Students

Materials *model heart with removable parts*
Time 15 minutes

This activity will benefit students who have difficulty seeing. Invite students to feel each part of the heart as you describe its function. Ask students to describe what they feel, noting differences in the size of the chambers and the thickness of the walls. Have students feel and describe the blood vessels that lead in and out of the chambers. **learning modality: kinesthetic**

Figure 2 This small stone sculpture, created by ancient Egyptians, represents the heart. Ancient Egyptians believed that feelings, thoughts, and memories were created by the heart.

The Heart

Without the heart, blood wouldn't go anywhere. The **heart** is a hollow, muscular organ that pumps blood throughout the body. Your heart, which is about the size of your fist, is located in the center of your chest. The heart lies beneath the breastbone and inside the ribs. These bones protect the heart from injury.

Each time the heart beats, it pushes blood through the blood vessels of the cardiovascular system. As you learned in Chapter 2, the heart is made of cardiac muscle, which can contract over and over without getting tired. The heart beats continually throughout a person's life, resting only between beats. During your lifetime, your heart may beat over 3 billion times. In a year, it pumps enough blood to fill over 30 competition-size swimming pools.

The Heart's Structure Look closely at *Exploring the Heart* as you read about the structure of the heart. Notice that the heart has two sides—a right side and a left side—completely separated from each other by a wall of tissue. Each side has two compartments, or chambers—an upper and a lower chamber. Each of the two upper chambers, called an **atrium** (AY tree um) (plural *atria*), receives blood that comes into the heart. Each lower chamber, called a **ventricle,** pumps blood out of the heart. The atria are separated from the ventricles by valves. A **valve** is a flap of tissue that prevents blood from flowing backward. Valves are also located between the ventricles and the large blood vessels that carry blood away from the heart.

How the Heart Works The action of the heart has two main phases. In one phase, the heart muscle relaxes and the heart fills with blood. In the other phase, the heart muscle contracts and pumps blood forward. A heartbeat, which sounds something like *lub-dup,* can be heard during the pumping phase.

Figure 3 As blood flows out of the heart and toward the lungs, it passes through the valve shown in the photograph. The illustration shows how blood flows through the open valve.
Applying Concepts What is the function of the valves in the heart?

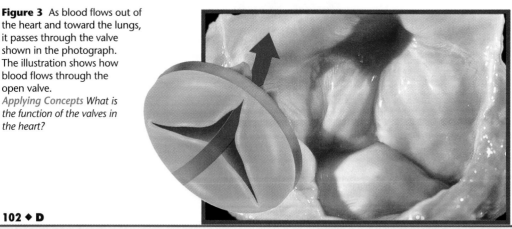

Background

Facts and Figures When doctors listen to their patients' hearts and blood vessels, they hope to hear the *lub-dup* sound of a healthy heart, but they listen for other sounds as well. For example, obstruction of or leakage through the heart valves causes turbulence in the flow of blood. This turbulence makes a prolonged noise called a heart murmur. Doctors can tell which valve is obstructed or damaged by listening to the location,

duration, intensity, pitch, and quality of the murmur.

When doctors listen to the blood vessels, they may hear bruits, which are blowing sounds made by blood vessels that are partially blocked. When the bruit is heard in the neck area, it may indicate an increased risk for a stroke. A bruit in the abdominal area may be a sign of an obstruction of the aorta or other major arteries.

When the heart muscle relaxes, blood flows into the chambers. Then the atria contract. This muscle contraction squeezes blood out of the atria, through the valves, and then into the ventricles. Next the ventricles contract. This contraction closes the valves between the atria and ventricles, making the *lub* sound and squeezing blood into large blood vessels. As the valves between the ventricles and the blood vessels snap shut, they make the *dup* sound. All of this happens in less than a second.

☑ *Checkpoint* **Contrast the functions of atria and ventricles.**

EXPLORING *the Heart*

Every second of your life, your heart pumps blood through your body. The right side of the heart pumps blood to the lungs, while the left side pumps blood to the rest of the body.

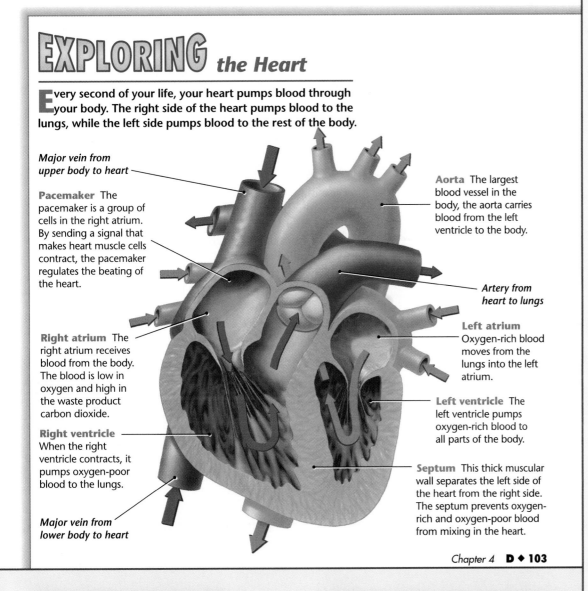

Major vein from upper body to heart

Pacemaker The pacemaker is a group of cells in the right atrium. By sending a signal that makes heart muscle cells contract, the pacemaker regulates the beating of the heart.

Right atrium The right atrium receives blood from the body. The blood is low in oxygen and high in the waste product carbon dioxide.

Right ventricle When the right ventricle contracts, it pumps oxygen-poor blood to the lungs.

Major vein from lower body to heart

Aorta The largest blood vessel in the body, the aorta carries blood from the left ventricle to the body.

Artery from heart to lungs

Left atrium Oxygen-rich blood moves from the lungs into the left atrium.

Left ventricle The left ventricle pumps oxygen-rich blood to all parts of the body.

Septum This thick muscular wall separates the left side of the heart from the right side. The septum prevents oxygen-rich and oxygen-poor blood from mixing in the heart.

Chapter 4 **D ◆ 103**

As students read the descriptions of the parts of the heart, ask: **Which chambers of the heart contain oxygen-rich blood?** *(The left atrium and left ventricle)* Ask students to identify the locations of valves they can see. *(Between the left atrium and the left ventricle; between the right atrium and the right ventricle; between the right ventricle and the artery to the lungs; between the left ventricle and the aorta)* Point out that the walls of the ventricles are much thicker than the walls of the atria. Then ask: **How could having thick walls benefit the ventricles?** *(Thick walls give ventricles the muscular strength necessary to pump blood out of the heart.)*

Extend Have students work in pairs to draw flowcharts describing the path of blood through the heart. **learning modality: visual**

Media and Technology

 Transparencies "Exploring the Heart," Transparency 8

Answers to Self-Assessment

Caption Question

Figure 3 Valves prevent blood from flowing backward.

☑ *Checkpoint*

The atria receive blood that comes into the heart. The ventricles pump blood out of the heart.

Ongoing Assessment

Drawing Have students draw a heart, label its chambers, and write brief captions describing the function of each chamber.

 Students can save their drawings in their portfolios.

Regulation of Heartbeat

Building Inquiry Skills: Interpreting Data

Materials *watch with second hand*

Time 10 minutes each day over 1 week

Allow students time to practice taking their pulse; have them follow the instructions in the Skills Lab on page 112. Then direct students to take their pulse three times a day for one school week—when they wake up in the morning, after exercising, before going to bed—and record their pulse rates in data tables. Caution students not to exercise if they have a medical condition that rules out vigorous exercise. At the end of the week, students can look for patterns in their data. Ask: **How does your heart rate at a certain time of the day relate to your body's need for oxygen at that time?** *(Students should find a positive correlation between high pulse rate and high demand for oxygen.)* **learning modality: logical/mathematical**

Integrating Technology

Tell students that scientists have developed artificial pacemakers that are sensitive to changes in body temperature and oxygen needs. Ask: **Why would these be more efficient than pacemakers that do not have these features?** *(They could match the person's heart rate with his or her activity level.)* **learning modality: verbal**

Language Arts
CONNECTION

To help students understand what an idiom is, discuss other examples, such as "on my mind," "icy stare," "she was broken up by the news," and "that idea didn't fly."

In Your Journal Change of heart—change of attitude; heart-to-heart talk—serious discussion; making the blood boil—making someone angry.
learning modality: verbal

Language Arts
CONNECTION

When you say that a person has a "heart of gold," you mean that the person is kind and generous—not that the person's heart is actually made of gold metal. "Heart of gold" is an idiom—an expression with a meaning that cannot be understood from the ordinary meanings of the words in it. The words *heart* and *blood* are found in many idioms. For example, a "blood-chilling scream" frightens you, but it doesn't lower the temperature of your blood.

In Your Journal

Learn what each of the following idioms means:
◆ a change of heart
◆ a heart-to-heart talk
◆ make the blood boil
Then write a sentence using each of these idioms.

Regulation of Heartbeat

A group of cells called the **pacemaker,** which is located in the right atrium, sends out signals that make the heart muscle contract. The pacemaker constantly receives messages about the body's oxygen needs. It then adjusts the heart rate to match. Your heart beats much faster when you are exercising than when you are sitting quietly. When you are exercising, the entire process from the beginning of one heartbeat to the beginning of the next can take less than half a second. Your muscles need more oxygen during exercise. Your rapid heartbeat supplies blood that carries the oxygen.

INTEGRATING TECHNOLOGY In some people, the pacemaker becomes damaged as a result of disease or an accident. This often results in an irregular or slow heartbeat. In the 1950s, doctors and engineers developed an artificial, battery-operated pacemaker. The artificial pacemaker is implanted beneath the skin and connected by wires to the heart. Tiny electric impulses travel from the battery through the wires. These impulses make the heart contract at a normal rate.

✓ *Checkpoint* *What is the function of the pacemaker?*

Two Loops

After leaving the heart, blood travels in blood vessels through the body. Your body has three kinds of blood vessels—arteries, capillaries, and veins. **Arteries** are blood vessels that carry blood away from the heart. From the arteries, blood flows into tiny vessels called **capillaries.** In the capillaries, substances are exchanged between the blood and body cells. From capillaries, blood flows into **veins,** which are the vessels that carry blood back to the heart.

The overall pattern of blood flow through the body is something like a figure eight. The heart is at the center where the two

Figure 4 Activities such as swimming require a lot of energy. A person's heart beats fast in order to supply the muscles with the blood they need. The heart's pacemaker regulates the speed at which the heart beats.

Background

Integrating Science Until recently, patients with advanced heart failure who were waiting for transplants had to stay in the hospital, attached to machines that pumped their hearts for them. However, new heart pumps allow patients to wait for transplants at home.

The devices are implanted into the patient's abdomen and connected to the left ventricle. Powered by a battery pack worn at the waist or shoulder, the pumps move blood through the body just as the heart does. Heart pumps give patients waiting for transplants a better quality of life.

These pumps may be offered as a long-term alternative for those who are ineligible for transplants, as there are only enough donated hearts for 2,000 transplants a year, and some 20,000 Americans die each year of heart failure.

loops cross. **In the first loop, blood travels from the heart to the lungs and then back to the heart. In the second loop, blood is pumped from the heart throughout the body and then returns again to the heart.** The heart is really two pumps, one on the right and one on the left. The right side pumps blood to the lungs, and the left side pumps blood to the rest of the body.

Blood travels in only one direction. If you were a drop of blood, you could start at any point in the figure eight and eventually return to the same point. The entire trip would take less than a minute. As you read about the path that blood takes through the cardiovascular system, trace the path in Figure 5.

Loop One: to the Lungs and Back When blood from the body flows into the right atrium, it contains little oxygen but a lot of carbon dioxide. This oxygen-poor blood is dark red. The blood then flows from the right atrium into the right ventricle. Then the ventricle pumps blood into the arteries that lead to the lungs.

As blood flows through the lungs, large blood vessels branch into smaller ones. Eventually, blood flows through tiny capillaries that are in close contact with the air that comes into the lungs. The air in the lungs has more oxygen than the blood in the capillaries, so oxygen moves from the lung into the blood. In contrast, carbon dioxide moves in the opposite direction—from the blood into the lung. As the blood leaves the lungs, it is now rich in oxygen and poor in carbon dioxide. This blood, which is bright red, flows to the left side of the heart to be pumped through the second loop.

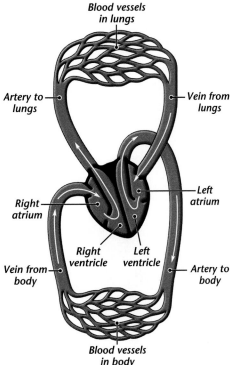

Blood vessels in lungs

Artery to lungs

Vein from lungs

Right atrium

Left atrium

Right ventricle

Left ventricle

Vein from body

Artery to body

Blood vessels in body

Figure 5 Blood circulates through the body in two loops with the heart at the center. Use the arrows to trace the path of blood, beginning at the right atrium. *Interpreting Diagrams Where does the blood that enters the left atrium come from?*

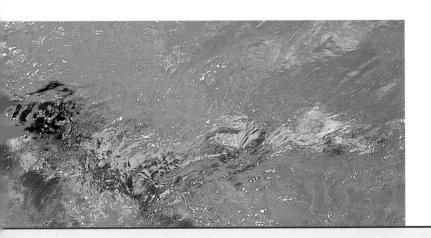

Using the Visuals: Figure 5

Point out that the left atrium is on the right side of the illustration, and the right atrium is on the left side. Explain that the heart and circulatory system are always diagrammed in this way. Also, explain that vessels shown in red carry oxygen-rich blood, while blue vessels carry oxygen-poor blood. Have students place a finger on the right ventricle and follow the arrows to trace the path of the blood as it flows out of the heart and around the body. Students should note that the blood goes through both loops before returning to the right ventricle. Ask: **When blood is pumped to the body cells, does it contain oxygen? How can you tell?** (*Yes; it has just come from the lungs.*) **learning modality: visual**

Addressing Naive Conceptions

Some students may think that some blood is actually blue. Explain that vessels shown in blue in illustrations carry blood that is dark red. Dark red blood contains mostly waste and little oxygen. Red vessels in illustrations carry bright red blood, which contains mostly oxygen and very little waste. **learning modality: verbal**

Answers to Self-Assessment

Caption Question

Figure 5 Blood that enters the left atrium comes from the lungs.

☑ *Checkpoint*

The pacemaker regulates the heartbeat by sending out signals that make the heart muscle contract.

Ongoing Assessment

Organizing Information Have students make flowcharts following the path of blood from one point in its circulation until it reaches the same point again. (*Sample: From the lungs, blood flows to the left atrium, then the left ventricle, and out into the body. From the body, the blood flows into the right atrium, then the right ventricle, then into the lungs.*)

The Force of the Ventricles

Integrating Physics

Ask: **Why doesn't the force exerted by the ventricles cause the blood to move back into the atria?** (*The valves between the ventricles and atria prevent the blood from flowing backward.*) **learning modality: verbal**

3 Assess

Section 1 Review Answers

1. The cardiovascular system carries needed substances to cells and carries wastes away from them.
2. The heart pumps blood through the vessels of the cardiovascular system.
3. Blood leaves the left ventricle and is pumped throughout the body. It returns to the right atrium and passes to the right ventricle. The right ventricle pumps the blood to the lungs. The blood then returns to the left atrium and the left ventricle.
4. The pacemaker is a group of cells in the right atrium that sends out signals for the heart muscle to contract. It adjusts heartbeat rate to the level of oxygen required by the body.
5. The artery carries blood from the right ventricle to the lungs.

Check Your Progress
CHAPTER PROJECT 4

Remind students that their displays need to show where the blood acquires and releases oxygen. Also check to make sure that students' plans are realistic.

Performance Assessment

Writing Have students explain the role of the heart in the circulatory system or describe the path the blood takes through the circulatory system.

Figure 6 If the batter hits the ball, the bat will exert a force on the ball. This force will make the ball zoom through the air. Similarly, when the ventricles of the heart contract, they exert a force on the blood inside them. This force pushes blood through the blood vessels.

Loop Two: to the Body and Back The second loop begins as the left atrium fills with oxygen-rich blood coming from the lungs. The blood then moves into the left ventricle. From the left ventricle, the blood is pumped into the **aorta** (ay AWR tuh), the largest artery in the body.

Eventually, after passing through branching arteries, blood flows through tiny capillaries in different parts of your body, such as your brain, liver, and legs. These vessels are in close contact with body cells. Oxygen moves out of the blood and into the body cells. At the same time, carbon dioxide passes from the body cells and into the blood. The blood then flows back to the right atrium of the heart through veins, completing the second loop.

The Force of the Ventricles

INTEGRATING PHYSICS When the ventricle muscles contract, they exert a force on the blood that is inside them. A **force** is a push or a pull. You see examples of forces all around you. When you lift a book off a table, for example, you exert a force on the book, making it move upward. The force exerted by the ventricles moves blood out of your heart and into arteries.

The contraction of the left ventricle exerts much more force than the contraction of the right ventricle. The right ventricle only pumps blood to the lungs. In contrast, the left ventricle pumps blood throughout the body. As a way of understanding this, think of the force it would take to bunt a baseball. Then think about how hard you would need to hit the ball if you wanted to hit a home run.

Section 1 Review

1. What is the function of the cardiovascular system?
2. What function does the heart perform?
3. Describe the route that blood takes through the cardiovascular system. Begin with blood leaving the left ventricle.
4. What is the heart's pacemaker? What causes the pacemaker to change the rate at which the heart beats?
5. **Thinking Critically** **Comparing and Contrasting** Most of the arteries in the body carry oxygen-rich blood away from the heart. One artery, however, carries blood that has little oxygen away from the heart. From which ventricle does that artery carry blood? To where does that artery carry blood?

Check Your Progress
CHAPTER PROJECT 4

At this point, you should have sketched out the two loops your red blood cell will travel. Make sure each pathway forms a complete circuit back to the heart. Begin to plan how you will construct your display. Keep a running list of the materials or equipment you'll need. (*Hint:* Think about how you will show the movement of the blood cell in your display.)

Program Resources

◆ **Teaching Resources** 4-1 Review and Reinforce, p. 95; 4-1 Enrich, p. 96

Media and Technology

 Interactive Student Tutorial CD-ROM D-4

DISCOVER •• ACTIVITY

How Does Pressure Affect the Flow of Blood?

1. Spread newspapers over a table or desktop. Then fill a plastic squeeze bottle with water.
2. Hold the bottle over a dishpan. Squeeze the bottle with one hand. Observe how far the water travels.
3. Now grasp the bottle with both hands and squeeze again. Observe how far the water travels this time.

Think It Over

Inferring Blood is pushed through arteries with much more force than it is pushed through veins. Which part of the activity models an artery? Which part models a vein? Which organ in the body provides the pushing force?

L ike corridors in a large building, blood vessels run through all of the tissues of your body. While some blood vessels are as wide as your thumb, most of them are much finer than a human hair. If all the arteries, capillaries, and veins in your body were hooked together, end to end, they would stretch a distance of almost 100,000 kilometers. That's long enough to wrap around Earth twice—with a lot left over!

Arteries

When blood leaves the heart, it travels through arteries. The right ventricle pumps blood into the arteries that go to the lungs. The left ventricle pumps blood into the aorta, the largest artery in your body. Every organ receives blood from arteries that branch off the aorta. The first branches, called the **coronary arteries,** carry blood to the heart itself. Other branches carry blood to the brain, intestines, and other organs. Each artery branches into smaller and smaller arteries.

Artery Structure The walls of arteries are generally very thick. In fact, artery walls consist of three layers. The innermost layer, which is made up of epithelial

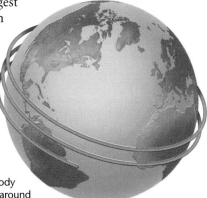

GUIDE FOR READING

◆ What are the functions of arteries, capillaries, and veins?

◆ What causes blood pressure?

Reading Tip As you read, use the text headings to make an outline of the information in this section.

Figure 7 If all the blood vessels in your body were joined end to end, they would wrap around the world almost two and a half times.

Chapter 4 **D ◆ 107**

READING STRATEGIES

Reading Tip After students read the text below the first heading, work as a class to outline the information. See the example below.
I. Arteries—vessels through which blood leaves the heart
  A. Arteries have three layers.
    1. smooth inner layer
    2. muscle tissue
    3. flexible connective tissue

Program Resources

◆ **Teaching Resources** 4-2 Lesson Plan, p. 97; 4-2 Section Summary, p. 98

Media and Technology

 Audiotapes English-Spanish Summary 4-2

SECTION
2 A Closer Look at Blood Vessels

Objectives

After completing the lesson, students will be able to
◆ describe the functions of the arteries, capillaries, and veins;
◆ identify the cause of blood pressure.

Key Terms coronary artery, diffusion, pressure, blood pressure, sphygmomanometer

1 Engage/Explore

Activating Prior Knowledge

Ask students to recall times when they have had their pulse taken. Ask questions such as these: **Where did the doctor or nurse put his or her fingers? What observations do you think the doctors and nurses made? Can pulse be felt in arteries, veins, or both?** At this point, do not correct any misconceptions. Tell students that they will learn more about pulse in this section. Later, after students have read the section, discuss pulse again, and ask whether students previously had any misconceptions about pulse or blood vessels.

•••••••• DISCOVER ••••••••

Skills Focus inferring
Materials *plastic squeeze bottle, dishpan, newspapers, paper towels*
Time 10 minutes
Tips Mop up spills immediately. Because of spillage, you may wish to do this activity outdoors.
Expected Outcome Water should travel farther when both hands are used.
Think It Over Squeezing with both hands models an artery, because more force is exerted. Squeezing with one hand models a vein. In the body, the heart provides the pushing force.

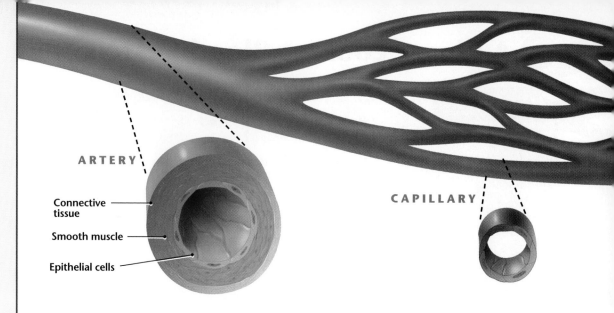

2 Facilitate

Arteries

Using the Visuals: Figure 8

You can use Figure 8 to help students understand the text differentiation between arteries, veins, and capillaries. Point out that the illustration shows the relative sizes of the three types of blood vessels. Ask which kind has the smallest diameter *(capillaries)*. Then have students note that arteries and veins have the same three layers. Ask student to contrast these three layers in veins and arteries. *(The smooth muscle layer is thicker in arteries.)* **limited English proficiency**

Math TOOLBOX

Explain that rates are often expressed as ratios. **ACTIVITY**
In this example, the pulse rate can be written as 71:1 or as 71 beats per minute. People often calculate their heart rate by counting their pulse for 15 or 30 seconds and then multiplying. Ask: **What are the units of a pulse rate?** *(Beats per minute)*
Extend Have students find the pulse rate of a person whose heart beats 23 times in 20 seconds. *(69 beats per minute)* **learning modality: logical/mathematical**

Building Inquiry Skills: Calculating

Have students take their pulses and determine **ACTIVITY**
how many heartbeats occur in one minute. The Skills Lab, page 112, has instructions for taking pulse. Then challenge students to calculate how many times their heart beats in one hour, one day, one week, one month, and one year. Ask: **What does the blood do on each trip through the body?** *(It delivers oxygen and glucose to the cells and removes wastes such as carbon dioxide.)* **learning modality: logical/mathematical**

ARTERY

Connective tissue

Smooth muscle

Epithelial cells

CAPILLARY

Math TOOLBOX

Pulse Rate

A rate is the speed at which something happens. When you calculate a rate, you compare the number of events with the time period in which they occur. Here is how you can calculate the pulse rate of a person whose heart beats 142 times in 2 minutes.

1. Write the comparison as a fraction.

$$\frac{142 \text{ heartbeats}}{2 \text{ minutes}}$$

2. Divide the numerator and the denominator by the denominator.

$$\frac{142 \div 2}{2 \div 2} = \frac{71}{1}$$

The person's pulse rate is 71 heartbeats per minute.

tissue, is smooth. This smooth surface enables blood to flow freely. The middle layer consists mostly of muscle tissue. The outer wall is made up of flexible connective tissue. Because of this layered structure, arteries have both strength and flexibility. Arteries are able to withstand the enormous pressure of blood pumped by the heart, and to expand and relax in response to that pumping.

Pulse If you lightly touch the inside of your wrist, you can feel the artery in your wrist rise and fall repeatedly. The pulse that you feel is caused by the alternating expansion and relaxation of the artery wall. Every time the heart's ventricles contract, they send a spurt of blood out through all the arteries in your body. As this spurt travels through the arteries, it pushes the artery walls and makes them expand. After the spurt passes, the artery walls become narrower again. When you count the number of times an artery pulses beneath your fingers, you are counting heartbeats. By taking your pulse rate, you can determine how fast your heart is beating.

Regulating Blood Flow The muscles in the middle wall of an artery are involuntary muscles, which contract without your thinking about it. When they contract, the opening in the artery becomes smaller. When they relax, the opening becomes larger. These muscles act as control gates, adjusting the amount of blood sent to different organs. For example, after you eat, your stomach

Background

History of Science The first person to identify the network of capillaries that connect small arteries to small veins was an Italian named Marcello Malpighi (1628–1694).

Malpighi was pursuing his microscopic research at the University of Bologna in 1661 when he identified the capillaries. In 1662, he moved to another Italian university and continued his research, while also teaching

and practicing medicine. He went on to identify the taste buds and describe the structure of the brain and optic nerves. In 1666, Malpighi was the first person to see red blood cells and to relate the red color of blood to the color of the cells.

Malpighi used the microscope to study the organization of living things up close. He is widely considered to be the founder of the study of microscopic anatomy.

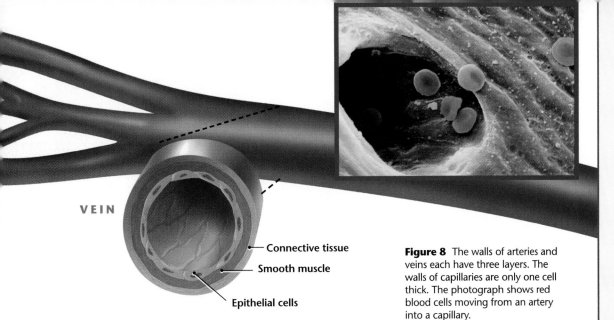

VEIN

— Connective tissue

— Smooth muscle

— Epithelial cells

Figure 8 The walls of arteries and veins each have three layers. The walls of capillaries are only one cell thick. The photograph shows red blood cells moving from an artery into a capillary.

and intestines need a greater blood supply to help power digestion. The arteries leading to those organs become larger, so that more blood flows through them. In contrast, when you are running, your stomach and intestines need less blood than the muscles in your legs. The arteries leading to the stomach and intestines become narrower, decreasing the blood flow to those organs.

☑ *Checkpoint* *What causes the pulse that you feel in your wrist?*

Capillaries

Eventually, blood flows from small arteries into the tiny capillaries. **In the capillaries, materials are exchanged between the blood and the body's cells.** Capillary walls are only one cell thick. Because capillaries have thin walls, materials can pass easily through them. Materials such as oxygen and glucose pass from blood, through the thin capillary walls, to the cells. Cellular waste products travel in the opposite direction—from cells, through the capillary walls, and into blood.

 INTEGRATING CHEMISTRY One way in which materials are exchanged between the blood and the body cells is by diffusion. **Diffusion** is the process by which molecules move from an area in which they are highly concentrated to an area in which they are less concentrated. For example, glucose is more highly concentrated in blood than it is in the body cells. Therefore, glucose diffuses from the blood, through the capillary wall, and into the body cells.

Media and Technology

📽 **Transparencies** "Artery, Capillary, and Vein," Transparency 9

Answers to Self-Assessment

☑ *Checkpoint*

The pulse in the wrist is caused by blood flowing through an artery. The artery wall expands and relaxes as the ventricles of the heart expand and relax, sending out spurts of blood.

Language Arts
CONNECTION

Tell students that the word *capillaries* comes from the Latin word *capillus*, which means "hair." Ask: **Why do you think capillaries have that name?** *(They are thin, like hair.)* Ask students if they know other words based on the same Latin word. *(Some students may know capellini, the Italian name for angel hair pasta.)* Encourage students to find the origins of other words in this section. (Sample: The word *sphygmomanometer* comes from a Greek word meaning "to beat or throb.") **learning modality: verbal**

🔵 Integrating Chemistry

Tell students that not all substances can diffuse through all membranes. Some membranes are selectively permeable, which means that they allow only certain substances to pass through. For example, a cell membrane may allow glucose molecules to pass through, but block starch molecules. **learning modality: verbal**

Ongoing Assessment

Oral Presentation Call on students to name and describe the three layers in an artery wall.

Veins

Blood Pressure

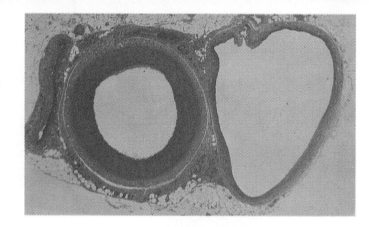

Figure 9 The wall of the artery (left) is much thicker than that of the vein (right).
Making Generalizations Why is it important for artery walls to be both strong and flexible?

Sharpen your Skills

Creating Data Tables

Scientists measured the volume of blood that different organs receive, first when a person was resting and then when the person was engaged in vigorous exercise.

- At rest, the organs of the abdomen received approximately 1,400 mL of blood per minute (mL/min). During vigorous exercise, they received 600 mL/min.

- At rest, skeletal muscles received about 1,200 mL/min. During vigorous exercise, the same muscles received about 12,500 mL/min.

- At rest, the kidneys received about 1,100 mL/min. During vigorous exercise, they received 600 mL/min.

Create a table to record these data. Then use the data to explain why some organs receive more blood during exercise, while some receive less.

Veins

After blood moves through capillaries, it enters larger blood vessels called veins, which carry blood back to the heart. The walls of veins, like those of arteries, have three layers, with muscle in the middle layer. However, the walls of veins are generally thinner than those of arteries.

By the time blood flows into veins, the pushing force of the heart has less effect than it did in the arteries. Several factors help move blood through veins. First, the muscles inside veins contract, narrowing the opening and pushing blood along, like toothpaste squeezed through a tube. Second, because many veins are located near skeletal muscles, the contraction of the muscles helps push the blood along. For example, as you run or walk, the skeletal muscles in your legs contract and squeeze the veins in your legs. Third, larger veins in your body have valves in them that prevent blood from flowing backward.

Checkpoint How do skeletal muscles help move blood in veins?

Blood Pressure

INTEGRATING PHYSICS Suppose that you are washing a car. You attach the hose to the faucet and turn on the faucet. The water flows out in a slow, steady stream. Then, while your back is turned, your little brother turns the faucet on all the way. Suddenly, the water spurts out rapidly, and the hose almost jumps out of your hand.

As water flows through a hose, it pushes against the walls of the hose, creating pressure on the walls. **Pressure** is the force that something exerts over a given area. When your brother turned on the faucet all the way, the additional water flow increased the pressure exerted on the inside of the hose. The extra pressure made the water spurt out of the nozzle faster.

What Causes Blood Pressure? Blood traveling through blood vessels behaves in a manner similar to that of water moving through a hose. Blood exerts a pressure, called **blood pressure,** against the walls of blood vessels. **Blood pressure is caused by the force with which the ventricles contract.** In general, as blood moves away from the heart, its pressure decreases. This happens because the farther away from the heart the blood moves, the lower the force of the ventricles. Blood flowing through arteries exerts the highest pressure. As blood flows through the capillaries, its pressure decreases. Blood pressure is lowest in veins.

Measuring Blood Pressure Blood pressure can be measured with an instrument called a **sphyg-momanometer** (sfig moh muh NAHM uh tur). Many sphygmo-manometers contain a tube of mercury. Blood pressure is expressed in millimeters of mercury and is recorded as two numbers. The first number is a measure of the blood pressure while the ventricles contract and pump blood into the arteries. The second number, which is lower, measures the blood pressure while the ventricles relax between heartbeats. The two numbers are expressed as a fraction: the contraction pressure over the relaxation pressure. A typical blood pressure reading for a young adult is 120/80. You will learn about the effects of high blood pressure in Section 4.

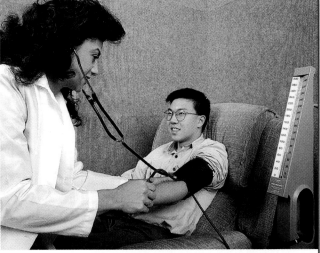

Figure 10 Blood pressure is measured with a sphygmoma-nometer. The cuff is wrapped around the patient's arm. His blood pressure is recorded by the height of the mercury column in the instrument on the right.

Section 2 Review

1. Contrast the functions of arteries, capillaries, and veins.
2. What causes blood pressure?
3. Explain the factors that enable blood in your leg veins to return to the heart in spite of the downward pull of gravity.
4. **Thinking Critically** **Applying Concepts** Arteries adjust the amount of blood flowing to different parts of the body, depending on where blood is needed. Use this fact to explain why it may not be a good idea to exercise vigorously shortly after you eat.

> **CHAPTER PROJECT 4**
> By now you should have begun constructing your display. Make sure that the blood vessels are depicted accurately. Also check that your display correctly shows the path of a red blood cell and identifies the place where the red blood cell picks up oxygen. *(Hint:* Start to prepare a rough draft of your written description at the same time as you begin constructing your display.)

Chapter 4 **D ◆ 111**

Answers to Self-Assessment

Caption Question

Figure 9 Artery walls need to be strong to withstand the pressure of blood; they must also be flexible in order to respond to changing blood volume.

✓ *Checkpoint*

They squeeze blood in the veins near them. This squeezing helps push the blood through the veins.

Real-Life Learning

Ask a medical professional to read the blood pressures of volunteers. Make sure volunteers have no medical problems that prohibit them from participating. Ask the professional to describe how a sphygmomanometer measures the two numbers in a blood pressure reading. Have volunteers describe what they feel during the reading. **learning modality: kinesthetic**

3 Assess

Section 2 Review Answers

1. Arteries carry blood away from the heart. Capillaries carry blood between arteries and veins and are the site of the exchange of materials. Veins return blood to the heart.
2. The force with which the ventricles contract
3. The pushing force of the heart still has same effect; muscles inside the veins contract, pushing blood along; skeletal muscles around the veins squeeze blood upward; valves prevent backward flow.
4. After eating, blood is routed to the digestive system. If someone exercises right after eating, the body might not be able to supply enough blood to both the digestive system and the skeletal muscles.

> **CHAPTER PROJECT 4**
> *Check Your Progress*
> Encourage students to use their rough drafts of their written descriptions to make sure their displays are accurate. Help students determine the best way to organize the information for their own understanding. Suggest students make flowcharts to help them prepare rough drafts.

Performance Assessment

Drawing Have students diagram the movement of blood through arteries, capillaries, veins, and the heart.

 Students can save their diagrams in their portfolios.

D ◆ 111

Heart Beat, Health Beat

Preparing for Inquiry

Key Concept Heart rate increases in response to physical activity.

Skills Objective Students will be able to
◆ measure their own pulse rates;
◆ measure the effects of physical activity.

Time 40 minutes

Advance Planning If any students have relevant health problems that restrict physical activity, they can keep time and record data.

Guiding Inquiry

Invitation Ask students to describe how they feel after exercising vigorously for several minutes. *(Samples: breathless, hot, feel their hearts beating)* Tell students that, in this lab, they measure how the heart responds to increased physical activity.

Introducing the Procedure

Have students practice taking their pulses.

Troubleshooting the Experiment

Ask the class to be quiet during the lab.

Expected Outcome

◆ Resting pulse rate should be around 70–80 beats per minute, increase more in response to running than walking, and return to near the resting rate.
◆ Students may show a great deal of variation in their heart rates.

Analyze and Conclude

1. Students' graphs should be clearly labeled and accurately plot data.
2. Pulse rate increases during exercise.
3. The pulse rate returns to the resting rate; the change may take a few minutes.
4. The heart is beating faster.
5. Answers will vary. One way to achieve accuracy would be to take the average of several measurements.

Extending the Inquiry

Design an Experiment Students' plans should include measuring the resting pulse rate of people of different ages.

Skills Lab

Measuring

Heart Beat, Health Beat

Problem

How does physical activity affect your pulse rate?

Materials

watch or clock with
second hand
graph paper

Procedure

1. Predict how your pulse rate will change as you go from resting to being active, then back to resting again. Then copy the data table into your notebook.
2. Locate your pulse by placing the index and middle finger of one hand on your other wrist at the base of your thumb. Move the two fingers slightly until you feel your pulse.
3. Work with a partner for the rest of this lab. Begin by determining your resting pulse rate. Count the number of beats in your pulse for exactly one minute while your partner times you. Record the number in your data table.
   CAUTION: *Do not complete the rest of these procedures if there is any medical reason why you should avoid physical activities.*

4. Walk in place for one minute while your partner times you. Stop and immediately take your pulse for one minute. Record the number in your data table.
5. Run in place for one minute. Take your pulse again, and record the result.
6. Sit down right away, and have your partner time you as you rest for one minute. Then take your pulse rate again.
7. Have your partner time you as you rest for 3 more minutes. Then take your pulse rate again and record it.

Analyze and Conclude

1. Use the data you obtained to create a bar graph of your pulse rate under the different conditions you tested.
2. What conclusion can you draw about the relationship between physical activity and a person's pulse rate?
3. What happens to the pulse rate when the physical activity has stopped?
4. What can you infer about the heartbeat when the pulse rate increases?
5. **Think About It** Do you think the pulse measurements you made are completely accurate? Why or why not? How could you improve the accuracy of your measurements?

Design an Experiment

Do the resting pulse rates of adults, teens, and young children differ? Write a plan to answer this question. Obtain your teacher's permission before carrying out your plan.

DATA TABLE

Activity	Pulse Rate
Resting	
Walking	
Running	
Resting after Exercise	
(1 min) Resting after Exercise	
(3+ min) Resting after Exercise	

112 ◆ D

Sample Data Table

Activity	Pulse Rate
Resting	75
Walking	88
Running	120
(1 min) Resting after Exercise	97
(3+ min) Resting after Exercise	81

Safety

Students who have medical reasons to avoid physical exercise should not complete the lab after Step 3.

Program Resources

◆ **Teaching Resources** Chapter 4 Skills Lab, pp. 109–110
◆ **Inquiry Skills Activity Book** Provides teaching and review of all inquiry skills.

DISCOVER ...... ACTIVITY

What Kinds of Cells Are in Blood?

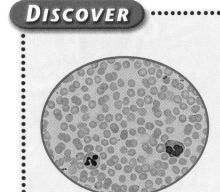

1. Obtain a microscope slide of human blood. Look at the slide under the microscope, first under low power and then under high power.

2. Look carefully at the different kinds of cells that you see.

3. Make several drawings of each kind of cell. Use red pencil for the red blood cells.

Think It Over

Observing How many kinds of cells did you see? How do they differ from each other?

I f someone fills a test tube with blood and lets it sit for a while, the blood separates into layers. The top layer is a clear, yellowish liquid. A dark red material rests on the bottom. The top layer is **plasma,** which is the liquid part of blood. The red material at the bottom is a mixture of blood cells. **Blood is made up of four components: plasma, red blood cells, white blood cells, and platelets.** About 45 percent of the volume of blood is made up of cells. The rest consists of plasma.

Plasma

Blood, as you have learned, transports materials from one part of the body to another. Most of those materials travel in plasma. In fact, 10 percent of plasma is made up of these dissolved materials. The other 90 percent of plasma is water.

Plasma carries molecules that come from the breakdown of digested food, such as glucose and fats. The vitamins and minerals your body needs also travel in plasma. Plasma also carries chemical messengers that direct body activities such as the uptake of glucose by your cells. In addition, many wastes produced by cell processes are carried away by plasma.

Protein molecules give plasma its yellow color. There are three groups of plasma proteins. One group helps to regulate the amount of water in blood. The second group, which is produced by white blood cells, helps fight disease. The third group of proteins interacts with platelets to form blood clots.

> **GUIDE FOR READING**
>
> ◆ What are the four components of blood?
>
> ◆ What determines the type of blood that a person can receive in transfusion?
>
> *Reading Tip* As you read, write definitions for each boldfaced term in your own words.

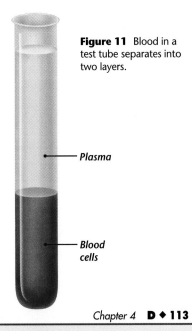

Figure 11 Blood in a test tube separates into two layers.

— Plasma

— Blood cells

Chapter 4 **D** ◆ **113**

Objectives

After completing the lesson, students will be able to

◆ name and describe the four components of blood;

◆ explain blood type and how it determines what blood a person can receive in a transfusion;

◆ describe the lymphatic system.

Key Terms plasma, red blood cell, hemoglobin, white blood cell, platelet, fibrin, blood transfusion, lymphatic system, lymph, lymph node

1 Engage/Explore

Activating Prior Knowledge

Fill five clear one-liter bottles with water. Add a few drops of red food coloring. Ask students if they would be surprised to learn that the bottles represent the amount of blood in an average human body. Ask students to name the components of blood with which they are familiar.

.... DISCOVER ....

Skills Focus observing
Materials *microscope, prepared slides of human blood*
Time 15 minutes
Tips Remind students to note the shapes and sizes of cells.
Expected Outcome Students should observe three kinds of blood cells. Students will see many more red blood cells than white blood cells or platelets.
Think It Over Students should describe three types of cells: round with a depressed center (red blood cells); irregularly shaped cells (white blood cells); and flat, fragmented bodies (platelets).

READING STRATEGIES

Reading Tip After students write definitions for the boldface terms, have them work in small groups to create vocabulary worksheets. Offer suggestions such as matching activities or fill-in-the-blank activities. Then have each group prepare the worksheet and an answer key. Direct groups to exchange worksheets and complete them. Then have students check their answers against the answer keys.

Program Resources

◆ **Teaching Resources** 4-3 Lesson Plan, p. 101; 4-3 Section Summary, p. 102

Media and Technology

 Audiotapes English-Spanish Summary 4-3

2 Facilitate

Plasma

Demonstration

Materials *test tubes, table salt, sugar, sand, measuring spoons, rubber stoppers*

Time 10 minutes setup; 10 minutes observation next day

This demonstration will help students understand that materials dissolve in plasma, as discussed on page 113. Label three test tubes *Salt, Sugar,* or *Sand,* and fill with water. Add a tablespoon of each material to the appropriate tube and shake. Have students observe the tubes and record their observations. Let the tubes stand overnight. Then have students compare the appearance of the materials in the test tubes with their appearance after they were shaken. Ask: **Which test tube most closely resembles Figure 11?** *(Sand)* Ask students to infer what parts of blood are modeled in this activity. *(Water—plasma; salt and sugar—materials carried in the plasma; sand —blood cells)* **learning modality: visual**

Red Blood Cells

EXPLORING
Blood Cells

This visual can help students who have difficulty comprehending written text. Ask them how many types of cells are found in blood. *(Three)* Have students contrast the relative sizes, structures, and numbers of the three types. Students should note that red blood cells are far more abundant than either white blood cells or platelets. Ask: **When does a red blood cell become bright red?** *(When its hemoglobin combines with oxygen)* **limited English proficiency**

Red Blood Cells

Without red blood cells, your body could not use the oxygen that you breathe in. **Red blood cells** take up oxygen in the lungs and deliver it to cells elsewhere in the body. Red blood cells, like most blood cells, are produced in bone marrow.

Exploring Blood Cells shows what red blood cells look like. Under a microscope, these cells look like disks with pinched-in centers. Because they are thin, red blood cells can bend and twist easily. This flexibility enables them to squeeze through narrow capillaries.

A red blood cell is made mostly of **hemoglobin** (HEE muh gloh bin), which is an iron-containing protein that binds chemically to oxygen molecules. When hemoglobin combines with oxygen, the cells become bright red. Without oxygen, they are dark red. Hemoglobin picks up oxygen in the lungs and releases it as blood travels through capillaries in the rest of the body. Hemoglobin also picks up some of the carbon dioxide produced by cells. However, most of the carbon dioxide is carried by plasma. The blood carries the carbon dioxide to the lungs, where it is released from the body.

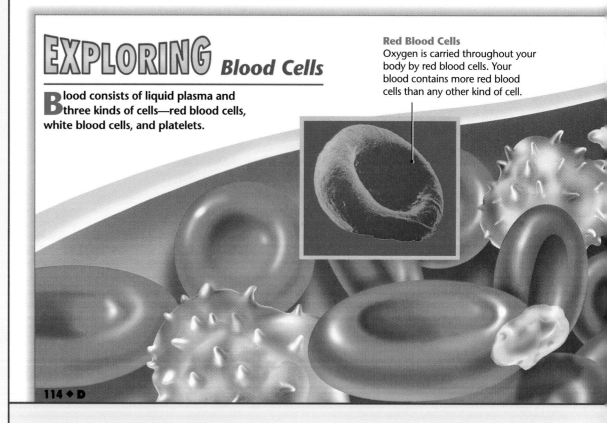

EXPLORING *Blood Cells*

Blood consists of liquid plasma and three kinds of cells—red blood cells, white blood cells, and platelets.

Red Blood Cells
Oxygen is carried throughout your body by red blood cells. Your blood contains more red blood cells than any other kind of cell.

114 ◆ D

Background

Integrating Science Suppose a forensic scientist is at the scene of a crime. The scientist finds some blood, but no body. How can he or she discover what animal the blood is from? The scientist can examine the hemoglobin in the blood. Hemoglobin carries oxygen in all vertebrates and some invertebrates. Mammalian hemoglobins differ in their amino acid composition, and the shape of hemoglobin crystals differs from species to species. For example, rat and horse hemoglobin crystallizes easily, but hemoglobin from humans, cattle, and sheep is more soluble and difficult to crystallize. If the blood is human, the forensic scientist can even find out where that human's ancestors came from. People whose ancestors came from Europe are likely to have hemoglobin D; those with ancestors from Southeast Asia, hemoglobin E.

Red blood cells have no nuclei. Without a nucleus, a red blood cell cannot live very long. In fact, red blood cells live only about 120 days. Every second, about 2 million red blood cells in your body die. Fortunately, your bone marrow produces new red blood cells at the same rate.

☑ *Checkpoint* *What is the shape of a red blood cell?*

White Blood Cells

Like red blood cells, white blood cells begin their existence in bone marrow. **White blood cells** are the body's disease fighters. Some white blood cells recognize disease-causing organisms such as bacteria, and alert the body that it has been invaded. Other white blood cells produce chemicals to fight the invaders. Still others surround and kill the organisms. You will learn more about the functions of white blood cells in Chapter 6.

White blood cells are different from red blood cells in several important ways. There are fewer of them—only about one white blood cell for every 500 to 1,000 red blood cells. White blood cells are also bigger than red blood cells, and they have nuclei. And most white blood cells live for months or even years.

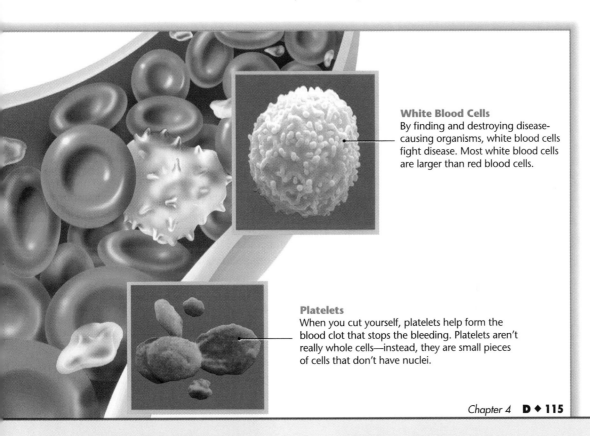

White Blood Cells
By finding and destroying disease-causing organisms, white blood cells fight disease. Most white blood cells are larger than red blood cells.

Platelets
When you cut yourself, platelets help form the blood clot that stops the bleeding. Platelets aren't really whole cells—instead, they are small pieces of cells that don't have nuclei.

Chapter 4 **D ◆ 115**

Answers to Self-Assessment

☑ *Checkpoint*
Red blood cells are shaped like disks with pinched-in centers.

White Blood Cells

Platelets

Skills Focus making models

Materials *two sturdy plastic cups, 20-cm-square piece of cheesecloth, rubber band, water, paper clips, coins, newspapers, paper towels*

Time 15 minutes

Tips Have students spread newspapers on their work areas and place their cups on the newspapers.

Expected Outcome Students should note that the cheesecloth represents the fibrin net. Platelets release chemicals that eventually result in the production of fibrin.

Extend Ask students to infer what would happen if a person did not have platelets. *(Their blood could not clot and they might bleed to death if the bleeding were not stopped some other way.)*

learning modality: kinesthetic

Blood Types

Using the Visuals: Figure 13

Refer students to Figure 13. Ask them to look at blood type B. Ask: **What type of marker molecule is on type B blood?** *(B marker)* Ask: **Why are the clumping proteins on type B blood anti-A?** *(Clumping proteins recognize markers that are foreign or different. Since type B blood contains B markers, it recognizes A markers as foreign and is therefore anti-A.)* Ask: **What would happen if a person with type B blood received type A?** *(It would make the type A cells clump together; the person would get sick and could die.)* Ask: **Why can a person with type B blood receive type O in a transfusion?** *(Type O has no markers.)* Tell students that blood type O is often referred to as the universal donor because it has no markers and therefore is not recognized as foreign by the clumping proteins of the other blood types.* **learning modality: logical/ mathematical**

Figure 12 When you cut your skin, a blood clot forms. The blood clot consists of blood cells trapped in a fiber net. Platelets produce the material of which the fibers are made.

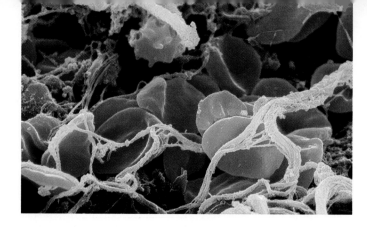

Caught in the Web

In this activity, you will model part of the process by which a blood clot forms.

1. Cover the opening of a sturdy plastic cup with a piece of cheesecloth. Use a rubber band to hold the cheesecloth in place.

2. Put some water, paper clips, and coins in another cup.

3. Carefully pour the water, coins, and paper clips into the middle of the cheesecloth.

Making Models The paper clips and coins represent blood cells. What does the cheesecloth represent? What starts the production of the substance that the cheesecloth represents?

Platelets

When you cut your finger, blood flows out of the cut. After a short time, however, a blood clot forms, stopping the blood flow. **Platelets** (PLAYT lits) are cell fragments that play an important part in forming blood clots.

When a blood vessel is cut, platelets collect and stick to the vessel at the site of the wound. The platelets release chemicals that start a chain reaction. This series of reactions eventually produces a chemical called **fibrin** (FY brin). Fibrin gets its name from the fact that it weaves a net of tiny fibers across the cut in the blood vessel. The fiber net traps blood cells. As more and more platelets and blood cells become trapped in the net, a blood clot forms. A scab is a dried blood clot on the skin surface.

☑ *Checkpoint* *What role do platelets play in forming blood clots?*

Blood Types

If a person loses a lot of blood—from a wound or during surgery—he or she may be given a **blood transfusion**. A blood transfusion is the transference of blood from one person to another. Most early attempts at blood transfusion failed, but no one knew why until the early 1900s. At that time Karl Landsteiner, an Austrian American physician, tried mixing blood samples from pairs of people. Sometimes the two blood samples blended smoothly. In other cases, however, the red blood cells clumped together. This clumping accounted for the failure of many blood transfusions. If clumping occurs within the body, it clogs the capillaries and may kill the person.

Marker Molecules Landsteiner went on to discover that there are four types of blood—A, B, AB, and O. Blood types are determined by marker molecules on red blood cells. If your blood type is A, you have the A marker. If your blood type is B, you

---

have the B marker. People with type AB blood have both A and B markers. The red blood cells of people with type O blood contain neither A nor B markers.

Your plasma contains clumping proteins that recognize red blood cells with "foreign" markers and make those cells clump together. For example, if you have blood type A, your blood contains clumping proteins that act against cells with B markers. So if you receive a transfusion of type B blood, your clumping proteins will make the "foreign" type B cells clump together.

Safe Transfusions Landsteiner's work led to a better understanding of transfusions. **The marker molecules on your red blood cells determine your blood type and the type of blood that you can safely receive in transfusions.** A person with type A blood can receive transfusions of either type A or type O blood. Neither of these two blood types has B markers. Thus they would not be recognized as foreign by the clumping proteins in type A blood. A person with type AB blood can receive all blood types in transfusion, because type AB blood has no clumping proteins. Figure 13 shows which transfusions are safe for each blood type.

If you ever receive a transfusion, your blood type will be checked. Then donated blood that you can safely receive will be found. This process is called cross matching. You may have heard a doctor on a television show give the order to "type and cross." The doctor wants to find out what blood type the patient has and then cross match it against donated blood.

Blood Types

Blood Type	Marker Molecules on Red Blood Cells	Clumping Proteins	Blood Types That Can Be Safely Received in a Transfusion
A		anti-B	A and O
B		anti-A	B and O
AB		no clumping proteins	A, B, AB, and O
O		anti-A and anti-B	O

Figure 13 The chemical markers on a person's red blood cells determine the types of blood he or she can safely receive in a transfusion. *Interpreting Charts* What types of blood can be given safely to a person with blood type AB? Who can safely receive blood type O?

Real-Life Learning

Materials *4 colors of removable sticky notes, graph paper*
Time 30 minutes

In this activity, students can find out what type of blood is most common in their class, and compare this information to national statistics. If possible, have students find out their blood types by asking at home. If they cannot determine their own blood type, have them list the blood type of a parent, sibling, or other relative. Because of potential privacy issues, make sure that this is not a sensitive issue for some students; also check state and local guidelines to make sure that this activity is acceptable. To begin, have students record their blood types or their relatives' blood types on sticky notes, using a different color for each blood type. They should not list their names. Then collect the notes, shuffle them, and sort them by color on a wall or other suitable surface to form a simple bar graph. Record the number of students with each type, then have students calculate what percentage of the class has each blood type. Inform students that in the United States, 40% of people have type A, 11% type B, 4% type AB, and 45% type O. Have students compare the class and national frequencies. This activity will also work as a class activity. **learning modality: logical/mathematical**

Answers to Self-Assessment

Caption Question

Figure 13 A person with type AB blood can receive AB, A, B, or O. Anyone can safely receive type O.

☑ *Checkpoint*

Platelets collect at the site of a wound and release chemicals that lead to the production of fibrin, which forms a net that catches blood cells and forms a clot.

Ongoing Assessment

Writing Have students choose one blood type, identify which other blood types a person with that blood type may safely receive in a transfusion, and explain why this is the case.

The Lymphatic System

Using the Visuals: Figure 14

Have students trace lymph as it enters the lymph vessels and passes through the nodes. Remind students that lymph passes through the nodes to remove bacteria and other microorganisms. Lymph vessels empty into the large veins of the chest, from which lymph reenters the bloodstream. **learning modality: visual**

3 Assess

Section 3 Review Answers

1. Plasma (liquid), red blood cells, white blood cells, platelets (part of a cell)
2. People with type O blood have anti-A and anti-B clumping proteins in their plasma. If they receive type A blood, the clumping proteins will make the type-A red blood cells clump together.
3. Lymph is a fluid that leaks out of blood vessels and bathes the cells. After it travels through the lymphatic system, it enters into large veins in the chest and becomes part of blood plasma again.
4. Because hemophiliacs do not have fibrin, their blood does not clot properly. The condition can lead to the loss of great amounts of blood.

Check Your Progress

CHAPTER PROJECT 4

Students should test their displays or practice their presentations as they add the finishing touches. Remind students to check their final written descriptions against their displays to make sure they match and are both correct.

Performance Assessment

Organizing Information Have students work in pairs to create illustrated charts that describe the four components of blood and the roles of each.

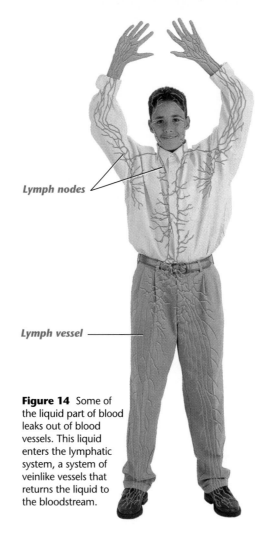

Lymph nodes

Lymph vessel

Figure 14 Some of the liquid part of blood leaks out of blood vessels. This liquid enters the lymphatic system, a system of veinlike vessels that returns the liquid to the bloodstream.

The Lymphatic System

As blood travels through the capillaries in the cardiovascular system, some of the fluid leaks out. It moves through the walls of capillaries and into surrounding tissues. This fluid carries materials that the cells in the tissues need.

After bathing the cells, this fluid moves into the lymphatic system. The **lymphatic system** (lim FAT ik) is a network of veinlike vessels that returns the fluid to the bloodstream. The lymphatic system acts something like rain gutters after a rainstorm, carrying the fluid away.

Lymph Once the fluid is inside the lymphatic system, it is called **lymph.** Lymph consists of water and dissolved materials such as glucose. It also contains some white blood cells that have left the capillaries.

The lymphatic system has no pump, so lymph moves slowly. Lymphatic vessels, which are part of the cardiovascular system, connect to large veins in the chest. Lymph empties into these veins and once again becomes part of blood plasma.

Lymph Nodes As lymph flows through the lymphatic system, it passes through small knobs of tissue called **lymph nodes.** Lymph nodes filter the lymph, trapping bacteria and other microorganisms that cause disease. When the body is fighting an infection, the lymph nodes enlarge. If you've ever had "swollen glands" when you've been sick, you've actually had swollen lymph nodes.

 ## Section 3 Review

1. List the four components of blood. Identify whether each is a cell, a part of a cell, or a liquid.
2. Explain why a person with type O blood cannot receive a transfusion of type A blood.
3. Where does lymph come from? What happens to lymph after it travels through the lymphatic system?
4. **Thinking Critically Relating Cause and Effect** People with the disease hemophilia do not produce the chemical fibrin. Explain why hemophilia is a serious disease.

Check Your Progress

CHAPTER PROJECT 4

By now, you should be completing your display. Write out your description using the correct names of blood vessels and other terms that you've learned in this chapter. (*Hint:* If your display has moving parts, test it to make sure that it works the way you expect it to.)

Program Resources

◆ **Teaching Resources** 4-3 Review and Reinforce, p. 103; 4-3 Enrich, p. 104

Media and Technology

Interactive Student Tutorial CD-ROM D-4

Do You Know Your A-B-O's?

Donated blood is used for blood transfusions. But not every type of blood can be safely donated to every individual. In this lab, you'll investigate why type O blood is especially useful in blood transfusions.

Problem

Which blood types can safely receive transfusions of type A blood? Which can receive type O blood?

Materials

4 paper cups
4 plastic droppers
white paper
four model "blood" types
marking pen
8 plastic petri dishes
toothpicks

Procedure

1. Write down your ideas about why type O blood might be in higher demand than other blood types. Then make two copies of the data table in your notebook.
2. Label 4 paper cups A, B, AB, and O. Fill each cup about one-third full with the model "blood" supplied by your teacher. Insert one clean plastic dropper into each cup. Use each dropper to transfer only that one type of blood.
3. Label the side of each of 4 petri dishes with a blood type: A, B, AB, or O. Place the petri dishes on a sheet of white paper.
4. Use the plastic droppers to place 10 drops of each type of blood in its labeled petri dish. Each sample represents the blood of a potential receiver of a blood transfusion. Record the original color of each sample in your data table as yellow, blue, green, or colorless.

DATA TABLE

Donor: Type _____

Potential Receiver	Original Color	Final Color of Mixture	Safe or Unsafe?
A			
B			
AB			
O			

5. Label your first data table Donor: Type A. To test whether each potential receiver can safely receive type A blood, add 10 drops of type A blood to each sample. Stir each mixture with a separate, clean toothpick.
6. Record the final color of each mixture in the data table. If the color stayed the same, write "safe" in the last column. If the color of the mixture changed, write "unsafe."
7. Label your second data table Donor: Type O. Obtain four clean petri dishes, and repeat Steps 3 through 6 to determine who could safely receive type O blood.

Analyze and Conclude

1. Which blood types can safely receive a transfusion of type A blood? Type O blood?
2. If some blood types are not available, how might type O blood be useful?
3. **Apply** Why should hospitals have an adequate supply of different types of blood?

More to Explore

Repeat this activity to find out which blood types can safely receive donations of type B and type AB blood.

Analyze and Conclude
1. Types A and AB can receive type A blood. Types A, B, AB, and O can receive type O.
2. Type O can safely be given to anyone.
3. To provide blood for people who have lost blood through injury, who are having surgery, or who need regular transfusions

Extending the Inquiry
More to Explore Colors should change when B is added to A or O, and when AB is added to A, B, or O.

Safety

Caution students not to taste any mixtures and to wash their hands thoroughly after the activity. Review the safety guidelines in Appendix A.

Program Resources

◆ **Teaching Resources** Chapter 4 Real-World Lab, pp. 111–113

Do You Know Your A-B-O's?

Preparing for Inquiry

Key Concept Some blood types cannot receive type A transfusions, while all can receive type O.

Skills Objective Students will be able to
◆ model the four blood types using colored water;
◆ infer the compatibilities between blood types by mixing.

Time 40 minutes

Advance Planning To make up the "blood types" for type O, use uncolored water. For A, use 20 drops of yellow dye per liter of water. For B, use 20 drops of blue dye per liter of water. For AB, use 50 drops of yellow plus 50 drops of blue per liter of water. To test the colors, place 10 drops of AB solution in each of four petri dishes, then add 10 drops of a different "blood type" to each. Mix with separate toothpicks; the four mixtures should be about the same green. If some mixtures are too yellowish or bluish, add more dye to darken the AB solution.

Guiding Inquiry

Invitation

Discuss blood transfusions and the need to make sure that the blood types of the donor and the recipient are compatible. Ask students if they know their blood types, and discuss the four types with them (A, B, AB, and O).

Introducing the Procedure

Explain that the four cups of water will model the four blood types.

Troubleshooting the Experiment

Make sure students do not interpret a change in intensity as a change in color.

Expected Outcome

Colors should change only when A is added to B and O.

SECTION 4 Cardiovascular Health

Objective

After completing the lesson, students will be able to
- describe behaviors that maintain cardiovascular health;
- list and describe types of cardiovascular disease.

Key Terms atherosclerosis, cholesterol, heart attack, hypertension

1 Engage/Explore

Activating Prior Knowledge

Ask students: **What factors do you think make a person more likely to have a heart attack?** *(Accept all reasonable answers at this time. Students might mention: high-fat diet; high salt intake; little or no exercise.)* Tell students that in this section they will learn about heart disease and the steps they can take to prevent it.

 DISCOVER

Skills Focus forming operational definitions

Materials *assortment of foods*

Time 20 minutes

Tips Provide heart-healthy foods such as fresh fruit and vegetables, unbuttered popcorn, low-fat yogurt, and skim milk. Also provide items such as potato chips, crackers, and processed foods high in sodium or fat (especially saturated fat). Information about sodium and fat content is found on food labels.

Think It Over Students' answers will depend on their knowledge of nutrition and the cardiovascular system. Heart-healthy foods include those low in fat and sodium.

SECTION 4 Cardiovascular Health

DISCOVER **ACTIVITY**

Which Foods Are "Heart Healthy"?

1. Your teacher will give you an assortment of foods. If they have nutrition labels, read the information.

2. Sort the foods into three groups. In one group, put those foods that you think are good for your cardiovascular system. In the second group, put foods that you think might damage your cardiovascular system if eaten often. Place foods you aren't sure about in the third group.

Think It Over
Forming Operational Definitions How did you define a "heart-healthy" food?

GUIDE FOR READING

- What behaviors can help maintain cardiovascular health?

Reading Tip Before you read, rewrite the headings in the section as questions that begin with *how*, *why*, or *what*. Write short answers to these questions as you read.

Shortly after sunrise, when most people are just waking up, the rowers are already out on the river. Rhythmically, with perfectly coordinated movement, the rowers pull on the oars, making the boat glide swiftly through the water. Despite the chilly morning air, sweat glistens on the rowers' faces and arms. And inside their chests, their hearts are pounding, delivering blood to the arm and chest muscles that power the oars.

Rowers cannot perform at their peaks unless their cardiovascular systems are in excellent condition. But cardiovascular health is important to all people, not just athletes. Cardiovascular

READING STRATEGIES

Reading Tip As students generate questions based on the section headings, suggest that students predict answers to some or all of the questions. Then direct students to answer the questions based on their reading.

Study and Comprehension After students read the section, have them write the major headings and subheadings on a sheet of paper, leaving several lines of space after each heading. Then have students review the section and write down the main ideas and important details that apply to each heading. Encourage students to use their own words to paraphrase the information they write for each heading. Invite students to read their information aloud.

disease is the leading cause of death in the United States. However, people can practice behaviors that decrease their risks of developing cardiovascular problems.

Cardiovascular Disease

Compare the two arteries shown in Figure 15. The one on the left is a healthy artery. It has a large space in the center through which blood can flow easily. The artery on the right, in contrast, has a thick wall and only a small space in the middle. This artery exhibits **atherosclerosis** (ath uh roh skluh ROH sis), a condition in which an artery wall thickens as a result of the buildup of fatty materials. One of these fatty materials is **cholesterol** (kuh LES tuh rahl), a waxy, fatlike substance. Atherosclerosis restricts the flow of blood in the arteries.

Atherosclerosis can develop in the coronary arteries that supply the heart. When that happens, the heart muscle receives less blood and therefore less oxygen. This condition may lead to a heart attack. A **heart attack** occurs when blood flow to part of the heart muscle is blocked. Cells die in the part of the heart that does not receive blood. This permanently damages the heart.

Treatment for mild atherosclerosis usually includes a low-fat diet and a moderate exercise program. In addition, medications that lower the levels of cholesterol and fats in the blood may be prescribed. People with severe atherosclerosis may need to undergo surgery or other procedures to unclog blocked arteries.

☑ *Checkpoint* *Why is atherosclerosis especially serious when it affects the coronary arteries?*

Hypertension

High blood pressure, or **hypertension** (hy pur TEN shun), is a disorder in which a person's blood pressure is consistently higher than normal—greater than 140/90. Hypertension makes the heart work harder. It also may damage the walls of the blood

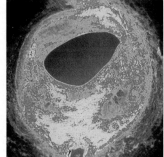

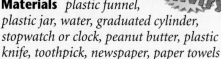

Blocking the Flow

Use this activity to find out how fatty deposits affect the flow of blood through an artery.

1. Put a funnel in the mouth of a plastic jar. The funnel will represent an artery.

2. To model blood flowing through the artery, slowly pour 100 mL of water into the funnel. Have your partner time how many seconds it takes for all the water to flow through the funnel. Then discard the water.

3. Use a plastic knife to spread a small amount of peanut butter along the bottom of the funnel's neck. Then, with a toothpick, carve out a hole in the peanut butter so that the funnel is partly, but not completely, clogged.

4. Repeat Steps 1 and 2.

Predicting If the funnels were arteries, which one—blocked or unblocked—would do a better job of supplying blood to tissues? Explain.

Figure 15 The healthy artery on the left is unblocked. In contrast, notice the narrow opening in the artery on the right. This person has atherosclerosis, which is caused by fatty deposits on the artery walls. *Relating Cause and Effect What kind of diet can lead to atherosclerosis?*

Answers to Self-Assessment

Caption Question

Figure 15 A diet high in fat and cholesterol can lead to atherosclerosis.

☑ *Checkpoint*

When atherosclerosis affects coronary arteries, it causes decreased blood flow to the heart and can lead to a heart attack.

2 Facilitate

Cardiovascular Disease

TRY THIS

Skills Focus predicting
Materials *plastic funnel, plastic jar, water, graduated cylinder, stopwatch or clock, peanut butter, plastic knife, toothpick, newspaper, paper towels*
Time 20 minutes
Tips If peanut butter is not available, use modeling clay to block the funnel.
Expected Outcome The unblocked funnel would do a better job of supplying blood, because more liquid can flow through it.
Extend Ask which photo in Figure 15 is represented by the peanut-butter-clogged funnel. *(The one on the right)* **learning modality: kinesthetic**

Hypertension

Language Arts
CONNECTION

Ask students to list other words they know that begin with the prefix *hyper*. *(Samples: hyperactivity, hyperspace, hyperventilate)* Write the list on the board, then ask students to infer the meaning of the prefix. *(Very, high, extra)* Explain that *hyper* is a Greek prefix often used in the names of medical conditions. Tell students that the opposite of *hyper* is *hypo*. Ask students to infer what the medical name for dangerously low blood pressure is. *(hypotension)* **learning modality: verbal**

Ongoing Assessment

Writing Have students describe how atherosclerosis causes heart attacks.

SCIENCE & *History*

For each item, have students summarize in their own words how the advancement has helped save lives. Then ask: **Why would some kinds of surgery have been impossible before the discovery of blood types?** *(Some kinds of surgery require blood transfusions.)*

Extend Ask students to speculate why these advances were not made until the twentieth century. *(Sample: Scientists needed technology such as lasers or improved surgical procedures in order to perform this work.)*

In Your Journal You may wish to allow students time to find information about their chosen scientists. When students have written their speeches, they may enjoy role-playing an awards ceremony at which they read their speeches. **learning modality: verbal**

vessels. Over time, both the heart and arteries can be severely harmed by hypertension. Because people with hypertension often have no obvious symptoms to warn them, hypertension is sometimes called the "silent killer."

Hypertension and atherosclerosis are closely related. As the arteries narrow, blood pressure increases. Being overweight and failing to get enough exercise can also increase a person's risk of developing hypertension.

SCIENCE & History

Cardiovascular Advances in the Twentieth Century

Scientists today have an in-depth understanding of how the cardiovascular system works and how to treat cardiovascular problems. This time line describes some advances of the twentieth century.

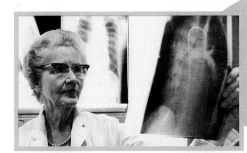

1944
Treatment for "Blue Babies"

Helen Taussig identified the heart defect that causes the skin of some newborn babies to be bluish in color. The blood of these "blue babies" does not receive an adequate amount of oxygen. Taussig and another surgeon, Alfred Blalock, developed an operation to correct the defect and save these babies' lives.

1900	1920	1940

1901
Discovery of Blood Types

Karl Landsteiner demonstrated that people have different blood types, which are determined by marker molecules on their red blood cells. Landsteiner's discovery enabled blood transfusions to be done safely.

1930s–1940s
Blood Banks

Charles Drew demonstrated that emergency transfusions could successfully be done with plasma if whole blood was not available. During World War II, Drew established blood banks for storing donated blood. His work helped save millions of lives on and off the battlefield.

122 ◆ D

Background

Facts and Figures After World War II, America experienced an epidemic of heart disease. The U.S. Public Health Service decided to find out why. In 1948, they went to Framingham, Massachusetts, and signed up 5,209 healthy residents to take part in the Framingham Heart Study. Since that time, participants have had health checkups every two years. Doctors recorded anything that might have an effect on the heart.

Among the findings:
◆ High blood pressure appears to trigger heart attacks.
◆ Cigarette smoking is bad for the heart.
◆ Too much cholesterol in the blood raises the risk of heart attacks.
◆ Physical exercise lowers the risk of heart disease; being overweight increases it.
◆ Diabetes is an important underlying cause of heart disease.

For mild hypertension, regular exercise and careful food choices may be enough to lower blood pressure. People with hypertension need to limit their intake of sodium, which can increase their blood pressure. Sodium is found in salt and in processed foods such as soups and packaged snack foods. For some people who have hypertension, however, medications are needed to reduce their blood pressure.

☑ *Checkpoint* **Why is hypertension called the "silent killer"?**

In Your Journal

Choose one of the scientists whose work is described here. Imagine that you are on a committee that has chosen him or her to receive an award. Write the speech you would give at the award ceremony. The speech should explain the importance of the scientist's contributions.

1967

First Heart Transplant

Christiaan Barnard, a South African surgeon, performed the first transplant of a human heart. Louis Washkansky, the man who received the heart, lived for only 18 days after the transplant. But Barnard's work paved the way for future successes in transplanting hearts and other organs.

1992

Laser Beam Unclogs Arteries

The United States government approved a device that uses a laser beam to burn away the material causing blockage in some arteries. This device can help some people with atherosclerosis.

1960	1980	2000

1982

Artificial Heart

An artificial heart, developed by Robert Jarvik, was implanted into a patient by surgeon William DeVries at the University of Utah. Barney Clark, the man who received the artificial heart, lived for 112 days. Today artificial hearts are sometimes used temporarily in people waiting for heart transplants.

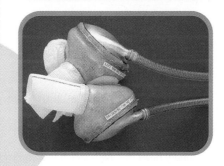

Chapter 4 **D ◆ 123**

Answers to Self-Assessment

☑ *Checkpoint*

People with hypertension often have no symptoms to warn them of the disease.

Building Inquiry Skills: Predicting

Materials *empty food containers with nutrition labels*
Time 15 minutes

Have students bring in the food containers from home. Group students. Display the containers and ask students to predict which foods are high in sodium. Then have group members work together to examine the labels on all the containers and compare the label information with their predictions. Students may be surprised at the amounts of sodium in foods they might otherwise think of as healthy.
cooperative learning

Building Inquiry Skills: Making Models

Materials *plastic drinking straws, thin plastic coffee stirring straws*
Time 5 minutes

To help students understand the physical reason for the increase in blood pressure when arteries narrow, have them first blow gently through a regular drinking straw. Students can hold one hand a few centimeters below the end of the straw to feel the pressure of the air. Then have students use the same force to blow through the thinner straw. Have them hold their hand the same distance below the end of the straw and compare the pressure they felt through the thin straw. *(When the same force is exerted through a thinner tube, the pressure is higher.)*
limited English proficiency

Ongoing Assessment

Writing Ask students to list and describe at least three cardiovascular advances made since 1900.

Portfolio Students can save their descriptions in their portfolios.

Keeping Your Cardiovascular System Healthy

Keeping Your Cardiovascular System Healthy

Few young people have heart attacks, but atherosclerosis can begin to develop in people as young as 20 years old. You can establish habits now that will lessen your risk of developing atherosclerosis and hypertension. **To help maintain cardiovascular health, people should exercise regularly; eat a balanced diet that is low in fat, cholesterol, and sodium; and avoid smoking.**

Figure 16 Eating foods that are low in fat can help keep your cardiovascular system healthy.

Exercise Do you participate in sports, ride a bike, swim, dance, or climb stairs instead of taking the elevator? Every time you do one of those activities, you are helping to maintain your cardiovascular health. Exercise strengthens your heart muscle and also helps prevent atherosclerosis.

A Balanced Diet Foods that are high in cholesterol and fats can lead to a buildup of fatty deposits on artery walls. In addition, eating too many high-fat foods can lead to excessive weight gain. Foods such as red meats, eggs, and cheese are high in cholesterol. These foods also contain substances that your body needs. Therefore, a smart approach might be to eat them, but only in small quantities. Some foods that are especially high in fat include butter and margarine, potato chips, doughnuts, and fried foods such as French fries. Eat high-fat foods only occasionally, if at all.

Avoid Smoking Smokers are more than twice as likely to have a heart attack than are nonsmokers. Every year, almost 180,000 people in the United States die from cardiovascular disease caused by smoking. If smokers quit, however, their risk of death from cardiovascular disease decreases.

Section 4 Review

1. List three things you can do to help your cardiovascular system stay healthy.
2. What is atherosclerosis?
3. How does hypertension affect blood vessels?
4. **Thinking Critically Relating Cause and Effect** Coronary heart disease is much less common in some countries than it is in the United States. What factors might account for this difference?

124 ◆ D

Science at Home

With your family, discuss some things that you all can do to maintain healthy cardiovascular systems. Make a list of exercise activities, such as bicycling and swimming, that family members can enjoy together. You might also work with your family to cook and serve a "heart-healthy," low-fat meal.

SECTION 1 The Body's Transportation System

Key Ideas

◆ The cardiovascular system consists of the heart, blood vessels, and blood.

◆ The heart pumps blood through the blood vessels. The heart has four chambers. The two atria receive blood, and the two ventricles pump blood out of the heart.

◆ Blood travels from the heart to the lungs and back to the heart. It is then pumped to the body and returns again to the heart.

◆ A group of cells called the pacemaker regulates the rate at which the heart beats.

Key Terms

cardiovascular system   artery
heart   capillary
atrium   vein
ventricle   aorta
valve   force
pacemaker

SECTION 2 A Closer Look at Blood Vessels

Key Ideas

◆ Arteries carry blood from the heart to capillaries. In the capillaries, materials are exchanged between the blood and the body's cells. From the capillaries, blood flows into veins that carry it back to the heart.

◆ Blood pressure is caused by the force with which the ventricles contract. Blood pressure is highest in arteries and lowest in veins.

Key Terms

coronary artery   blood pressure
diffusion   sphygmomanometer
pressure

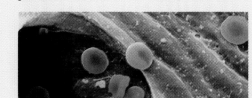

SECTION 3 Blood and Lymph

Key Ideas

◆ Plasma, the liquid part of blood, transports materials such as glucose, vitamins, and waste products.

◆ Red blood cells, which contain hemoglobin, carry oxygen and deliver it to body cells. White blood cells fight disease. Platelets are important in forming blood clots.

◆ There are four blood types—A, B, AB, and O. A person's blood type determines the types of blood he or she can receive in transfusions.

◆ Some fluid escapes from blood vessels. The lymphatic system transports this fluid, called lymph, and empties it back into the blood.

Key Terms

plasma   fibrin
red blood cell   blood transfusion
hemoglobin   lymphatic system
white blood cell   lymph
platelet   lymph node

SECTION 4 Cardiovascular Health

INTEGRATING HEALTH

Key Ideas

◆ Atherosclerosis is a condition in which an artery wall thickens due to the buildup of cholesterol and other fatty materials.

◆ Hypertension is a disorder in which the blood pressure is higher than normal.

◆ To help prevent atherosclerosis and hypertension, people need to exercise regularly; eat a diet low in fat, cholesterol, and salt; and avoid smoking.

Key Terms

atherosclerosis   heart attack
cholesterol   hypertension

USING THE INTERNET
ACTIVITY

www.science-explorer.phschool.com

Chapter 4 **D ◆ 125**

Program Resources

◆ **Teaching Resources** Chapter 4 Project Scoring Rubric, p. 92; Chapter 4 Performance Assessment Teacher Notes, p. 257; Chapter 4 Performance Assessment Student Worksheet, pp. 258–259; Chapter 4 Test, pp. 260–263

Reviewing Content:
Multiple Choice

1. b   2. a   3. a   4. a   5. c

True or False

6. true   7. red blood cells   8. true   9. O
10. true

Checking Concepts

11. The cell will pass into a capillary in your leg and into a vein that returns blood to the heart. A vein will then carry the cell to the right atrium.
12. The left ventricle contracts with more force than the right. The left ventricle needs to contract with enough force to pump blood throughout the entire body, while the right pumps blood to the lungs only.
13. Capillaries have thin walls, allowing substances to move in and out of the them easily.
14. Hemoglobin carries oxygen from the lungs and releases it in the body.
15. Accept any two: A high-fat, high-cholesterol diet can lead to atherosclerosis; overeating can lead to excessive weight gain, which puts strain on the heart; dietary sodium can aggravate hypertension.
16. Ads should point out the specific benefits of exercise, show at least two or three ways in which teenagers can obtain exercise, and be appropriate for a teenage audience.

Thinking Visually

17. **a.** carries blood away from the heart
b. capillary **c.** one layer of epithelial cells
d. carries blood from capillaries to heart
e. three layers: inner epithelial, middle muscle, and outer connective tissue

Applying Skills

18. A man. The line for men is above the line for women for all ages on the graph.
19. Both lines show that, on average, people's blood pressure increases as they age.
20. Yes. The two lines seem to be converging and will probably intersect at some age above 45.

Reviewing Content

 For more review of key concepts, see the Interactive Student Tutorial CD-ROM.

Multiple Choice
Choose the letter of the best answer.

1. The heart's upper chambers are called
   a. ventricles.
   b. atria.
   c. valves.
   d. hemoglobins.
2. Oxygen-rich blood enters the heart through the
   a. left atrium.
   b. right atrium.
   c. left ventricle.
   d. right ventricle.
3. Which of the following is *not* important in moving blood through veins?
   a. the force with which the atria contract
   b. valves
   c. muscles in the walls of veins
   d. the contraction of skeletal muscles
4. Platelets help the body to
   a. control bleeding.
   b. carry oxygen.
   c. fight infection.
   d. regulate the amount of water in plasma.
5. Cholesterol is a fatlike substance associated with
   a. lymph nodes.
   b. fibrin.
   c. atherosclerosis.
   d. salt.

True or False
If the statement is true, write true. If it is false, change the underlined word or words to make the statement true.

6. The two lower heart chambers are called <u>ventricles</u>.
7. <u>White blood cells</u> contain hemoglobin.
8. The <u>capillaries</u> are the narrowest blood vessels in the body.
9. A person with blood type B can receive a transfusion of blood types B and <u>AB</u>.
10. Elevated blood pressure is called <u>hypertension</u>.

Checking Concepts

11. A red blood cell is moving through an artery in your leg. Describe the path that blood cell will follow back to your heart. Identify the chamber of the heart to which it will return.
12. Contrast the forces with which the right and left ventricles contract. How does this relate to each ventricle's function?
13. How is a capillary's structure adapted to its function?
14. What is the function of hemoglobin?
15. Give two reasons why the food choices that people make are important to their cardiovascular health.
16. **Writing to Learn** Write an ad that encourages teenagers to exercise. Your ad will appear in a teen magazine. The ad should point out the health benefits of exercise and identify some ways that teenagers can exercise.

Thinking Visually

17. **Compare/Contrast Table** Compare the three types of blood vessels by copying and completing the table below. (For more on compare/contrast tables, see the Skills Handbook.)

Blood Vessel	Function	Structure of Wall
Artery	a. ?	3 layers: inner–epithelial tissue middle–muscle outer–connective tissue
b. ?	exchange of materials between cells and blood	c. ?
Vein	d. ?	e. ?

Thinking Critically

21. Oxygen-poor blood from the right ventricle could flow to the left ventricle and be pumped to the rest of the body, impairing the delivery of oxygen.
22. In lung capillaries, oxygen moves from the lungs into the capillaries. In capillaries in other parts of the body, oxygen moves out of the capillaries and into body cells.

23. Iron is an important component of hemoglobin, which is used to transport oxygen. Without enough iron, people could not carry as much oxygen in their blood.
24. Atherosclerosis and hypertension are affected by eating habits and behavior. The risk of these diseases can be lowered with a diet low in fat, cholesterol, and salt; by regular exercise; and by not smoking.

Applying Skills

The graph below shows how average blood pressure, measured when the ventricles contract, changes as men and women grow older. Use the graph to answer Questions 18–20.

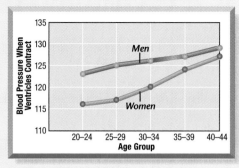

18. **Interpreting Data** At age 20, who is likely to have the higher blood pressure—a man or a woman?

19. **Drawing Conclusions** In general, what happens to people's blood pressure as they age?

20. **Predicting** Do you think that there is some age at which both men and women have about the same blood pressure? Use the graph lines to explain your prediction.

Thinking Critically

21. **Predicting** Some babies are born with an opening between the left and right ventricles. How would this heart defect affect the ability of the cardiovascular system to deliver oxygen to body cells?

22. **Comparing and Contrasting** Contrast the direction of movement of oxygen in lung capillaries and other capillaries in the body.

23. **Relating Cause and Effect** People who do not have enough iron in their diets sometimes develop a condition in which their blood cannot carry a normal amount of oxygen. Explain why this is so.

24. **Making Generalizations** Why are atherosclerosis and hypertension sometimes called "lifestyle diseases"?

C H A P T E R 4 R E V I E W

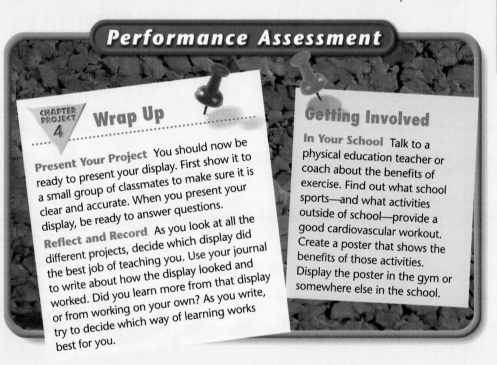

CHAPTER PROJECT 4 **Wrap Up**

Present Your Project You should now be ready to present your display. First show it to a small group of classmates to make sure it is clear and accurate. When you present your display, be ready to answer questions.

Reflect and Record As you look at all the different projects, decide which display did the best job of teaching you. Use your journal to write about how the display looked and worked. Did you learn more from that display or from working on your own? As you write, try to decide which way of learning works best for you.

Getting Involved

In Your School Talk to a physical education teacher or coach about the benefits of exercise. Find out what school sports—and what activities outside of school—provide a good cardiovascular workout. Create a poster that shows the benefits of those activities. Display the poster in the gym or somewhere else in the school.

Chapter 4 **D ◆ 127**

Performance Assessment

CHAPTER PROJECT 4

Wrap Up
Present Your Project
If possible, allow one class period for students to work in small groups to present their projects to each other. Encourage students to provide constructive feedback to help each other improve their displays. In order to help students compare all the displays, try to schedule all presentations in two or three consecutive class periods. If possible, allow students to arrange their displays around the room in a large circle so all displays are visible at once.

Students' presentations should include descriptions of the travels of the red blood cell through the body as well as a clear explanation of how the student has chosen to represent the process in his or her display. Encourage other students to ask questions about each model as it is presented.

Reflect and Record Encourage students to identify one aspect of a particular display that helped them understand a concept. Some students may find that they learned more by making their own displays; others may find that they learned more by looking at other displays.

Getting Involved

In Your School Invite a coach or physical education teacher to participate in a question-and-answer session during class. Provide resources for students to research the benefits of outside activities they are involved in such as soccer, gymnastics, karate, or dancing. Encourage students to include exercises that can be performed by all students. If possible, obtain permission for students to display their posters in the gym or other common area.

D ◆ 127

Program Resources

◆ **Inquiry Skills Handbook** Provides teaching and review of all inquiry skills

Respiration and Excretion

Sections	Time	Student Edition Activities	ACTIVITY Other Activities	
CHAPTER PROJECT 5 **Get the Message Out** p. 129	Ongoing (1½ weeks)	Check Your Progress, pp. 144, 150 Wrap Up, p. 153	TE	Chapter 5 Project Notes, pp. 128–129
1 **The Respiratory System** pp. 130–139 ◆ Identify the functions of the respiratory system. ◆ Identify the structures that air passes through as it travels to the lungs. ◆ Describe how oxygen, carbon dioxide, and water move in the lungs. ◆ Explain the process by which people breathe and speak.	5 periods/ 2½ blocks	**Discover** How Big Can You Blow Up a Balloon?, p. 130 **Try This** Do You Exhale Carbon Dioxide?, p. 135 **Skills Lab: Making Models** A Breath of Fresh Air, p. 139	TE TE TE TE ISLM	Demonstration, p. 131 Integrating Earth Science, p. 131 Inquiry Challenge, p. 132 Integrating Math, p. 134 Integrating Physics, p. 137 D-5, "Measuring the Volume of Exhaled Air"
2 *INTEGRATING HEALTH* **Smoking and Your Health** pp. 140–144 ◆ List the harmful chemicals contained in tobacco smoke. ◆ Explain how tobacco smoke harms the respiratory and circulatory systems.	2½ periods/ 1–2 blocks	**Discover** What Are the Dangers of Smoking?, p. 140 **Sharpen Your Skills** Calculating, p. 143	TE	Real-Life Learning, p. 142
3 **The Excretory System** pp. 145–150 ◆ Identify the function of the excretory system. ◆ State how urine is produced in the kidneys' nephrons. ◆ Name the organs involved in excretion and describe their roles.	3 periods/ 1½ blocks	**Discover** How Does Filtering a Liquid Change What Is in It?, p. 145 **Real-World Lab: You Solve the Mystery** Clues About Health, pp. 148–149	TE TE	Demonstration, p. 147 Building Inquiry Skills: Inferring, p. 150
Study Guide/Chapter Review pp. 151–153	1 period/ ½ block		ISAB	Provides teaching and review of all inquiry skills

 For Standard or Block Schedule The Resource Pro® CD-ROM gives you maximum flexibility for planning your instruction for any type of schedule. Resource Pro® contains Planning Express®, an advanced scheduling program, as well as the entire contents of the Teaching Resources and the Computer Test Bank.

CHAPTER PLANNING GUIDE

Program Resources	Assessment Strategies	Media and Technology
TR Chapter 5 Project Teacher Notes, pp. 114–115 **TR** Chapter 5 Project Overview and Worksheets, pp. 116–119 **TR** Chapter 5 Project Scoring Rubric, p. 120	**SE** Performance Assessment: Chapter 5 Project Wrap Up, p. 153 **TE** Check Your Progress, pp. 144, 150 **TE** Performance Assessment: Chapter 5 Project Wrap Up, p. 153 **TR** Chapter 5 Project Scoring Rubric, p. 120	
TR 5-1 Lesson Plan, p. 121 **TR** 5-1 Section Summary, p. 122 **TR** 5-1 Review and Reinforce, p. 123 **TR** 5-1 Enrich, p. 124 **TR** Chapter 5 Skills Lab, pp. 133–134	**SE** Section 1 Review, p. 138 **SE** Analyze and Conclude, pp. 131, 133, 135, 137 **TE** Ongoing Assessment, pp. 17, 19 **TE** Performance Assessment, p. 138 **TR** 5-1 Review and Reinforce, p. 123	Exploring Earth Science Videodisc, Unit 2 Side 1, "Air Today, Gone Tomorrow" Audiotapes: English-Spanish Summary 5-1 Transparency 10, "Exploring the Respiratory System" Transparency 11, "Gas Exchange in the Alveoli" Interactive Student Tutorial CD-ROM, D-5
TR 5-2 Lesson Plan, p. 125 **TR** 5-2 Section Summary, p. 126 **TR** 5-2 Review and Reinforce, p. 127 **TR** 5-2 Enrich, p. 128	**SE** Section 2 Review, p. 144 **TE** Ongoing Assessment, pp. 141, 143 **TE** Performance Assessment, p. 144 **TR** 5-2 Review and Reinforce, p. 127	Exploring Life Science Videodisc, Unit 4 Side 1, "Caution: Breathing May Be Hazardous to Your Health" Audiotapes: English-Spanish Summary 5-2 Interactive Student Tutorial CD-ROM, D-5
TR 5-3 Lesson Plan, p. 129 **TR** 5-3 Section Summary, p. 130 **TR** 5-3 Review and Reinforce, p. 131 **TR** 5-3 Enrich, p. 132 **TR** Chapter 5 Real-World Lab, pp. 135–137	**SE** Section 3 Review, p. 150 **SE** Analyze and Conclude, pp. 148–149 **TE** Ongoing Assessment, p. 147 **TE** Performance Assessment, p. 150 **TR** 5-3 Review and Reinforce, p. 131	Exploring Life Science Videodisc, Unit 4 Side 1, "Cool Sweat" Transparency 12, "Exploring a Kidney" Audiotapes: English-Spanish Summary 5-3 Interactive Student Tutorial CD-ROM, D-5
TR Chapter 5 Performance Assessment, pp. 264–266 **TR** Chapter 5 Test, pp. 267–270	**SE** Chapter Review, pp. 151–153 **TR** Chapter 5 Performance Assessment, pp. 264–266 **TR** Chapter 5 Test, pp. 267–270 **CTB** Test D-5	Computer Test Bank, Test D-5 Interactive Student Tutorial CD-ROM, D-5 Science Explorer Internet Site

Key: **SE** Student Edition   **TE** Teacher's Edition   **TR** Teaching Resources
     CTB Computer Test Bank   **SES** Science Explorer Series Text   **ISLM** Integrated Science Laboratory Manual
     ISAB Inquiry Skills Activity Book   **PTA** Product Testing Activities by *Consumer Reports*   **IES** Interdisciplinary Explorations Series

Meeting the National Science Education Standards and AAAS Benchmarks

National Science Education Standards	Benchmarks for Science Literacy	Unifying Themes
Science as Inquiry (Content Standard A) ◆ **Ask questions that can be answered by scientific investigations** Students conduct an investigation to determine how air gets into the lungs. *(Skills Lab)* **Physical Science** (Content Standard B) ◆ **Properties and changes of properties in matter** During metabolism, oxygen combines with carbon to from carbon dioxide. Breathing is accomplished through the action of several groups of muscles that act together to enlarge the chest cavity. Air pressure then forces air into the lungs. *(Section 1)* **Life Science** (Content Standard B) ◆ **Structure and function of living systems** The respiratory and excretory systems work together to transport substances to and from the blood. *(Sections 1, 3)* **Science in Personal and Social Perspectives** (Content Standard B) ◆ **Personal health** Smoking can damage the respiratory system. Some of the damage can be repaired by the body when the smoker quits. *(Section 2)*	**4D The Structure of Matter** During metabolism, oxygen combines with carbon to form carbon dioxide. *(Section 1)* **5E Flow of Matter and Energy** The respiratory system provides body cells with the oxygen they need and combines it with nutrients to produce energy. The excretory system removes from the cells the waste products of energy production. *(Sections 1, 3)* **6C Basic Functions** The respiratory system permits the exchange of gases between the body cells and the environment. The excretory system removes wastes from the body. *(Sections 1, 3)* **6E Physical Health** Smoking causes changes in the structure of the respiratory system that limit its ability to function properly. *(Section 2)* **7A Cultural Effects on Behavior** Passive smoke is a recognized problem in society. Friends sometimes influence people to begin to smoke. *(Section 2)* **11C Constancy and Change** By delivering oxygen to the blood and removing wastes from the blood, the respiratory and excretory systems help to maintain homeostasis. *(Sections 1, 3)*	◆ **Energy** The respiratory system provides body cells with the oxygen they need and combines it with nutrients to produce energy. The excretory system removes the waste products of energy production. *(Sections 1, 3)* ◆ **Patterns of Change** The respiratory system brings about the exchange of gases (O_2 and CO_2) with the environment. Smoking damages the respiratory system. The excretory system carries waste products out of the body and returns them to the environment. *(Sections 1, 2, 3)* ◆ **Scale and Structure** The lungs are composed of structures called alveoli, in which the exchange of gases takes place. Smoking causes changes in the structure of the respiratory system that limit its ability to function properly. The kidneys contain structures called nephrons, which remove wastes from the blood. *(Sections 1, 2, 3)* ◆ **Systems and interactions** The respiratory system permits the exchange of gases between the body cells and the environment. The excretory system removes wastes from the body. *(Sections 1, 3)* ◆ **Unity and diversity** The structures of the respiratory system and the excretory system are different, yet they work together in transporting materials to and from the blood. *(Sections 1, 2, 3)* ◆ **Stability** The respiratory and excretory systems help to maintain homeostasis. *(Sections 1, 3)*

Media and Technology

Exploring Earth Science Videodisc
◆ **Section 1** "Air Today, Gone Tomorrow" examines the composition of the atmosphere and how it has changed since the content of Earth's original atmosphere was first identified.

Exploring Life Science Videodisc
◆ **Section 2** "Caution: Breathing May Be Hazardous to Your Health" demonstrates the effects of smog and indoor air pollution on the health of the respiratory system.

◆ **Section 3** "Cool Sweat" explains the function of the sweat glands and a NASA solution to a rare gland disease.

Interactive Student Tutorial CD-ROM
◆ **Chapter Review** Interactive questions help students to self-assess their mastery of key chapter concepts.

Student Edition Connection Strategies

◆ **Section 1**   Integrating Earth Science, p. 131
Integrating Mathematics, p. 135
Social Studies Connection, p. 136
Integrating Physics, p. 136
Integrating Physics, p. 137

◆ **Section 2**   Integrating Health, p. 140

◆ **Section 3**   Integrating Health, p. 148

USING THE INTERNET
www.science-explorer.phschool.com

Visit the Science Explorer Internet site to find an up-to-date activity for Chapter 5 of *Human Biology and Health*.

ACTIVITY	Time (minutes)	Materials Quantities for one work group	Skills
Section 1			
Discover, p. 130	15	**Nonconsumable** round balloon, metric measuring tape	Inferring
Try This, p. 135	20	**Consumable** bromthymol blue solution, plastic drinking straw, plastic wrap for covering test tubes **Nonconsumable** 2 test tubes, safety goggles	Predicting
Skills Lab, p. 139	30	**Consumable** transparent plastic bottle with narrow neck **Nonconsumable** small balloon, scissors, large balloon	Making Models
Section 2			
Discover, p. 140	20	**Consumable** No special materials are required.	Inferring
Sharpen your Skills, p. 143	5	**Consumable** No special materials are required.	Calculating
Section 3			
Discover, p. 145	15	**Consumable** glucose solution, sand, glucose test strip, filter paper **Nonconsumable** 2 small plastic containers, plastic funnel	Observing
Real-World Lab, pp. 148–149	40	**Consumable** glucose solution, glucose test strips, 3 simulated urine samples, water, protein solution, white paper towels, Biuret solution **Nonconsumable** 6 test tubes, 6 plastic droppers, marking pencil, test tube rack	Observing, Interpreting Data, Drawing Conclusions

A list of all materials required for the Student Edition activities can be found on pages T14–T15. You can order Materials Kits by calling 1-800-828-7777 or by accessing the Science Explorer Internet site at **www.science-explorer.phschool.com.**

CHAPTER PROJECT 5

Get the Message Out

Smoking causes damage to the respiratory and circulatory systems and affects smokers' overall health. Anti-smoking campaigns may help convince some adult smokers to quit, and some children and teenagers not to begin.

Purpose In this project, students design ads to discourage minors from smoking, and adults to quit if they do smoke. In the ads, students address the health risks of smoking and the pressures that influence people to smoke. Students use what they learn about respiratory functions and the effects of smoking to formulate compelling arguments against beginning this habit.

Skills Focus Students will be able to
- pose questions, make inferences, and draw conclusions about the detrimental effects of smoking;
- apply the concepts of healthy behavior to designing ads to discourage people from smoking, and to encourage people to quit if they do smoke;
- communicate their findings about smoking to people in three different age groups.

Project Time Line This project will take about three weeks. Spend one day talking about advertising and looking at ads. During the first week, students collect information from the chapter about respiratory functions and the detrimental effects of smoking on the body. In the second week, students address at least two pressures that influence people to start or to continue smoking as they plan, design, and produce their ads. During the third week, students present their work to their classmates and discuss reasons why they chose particular images and messages. Before beginning the project, see Chapter 5 Project Teacher Notes on pages 114–115 in Teaching Resources for more details on carrying out the project. Also distribute to students the Chapter 5 Project Overview and Worksheets and Scoring Rubric on pages 116–120 in Teaching Resources.

CHAPTER 5 Respiration and Excretion

WHAT'S AHEAD

SECTION 1 The Respiratory System

Discover How Big Can You Blow Up a Balloon?
Try This Do You Exhale Carbon Dioxide?
Skills Lab A Breath of Fresh Air

SECTION 2 *Integrating Health* Smoking and Your Health

Discover What Are the Dangers of Smoking?
Sharpen Your Skills Calculating

SECTION 3 The Excretory System

Discover How Does Filtering a Liquid Change What Is in It?
Real-World Lab Clues About Health

128 ◆ D

Possible Materials Fashion, sports, and entertainment magazines will be useful for brainstorming ideas for convincing ads. Students will need poster boards or large sheets of paper along with markers, crayons, or colored pencils for designing their posters. If students elect to do radio or television commercials, they will need to write scripts and bring in props and/or costumes.

Launching the Project Ask: **Why do people start smoking?** (*Samples: Peer pressure, to look "cool"*) Ask: **Why do people who smoke keep smoking?** (*Sample: They might try to stop, but find that they can't.*) Discuss reasons why people might smoke even though they know that smoking is unhealthy. Students should begin thinking about the detrimental effects of smoking and come up with ways to communicate this information to different age groups. To get them thinking about the influences that sway people of different ages, bring in several

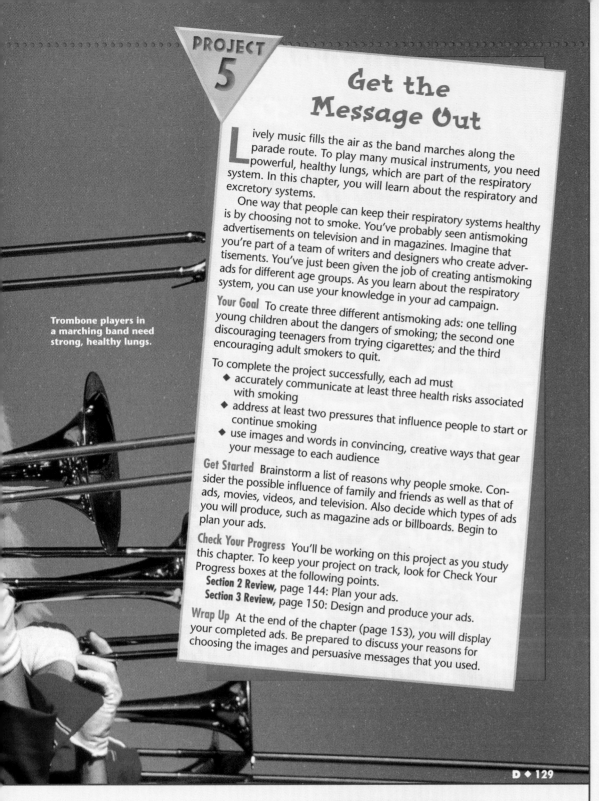

Get the Message Out

Lively music fills the air as the band marches along the parade route. To play many musical instruments, you need powerful, healthy lungs, which are part of the respiratory system. In this chapter, you will learn about the respiratory and excretory systems.

One way that people can keep their respiratory systems healthy is by choosing not to smoke. You've probably seen antismoking advertisements on television and in magazines. Imagine that you're part of a team of writers and designers who create advertisements. You've just been given the job of creating antismoking ads for different age groups. As you learn about the respiratory system, you can use your knowledge in your ad campaign.

Your Goal To create three different antismoking ads: one telling young children about the dangers of smoking; the second one discouraging teenagers from trying cigarettes; and the third encouraging adult smokers to quit.

To complete the project successfully, each ad must
◆ accurately communicate at least three health risks associated with smoking
◆ address at least two pressures that influence people to start or continue smoking
◆ use images and words in convincing, creative ways that gear your message to each audience

Get Started Brainstorm a list of reasons why people smoke. Consider the possible influence of family and friends as well as that of ads, movies, videos, and television. Also decide which types of ads you will produce, such as magazine ads or billboards. Begin to plan your ads.

Check Your Progress You'll be working on this project as you study this chapter. To keep your project on track, look for Check Your Progress boxes at the following points.
Section 2 Review, page 144: Plan your ads.
Section 3 Review, page 150: Design and produce your ads.

Wrap Up At the end of the chapter (page 153), you will display your completed ads. Be prepared to discuss your reasons for choosing the images and persuasive messages that you used.

Trombone players in a marching band need strong, healthy lungs.

D ◆ 129

ads for different products. Lead a class discussion about the target audience for each ad and have students explain why the ad would appeal to that audience. Allow time for students to read the description of the project in their text and Chapter 5 Project Overview on pages 116–117 in Teaching Resources. Chapter 5 Worksheet 1, page 118 in Teaching Resources will help students think about how they can use images and words in creative ways to target their messages to audiences of different ages. Chapter 5 Worksheet 2, page 119 in Teaching Resources will help students identify pressures that encourage people to start smoking.

Program Resources

◆ **Teaching Resources** Chapter 5 Project Teacher Notes, pp. 114–115; Chapter 5 Project Overview and Worksheets, pp. 116–119; Chapter 5 Project Scoring Rubric, p. 120

Performance Assessment

The Chapter 5 Project Scoring Rubric on page 120 of Teaching Resources will help you evaluate how well students complete the Chapter 5 Project. Students will be assessed on
◆ how well they support their decisions in terms of what messages will relate to the concerns of the three age groups;
◆ the accuracy of the information contained in their ads;
◆ the thoroughness and organization of their presentations;
◆ how well they work with other students.
By sharing the Chapter 5 Scoring Rubric with students at the beginning of the project, you will make it clear to them what they are expected to do.

Objectives

After completing the lesson, students will be able to
◆ identify the functions of the respiratory system;
◆ identify the structures that air passes through as it travels to the lungs;
◆ describe how oxygen, carbon dioxide, and water move in the lungs;
◆ explain the process by which people breathe and speak.

Key Terms cilia, pharynx, trachea, bronchi, lung, alveoli, diaphragm, larynx, vocal cord

1 Engage/Explore

Activating Prior Knowledge

Ask students to explain why astronauts wear space suits and carry oxygen with them when they walk outside a spacecraft. Then ask why deep-sea divers take oxygen with them on a dive. Most students will realize that astronauts and divers need oxygen to survive.

DISCOVER

Skills Focus inferring
Materials *round balloon, metric measuring tape*
Time 15 minutes
Tips Students should blow the balloon up several times and gently stretch it before beginning this activity. Remind students not to share balloons. Students with breathing difficulties may not be able to blow up the balloons. They can act as measurers or calculators.
Expected Outcome Measurements will vary depending upon the amount of air exhaled.
Think It Over Students may infer that factors such as smoking, air pollution, breathing difficulties, and colds may affect the volume of air a person can exhale.

DISCOVER · ACTIVITY

How Big Can You Blow Up a Balloon?

1. Take a normal breath, then blow as much air as possible into a balloon. Twist the end and hold it closed. Have your partner measure around the balloon at its widest point.

2. Let the air out of the balloon. Repeat Step 1 and calculate the average of the two measurements.

3. Compare your results with those of your classmates. The bigger the circumference, the greater the volume of air exhaled.

Think It Over
Inferring What factors might affect the volume of air a person can exhale?

GUIDE FOR READING

◆ What are the functions of the respiratory system?
◆ What structures does air pass through as it travels to the lungs?
◆ How do oxygen, carbon dioxide, and water move in the lungs?

Reading Tip Before you read, preview *Exploring the Respiratory System* on page 133. Write down any unfamiliar terms.

130 ◆ D

Jerry, the main character in Doris Lessing's story "Through the Tunnel," is on vacation at the seaside. Day after day, he watches some older boys dive into deep water on one side of a huge rock. The boys mysteriously reappear on the other side. Jerry figures out that there must be an underwater tunnel in the rock. He finds the tunnel beneath the water and decides to swim through it. Once inside, though, he is terrified. The walls are slimy, and rocks scrape his body. He can barely see where he is going. But worst of all, Jerry has to hold his breath for far longer than ever before. The author describes Jerry this way: "His head was swelling, his lungs were cracking."

Jerry's behavior could have killed him. No one can go for very long without breathing. Your body cells need oxygen, and they get that oxygen from the air you breathe. **The respiratory system moves oxygen from the outside environment into the body. It also removes carbon dioxide and water from the body.**

Why the Body Needs Oxygen

The energy-releasing chemical reactions that take place inside your cells require oxygen. As a result of these reactions, your cells are able to perform all the tasks that keep you alive. Like a fire, which cannot burn without oxygen, your cells cannot "burn" enough substances to keep you alive without oxygen.

READING STRATEGIES

Reading Tip After students preview *Exploring the Respiratory System,* call on volunteers to paraphrase the information in the visual. Suggest students write questions they have about the information. They can begin the questions with words such as *How, Why,* and *What.* Encourage them to find answers to their questions as they read the section.

Study and Comprehension After students read the section, have them outline the information under the headings *Why the Body Needs Oxygen, The Air You Breathe, The Path of Air, Gas Exchange, How You Breathe,* and *How You Speak.* Instruct students to review the information under the headings and write a short summary for each heading.

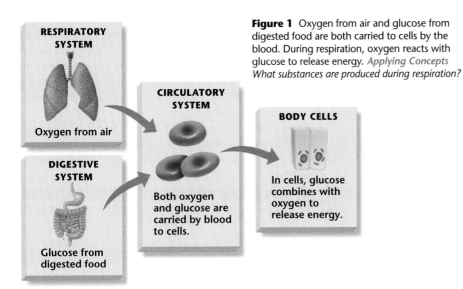

Figure 1 Oxygen from air and glucose from digested food are both carried to cells by the blood. During respiration, oxygen reacts with glucose to release energy. *Applying Concepts What substances are produced during respiration?*

RESPIRATORY SYSTEM
Oxygen from air

DIGESTIVE SYSTEM
Glucose from digested food

CIRCULATORY SYSTEM
Both oxygen and glucose are carried by blood to cells.

BODY CELLS
In cells, glucose combines with oxygen to release energy.

Respiration is the process in which oxygen and glucose undergo a complex series of chemical reactions inside cells. These chemical reactions release the energy that fuels growth and other cell processes. Besides releasing energy, respiration produces carbon dioxide and water. Your body eliminates the carbon dioxide and some of the water through your lungs. To a scientist, *breathing* and *respiration* mean different things. Respiration refers to the chemical reactions inside cells, while breathing refers to the movement of air into and out of the lungs.

Your respiratory system gets oxygen into your lungs. However, respiration could not take place without your circulatory and digestive systems. The digestive system absorbs glucose from food. The circulatory system carries both oxygen from your lungs and glucose from food to your cells.

☑ *Checkpoint Why does your body need oxygen?*

The Air You Breathe

 INTEGRATING EARTH SCIENCE The oxygen your body needs comes from the atmosphere, which is the blanket of gases that surrounds Earth. The atmosphere is made up of a mixture of gases. Only about 21 percent of air is oxygen. Nitrogen makes up about 78 percent, and the remaining 1 percent includes carbon dioxide, helium, and other gases. Your body doesn't use most of the air that you breathe into your lungs. When you exhale, most of the air that you inhaled goes back into the atmosphere.

Answers to Self-Assessment

Caption Question

Figure 1 Carbon dioxide and water

☑ *Checkpoint*

Without oxygen, cells cannot "burn" substances to release energy.

2 Facilitate

Why the Body Needs Oxygen

Demonstration

Materials *short candle, matches, metal pie plate, glass jar taller than the candle*
Time 15 minutes

A burning candle can serve as a model for respiration. Secure the candle on the pie plate, and then light the candle. Cover the candle with the jar and direct students to observe what happens. *(The candle flame will burn out within a few seconds.)* Ask students: **Why did the candle go out?** *(After a few seconds, there was not enough air—oxygen—in the jar for the candle to keep burning.)* Explain that just as the candle needs oxygen to burn, body cells need oxygen to break down food and release energy cells need.
learning modality: visual

The Air You Breathe

 Integrating Earth Science

Materials *blue, green, white marbles; bag*
Time 10 minutes

Place 21 blue marbles (to represent oxygen), 78 green marbles (to represent nitrogen), and 1 white marble (to represent other gases) in the bag. Ask volunteers to take handfuls of marbles from the bag and count how many blue marbles appear in each handful. Ask students to explain how this models the composition of the air they breathe. *(Air is about 21% oxygen, 78% nitrogen, and 1% other gases, including carbon dioxide and helium.)* **learning modality: kinesthetic**

Ongoing Assessment

Writing Ask students to write brief paragraphs, explaining the difference between breathing and respiration.

The Path of Air

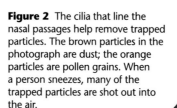
The Path of Air

If you look toward a window on a bright day, you may see tiny particles dancing in the air. These particles include such things as floating grains of dust, plant pollen, and ash from fires. In addition, air contains microorganisms, some of which can cause disease in humans. When you breathe in, all these materials enter your body along with the air.

However, most of these materials never enter your lungs. On its way to the lungs, air passes through a series of organs that filter and trap particles. These organs also warm and moisten the air. **As air travels from the outside environment to the lungs, it passes through the following organs: nose, pharynx, trachea, and bronchi.** It takes air only a few seconds to complete the route from the nose to the lungs. You can trace that route in *Exploring the Respiratory System.*

The Nose Your nose has two openings, or nostrils, which are separated by a thin wall. Air enters the body through the nostrils and then moves into the nose cavities, or nasal cavities. The lining of the nasal cavities contains many blood vessels. Warm blood flowing through these vessels heats the air. Some of the cells lining the cavities produce mucus. This sticky material moistens the air and keeps the delicate tissue from drying out. Mucus also traps particles, such as dust and bacteria. The cells that line the nasal cavities have **cilia** (SIL ee uh), tiny hairlike extensions that can move together like whips. The whiplike motion of these cilia sweeps the mucus into the throat, where you swallow it. In the stomach, the mucus, along with the particles and bacteria trapped in it, is destroyed by stomach acid.

Some particles and bacteria never make it to your stomach. They irritate the lining of your nose or throat, and you sneeze. The powerful force of a sneeze shoots the particles and bacteria out of your nose and into the air.

The Pharynx After flowing through the nasal cavities, air enters the **pharynx** (FAR ingks), or throat. The pharynx is the only part of the respiratory system that is shared with another system—the digestive system. If you look at *Exploring the Respiratory System,* you can see that both the nose and the mouth connect to the pharynx.

☑ *Checkpoint* To what two body systems does the pharynx belong?

Figure 2 The cilia that line the nasal passages help remove trapped particles. The brown particles in the photograph are dust; the orange particles are pollen grains. When a person sneezes, many of the trapped particles are shot out into the air.

The Trachea From the pharynx, air moves into the **trachea** (TRAY kee uh), or windpipe. You can feel your trachea if you gently run your fingers down the center of your neck. The trachea feels like a tube with a series of ridges. The firm ridges are rings of cartilage that strengthen the trachea and keep it open.

The trachea, like the nose, is lined with cilia and mucus. The cilia in the trachea sweep upward, moving mucus toward the pharynx, where it is swallowed. The trachea's cilia and mucus

 the Respiratory System

On its path from outside the body into the lungs, air passes through several structures that clean, warm, and moisten it. Once in the lungs, the oxygen in the air can enter your bloodstream.

Pharynx Air moves from the nose downward into the throat, or pharynx. Part of the pharynx is also a passageway for food.

Nose Air enters the body through two nostrils. The lining of the nose is coated with cilia and mucus, which trap particles and warm and moisten the air.

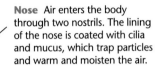

Epiglottis

Larynx

Trachea The trachea leads from the pharynx toward the lungs. The walls of the trachea are made up of rings of cartilage which protect the trachea and keep it from collapsing.

Bronchi Air moves from the trachea into the right and left bronchi. One bronchus leads to each lung. Part of each bronchus is outside the lung and part is inside.

Lungs After it reaches the lungs, air moves through smaller and smaller bronchi until it reaches the alveoli. In the alveoli, oxygen passes into the blood and carbon dioxide passes out of the blood.

Chapter 5 **D ◆ 133**

Suggest students finger trace the path of air as it enters the body. Ask students to infer why it is important for the air to be warmed and moistened when it enters the body. *(Because the inside of the body is warm and moist; this helps the body maintain a stable state.)* Instruct students to gently feel along their necks for their tracheas. Invite volunteers to describe what their trachea feels like. Then encourage students to consider the function of the rings of cartilage in the trachea. Ask: **What would happen if the trachea were to close?** *(No air would reach the lungs and the person would suffocate.)* **Extend** Suggest students compose three quiz questions based on the information in the visual. Students can then exchange and answer each other's questions. **learning modality: kinesthetic**

Media and Technology

 Transparencies "Exploring the Respiratory System," Transparency 10

Answers to Self-Assessment

☑ *Checkpoint*
Respiratory and digestive systems

Ongoing Assessment

Organizing Information Direct students to make flowcharts showing the movement of air through the organs in the respiratory system.

The Path of Air, continued

Including All Students

To help students whose understanding of English is limited, encourage them to write each new or unfamiliar term on the front of a note card and the definition of the term on the back. Students can also include an explanation of what role the organ or process plays in respiration, or draw a small diagram to describe or explain the term. Students can use the cards as flash cards to increase their familiarity with the terms. **limited English proficiency**

Using the Visuals: Figure 3

To help students understand how the processes in Figure 3 relate to the entire process of breathing, ask: **How does the oxygen get into the alveoli?** *(From the trachea to a bronchus, and then through the smaller branches of the bronchus.)* Ask students to infer what happens to the carbon dioxide the alveoli receive from the blood cells. *(It is exhaled when the person breathes out.)* **learning modality: visual**

 ### Integrating Mathematics

Materials *meter stick, masking tape*
Time 15 minutes

To help students comprehend just how large an area 70 square meters is, first help them visualize how large 1 square meter is. Provide students with the meter stick and masking tape, and allow them to mark a 1-m by 1-m square on the classroom floor. Invite students to estimate how many of these single square meters they can mark in the classroom. Then have them estimate how many classrooms they would need to be able to mark 70 square meters. **learning modality: visual**

---

continue the cleaning and moistening of air that began in the nose. If particles irritate the lining of the trachea, you cough. A cough, like a sneeze, sends harmful materials flying out of your body and into the air.

Normally, only air—not food—enters the trachea. If food does enter the trachea, the food can block the opening and prevent air from getting to the lungs. When that happens, a person chokes. Fortunately, food rarely gets into the trachea. Remember from Chapter 3 that the epiglottis is a small flap of tissue that folds over the trachea. The epiglottis seals the trachea off while you swallow.

The Bronchi and Lungs Air moves from the trachea to the **bronchi** (BRAHNG ky)(singular *bronchus*), the passages that direct air into the lungs. The **lungs** are the main organs of the respiratory system. The left bronchus leads into the left lung, and the right bronchus leads into the right lung. Inside the lungs, each bronchus divides into smaller and smaller tubes in a pattern that resembles the branches of a tree.

At the end of the smallest tubes are small structures that look like bunches of grapes. The "grapes" are **alveoli** (al VEE uh ly) (singular *alveolus*), tiny sacs of lung tissue specialized for the movement of gases between air and blood. Notice in Figure 3 that each alveolus is surrounded by a network of capillaries. It is here that the blood picks up its cargo of oxygen from the air.

☑ *Checkpoint* *Describe the structure of the bronchi.*

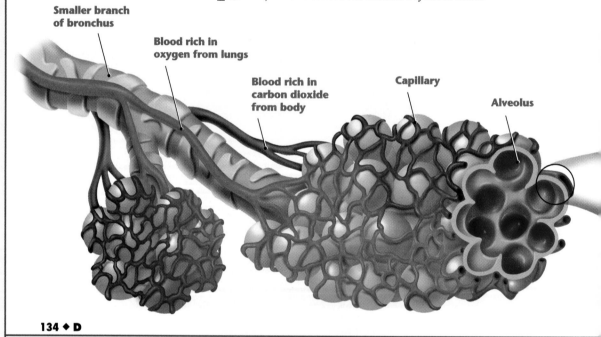

Smaller branch of bronchus

Blood rich in oxygen from lungs

Blood rich in carbon dioxide from body

Capillary

Alveolus

134 ◆ D

Gas Exchange

Because the walls of both the alveoli and the capillaries are very thin, materials can pass through them easily. **After air enters an alveolus, oxygen passes through the wall of the alveolus and then through the capillary wall into the blood. Carbon dioxide and water pass from the blood into the alveoli.** This whole process is known as gas exchange.

How Gas Exchange Occurs Imagine that you are a drop of blood beginning your journey through a capillary that wraps around an alveolus. When you begin that journey, you are carrying a lot of carbon dioxide and little oxygen. As you move through the capillary, oxygen gradually attaches to the hemoglobin in your red blood cells. At the same time, you are getting rid of carbon dioxide. At the end of your journey around the alveolus, you are rich in oxygen and poor in carbon dioxide.

A Large Surface Area Your lungs can absorb a large amount

INTEGRATING MATHEMATICS of oxygen because of the large surface area of the alveoli. An adult's lungs contain about 300 million alveoli. If you removed the alveoli, opened them, and spread them out on a flat surface, you would have a surface area of about 70 square meters. That's about the area of three lanes in a bowling alley!

The huge surface area of the alveoli enables the lungs to absorb a large amount of oxygen. The lungs can therefore supply the oxygen that people need—even when they are performing strenuous activities. When you play a musical instrument or a fast-paced game of basketball, you have your alveoli to thank.

Your lungs are not the only organs that provide a large surface area in a relatively small space. Remember that the small intestine contains numerous, tiny villi that increase the surface available to absorb food molecules.

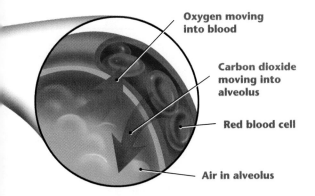

- Oxygen moving into blood
- Carbon dioxide moving into alveolus
- Red blood cell
- Air in alveolus

Do You Exhale Carbon Dioxide?

Use this activity to learn whether carbon dioxide is present in exhaled air.

1. Put on your goggles. Label two test tubes A and B.
2. Fill each test tube with 10 mL of water and a few drops of bromthymol blue solution. Bromthymol blue solution turns green or yellow in the presence of carbon dioxide.
3. Using a straw, blow air into the liquid in test tube A for a few seconds. Blow gently—if you blow hard, the liquid will bubble out of the test tube. **CAUTION:** *Use the straw to exhale only. Do not suck the solution back through the straw.*
4. Compare the solutions in the test tubes. Wash your hands when you have finished.

Predicting Suppose you had exercised immediately before you blew into the straw. Predict how this would have affected the results.

Figure 3 Alveoli are hollow air sacs surrounded by capillaries. As blood flows through the capillaries, oxygen moves from the alveoli into the blood. At the same time, carbon dioxide moves from the blood into the alveoli. *Interpreting Diagrams How is the structure of the alveoli important for gas exchange?*

TRY THIS

Skills Focus predicting
Materials *bromthymol blue solution, 2 test tubes, plastic drinking straw, plastic wrap for covering test tubes (optional), safety goggles*
Time 20 minutes
Tips Caution students to blow gently, and to not suck the liquid up through the straw. Students can cover the test tube with plastic wrap to prevent liquid from bubbling out of the tube.
Expected Outcome The blue solution in test tube A will turn yellow when students blow into it, indicating the presence of carbon dioxide. Students should predict that, had they exercised before the activity, the color change would have occurred more quickly because their bodies would have been generating more carbon dioxide.
Extend Have students test their predictions by doing several jumping jacks or other exercises and repeating the activity. Before allowing students to exercise, make certain that they do not have a medical condition that precludes exercising. **learning modality: visual**

Media and Technology

Transparencies "Gas Exchange in the Alveoli," Transparency 11

Exploring Earth Science Videodisc Unit 2, Side 1, "Air Today, Gone Tomorrow"

Chapter 2

Answers to Self-Assessment

Caption Question
Figure 3 The thin walls and huge surface area allow high-volume gas exchange.

✓ *Checkpoint*
The bronchi are tubelike structures that lead into the lungs. Inside the lungs, the bronchi divide into smaller and smaller branches. At the ends of the branches are the alveoli.

Ongoing Assessment

Writing Ask students to write explanations of what happens in the alveoli during gas exchange.

How You Breathe

Social Studies
CONNECTION

Display a large map of South America and Asia. Inform students that the Andes are about 8,900 kilometers long. Ask: **In which countries are the Andes located?** *(Venezuela, Colombia, Ecuador, Peru, Bolivia, Chile, and Argentina)* Invite a volunteer to locate Mt. Aconcagua, the highest peak of the Andes at 6,959 meters, on the border of Argentina and Chile. On the map of Asia, show students the Himalayan Range, telling them it is about 2,500 kilometers long. Locate Nepal and tell students that 9 of the 14 highest peaks of the world are found in Nepal. Ask a volunteer to locate Mt. Everest. *(On the border between Nepal and Tibet)*

In Your Journal Students can include descriptions of symptoms associated with mountain sickness in their journals. They should consider how the thin air might affect their judgment and their ability to react quickly.
learning modality: verbal

Integrating Physics

Remind students that gases and liquids generally move from an area of high pressure to an area of low pressure. Point out that the flow of air into and out of the lungs is determined by the difference in pressure between the lungs and the atmosphere. Ask students to use this relationship to explain how relaxed rib and diaphragm muscles cause air to move out of the lungs. *(When the muscles relax, the volume of the lungs decreases. With the same amount of air in a smaller space, the air pressure inside the lungs is greater than the pressure outside, so the air moves outside.)* **learning modality: logical/mathematical**

136 ◆ D

Social Studies
CONNECTION

Have you ever seen movies or read about climbers scaling mountains in the Andes or Himalayas? Some of the peaks in the Andes rise to almost 7,000 meters. Mount Everest in the Himalayas, which rises to 8,848 meters, is the world's tallest mountain. People who climb these mountains usually experience mountain sickness—dizziness, headaches, and shortness of breath. Their symptoms are due to a shortage of oxygen in their blood. The amount of oxygen in air decreases the farther one goes above sea level.

In contrast to visitors, people who live high in these mountain ranges do not experience these symptoms. Their respiratory and circulatory systems have adjusted to compensate for the low levels of oxygen. For example, they inhale a greater volume of air with each breath than do people at lower levels. In addition, their blood contains a greater number of red blood cells for transporting oxygen.

In Your Journal

Locate the Andes Mountains and Himalaya Mountains on a globe or map. Then imagine that you are climbing a mountain in one of these ranges. Write a diary entry describing your physical reactions and what you might see.

136 ◆ D

How You Breathe

In an average day, you may breathe more than 20,000 times. The rate at which you breathe depends on your body's need for oxygen. When you exercise, your body needs a lot of oxygen to supply energy. The more oxygen you need, the faster you breathe.

Muscles for Breathing Pay attention to your breathing as you read this paragraph. Can you feel the air flowing in and out through your nose? Do you notice the gentle lift and fall of your chest?

Breathing, like other body movements, is controlled by muscles. Figure 5 shows the structure of the chest, including the muscles that enable you to breathe. Notice that the lungs are surrounded by the ribs, which have muscles attached to them. At the base of the lungs is the **diaphragm** (DY uh fram), a large, dome-shaped muscle that plays an important role in breathing.

The Process of Breathing Here is what happens when you *INTEGRATING PHYSICS* inhale, or breathe in. The rib muscles contract, lifting the chest wall upward and outward. At the same time, the diaphragm contracts and moves downward. The combined action of these muscles makes the chest cavity larger, providing extra space for the lungs to expand.

When the chest cavity has expanded, there is more room for air. For a brief moment, however, there is no extra air to fill the space. Because the same amount of air now occupies a larger

Figure 4 These people live high in the Andes Mountains in Ecuador. Despite the low oxygen levels, these people experience no symptoms of mountain sickness. Their respiratory systems have adjusted in order to get enough oxygen into their bodies.

Background

Integrating Technology Sometimes, a person who has throat cancer has to have his or her larynx removed. When the larynx must be totally removed, doctors stitch the remaining trachea into a hole above the patient's breastbone, and from then on, the patient breathes through this hole. Without a larynx and the flow of air through it, the person cannot speak.

To give a person without a larynx a "voice," therapists often provide him or her with an artificial larynx, or electrolarynx. To "speak," the person holds the vibrating head of the electrolarynx against his or her throat. The buzzing sound enters through the skin, producing vibrations that can be articulated into speech. With practice, speech becomes more intelligible, though there remains a mechanical quality to the voice.

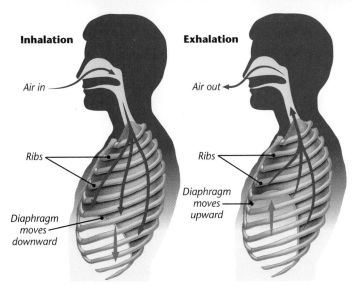

Inhalation   Exhalation

Air in   Air out

Ribs   Ribs

Diaphragm
moves
upward

Diaphragm
moves
downward

Figure 5 When you inhale, the diaphragm moves downward, allowing more room in the lungs for air. In contrast, when you exhale, the diaphragm moves upward. This upward movement increases the pressure in the lungs and pushes the air out.
Interpreting Diagrams How does the downward movement of the diaphragm affect the pressure of air inside the chest cavity?

space, the pressure of the air inside your lungs decreases. This means that the pressure of air inside the chest cavity is lower than the pressure of the atmosphere pushing on the body. Because of this difference in air pressure, air rushes into your chest, in the same way that air is sucked into a vacuum cleaner. You have inhaled.

In contrast, when you exhale, or breathe out, the rib muscles and diaphragm relax, and the chest cavity becomes smaller. This decrease in size squeezes air out of the lungs, the way squeezing a container of ketchup pushes ketchup out of the opening.

✓ *Checkpoint* *What muscles cause the chest to expand during breathing?*

How You Speak

The **larynx** (LAR ingks), or voice box, is located in the top part of the trachea, underneath the epiglottis. You can see the larynx if you look back at *Exploring the Respiratory System* on page 133. Place your fingers on your Adam's apple, which sticks out from the front of your neck. You can feel some of the cartilage that makes up the larynx. Two **vocal cords,** which are folds of connective tissue that produce your voice, stretch across the opening of the larynx.

How the Vocal Cords Work If you've ever let air out of a balloon while stretching its neck, you've heard the squeaking sound that the air makes. The neck of the balloon is something like your vocal cords.The vocal

 INTEGRATING PHYSICS

How You Speak

Integrating Physics

Materials *pieces of rubber with a small slit in the center*
Time 10 minutes

Cut small slits in the center of the rubber pieces prior to the activity. You can use a piece of rubber from a balloon. Some students may have difficulty visualizing how stretched tissue can be used to produce sounds. To demonstrate this, provide students with the prepared pieces of rubber. Instruct them to stretch the rubber until it is taut. Next, have the students take deep full breaths and blow across the piece of rubber at different angles. Ask: **What produces the sound?** *(Air flowing through the opening causes the rubber to vibrate. The vibrating rubber causes the air to vibrate and produces sound.)* Have students identify what the rubber represents. *(Vocal cords)*
learning modality: kinesthetic

Answers to Self-Assessment

Caption Question

Figure 5 Downward movement of the diaphragm causes a decrease in air pressure inside the chest cavity.

✓ *Checkpoint*
Rib and diaphragm muscles

Ongoing Assessment

Writing Ask students to write short paragraphs describing what happens during the breathing process.

Section 1 Review Answers

1. It moves oxygen from the outside environment into the body and removes carbon dioxide and water from the body.

2. The oxygen molecule moves through the nostrils, pharynx, trachea, bronchus, smaller and smaller bronchi, and then into the alveolus.

3. Carbon dioxide passes from the blood through the thin capillary wall and the wall of the alveolus into the alveolus.

4. When you inhale, the chest cavity becomes larger, decreasing the air pressure inside the lungs. This decrease in air pressure causes air to rush into the lungs.

5. Dust irritates breathing passages. Coughs and sneezes are the body's response to the irritation; they act to remove the irritants.

Science at Home

Materials *shoe box, set of wooden blocks*

Encourage students to develop a mathematical expression to describe the surface area of a block. Remind them that the surface area of a single block is the sum of the areas of each of its surfaces. Have students imagine a cube with a side length of 1 cm as an example. Explain that each side has an area of 1 square cm (length $\propto$ width). Because the cube has six surfaces (four sides, the top, and the bottom), the surface area of the cube is 6 cm^2.

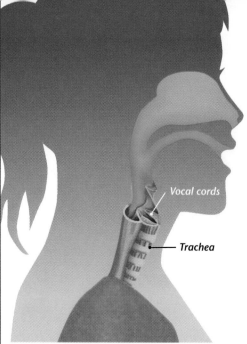

Vocal cords

Trachea

Figure 6 Air moving over this singer's vocal cords causes them to vibrate and produce sound. When her vocal cords contract, or shorten, she sings higher notes. When her vocal cords lengthen, she sings lower notes.

cords have a slitlike opening between them. When you speak, muscles make the vocal cords contract, narrowing the opening. Air from the lungs rushes through this opening. The movement of the vocal cords makes the air particles vibrate, or move rapidly back and forth. This vibration creates a sound—your voice.

High and Low Tones The length of the vocal cords affects whether you produce low or high tones. When the vocal cords contract and shorten, you speak in a higher voice. When they are longer and in a relaxed position, you speak in a lower voice.

The length of vocal cords changes during a person's lifetime. Small children have high-pitched voices because their larynxes are small and their vocal cords are short. The vocal cords of both boys and girls are about the same length. During the teenage years, however, the vocal cords of boys grow longer than those of girls. This is why men have deeper voices than women.

Section 1 Review

1. List the functions of the respiratory system.
2. Describe the path that a molecule of oxygen takes as it moves from the air into the alveoli.
3. Explain what happens to carbon dioxide in the blood that flows through capillaries in the alveoli.
4. Why does air rush into your body when you inhale?
5. **Thinking Critically** **Relating Cause and Effect** When there is a lot of dust in the air, people often cough and sneeze. Explain why this happens.

Science at Home

Use a shoe box and a set of blocks to show your family how the alveoli increase the surface area of the lungs. The shoe box represents a lung, and each block represents an alveolus. Fill the box with as many blocks as will fit inside. Then have your family imagine how much surface would be covered if all of the blocks were opened up and put together to form a large sheet. How would the surface area of the blocks compare with that of the shoe box?

Performance Assessment

Writing Have students write short stories describing the adventures of an oxygen molecule during respiration. Reports should indicate where the molecule traveled, what sights it saw, and how it was changed by the adventure.

 Students can save their short stories in their portfolios.

Program Resources

◆ **Teaching Resources** 5-1 Review and Reinforce, p. 123; 5-1 Enrich, p. 124

Media and Technology

Interactive Student Tutorial CD-ROM D-5

Skills Lab

A Breath of Fresh Air

How does air get into your lungs? In this lab, you will make a model of the lungs to demonstrate how breathing takes place.

Problem

What causes your body to inhale and exhale air?

Materials

small balloon   large balloon
scissors
transparent plastic bottle with narrow neck

Procedure ✂

1. In your notebook, explain how you think air gets into the lungs during the breathing process.
2. Cut off and discard the bottom of a small plastic bottle. Trim the cut edge so there are no rough spots.
3. Stretch a small balloon, then blow it up a few times to stretch it further. Insert the round end of the balloon through the mouth of the bottle. Then, with a partner holding the bottle, stretch the neck of the balloon and pull it over the mouth of the bottle.
4. Stretch a large balloon, then blow it up a few times to stretch it further. Cut off the balloon's neck, and discard it.
5. Have a partner hold the bottle while you stretch the remaining part of the balloon over the bottom opening of the bottle, as shown in the photo.

6. Use one hand to hold the bottle firmly. With the knuckles of your other hand, push upward on the large balloon, causing it to form a dome. Remove your knuckles from the balloon, letting the balloon flatten. Repeat this procedure a few times. Observe what happens to the small balloon. Record your observations in your notebook.

Analyze and Conclude

1. Make a diagram of the completed model in your notebook. Add labels to show which parts of your model represent the chest cavity, diaphragm, lungs, and trachea.
2. In this model, what is the position of the diaphragm just after you have exhaled? What do the lungs look like just after you have exhaled?
3. In this model, how does the diaphragm move? How do these movements of the diaphragm affect the lungs?
4. **Think About It** How does this model show that pressure changes are responsible for breathing?

More to Explore

How could you improve on this model to more closely show what happens in the chest cavity during the process of breathing? Obtain your teacher's permission before making a new model.

Extending the Inquiry

More to Explore Samples: To improve their models, students could:
◆ use many small balloons and straws to show that the surface area of the lungs is large because of numerous alveoli;
◆ use a flexible plastic bottle to show that the ribs also move during inhalation, increasing the volume of the chest cavity.

Safety

You may want to cut the plastic bottles yourself or make the process easier by making the first cut.

Program Resources

◆ **Teaching Resources** Chapter 5 Skills Lab, pp. 133–134
◆ **Inquiry Skills Activity Book** Provides teaching and review of all inquiry skills

---

A Breath of Fresh Air

Preparing for Inquiry

Key Concept A model of the lungs will demonstrate what happens during inhalation and exhalation.
Skills Objective Students will be able to
◆ make a model of the lungs.
Time 30 minutes
Advance Planning Obtain balloons and small, transparent, plastic bottles.
Alternative Materials You can use different sizes of bottles and balloons, but make sure the small balloon hangs freely. If a balloon does not make an airtight seal with the bottle, tape the seal.

Guiding Inquiry

Invitation
Encourage students to share their responses to Step 1 in the Procedure.

Introducing the Procedure
Have students refer to the photo in the book as they prepare the model.

Troubleshooting the Experiment
Be sure students do not pull the large balloon down to model inhalation. To show the relaxed (exhaled) state, the balloon should be dome shaped. The balloon flattens during inhalation.

Analyze and Conclude
1. Bottle—chest cavity; large balloon—diaphragm; neck of the bottle —trachea; small balloon—lungs
2. The diaphragm rises into the chest cavity. The lungs are deflated.
3. The diaphragm moves down, becoming flat, then moves upward into its domed shape. When it moves upward, the lungs deflate. When it moves down, the lungs inflate.
4. When the volume inside the plastic bottle increases, it decreases the air pressure inside, and the small balloon inflates. When the volume inside the bottle decreases, it increases the air pressure inside and causes the small balloon to deflate.

SECTION 2 Smoking and Your Health

Objectives

After completing the lesson, students will be able to

◆ list the harmful chemicals contained in tobacco smoke;

◆ explain how tobacco smoke harms the respiratory and circulatory systems.

Key Terms tar, carbon monoxide, nicotine, addiction, bronchitis, emphysema, passive smoking

1 Engage/Explore

Activating Prior Knowledge

Have students discuss their perceptions of smoking and popular culture. Encourage students to talk about how the image of smoking has changed over the years. Students may be aware of laws that restrict the areas where smoking is permitted or of lawsuits that have been brought against cigarette manufacturers.

•••••••• DISCOVER ••••••••

Skills Focus inferring
Time 20 minutes
Tips Encourage students to discuss their answers with their partners. After students record their answers, provide the actual answers listed below. Prompt students to discuss any differences between their estimates and the actual numbers.
Answers 1. 400,000 2. 87% 3. 7 years longer 4. About 70% 5. About 25% (Sources: 1 and 3—Centers for Disease Control; 2—American Cancer Society; 4 and 5—Koop-Kessler Report on Tobacco Policy and Public Health)
Think It Over Samples: peer pressure, advertising, family members smoke

SECTION 2 Smoking and Your Health

DISCOVER •••••••••••••••••••••••••••••• ACTIVITY

What Are the Dangers of Smoking?

Pair up with a partner. Read each question below and decide on a reasonable answer based on your current knowledge.

1. In the United States, about how many people die each year from smoking-related illnesses?

2. What percentage of lung cancer deaths are related to smoking?

3. On the average, how much longer do nonsmokers live than smokers?

4. What percentage of smokers say they want to quit smoking?

5. What percentage of smokers actually succeed in quitting?

Think It Over
Inferring Why do you think people start smoking when they know that smoking can cause serious health problems?

GUIDE FOR READING

◆ What harmful chemicals are contained in tobacco smoke?

◆ How does tobacco smoke harm the respiratory and circulatory systems?

Reading Tip Before you read, make a list of smoking-related health problems that you already know about. Add to your list as you read.

Whoosh! Millions of tiny but dangerous aliens are invading the respiratory system. The aliens are pulled into the nose with an inhaled breath. The cilia in the nasal cavities trap some aliens, and others get stuck in mucus. But many aliens get past these defenses. After tumbling in air currents, thousands of the invaders enter the lungs. The aliens implant themselves in the alveoli!

The "aliens" are not tiny creatures from space. They are the substances found in cigarette smoke. In this section you will learn how tobacco smoke damages the respiratory system.

Chemicals in Tobacco Smoke

With each puff, a smoker inhales over 4,000 different chemicals. **Some of the most deadly chemicals in tobacco smoke are tar, carbon monoxide, and nicotine.**

Tar The dark, sticky substance that forms when tobacco burns is called **tar.** When someone inhales tobacco smoke, some tar settles on cilia that line the trachea and other respiratory organs. Tar makes cilia clump together so they can't function to prevent harmful materials from getting into the lungs. Tar also contains chemicals that have been shown to cause cancer.

READING STRATEGIES

Reading Tip After students make their lists, invite volunteers to read items from their lists to the class. Record the information on the board. Then lead students in a discussion of other types of problems related to smoking, such as stained fingers and teeth, litter from cigarettes and their packaging, and fires.

Vocabulary Students should write each boldfaced term and its definition in their journals as they read.

Study and Comprehension Students can create concept maps to organize information about smoking and health. Have students choose between these topics: *Harmful Chemicals in Tobacco Smoke* or *Respiratory and Circulatory Problems Caused by Tobacco Smoke*. Refer students to the explanation of concept mapping in the Skills Handbook, page 268.

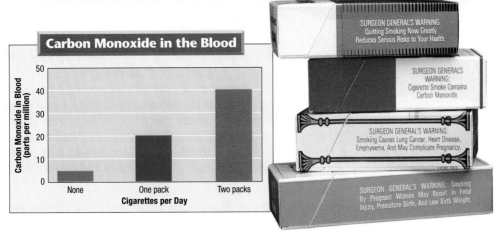

Carbon Monoxide in the Blood

Figure 7 The more cigarettes a person smokes, the more carbon monoxide he or she inhales. *Relating Cause and Effect How does carbon monoxide deprive the body of oxygen?*

Carbon Monoxide When substances—including tobacco—are burned, a colorless, odorless gas called **carbon monoxide** is produced. Carbon monoxide is dangerous to inhale because its molecules bind to hemoglobin in red blood cells. When carbon monoxide binds to hemoglobin, it takes the place of some of the oxygen that the red blood cells normally carry. The carbon monoxide molecules are something like cars that have taken parking spaces reserved for other cars.

When carbon monoxide binds to hemoglobin, red blood cells carry less than their normal load of oxygen throughout the body. To make up for the decrease in oxygen, the breathing rate increases and the heart beats faster. Smokers' blood may contain too little oxygen to meet their bodies' needs.

Nicotine Another dangerous chemical found in tobacco smoke is **nicotine.** Nicotine is a drug that speeds up the activities of the nervous system, heart, and other organs. It makes the heart beat faster and blood pressure rise. Nicotine produces an **addiction,** or physical dependence. Smokers feel an intense need, or craving, for a cigarette if they go without one. Addiction to nicotine is one reason why smokers have difficulty quitting.

☑ *Checkpoint How does the tar in cigarette smoke affect the body?*

Respiratory System Problems

Tobacco smoke harms the respiratory system in several ways. For example, because their cilia can't sweep away mucus, many smokers have a frequent cough. The mucus buildup also limits the space for air flow, and this decreases oxygen intake. Because

---

Answers to Self-Assessment

Caption Question

Figure 7 Carbon monoxide binds to the hemoglobin in red cells, taking the place of some of the oxygen.

☑ *Checkpoint*

Tar makes cilia clump together so they cannot stop harmful materials from traveling to the lungs. Tar also contains chemicals that cause cancer.

---

2 Facilitate

Chemicals in Tobacco Smoke

Using the Visuals: Figure 7

Ask students what they think the phrase "parts per million" means. Help students understand that the phrase expresses concentration, or the amount of one substance in a certain volume of another substance. If the carbon monoxide in a person's blood has a concentration of two parts per million, that means that there is 500,000 times more blood than carbon dioxide. **limited English proficiency**

Addressing Naive Conceptions

Students may believe smokers can control the amount of dangerous chemicals they receive by smoking "light" or filtered cigarettes. Tell students researchers have found that many people who smoke these cigarettes smoke them in such a way that they actually receive the same amounts of tar and other chemicals as people who smoke "regular" cigarettes. Point out that no cigarettes are safe to smoke. **learning modality: verbal**

Respiratory System Problems

Real-Life Learning

Ask students if they know anyone with bronchitis, emphysema, or lung cancer. Encourage those who do to describe how these illnesses affect quality of life and affect families. **learning modality: verbal**

Ongoing Assessment

Oral Presentation Call on students to name three harmful chemicals in tobacco smoke and to explain the health effects of each of them.

Respiratory System Problems, continued

Real-Life Learning

Materials *2 plastic cups, eraser, water, pencil, blindfold*

Time 5 minutes

Ask students if they have ever seen a doctor or nurse "thumping" on a person's back on television or in a movie. Explain that this is one way the doctor or nurse can tell whether the lungs are clear or have liquid in them. Pairs of students can model this procedure by standing two plastic drinking cups side-by-side, one filled with water, the second containing an eraser to weigh it down. Have one partner put on the blindfold. The other student will tap each cup with a pencil. The blindfolded student can note the differences in sound and try to identify the cup of water. Ask: **How can you tell which cup has the liquid in it?** *(They sound different.)* **cooperative learning**

Addressing Naive Conceptions

Students may have heard statements that nicotine is not an addictive drug like heroin or cocaine, leading them to think that quitting smoking is much easier than quitting a so-called "hard" drug. Inform students that researchers have recently discovered that nicotine releases the same chemicals in the brain that heroin, cocaine, and other drugs release. Explain that this research points to a physical basis for nicotine addiction. Ask students: **What are the implications of the recent research on nicotine addiction?** *(Samples: A physical addiction to nicotine makes it more difficult to quit smoking; nicotine is a dangerous drug.)* **learning modality: verbal**

they are not getting enough oxygen, smokers may not be able to participate in vigorous sports. Long-term or heavy smokers may be short of breath during even light exercise.

Some serious respiratory problems can result from long-term smoking. **Over time, smokers can develop bronchitis, emphysema, and lung cancer.** Every year in the United States, more than 400,000 people die from smoking-related illnesses. That's one out of every five deaths. Tobacco smoke is the most important preventable cause of major illness and death.

Bronchitis Over time, mucus buildup can lead to bronchitis. **Bronchitis** (brahng KY tis) is an irritation of the breathing passages in which the small passages become narrower than normal and may be clogged with mucus. People with bronchitis have a hard time breathing. Bronchitis is often accompanied by infection with disease-causing microorganisms. If bronchitis lasts a long time, it can cause permanent damage to the breathing passages. Long-term bronchitis is five to ten times more common in heavy smokers than in nonsmokers.

Figure 8 These people stay healthy by exercising and by choosing not to smoke.

Emphysema The chemicals in tobacco smoke damage lung tissue as well as breathing passages. **Emphysema** (em fuh SEE muh) is a serious disease that destroys lung tissue and causes difficulty in breathing. People with emphysema do not get enough oxygen and cannot adequately eliminate carbon dioxide. Therefore, they are always short of breath. Some people with emphysema even have trouble blowing out a match. Unfortunately, the damage caused by emphysema is permanent, even if a person stops smoking.

Lung Cancer About 140,000 Americans die each year from lung cancer caused by smoking. Cigarette smoke contains over 40 different chemicals that cause cancer, including chemicals in tar. Cancerous growths, or tumors, take away space in the lungs that should be used for gas exchange. Unfortunately, lung cancer is difficult to detect early, when treatment would be most effective.

☑ *Checkpoint* *How does emphysema affect a person's lungs?*

Background

Integrating Health Many teenagers think smokeless tobacco is a safe alternative to smoking cigarettes. The truth, however, is quite different. Smokeless tobacco includes chewing tobacco and snuff, a powdered tobacco. Like inhaled tobacco smoke, smokeless tobacco contains nicotine and carcinogens that get into the body and damage it.

Researchers have found a positive correlation between the use of smokeless tobacco and cancers of the oral cavity, pharynx, larynx, and esophagus. In addition to cancer, smokeless tobacco is responsible for nicotine addiction, increased heart rate and blood pressure, and reduced physical performance and productivity. Users of smokeless tobacco may also develop gum disease.

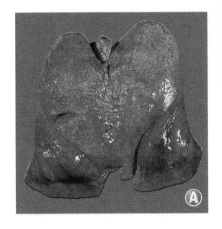
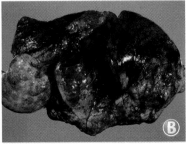
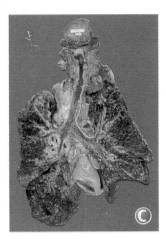

Figure 9 Over time, smoking damages the lungs and leads to serious health problems. Compare the lungs of a nonsmoker (**A**) to those of a person with emphysema (**B**) and a person with lung cancer (**C**).

Circulatory System Problems

The chemicals in tobacco smoke that damage the lungs also harm the circulatory system. Some of the chemicals get into the blood and are absorbed by the blood vessels. The chemicals then irritate the walls of the blood vessels. This irritation contributes to the buildup of the fatty material that causes atherosclerosis. Atherosclerosis can lead to heart attacks. **Compared to nonsmokers, smokers are more than twice as likely to have heart attacks.**

Conditions that harm the lungs, such as bronchitis and emphysema, also strain the circulatory system. The respiratory and circulatory systems work together to get oxygen to the cells and to remove carbon dioxide from the body. If either system is damaged, the other one must work harder.

Passive Smoking

Smokers are not the only people to suffer from the effects of tobacco smoke. In **passive smoking,** people involuntarily inhale the smoke from other people's cigarettes, cigars, or pipes. Since this smoke contains the same harmful chemicals that smokers inhale, it can cause health problems. Each year, passive smoking causes about 300,000 young children in the United States to develop respiratory problems such as bronchitis. In addition, long-term exposure to cigarette smoke increases people's risks of heart disease and cancer.

Sharpen your Skills

Calculating

Heavy smokers may smoke two packs of cigarettes every day. Find out what one pack of cigarettes costs. Then use that price to calculate how much a person would spend on cigarettes if he or she smoked two packs a day for 30 years.

Chapter 5 **D ◆ 143**

Media and Technology

 Exploring Life Science Videodisc
Unit 4, Side 1, "Caution: Breathing May Be Hazardous to Your Health"

Chapter 8

Answers to Self-Assessment

☑ *Checkpoint*

Emphysema destroys lung tissue and causes difficulty in breathing.

Circulatory System Problems

Using the Visuals: Figure 9

Ask students to use the photographs to infer how the condition of the lungs shown in each photograph would probably affect a person's circulatory health. Point out how pink and moist the healthy lungs look compared to the lungs in the other two photos. *(Students may speculate that the lungs in B and C would not be able to take in very much air, and that they would not be able to exchange gas with the circulatory system.)*
learning modality: visual

Sharpen your Skills

Calculating

Ask students to provide a range of costs for a pack of cigarettes based on advertising, or give them an average price to work with. Answers will depend on the price of cigarettes.
Extend Have students figure out some things that the person could have bought if he or she had saved the money spent on cigarettes. For example, if an apartment rents for $500 per month, how many months' rent would the saved money pay for?

Passive Smoking

Real-Life Learning

Tell students that smoking is now forbidden in many workplaces, restaurants, public buildings, and aircraft. Ask if students can explain why these restrictions have been imposed and who they were designed to protect. Interested students can research the laws governing smoking in your community.
learning modality: verbal

Ongoing Assessment

Oral Presentation Ask students to identify and describe three respiratory system problems that result from cigarette smoking.

Choosing Not to Smoke

Real-Life Learning

Inform students that most smokers started smoking as teenagers. Ask: **If most smokers who try to quit are unsuccessful, what is a simple way to avoid becoming part of these statistics?** (*Never start smoking.*) **learning modality: verbal**

3 Assess

Section 2 Review Answers

1. Tar— damages cilia and contains chemicals that cause cancer; carbon monoxide—takes the place of oxygen in hemoglobin and deprives the body of oxygen; nicotine—addictive and speeds up body systems, making the heart beat faster and blood pressure rise
2. Any three: frequent cough, decreased oxygen intake, shortness of breath, bronchitis, emphysema, lung cancer
3. Chemicals in cigarette smoke contribute to a buildup of substances in blood vessels that cause atherosclerosis; problems in the respiratory system put a strain on the cardiovascular system.
4. Peer pressure and advertisements
5. Nonsmokers develop cancer because they are passive smokers—they have inhaled the cigarette smoke produced by other people's cigarettes.

Check Your Progress
CHAPTER PROJECT 5

Review students' ads to make sure they indicate a relationship between what students are learning about respiratory function and health problems associated with smoking.

Performance Assessment

Writing Have students write paragraphs in which they convince a friend not to smoke.

 Students can save their paragraphs in their portfolios.

Figure 10 This antismoking advertisement was created by a teenager to encourage smokers to quit.

Choosing Not to Smoke

Today about 50 million Americans are smokers. Of those people, more than 90 percent began smoking when they were teenagers. Studies show that if people do not start smoking when they are teenagers, they probably will not start smoking later in life.

You may be tempted to try smoking. Friends may pressure you, or advertisements may appeal to you. Tobacco advertisements show smokers as young, attractive, popular people. The ads try to make you think that you will be like these people if you use tobacco products.

It is important to remember that it's very hard to quit smoking once you start. Many teenage smokers think that they will quit when they are older—but because nicotine is addictive, they have trouble doing so. And smoking hurts people right away, not just later in life. The lungs of teenagers who smoke develop more slowly than those of nonsmokers and may never reach the same peak level of functioning. In addition, teenage smokers may develop coughs and bronchitis. If someone asks you to try a cigarette, think of your health and politely refuse.

Section 2 Review

1. Name three harmful substances in tobacco smoke. Describe the effects of each substance.
2. Identify three respiratory problems caused by smoking.
3. Describe the effect of smoking on the circulatory system.
4. Identify two factors that may pressure teenagers to try smoking.
5. **Thinking Critically Relating Cause and Effect** Scientists estimate that about 3,000 nonsmoking Americans die every year from smoking-related lung cancer. Explain why.

Check Your Progress
CHAPTER PROJECT 5

By now you should have sketched what your ads might look like and written what they might say. In planning your ads, be sure to consider all the effects of smoking, not just those related to health—for example, the expense of smoking. Plan to use ideas and images that are appropriate for each age group. (*Hint:* Look through a variety of magazines to find ads aimed at different age groups. Which techniques seem to work best? How can you use those techniques in your ads?)

Program Resources

◆ **Teaching Resources** 5-2 Review and Reinforce, p. 127; 5-2 Enrich, p. 128

Media and Technology

 Interactive Student Tutorial CD-ROM D-5

SECTION 3 The Excretory System

SECTION 3 The Excretory System

DISCOVER ••••••••••••••••••••••••••• ACTIVITY

How Does Filtering a Liquid Change What Is in It?

1. Your teacher will give you 50 milliliters of a liquid in a small container. Pour a small amount of sand into the liquid.

2. Use a glucose-test strip to determine whether glucose is present in the liquid.

3. Put filter paper in a funnel. Then put the funnel into the mouth of a second container. Slowly pour the liquid through the funnel into the second container.

4. Look for any solid material on the filter paper. Remove the funnel and carefully examine the liquid that passed through the filter.

5. Test the liquid again to see whether it contains glucose.

Think It Over

Observing Which substances passed through the filter, and which did not? How might a filtering device be useful in the body?

The human body faces a challenge that is a bit like trying to keep a home clean. You learned in Chapter 3 that the body takes in foods through the digestive system and breaks them down into nutrients. As cells use those nutrients in respiration and other processes, wastes are created. **The excretory system is the system in the body that collects wastes produced by cells and removes the wastes from the body.** The removal process is known as **excretion.**

If wastes were not taken away, they would pile up and make you sick. Excretion helps maintain homeostasis by keeping the body's internal environment stable and free of harmful materials.

The Kidneys

As you already know, some wastes that your body must eliminate are carbon dioxide and excess water. Another waste product is urea. **Urea** (yoo REE uh) is a poisonous chemical that comes from the breakdown of proteins. Your two **kidneys,** which are the major organs of the excretory system, eliminate urea, excess water, and some other waste materials. These wastes are eliminated in **urine,** a watery fluid produced by your kidneys.

The kidneys act something like filters. As blood flows through the kidneys, they remove wastes from the blood. After the process is complete, urine flows from the kidneys through two narrow tubes called **ureters** (yoo REE turz). The ureters carry the urine

> ### GUIDE FOR READING
> ◆ What is the function of the excretory system?
> ◆ How is urine produced in the kidneys' nephrons?
> ◆ In addition to the kidneys, what other organs play a role in excretion?
>
> *Reading Tip* As you read, write a brief summary of the information under each heading.

Chapter 5 **D ◆ 145**

Objectives

After completing the lesson, students will be able to

◆ identify the function of the excretory system;
◆ state how urine is produced in the kidneys' nephrons;
◆ name the organs involved in excretion and describe their roles.

Key Terms excretion, urea, kidney, urine, ureter, urinary bladder, urethra, nephron

1 Engage/Explore

Activating Prior Knowledge

Have students list some typical items that families discard as trash. Ask students what would happen if no one ever removed this trash from their apartment or house. Then point out that the body produces "trash" substances that need to be eliminated.

•••••••• DISCOVER ••••••••

Skills Focus observing
Materials *glucose solution, sand, two small plastic containers, glucose test strip, plastic funnel, filter paper*
Time 15 minutes
Tips Prepare the glucose solution using 5 grams of glucose per liter of water. Each plastic container should hold at least 75 mL.
Expected Outcome The glucose solution will pass through the filter, but the sand will not.
Think It Over The glucose and water passed through the filter; the sand did not. A filtering device could remove wastes in the body.

The Kidneys

Real-Life Learning

Have students predict what happens when the kidneys fail. *(Students may speculate that urination may cease and the body may fill with waste products.)* Tell students that sometimes, because of disease, people's kidneys stop functioning. Have them develop a list of questions about kidney failure, including symptoms and treatment options. Invite a specialist to talk to the class and answer students' questions, or provide resources for students to perform their own research. Students can present their findings in a poster or pamphlet. **learning modality: verbal**

The Filtering Process

EXPLORING
a Kidney

Refer students to the visual essay on the kidney. Ask: **How are the three diagrams related?** *(The first diagram shows the location of the kidneys in the excretory system; the second shows a close-up of a kidney; the third shows details of a nephron inside a kidney.)* Direct students' attention to the illustration of the nephron. After students have examined the illustration, ask them to identify the function of the capillary cluster. *(Filters urea, water, glucose, and other substances out of the blood.)* Students can then make flowcharts that trace the path of filtered material through the tube. Once the flowcharts are completed, ask: **What is the purpose of the nephrons?** *(The nephrons remove wastes and produce urine.)* **learning modality: visual**

Portfolio Students can save their flowcharts in their portfolios.

to the **urinary bladder,** a sacklike muscular organ that stores urine. When the bladder is full enough that its walls are stretched, you feel a need to urinate. Urine flows from the body through a small tube called the **urethra** (yoo REE thruh), which you can see in *Exploring a Kidney.*

✓ *Checkpoint* **What is the role of the ureters?**

The Filtering Process

The kidneys are champion filters. Every drop of blood in your body passes through your kidneys and is filtered more than 300 times a day. Contrast this to a typical swimming-pool filter, which only cleans the pool water about 5 times a day.

Each of your kidneys contains about a million tiny filtering factories called **nephrons.** The nephrons are the tiny structures that remove wastes from blood and produce urine. **Urine formation takes place in two stages. First, both wastes and needed materials, such as glucose, are removed from the blood. Second, much of the needed material is returned to the blood.**

Filtering Out Wastes After entering the kidneys, blood flows through smaller and smaller arteries. Eventually it reaches a cluster of capillaries in a nephron. These capillaries are surrounded

EXPLORING *a Kidney*

Each kidney contains about a million tiny filtering units called nephrons. Urine is produced in the nephrons.

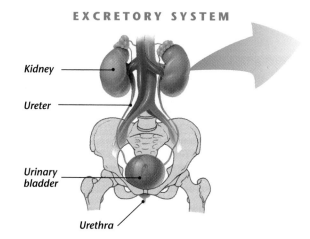

EXCRETORY SYSTEM

Kidney

Ureter

Urinary bladder

Urethra

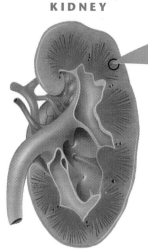

KIDNEY

Background

Facts and Figures People whose kidneys do not function have to undergo dialysis. In this procedure, the patients' blood is removed from their body, purified by an artificial kidney (called a dialyzer), and then returned to their bloodstream. During the procedure, the patient's blood is diverted from an artery into the dialyzer, where it flows along one surface of a membrane. The waste materials pass through the membrane into a sterile

solution on the other side. Substances required by the body, such as sugars, amino acids, and salts are added to the sterile solution where they move through the membrane into the blood. After water is returned across the membrane and the blood is completely filtered, clots and bubbles are removed before the blood flows back into one of the patient's veins.

by a thin-walled, hollow capsule that is connected to a long tube. Find the capillary cluster, the capsule, and the tube in *Exploring a Kidney*. In the capillary cluster, urea, glucose, other chemicals, and some water move out of the blood and into the capsule. In contrast, blood cells, some water, and some other materials do not move into the capsule. Instead, they remain in the capillaries.

Formation of Urine Urine forms from the filtered material that passes into the capsule. This filtered material flows through the long, twisting tube. Some of the substances that collect in the capsule are needed by the body. As the liquid moves through the tube, many of these substances are reabsorbed, or returned to the blood. Normally all the glucose, most of the water, and small amounts of other materials pass back into the blood in the capillaries that surround the tube. In contrast, urea and other wastes remain in the tube.

The filtering process is something like cleaning your locker by throwing everything in your locker into a wastebasket, and then putting back the things that you want to keep. You can think of the locker as your blood and the wastebasket as the capsule. After the entire filtering and reabsorbing process is complete, the fluid that remains in the tube is urine.

NEPHRON

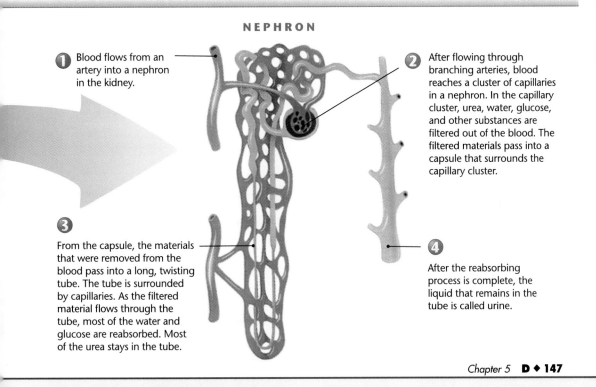

1. Blood flows from an artery into a nephron in the kidney.

2. After flowing through branching arteries, blood reaches a cluster of capillaries in a nephron. In the capillary cluster, urea, water, glucose, and other substances are filtered out of the blood. The filtered materials pass into a capsule that surrounds the capillary cluster.

3. From the capsule, the materials that were removed from the blood pass into a long, twisting tube. The tube is surrounded by capillaries. As the filtered material flows through the tube, most of the water and glucose are reabsorbed. Most of the urea stays in the tube.

4. After the reabsorbing process is complete, the liquid that remains in the tube is called urine.

Chapter 5 **D ◆ 147**

Media and Technology

📺 **Transparencies** "Exploring a Kidney," Transparency 12

💿 **Exploring Life Science Videodisc** Unit 4, Side 1, "Cool Sweat"

Chapter 7

Answers to Self-Assessment

☑ *Checkpoint*
Ureters carry urine to the urinary bladder.

Demonstration

Materials *30-cm section of cellophane dialysis tubing, 2 large beakers, string, 10 mL of a solution of salt water, distilled water, hand held conductivity tester*

Time 40 minutes

For the benefit of students who had difficulty comprehending the text description of kidney function, you can use a model to demonstrate how salt passes back into the blood during the formation of urine. Soak the tubing for several hours in a beaker filled with distilled water. Use string to tie one end of the dialysis tubing tightly closed. After the tubing is tied, store it in the container of distilled water. On the day of the activity, prepare the salt solution by mixing a few teaspoons of table salt in 100 mL of water. Fill the tubing three-quarters full with the salt solution, then tie the open end of the bag tightly closed with string. Suspend the tubing in a beaker of distilled water by tying it to a ruler placed across the rim. Do not allow the beaker to overflow. To begin the demonstration, tell students that the bag contains a salt solution, and that the tester indicates the presence of salt in a solution. After 20 minutes, test the solution in the beaker. The conductivity tester should light. Have students explain how the salt got into the distilled water and how this models the movement of salt during the formation of urine. (*The salt in the tubing passes into the water the way salt in the kidney tubes passes back into the blood in the capillaries that surround the tubes.*)

Alternative Materials If you do not have a conductivity tester, pour some of the water from the beaker into an evaporating dish and heat it gently until the water evaporates. (Do not boil.) Students should be able to see a white residue in the dish, indicating the presence of salt. **limited English proficiency**

Ongoing Assessment

Writing Have students list the functions of the kidneys.

You Solve the Mystery

Clues About Health

Preparing for Inquiry

Key Concept Urine tests can provide evidence of disease.

Skills Objectives Students will be able to
- observe color changes as solutions react with the test solutions;
- interpret data and draw conclusions about the presence or absence of glucose and protein in the solutions.

Time 40 minutes

Advance Planning Make up the patients' samples to match the Sample Data Table below or according to your own preferences. Prepare a 1% glucose solution by dissolving 10 g of glucose in 990 mL of water. Make a 1% protein solution by dissolving 10 g of albumin or pepsin in 990 mL of water. Add food coloring to make the solutions a pale yellow color (like urine), if desired. Use these solutions to make the simulated urine samples. Glucose test strips and Biuret solution can be obtained from biological supply companies.

Guiding Inquiry

Invitation

Ask students to list substances that are filtered from the blood and to identify which of those substances should be reabsorbed. Students should conclude that some substances should not be in the urine of a healthy person.

Introducing the Procedure

Ask: **What is the purpose of testing known solutions?** *(They show how the test materials work.)*

Troubleshooting the Experiment

- Food coloring may distort color changes and make them less noticeable.
- Droppers should be labeled and returned to the proper test tube to avoid contamination.

Analyzing Urine for Signs of Disease When people go to a **INTEGRATING HEALTH** doctor for a medical checkup, they usually have their urine analyzed. A chemical analysis of urine can be useful in detecting some medical problems. Normally, urine contains almost no glucose or protein. If glucose is present in urine, it may indicate that a person has diabetes, a condition in which body cells cannot absorb enough glucose from the blood. Protein in urine can be a sign that the kidneys are not functioning properly.

Real-World Lab

.... **You Solve the Mystery** ....

CLUES ABOUT HEALTH

In this lab, you'll become a medical detective as you carry out urine tests to uncover evidence of disease.

Problem

How can you test urine for the presence of glucose and protein?

Skills Focus

observing, interpreting data, drawing conclusions

Materials

test tubes, 6	test tube rack
plastic droppers, 6	water
glucose solution	protein solution
marking pencil	white paper towels
glucose test strips	Biuret solution
simulated urine samples, 3	

Procedure

Part 1 Testing for Glucose

1. Label six test tubes as follows: "W" for water, "G" for glucose, "P" for protein, and "A," "B," and "C" for three patients' "urine samples."

2. Place the test tubes in a test tube rack. Label six glucose test strips with the same letters.

3. Copy the data table into your notebook.

4. Fill each test tube about 3/4 full with the solution that corresponds to its label.

5. Place the W glucose test strip on a clean, dry section of a paper towel. Then use a clean plastic dropper to place 2 drops of the water from test tube W on the test strip. Record the resulting color of the test strip in your data table. If no color change occurs, write "no reaction."

Expected Outcome
- Glucose test strips will turn green if glucose is present.
- The solution will turn purple-pink when Biuret solution is added if protein is present.
- A 50/50 mix (simulated urine sample) should give positive results for both glucose and protein.

Analyze and Conclude

1. The normal urine sample (B) is negative in both the glucose and protein tests.

2. The urine sample that tests positive for glucose (C) indicates possible diabetes.

3. A urine sample that tests positive for protein (A) indicates possible kidney disease.

4. Normally, the kidneys reabsorb glucose and protein into the blood.

5. No. A single test does not provide enough evidence. The person should go for further testing.

Water Balance in the Body

The kidneys also help maintain homeostasis by regulating the amount of water in your body. Remember that as urine is being formed, water passes from the tube back into the bloodstream. The exact amount of water that is reabsorbed depends on conditions both outside and within the body. Suppose that it's a hot day. You've been sweating a lot, and you haven't had much to drink. In that situation, almost all of the water in the tube will be reabsorbed, and you will excrete only a small amount of urine. If,

DATA TABLE
Test Tube

Test for	W (water)	G (glucose)	P (protein)	A (Patient A)	B (Patient B)	C (Patient C)
Glucose						
Protein						

6. Use the procedure in Step 5 to test each of the other five solutions with the correctly labeled glucose test strip. Record the color of each test strip in the data table.

Part 2 Testing for Protein

7. Obtain a dropper bottle containing Biuret solution. Record the original color of the solution in your notebook.

8. Carefully add 10 drops of Biuret solution to test tube W. **CAUTION:** *Biuret solution can harm skin and damage clothing. Handle it with care.* Gently swirl the test tube to mix the two solutions together. Hold the test tube against a white paper towel to help you detect any color change. Observe the color of the final mixture, and record that color in your data table.

9. Repeat Step 8 for each of the other test tubes.

Analyze and Conclude

1. Which of the three patients' urine samples tested normal? How do you know?

2. Which urine sample(s) indicated that diabetes might be present? How do you know?

3. Which urine sample(s) indicated that kidney disease might be present? How do you know?

4. When a person's health is normal, how are the kidneys involved in keeping glucose and protein out of urine?

5. **Apply** Do you think a doctor should draw conclusions about the presence of a disease based on a single urine sample? Explain.

More to Explore

Propose a way to determine whether a patient with glucose in the urine could reduce the level through changes in diet.

Extending the Inquiry

More to Explore Students might suggest the patient eat fewer sugary foods. The amount of glucose in the patient's urine can be monitored to determine if diet affects the glucose level.

Sample Data Table

Test for	W (water)	G (glucose)	P (protein)	A (Patient A)	B (Patient B)	C (Patient C)
Glucose	Yellow	Green	Yellow	Yellow	Yellow	Green
Protein	Lt. Blue	Lt. Blue	Purple	Purple	Lt. Blue	Lt. Blue

Safety

Students should wear aprons and safety goggles and use glassware carefully. Biuret solution can harm skin and damage clothing. Review the safety guidelines in Appendix A.

Program Resources

◆ **Teaching Resources** Chapter 5 Real-World Lab, pp. 135–137

 Integrating Health

Inform students that doctors can find evidence of illness or injury by studying changes in the color, density, and amount of the urine. Tell them that urinalysis can also show whether a person has used steroids, marijuana, or other illegal substances. Ask: **What does it indicate when a substance not normally a waste product is found in a urine sample?** *(Sample: The body cannot fully absorb or process the substance.)* **learning modality: verbal**

Water Balance in the Body

Building Inquiry Skills: Predicting

Ask students to predict what would happen if they took in significantly more than 2 liters of water each day. *(Sample: The body would produce a volume of urine large enough to maintain homeostasis.)* **learning modality: verbal**

Other Organs of Excretion

Building Inquiry Skills: Inferring

Have each student place a plastic sandwich bag over one of his or her hands, then use masking tape to close the bag at the wrist. After a few minutes, students should observe condensation inside the bags. Ask students to infer whether the skin removes wastes from the body all the time, or just when they are aware they are perspiring. (*All the time*)
learning modality: kinesthetic

3 Assess

Section 3 Review Answers

1. To collect and remove wastes from the body.
2. First, both wastes and needed substances are removed from the blood. Then, the substances the body needs are returned to the blood. Once the filtering and reabsorbing processes are complete, the fluid remaining is urine.
3. Lungs remove carbon dioxide and some water; sweat glands in skin excrete water and some chemical waste; the liver breaks large proteins into smaller ones so they can be excreted.
4. They adjust the amount of water reabsorbed during excretion.
5. Laura will probably produce less urine, because most of the water she is taking in will be reabsorbed.

Check Your Progress CHAPTER PROJECT 5

Groups should have assigned roles for the production of their ads. Arrange a place for students to display their work. If possible, use a common hallway where other students can see the ads. Effective posters may discourage other students from smoking.

Performance Assessment

Writing Have students explain how one organ in the excretory system functions.

Figure 11 Your skin and lungs also function as excretory organs. Water and some chemical wastes are excreted in perspiration. And when you exhale on a cold morning, you can see the water in your breath. *Applying Concepts What other waste product does your exhaled breath contain?*

however, the day is cool and you've drunk a lot of water, less water will be reabsorbed. Your body will produce a larger volume of urine.

Every day, you need to take at least 2 liters of water into your body. You can do this either by drinking or by eating foods such as apples that contain a lot of water. This helps your kidneys maintain the proper water balance in your body.

Other Organs of Excretion

Most of the wastes produced by the body are removed through the kidneys, but not all. **The other organs of excretion are the lungs, skin, and liver.** You've already learned how the lungs and skin remove wastes. When you breathe out, carbon dioxide and some water are removed from the body. Sweat glands also function in excretion, because water and some chemical wastes are excreted in perspiration.

Have you ever torn apart a large pizza box so that it could fit in a wastebasket? If so, then you can understand that some wastes need to be broken down before they can be excreted. The liver performs this function. For example, urea, which comes from the breakdown of proteins, is produced by the liver. The liver also converts part of the hemoglobin molecule from old red blood cells into substances such as bile. Recall from Chapter 3 that bile helps break down fats during digestion. Because the liver produces a usable material from old red blood cells, you can think of the liver as a recycling factory.

Section 3 Review

1. What is the function of the excretory system?
2. Describe the two stages of urine formation.
3. What roles do the lungs, skin, and liver play in excretion?
4. How do the kidneys help regulate the amount of water in the body?
5. **Thinking Critically Predicting** On a long bus trip, Laura does not drink any water for several hours. How will the volume of urine she produces that day compare to the volume on a day when she drinks several glasses of water? Explain.

Check Your Progress CHAPTER PROJECT 5

By now you should be creating your ads. If you are producing ads for a newspaper or magazine, you need to create original drawings or use images from other sources. If you are preparing television or radio ads, you need to arrange for actors and any necessary props. Write and edit the text or script of your ads. Arrange for a place to display your ads or for a time to present the ads.

Program Resources

◆ **Teaching Resources** 5-3 Review and Reinforce, p. 131; 5-3 Enrich, p. 132

Answers to Self-Assessment

Caption Question
Figure 11 Carbon dioxide

The Respiratory System

Key Ideas

◆ The respiratory system moves oxygen into the body and removes carbon dioxide from the body.

◆ In the process of respiration in cells, glucose is broken down using oxygen to produce energy.

◆ As air travels from the outside environment to the lungs, it passes through the nose, pharynx, trachea, and bronchi. The air is warmed, moistened, and filtered.

◆ In the alveoli, oxygen moves from the air into the blood, while carbon dioxide and water pass from the blood into the air. This process is known as gas exchange.

◆ During inhalation, the diaphragm and rib muscles make the chest cavity expand. The air pressure inside the lungs decreases, and air rushes into the lungs. During exhalation, the chest cavity becomes smaller, pushing air out of the body.

◆ When air passes over the vocal cords, which are folds of tissue in the larynx, they vibrate to produce sound.

Key Terms

respiration   bronchi   diaphragm
cilia   lungs   larynx
pharynx   alveoli   vocal cords
trachea

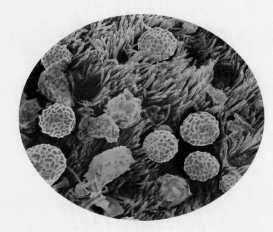

 Smoking and Your Health

INTEGRATING HEALTH

Key Ideas

◆ The most harmful substances in tobacco smoke are tar, carbon monoxide, and nicotine.

◆ When people inhale tobacco smoke, they increase their chances of developing respiratory diseases such as bronchitis, emphysema, and lung cancer.

◆ Smokers are more likely to have heart attacks than are nonsmokers.

Key Terms

tar   bronchitis
carbon monoxide   emphysema
nicotine   passive smoking
addiction

The Excretory System

Key Ideas

◆ The excretory system removes carbon dioxide, urea, water, and other wastes from the body.

◆ The kidneys are the major organs of excretion. By filtering the blood, the kidneys produce urine.

◆ Urine travels from the kidneys through the ureters to the urinary bladder. Urine is eliminated through the urethra.

◆ In the kidney's nephrons, wastes and other materials are filtered from the blood. Some useful substances, such as glucose and water, are then reabsorbed into the blood.

◆ The lungs, skin, and liver are also organs of excretion.

Key Terms

excretion   ureters
urea   urinary bladder
kidney   urethra
urine   nephron

USING THE INTERNET
www.science-explorer.phschool.com

Program Resources

◆ **Teaching Resources** Chapter 5 Project Scoring Rubric, p. 120; Chapter 5 Performance Assessment Teacher Notes, pp. 264–265; Chapter 5 Performance Assessment Student Worksheet, p. 266; Chapter 5 Test, pp. 267–270

Media and Technology

 Interactive Student Tutorial CD-ROM D-5

Reviewing Content:
Multiple Choice
1. b **2.** a **3.** b **4.** a **5.** d

True or False
6. cilia **7.** true **8.** nicotine **9.** urethra
10. true

Checking Concepts

11. Breathing consists of taking air into the body and removing it from the body. Respiration is the series of chemical reactions in cells in which glucose and oxygen react to release energy.

12. Because there are an enormous number of alveoli, they have an extremely large surface area.

13. During inhalation, the diaphragm moves downward, and the rib muscles lift the chest wall upward and outward. This increases the volume of the chest cavity so air rushes into the lungs. During exhalation, the diaphragm moves upward and the rib muscles relax. This makes the chest cavity smaller and pushes air out of the lungs.

14. Men have longer vocal cords.

15. Carbon monoxide binds to hemoglobin, taking the place of oxygen. This deprives the body of oxygen.

16. Kidneys maintain homeostasis by removing wastes from the body; if wastes were not removed, they would poison body cells. In addition, by adjusting the amount of water reabsorbed, kidneys maintain water balance.

17. Stories should trace the path of the molecule from a nostril, through the pharynx, trachea, and bronchi, and into an alveolus. From there, the oxygen molecule passes into a capillary and enters the blood, which carries it to a body cell. Then it is used in a chemical reaction to release energy.

Thinking Visually

18. a. Water, urea, glucose, and some chemicals are removed from the blood and flow into the capsule. **b.** From the capsule, the substances flow into a long tube. **c.** Urine flows from the kidneys through ureters to the urinary bladder.

Reviewing Content

 For more review of key concepts, see the Interactive Student Tutorial CD-ROM.

Multiple Choice

1. The process in which glucose and oxygen react in cells to release energy is called
 a. digestion.
 b. respiration.
 c. breathing.
 d. gas exchange.

2. The trachea divides into two tubes called
 a. bronchi.
 b. alveoli.
 c. windpipes.
 d. diaphragms.

3. Your voice is produced by the
 a. pharynx.
 b. larynx.
 c. trachea.
 d. alveoli.

4. The disease in which the respiratory passages become narrower than normal is called
 a. bronchitis.
 b. lung cancer.
 c. diabetes.
 d. emphysema.

5. Normal urine contains both
 a. water and carbon monoxide.
 b. water and large amounts of glucose.
 c. urea and proteins.
 d. urea and water.

True or False

If the statement is true, write true. If it is false, change the underlined word or words to make the statement true.

6. Dust particles in incoming air are trapped by tiny, hairlike <u>blood vessels</u> in the nose.

7. The clusters of air sacs in the lungs are called <u>alveoli</u>.

8. <u>Tar</u> is a chemical in tobacco smoke that makes the heart beat faster.

9. The <u>ureter</u> is the tube through which urine leaves the body.

10. The <u>lungs</u> are excretory organs.

Applying Skills

19. Carbon dioxide; as a waste product of cellular activity, it is released into the air from the lungs.

20. Oxygen; its percentage is lower in exhaled air than in inhaled air. Oxygen is used in respiration within cells.

21. Nitrogen is not used by the body and is not a waste product.

Checking Concepts

11. Explain the difference between breathing and respiration.

12. Explain how the alveoli provide a large surface area for gas exchange.

13. Describe how the diaphragm and rib muscles control inhaling and exhaling.

14. Why do men have deeper voices than women?

15. Describe what happens when carbon monoxide enters the body. How does this affect the body?

16. Explain two ways in which the kidneys maintain homeostasis.

17. Writing to Learn Imagine that you are a molecule of oxygen. Write an adventure story that describes what happens to you between the time you are inhaled through someone's nose and the time you are used in respiration in a body cell.

Thinking Visually

18. Flowchart The kidneys eliminate wastes from the body in a series of steps. Copy the flowchart below and complete it by filling in the missing steps. (For more on flowcharts, see the Skills Handbook.)

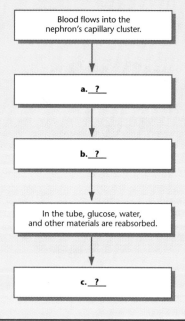

Blood flows into the nephron's capillary cluster.

a. ?

b. ?

In the tube, glucose, water, and other materials are reabsorbed.

c. ?

Thinking Critically

22. Water vapor is present in exhaled air, and it condenses on the mirror.

23. If babies inhale smoke from people's cigarettes, this smoke can damage their respiratory systems.

24. Blood cells could pass into the nephron and end up in urine.

25. Students' judgments will vary. Check for supported arguments.

Applying Skills

Use your knowledge of the respiratory system and the information in the data table to answer Questions 19–21.

Gases in Inhaled and Exhaled Air		
Gas	Inhaled Air	Exhaled Air
Nitrogen	78%	78%
Oxygen	21%	16%
Carbon dioxide	0.03%	4%

19. **Interpreting Data** Which gas makes up a higher percentage of exhaled air than inhaled air? How can you account for this difference?

20. **Drawing Conclusions** Based on the data, which gas is used by the body? How is this gas used?

21. **Inferring** Explain why the percentage of nitrogen is the same in both inhaled air and exhaled air.

Thinking Critically

22. **Inferring** If you exhale onto a mirror, the mirror will become clouded with a thin film of moisture. Explain why this happens.

23. **Applying Concepts** Explain how babies can develop smoking-related respiratory problems.

24. **Predicting** If the walls of the capillary cluster in a nephron were damaged or broken, what substance might you expect to find in urine that is not normally present? Explain.

25. **Making Judgments** Do you think that drugstores, which sell medicines, should also sell cigarettes and other tobacco products? Why or why not?

26. **Comparing and Contrasting** How is respiration similar to the burning of fuel? How is it different?

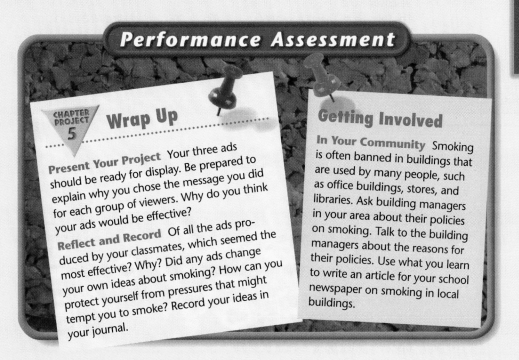

Performance Assessment

CHAPTER PROJECT 5

Wrap Up

Present Your Project Your three ads should be ready for display. Be prepared to explain why you chose the message you did for each group of viewers. Why do you think your ads would be effective?

Reflect and Record Of all the ads produced by your classmates, which seemed the most effective? Why? Did any ads change your own ideas about smoking? How can you protect yourself from pressures that might tempt you to smoke? Record your ideas in your journal.

Getting Involved

In Your Community Smoking is often banned in buildings that are used by many people, such as office buildings, stores, and libraries. Ask building managers in your area about their policies on smoking. Talk to the building managers about the reasons for their policies. Use what you learn to write an article for your school newspaper on smoking in local buildings.

26. Similar—Both are energy-releasing chemical reactions that require oxygen. Different—Respiration takes place within cells and produces carbon dioxide and water as waste products. Burning takes place outside cells.

Program Resources

◆ **Inquiry Skills Handbook** Provides teaching and review of all inquiry skills

---

Performance Assessment

Wrap Up
CHAPTER PROJECT 5

Present Your Project
During their presentations, students should discuss messages and images they chose and why they think their ads will be effective in discouraging people in each age group from smoking. After all presentations have been made, lead a discussion on the effectiveness of advertising.

Reflect and Record Encourage students to reflect on advertising tactics that appealed to them personally. Some students may find they respond to colorful graphics or catchy phrases; others may be interested in statistics or personal stories. Encourage students to identify specific images or attitudes that might influence them to start smoking. Have students develop a plan to combat those influences.

Getting Involved

In Your Community In many public buildings, smoking policy may be regulated by law. However, building managers can still provide insight into how smokers are accommodated without endangering the health of nonsmokers. For example, some buildings have designated smoking areas outside the building, special smoking sections, or smoking lounges. Check students' articles for accuracy and journalistic style. If your school does not have a student newspaper, students can write essay-style articles to be displayed with the chapter projects.

CHAPTER 6 Fighting Disease

Sections	Time	Student Edition Activities	Other Activities
CHAPTER PROJECT 6 **Stop the Invasion** p. 155	Ongoing (3 weeks)	Check Your Progress, pp. 160, 167, 184 Wrap Up, p. 187	TE Chapter 6 Project Notes, pp. 154–155
1 Infectious Disease pp. 156–160 ◆ Explain the cause of infectious disease and identify the kinds of organisms that cause disease. ◆ Describe methods in which pathogens enter the body.	2½ periods/ 1–2 blocks	**Discover** How Does a Disease Spread?, p. 156 **Sharpen Your Skills** Posing Questions, p. 159	TE Building Inquiry Skills: Communicating, p. 159 IES "Soap From Concept to Consumer," pp. 12–13
2 The Body's Defenses pp. 161–169 ◆ Identify the body's barriers against pathogens. ◆ Describe the role of the inflammatory response in fighting disease. ◆ State how the immune system responds to pathogens.	4½ periods/ 2–3 blocks	**Discover** Which Pieces Fit Together?, p. 161 **Try This** Stuck Together, p. 166 **Real-World Lab: How It Works** The Skin as a Barrier, pp. 168–169	TE Demonstration, p. 162 TE Including All Students, p. 163 TE Including All Students, p. 164 TE Inquiry Challenge, p. 164
3 Preventing Infectious Disease pp. 170–174 ◆ Define and explain active immunity. ◆ Define and explain passive immunity. ◆ Identify some strategies for staying healthy.	2½ periods/ 1–2 blocks	**Discover** What Substances Can Kill Pathogens?, p. 170	TE Inquiry Challenge, p. 172 IES "Fate of the Rain Forest," pp. 35–36
4 Noninfectious Disease pp. 175–181 ◆ Define an allergy. ◆ Explain how diabetes affects the body. ◆ Explain how cancer affects the body.	3½ periods/ 1–2 blocks	**Discover** What Happens When Airflow Is Restricted?, p. 175 **Sharpen Your Skills** Drawing Conclusions, p. 176 **Skills Lab: Interpreting Data** Causes of Death, Then and Now, pp. 180–181	TE Building Inquiry Skills: Communicating, p. 177 IES "Fate of the Rain Forest," pp. 12–13
5 INTEGRATING ENVIRONMENTAL SCIENCE **Cancer and the Environment** pp. 182–184 ◆ Identify the environmental factors related to cancer.	1½ periods/ ½–1 block	**Discover** What Does Sunlight Do to the Beads?, p. 182	
Study Guide/Chapter Review pp. 185–187	1 period/ ½ block		ISAB Provides teaching and review of all inquiry skills

For Standard or Block Schedule The Resource Pro® CD-ROM gives you maximum flexibility for planning your instruction for any type of schedule. Resource Pro® contains Planning Express®, an advanced scheduling program, as well as the entire contents of the Teaching Resources and the Computer Test Bank.

154a

CHAPTER PLANNING GUIDE

Program Resources	Assessment Strategies	Media and Technology
TR Chapter 6 Project Teacher Notes, pp. 138–139 **TR** Chapter 6 Project Overview and Worksheets, pp. 140–143 **TR** Chapter 6 Project Scoring Rubric, p. 144	**SE** Performance Assessment: Chapter 6 Project Wrap Up, p. 187 **TE** Check Your Progress, pp. 160, 167, 184 **TE** Performance Assessment: Chapter 6 Project Wrap Up, p. 187 **TR** Chapter 6 Project Scoring Rubric, p. 144	
TR 6-1 Lesson Plan, p. 145 **TR** 6-1 Section Summary, p. 146 **TR** 6-1 Review and Reinforce, p. 147 **TR** 6-1 Enrich, p. 148	**SE** Section 1 Review, p. 160 **TE** Ongoing Assessment, pp. 157, 159 **TE** Performance Assessment, p. 160 **TR** 6-1 Review and Reinforce, p. 147	Exploring Life Science Videodisc, Unit 2 Side 1, "On the Trail of a Disease" Audiotapes: English-Spanish Summary 6-1 Interactive Student Tutorial CD-ROM, D-6
TR 6-2 Lesson Plan, p. 149 **TR** 6-2 Section Summary, p. 150 **TR** 6-2 Review and Reinforce, p. 151 **TR** 6-2 Enrich, p. 152 **TR** Chapter 6 Real-World Lab, pp. 165–166 **SES** Book K, *Chemical Building Blocks,* Chapter 4	**SE** Section 2 Review, p. 167 **SE** Analyze and Conclude, p. 169 **TE** Ongoing Assessment, pp. 163, 165 **TE** Performance Assessment, p. 167 **TR** 6-2 Review and Reinforce, p. 151	Audiotapes: English-Spanish Summary 6-2 Transparency 13, "Exploring the Immune Response" Interactive Student Tutorial CD-ROM, D-6
TR 6-3 Lesson Plan, p. 153 **TR** 6-3 Section Summary, p. 154 **TR** 6-3 Review and Reinforce, p. 155 **TR** 6-3 Enrich, p. 156	**SE** Section 3 Review, p. 174 **TE** Ongoing Assessment, pp. 171, 173 **TE** Performance Assessment, p. 174 **TR** 6-3 Review and Reinforce, p. 155	Exploring Life Science Videodisc, Unit 2 Side 1, "Have You Had Your Shots?" Audiotapes: English-Spanish Summary 6-3 Interactive Student Tutorial CD-ROM, D-6
TR 6-4 Lesson Plan, p. 157 **TR** 6-4 Section Summary, p. 158 **TR** 6-4 Review and Reinforce, p. 159 **TR** 6-4 Enrich, p. 160 **TR** Chapter 6 Skills Lab, pp. 167–169 **SES** Book O, *Sound and Light,* Chapter 1	**SE** Section 4 Review, p. 179 **SE** Analyze and Conclude, p. 181 **TE** Ongoing Assessment, p. 177 **TE** Performance Assessment, p. 179 **TR** 6-4 Review and Reinforce, p. 159	Exploring Life Science Videodisc, Unit 4 Side 1, "Caution: Breathing May Be Hazardous to Your Health" Audiotapes: English-Spanish Summary 6-4 Interactive Student Tutorial CD-ROM, D-6
TR 6-5 Lesson Plan, p. 161 **TR** 6-5 Section Summary, p. 162 **TR** 6-5 Review and Reinforce, p. 163 **TR** 6-5 Enrich, p. 164	**SE** Section 5 Review, p. 184 **TE** Ongoing Assessment, p. 183 **TE** Performance Assessment, p. 184 **TR** 6-5 Review and Reinforce, p. 163	Exploring Life Science Videodisc, Unit 5 Side 2, "Fossils" Exploring Life Science Videodisc, Unit 5 Side 2, "The Earth Library" Audiotapes: English-Spanish Summary 6-5 Interactive Student Tutorial CD-ROM, D-6
TR Chapter 6 Performance Assessment, pp. 271–273 **TR** Chapter 6 Test, pp. 274–277	**SE** Chapter Review, pp. 185–187 **TR** Chapter 6 Performance Assessment: pp. 271–273 **TR** Chapter 6 Test, pp. 274–277 **CTB** Test D-6	Computer Test Bank, Test D-6 Interactive Student Tutorial CD-ROM, D-6 Science Explorer Internet Site

Key: **SE** Student Edition   **TE** Teacher's Edition   **TR** Teaching Resources
      CTB Computer Test Bank   **SES** Science Explorer Series Text   **ISLM** Integrated Science Laboratory Manual
      ISAB Inquiry Skills Activity Book   **PTA** Product Testing Activities by *Consumer Reports*   **IES** Interdisciplinary Explorations Series

Meeting the National Science Education Standards and AAAS Benchmarks

National Science Education Standards	Benchmarks for Science Literacy	Unifying Themes
Science as Inquiry (Content Standard A) ◆ **Develop descriptions, explanations, predictions, and models using evidence** Students develop a model to show how the skin acts as a barrier against infectious diseases. *(Real-World Lab)* ◆ **Use mathematics in all aspects of scientific inquiry** Students use data and create graphs to compare the leading causes of death today with those in 1900. *(Skills Lab)* **Life Science** (Content Standard C) ◆ **Structure and function in living systems** The human organism has systems for protection from disease that interact with other systems. *(Section 2)* **Science in Personal and Social Perspectives** (Content Standard F) ◆ **Personal health** Environments contain substances that are harmful to human beings and that must be monitored to maintain quality standards. *(Section 5)*	**1A The Scientific World View** Students learn about how the work of Pasteur and Koch contributed to the understanding of infectious disease. *(Section 1)* **1C The Scientific Enterprise** Many people investigated the causes of infectious disease and discovered methods of prevention. *(Section 3)* **6E Physical Health** Pathogens such as bacteria and viruses can infect the human body and interfere with normal human functions. The immune system responds to pathogens by producing antibodies that attack pathogens and by engulfing them with white blood cells. Antibodies remain in the body and can fight off subsequent invaders of the same kind. The environment contains dangerous substances that are harmful to the human body. *(Sections 1, 2, 3; Chapter Project)* **10I Discovering Germs** The work of Louis Pasteur and others in the 19th century led to the modern belief that many diseases are caused by microorganisms, such as bacteria and viruses. *(Sections 1, 3)* **12D Communication Skills** Students use information in data tables to create graphs to compare the leading causes of death today with those in 1900. *(Skills Lab)*	◆ **Energy** Energy is required by the body to fight off disease. *(Section 2)* ◆ **Scale and Structure** The body's three lines of defense are: 1) the skin, mucous, and cilia; 2) white blood cells; and 3) antibodies. *(Section 2)* ◆ **Unity and Diversity** There are two types of immunity: passive immunity and active immunity. *(Section 3)* ◆ **Systems and Interactions** The body's immune system and the structures that are part of it protect the body by attacking and destroying pathogens. By introducing antigens, vaccination allows the body to fight pathogens as if the antigen had naturally occurred. *(Section 2; Real-World Lab)* ◆ **Stability** The body's immune system helps the body maintain normal functions by attacking and destroying harmful pathogens. *(Sections 2, 3)* ◆ **Modeling** Students model the way a disease spreads by shaking hands with their classmates. Students model how the skin acts as a barrier to disease by infecting apples with a rotting apple. They also model the use of a disinfectant. *(Section 1; Real-World Lab)*

Media and Technology

Exploring Life Science Videodisc

◆ **Section 1** "On the Trail of a Disease" tracks an outbreak of the Ebola virus from "patient zero" and notes how the scientists attempt to protect the population.

◆ **Section 3** "Have You Had Your Shots?" describes the role of vaccines and antibiotics in protecting against deadly diseases.

◆ **Section 4** "Caution: Breathing May Be Hazardous to Your Health" demonstrates the effects of smog and indoor pollution on the health of the respiratory system.

Interactive Student Tutorial CD-ROM

◆ **Chapter Review** Interactive questions help students to self-assess their mastery of key chapter concepts.

Student Edition Connection Strategies

◆ **Section 2** Social Studies Connection, p. 163
Integrating Chemistry, p. 164
Integrating Chemistry, p. 165

◆ **Section 3** Science and History, pp. 172–173
Integrating Health, p. 174

◆ **Section 4** Integrating Physics, p. 178

◆ **Section 5** Integrating Environmental Science, p. 182

USING THE INTERNET

www.science-explorer.phschool.com

Visit the Science Explorer Internet site to find an up-to-date activity for Chapter 6 of *Human Biology and Health.*

ACTIVITY	Time (minutes)	Materials *Quantities for one work group*	Skills
Section 1			
Discover, p. 156	10	**Consumable** No special materials are required.	Calculating
Sharpen Your Skills, p. 159	10	**Consumable** No special materials are required.	Posing Questions
Section 2			
Discover, p. 161	10	**Consumable** sheets of paper, each cut into two matching jigsaw pieces	Inferring
Try This, p. 166	10	**Consumable** tape **Nonconsumable** large ball, small ball, modeling clay	Making Models
Real-World Lab, pp. 168–169	30	**Consumable** 4 sealable plastic bags, 4 fresh apples, rotting apple, cotton swabs, paper towels, toothpick, rubbing alcohol **Nonconsumable** marking pen	Making Models, Controlling Variables, Drawing Conclusions
Section 3			
Discover, p. 170	15	**Nonconsumable** disinfectants and antibacterial products such as creams, mouthwashes, hand soaps, household cleaners, and spray disinfectants	Designing Experiments
Section 4			
Discover, p. 175	10	**Consumable** plastic drinking straws	Observing
Sharpen Your Skills, p. 176	10	**Consumable** No special materials are required.	Drawing Conclusions
Skills Lab, pp. 180–181	20–30	**Nonconsumable** colored pencils, calculator (optional), compass, ruler, protractor	Interpreting Data
Section 5			
Discover, p. 182	10	**Nonconsumable** pipe cleaners, ultraviolet-light detecting beads	Developing Hypotheses

A list of all materials required for the Student Edition activities can be found on pages T14–T15. You can order Materials Kits by calling 1-800-828-7777 or by accessing the Science Explorer Internet site at **www.science-explorer.phschool.com.**

154d

Stop the Invasion

Students may think of illness and wellness as opposite states, without really considering the processes the body uses to defend itself against pathogens. This project will allow students to gain an understanding of the ongoing activity of the immune system.

Purpose In this project, students will represent the body's responses to illness as battles in a war. Students will write and present a series of news reports that uses scientific information, visual aids, and creative writing to describe how the body defends itself against pathogens at each stage of infection.

Skills Focus After completing the Chapter 6 Project, students will be able to
♦ pose questions about the progression of a disease;
♦ apply concepts learned in the chapter to their study of a specific disease;
♦ communicate information on how the disease affects the body in the format of a series of news reports.

Project Time Line The entire project should take two to three weeks. Spend one or two days in class discussing how news reports tell stories as they convey information. Allow students to discuss options for presenting their projects, such as using recording equipment or visual aids. By the end of the first week, students should have chosen a disease and begun researching the stages of infection. At this time you may want to distribute the Chapter 6 Project Overview and Worksheets on pages 140–143 in Teaching Resources for students to review. Allow students to spend the next week preparing three news reports. Provide class time for all presentations, or allow students to write or record their reports and turn them in.

Suggested Shortcuts You can simplify the project by restricting students to newspaper or radio reports. If there is not enough time for each student to research and present a project, have students work in small groups, pooling their knowledge of disease, as well as their artistic and verbal talents.

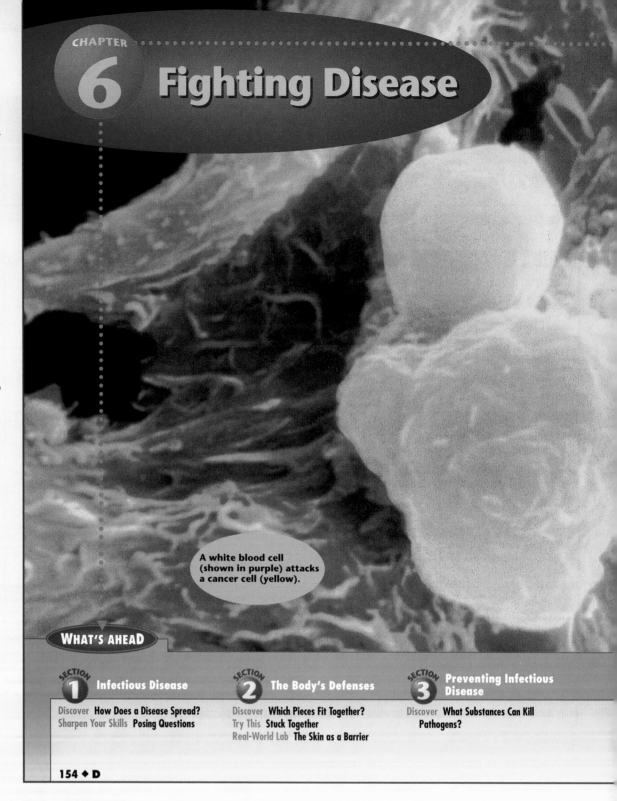

CHAPTER

6 Fighting Disease

A white blood cell (shown in purple) attacks a cancer cell (yellow).

WHAT'S AHEAD

SECTION **1** Infectious Disease
Discover How Does a Disease Spread?
Sharpen Your Skills Posing Questions

SECTION **2** The Body's Defenses
Discover Which Pieces Fit Together?
Try This Stuck Together
Real-World Lab The Skin as a Barrier

SECTION **3** Preventing Infectious Disease
Discover What Substances Can Kill Pathogens?

154 ♦ D

Possible Materials For newspaper or radio reports, students will need only writing materials. If the presentations will include pictures or sound effects, you will need to make art materials available to students. You may want to provide class time for students to prepare their visual aids. Provide
♦ markers;
♦ poster board;
♦ audio or video tape recorders;
♦ newspapers, magazines, and transcripts of radio or television news broadcasts for students to examine.

Stop the Invasion!

When you catch a cold, your body is being attacked. The attackers are cold viruses. If they're not stopped, they'll multiply in great numbers and cause infection. Many other diseases are also caused in this way—by viruses or bacteria that invade your body. In this chapter, you'll learn how your body defends itself against such invasions. And you'll put that knowledge to use as you develop a series of informative news reports in this chapter project.

Your Goal To create a series of imaginary news broadcasts from "battlefield sites" where the body is fighting an infectious disease.

To complete the project successfully you must
◆ choose a specific disease and represent the sequence of events that occur when that disease strikes the body
◆ describe the stages of the disease as if they were battles between two armies
◆ present your story creatively in at least three reports using newspaper, radio, or television news-reporting techniques

Get Started With some classmates, list your ideas about delivering a good newspaper, radio, or television news report. Think about what techniques reporters use to make stories interesting or to explain complicated information. Also, recall the times you've had a cold, flu, or other infectious disease. Write down how your body responded, how long you were sick, and any other useful information you can remember.

Check Your Progress You'll be working on this project as you study this chapter. To keep your project on track, look for Check Your Progress boxes at the following points.
Section 1 Review, page 160: Select a specific disease to research. Learn how it affects the body and how the body responds.
Section 2 Review, page 167: Write scripts for your news reports.
Section 5 Review, page 184: Make any necessary revisions, and practice your presentation.

Wrap Up At the end of the chapter (page 187), you will "broadcast" your news reports for the rest of the class.

Program Resources

◆ **Teaching Resources** Chapter 6 Project Teacher Notes, pp. 138–139; Chapter 6 Project Overview and Worksheets, pp. 140–143; Chapter 6 Project Scoring Rubric, p. 144

Launching the Project Ask students to speculate on what it means to "fight a cold." Ask: **What weapons do you use in the fight?** *(Samples: Lots of rest, plenty of fluids, vitamins, cold medicine, hot tea, tissues)*

Allow time for students to read the description of the project in their text and the Chapter Project Overview on pages 140–141 in Teaching Resources. Then encourage discussions on the stages of specific diseases and on any initial questions students may have.

This is a good opportunity to illustrate how knowledge about the body's active defense systems explains common symptoms such as fever, tiredness, and mucus production. Record any questions that come up about specific effects of illness. You might want to have students read ahead in the text to answer any questions they may have about immune responses.

Performance Assessment

The Chapter 6 Project Scoring Rubric on page 144 of Teaching Resources will help you evaluate how well students complete the Chapter 6 Project. Students will be assessed on
◆ the thoroughness of their research on their chosen diseases, including pathogens, transmission, symptoms, treatments, and recovery stages;
◆ the thoroughness and organization of their presentations, and how well they apply chapter concepts to their research;
◆ the organization of their written or oral analyses;
◆ their group participation, if they worked in groups.
By sharing the Chapter 6 Scoring Rubric with students at the beginning of the project, you will make it clear to them what they are expected to do.

SECTION 1 — Infectious Disease

Objectives

After completing the lesson, students will be able to

- explain the cause of infectious disease and identify the kinds of organisms that cause disease;
- describe methods in which pathogens enter the body.

Key Terms pathogen, infectious disease, toxin

1 Engage/Explore

Activating Prior Knowledge

Ask students to brainstorm a list of familiar diseases. Then divide the diseases into two groups: those students think can be spread from one person to another and those they think cannot. Ask students to explain their decisions.

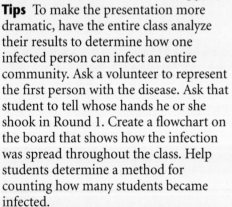

DISCOVER

Skills Focus calculating
Time 10 minutes
Tips To make the presentation more dramatic, have the entire class analyze their results to determine how one infected person can infect an entire community. Ask a volunteer to represent the first person with the disease. Ask that student to tell whose hands he or she shook in Round 1. Create a flowchart on the board that shows how the infection was spread throughout the class. Help students determine a method for counting how many students became infected.
Think It Over In each round, the student infects 2 students, so the student directly infects 6. The 2 infected in Round 2 infect 2 each in Rounds 2 and 3, for a total of 8. The 6 infected in Round 2 infect 2 each in Round 3, for a total of 12. Therefore, each student infects 26 other students, assuming that no student shakes the hand of a student whose hand had already been shaken.

SECTION 1 — Infectious Diseases

DISCOVER .... ACTIVITY

How Does a Disease Spread?

1. On a sheet of paper, write three headings: *Round 1, Round 2,* and *Round 3.*

2. Everyone in the class should shake hands with two people. Under *Round 1,* record the names of the people whose hand you shook.

3. Now shake hands with two different people. Record the name of each person whose hand you shook under *Round 2.*

4. Once again, shake hands with two additional people. Under *Round 3,* record the names of the people whose hand you shook.

Think It Over
Calculating Suppose you had a disease that was spread by shaking hands. Everyone whose hand you shook has caught the disease. So has anyone who later shook those people's hands. Calculate how many people you "infected."

GUIDE FOR READING

- What kinds of organisms cause disease?
- Where do pathogens come from?

Reading Tip As you read, use the headings in the section to make an outline. Write the important concepts under each heading.

Before the twentieth century, surgery was a very risky business. Even if people lived through an operation, they were not out of danger. After the operation, many patients' wounds became infected, and the patients often died. No one knew what caused these infections.

In the 1860s, a British surgeon named Joseph Lister hypothesized that microorganisms caused the infections. To protect his patients, Lister used carbolic acid, a chemical that kills microorganisms. Before performing an operation, Lister washed his hands and surgical instruments with carbolic acid. After the surgery, he covered the patient's wounds with bandages dipped in carbolic acid.

Figure 1 Doctors at Massachusetts General Hospital perform surgery on a patient in 1846. In the 1800s, surgery was performed under conditions that were very different from those used today.

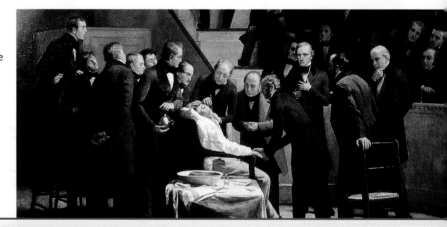

READING STRATEGIES

Reading Tip With the class, outline the information under the first heading.
Sample:
I. Diseases and Pathogens
   A. Organisms that cause disease are called pathogens.
   B. An infectious disease can pass from one organism to another.
   C. Pathogens get inside the body and damage its cells.

Study and Comprehension After students read the section, have them use the outlines they created to generate questions about infectious diseases and pathogens. Instruct students to write five questions and their answers on a sheet of paper. Then have partners use the questions to quiz each other on the information in the section. Suggest students save their questions to use as study guides.

Lister's results were dramatic. Before he used his new method, about 45 percent of his surgical patients died from infection. With Lister's new techniques, only 15 percent died.

Disease and Pathogens

Like the infections that Lister observed after surgery, many illnesses, such as ear infections and food poisoning, are caused by living things that are too small to see. Organisms that cause disease are called **pathogens.** Diseases caused by pathogens are infectious. An **infectious disease** is a disease that can pass from one organism to another.

When you have an infectious disease, pathogens have gotten inside your body and harmed it. Pathogens make you sick by damaging individual cells, even though you may feel pain in a whole organ or throughout your body. For example, when you have strep throat, pathogens have damaged cells in your throat.

✓ *Checkpoint* What causes infectious disease?

Understanding Infectious Disease

Until Lister's time, few people thought that living organisms could cause disease. Before that, people believed that things like evil spirits or swamp air made people sick.

Several scientists in the late 1800s contributed to the understanding of infectious diseases. Joseph Lister was influenced by the work of Louis Pasteur, a French scientist. In the 1860s, Pasteur showed that microorganisms cause certain kinds of diseases. In addition, Pasteur showed that killing the microorganisms could prevent the spread of those diseases. In the 1870s and 1880s, a German physician named Robert Koch demonstrated that each infectious disease is caused by a specific kind of pathogen. In other words, one kind of pathogen causes pneumonia, another kind causes chicken pox, and still another kind causes rabies.

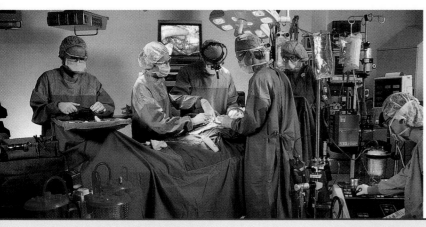

Figure 2 Surgery today is performed in operating rooms that have been cleaned thoroughly to eliminate disease-causing organisms.
Comparing and Contrasting Contrast Figures 1 and 2. How does surgery today differ from surgery in 1846?

Chapter 6 **D ◆ 157**

Program Resources

◆ **Teaching Resources** 6-1 Lesson Plan, p. 145; 6-1 Section Summary, p. 146

Media and Technology

🎧 **Audiotapes** English-Spanish Summary 6-1

Answers to Self-Assessment

Caption Question

Figure 2 The doctors in Figure 1 wear no special clothing. In contrast, the doctors and nurses in Figure 2 wear protective clothing and masks to prevent the transfer of pathogens to the patient.

✓ *Checkpoint*

Infectious diseases are caused by organisms called pathogens.

---

2 Facilitate

Disease and Pathogens

Language Arts
CONNECTION

Point out that the word *pathogen* comes from the Greek *patho*, meaning "disease," and *gennan*, meaning "origin." Tell students that they can think of pathogens as "disease-causers." **limited English proficiency**

Understanding Infectious Disease

Real-Life Learning

Invite a surgeon or a surgical nurse to the class to talk about sterile procedure in modern operating rooms. Have students prepare a list of questions before the visit. Encourage students to ask questions about specific pathogens that once threatened surgical patients and how surgeons prevent infection from those pathogens today. **learning modality: verbal**

Ongoing Assessment

Writing Have students explain the contributions of Lister, Pasteur, and Koch to the understanding of infectious disease.

D ◆ 157

Kinds of Pathogens

Building Inquiry Skills: Inferring

Ask students to speculate how scientists identify the pathogen that causes a specific disease. *(By determining whether the pathogen is present in everyone who has the disease; by testing the pathogen on another organism to see if it produces the same illness.)* **learning modality: logical/mathematical**

Addressing Naive Conceptions

Students may think that the common cold is a single disease, caused by a single virus. Point out that over 200 different viruses can cause the symptoms associated with colds. In fact, the symptoms of colds tend to vary more from person to person than from virus to virus; an individual tends to experience the same symptoms even when infected with different viruses. Ask students why they think there is still no cure for the common cold. *(Students may speculate that it is because it is caused by so many viruses. There would have to be 200 cures, and people would have to be able to determine which one to use.)* **learning modality: verbal**

Kinds of Pathogens

You share Earth with many kinds of organisms. Most are harmless, but some can make you sick. Some diseases are caused by many-celled animals, such as worms. However, most pathogens are too small to be seen without a microscope. **The four major groups of human pathogens are bacteria, viruses, fungi, and protists.** Look at Figure 3 to see examples of pathogens.

Bacteria Bacteria are one-celled microorganisms. They cause a wide variety of diseases, including ear infections, food poisoning, and tuberculosis, which is a disease of the lungs. Some bacterial pathogens damage body cells directly. Strep throat, for example, is caused by streptococcus bacteria that invade cells in your throat. Other bacterial pathogens do not enter cells, but instead produce a poison, or **toxin,** that damages cells. For example, when the bacteria that cause tetanus get into a wound, they can produce a toxin that damages the nervous system. Tetanus is also called lockjaw because the nerve damage can lock the muscles that control the jaws.

Figure 3 Most infectious diseases are caused by microscopic organisms. **A.** Bacteria like this rod-shaped one cause tetanus, a disease that harms the nervous system. **B.** When you have a cough and a sore throat, this round virus, called an adenovirus may be to blame. **C.** This fungus causes ringworm, a skin disease.

Viruses Viruses are tiny particles, much smaller than bacteria and other pathogens. Viruses cannot reproduce unless they are inside living cells. The cells are damaged or destroyed in the process, releasing new viruses to infect other cells. Both colds and influenza—or flu—are caused by viruses that invade cells in the respiratory system. In fact, there are over 200 different kinds of cold viruses, and each of them can give you a sore throat and a runny nose! Chicken pox and AIDS are also caused by viruses. You will learn more about AIDS later in the chapter.

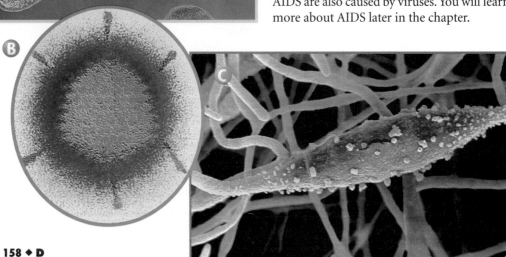

Background

History of Science During and shortly after World War I, an estimated 30 million people died from a single cause—the Influenza Epidemic of 1918–1919. Soldiers from the United States apparently spread the virus to Europe. During the following months, the virus spread all over the world, first in ports and then in cities along transportation routes. By August 1918, the virus had mutated into a much more deadly form, and by the winter it had changed into a third.

The second and third phases of the epidemic proved to be the most lethal. After the virus mutated in the summer of 1918, people often died within two days of their first symptoms. The epidemic lasted about a year, and died out in the spring of 1919.

Fungi and Protists Fungi, which include molds, yeasts, and other organisms, cause some infectious diseases, including athlete's foot. Malaria, an infection of the blood that is common in tropical areas, is one disease caused by protists.

☑ *Checkpoint* *What are two ways in which bacteria cause disease?*

How Diseases Are Spread

Pathogens are something like ants at a picnic. They aren't trying to harm you. However, like the ants, pathogens need food. They also need a place to live and reproduce. Unfortunately, your body may be just the right place for a pathogen to meet those needs.

You can become infected by a pathogen in one of several ways. **Sources of pathogens include another person, a contaminated object, an animal bite, and the environment.**

Person-to-Person Transfer Many pathogens are transferred from one person to another person. Pathogens often pass from one person to another through direct physical contact, such as kissing, hugging, and shaking hands. For example, if you kiss someone who has a cold sore, cold-sore viruses can then get into your body.

Diseases are also spread through indirect contact with an infected person. For example, if a person with pneumonia sneezes, pathogens shoot into the air. Pathogens from a sneeze can travel most of the way across a small room! Other people may catch pneumonia if they inhale these pathogens. Colds, flu, and tuberculosis can be spread through coughing and sneezing.

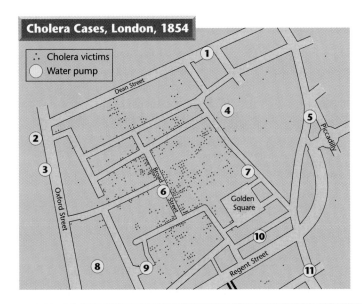

Cholera Cases, London, 1854

∴ Cholera victims
◯ Water pump

Sharpen your Skills

Posing Questions

Cholera is a deadly disease that is spread through food or water contaminated with cholera bacteria. In 1854, cholera spread through London, England. Dr. John Snow analyzed where most of the cholera victims lived, as well as the locations of the water pumps in the area. The map in Figure 4 shows Dr. Snow's findings. Dr. Snow hypothesized that the disease was spread by water that came from one of the pumps. Which pump was probably the source of the contaminated water?

Suppose that Dr. Snow just learned that two additional people had died of cholera. What questions would Dr. Snow most likely ask about the additional cholera cases?

Figure 4 The map shows the location of cholera cases in the 1854 epidemic in London, England.

How Diseases Are Spread

Building Inquiry Skills: Communicating

Time 30 minutes

Divide the class into an even number of small groups. Have each group develop and write a story describing how a group of people contracted a disease. Encourage students to be creative, but make sure their stories are consistent with the sources of pathogens identified in the text. When the stories are finished, have two groups work together. One group should play the part of medical workers and ask questions to determine how the other group became infected. Have groups switch roles. As a class, discuss what kinds of questions were most helpful and write a master list of questions that should be asked when doctors try to determine the cause of an outbreak.
cooperative learning

Sharpen your Skills

Posing Questions

Time 10 minutes
Tips Ask students to point out the location of the pumps and of the cholera victims. Pump 6 was the source of the contaminated water. Dr. Snow would probably ask where the latest cholera victims lived and from which pumps they obtained water.
Extend Have students write a newspaper story about Dr. Snow's work, including a caption that could accompany the map in Figure 4.
learning modality: visual

Portfolio Students can save their newspaper stories in their portfolios.

Media and Technology

🔘 **Exploring Life Science Videodisc**
Unit 2, Side 1,
"On the Trail
of a Disease"
Chapter 2

Answers to Self-Assessment

☑ *Checkpoint*

Bacteria can cause disease by entering cells and damaging them directly or by producing toxins that damage cells.

Ongoing Assessment

Oral Presentation Ask students to identify the four main groups of human pathogens. (*Bacteria, viruses, fungi, and protists*)

3 Assess

Section 1 Review Answers

1. Bacteria, viruses, fungi, and protists
2. Pathogens may come from other people, contaminated objects, animal bites, and the environment.
3. Pasteur showed that microorganisms cause certain diseases and that killing microorganisms prevents the spread of diseases. Koch showed that specific kinds of pathogens cause specific diseases.
4. Avoid contact with others, wash utensils carefully, do not share food or utensils with others, cover your mouth and nose when sneezing or coughing. These steps help prevent the cold virus from entering the body of another person.

Check Your Progress

CHAPTER PROJECT 6

Encourage students to make a list of questions that a good news story should answer so they can make sure they answer these questions when they do their research. In addition to providing the essential information, students should be encouraged to highlight interesting facts or stories about the disease. Provide students with newspapers and magazines in a variety of styles to give them ideas for presenting their stories.

Performance Assessment

Writing Have students imagine they are a kind of pathogen. Students should describe themselves and tell how they infected a human.

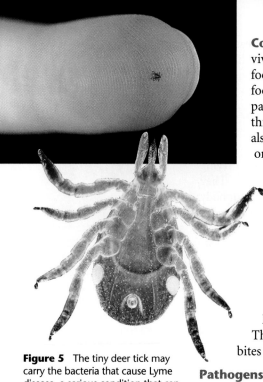

Figure 5 The tiny deer tick may carry the bacteria that cause Lyme disease, a serious condition that can damage the joints. If a deer tick that is carrying Lyme disease bacteria bites a person, the person may get Lyme disease. *Problem Solving How might people reduce their risk of catching Lyme disease?*

Contaminated Objects Some pathogens can survive for a time outside a person's body. Water and food can become contaminated. If people then eat the food or drink the water, they may become sick. Some pathogens that cause severe diarrhea are spread through contaminated food and water. People can also pick up pathogens by using objects, such as towels or silverware, that have been handled by an infected person. Colds and flu can be spread in this way. Tetanus bacteria can enter the body if a person steps on a contaminated nail.

Animal Bites If an animal is infected with certain pathogens and then bites a person, it can pass the pathogens to the person. People can get rabies, a serious disease that affects the nervous system, from the bite of an infected animal, such as a dog or a raccoon. Lyme disease and Rocky Mountain spotted fever are both spread by tick bites. The protist that causes malaria is transferred by the bites of mosquitoes that live in tropical regions.

Pathogens from the Environment Some pathogens occur naturally in the environment. The bacteria that cause tetanus live in soil or water. The bacteria that cause botulism, an especially severe form of food poisoning, also live in soil. Botulism bacteria can produce a toxin in foods that have been improperly canned. The toxin is extremely powerful.

Section 1 Review

1. Name four kinds of pathogens that cause disease in humans.
2. Describe four ways that pathogens can infect humans.
3. Explain how Pasteur and Koch contributed to the understanding of infectious disease.
4. **Thinking Critically Applying Concepts** If you have a cold, what steps can you take to keep from spreading it to other people? Explain.

Check Your Progress

CHAPTER PROJECT 6

At this stage, you should have chosen a specific infectious disease to research. You should also decide whether to do newspaper articles, radio programs, or a television series. Begin to plan how you will explain the way in which the body is invaded by pathogens. Also begin thinking about how you will make your show appropriate for your audience. (*Hint:* To get ideas on how to present news stories, read newspapers or watch or listen to real news programs about international conflicts.)

Program Resources

◆ **Interdisciplinary Exploration Series** "Soap from Concept to Consumer," pp. 12–13
◆ **Teaching Resources** 6-1 Review and Reinforce, p. 147; 6-1 Enrich, p. 148

Media and Technology

 Interactive Student Tutorial CD-ROM D-6

Answers to Self-Assessment

Caption Question

Figure 5 A person could avoid walking through areas where ticks may live. People should also cover their legs and arms when hiking and wear tick repellent.

SECTION 2 The Body's Defenses

Which Pieces Fit Together?

1. Your teacher will give you a piece of paper with one jagged edge.
2. One student in the class has a piece of paper whose edges match your paper edge, like two pieces of a jigsaw puzzle.
3. Find the student whose paper matches yours and fit the two edges together.

Think It Over

Inferring Imagine that one of each pair of matching pieces is a pathogen. The other is a cell in your body that defends your body against the invading pathogen. How many kinds of invaders can each defender cell recognize?

Y our eyes are glued to the screen. The situation in the video game is desperate. Enemy troops have gotten through an opening in the wall. Your soldiers have managed to hold back most of the invaders. However, some enemy soldiers are breaking through the defense lines. You need your backup defenders. They can zap the invaders with their powerful weapons. If your soldiers can fight off the enemy until the backup team arrives, you can save your fortress.

Video games create fantasy wars, but in your body, real battles happen all the time. In your body, the "enemies" are invading pathogens. You are hardly ever aware of these battles. The body's disease-fighting system is so effective that most people get sick only occasionally. By eliminating pathogens that can destroy your cells, your body maintains homeostasis.

GUIDE FOR READING

♦ What is the body's first line of defense against pathogens?
♦ What happens during the inflammatory response?
♦ How does the immune system respond to pathogens?

Reading Tip Before you read, preview *Exploring the Immune Response* on page 165. List any unfamiliar terms. As you read, write definitions of those terms in your own words.

Figure 6 The pathogens that invade your body are something like the enemy soldiers in a video game. Your body has to defend itself against the pathogens.

SECTION 2 The Body's Defenses

Objectives

After completing the lesson, students will be able to
♦ identify the body's barriers against pathogens;
♦ describe the role of the inflammatory response in fighting disease;
♦ state how the immune system responds to pathogens.

Key Terms inflammatory response, phagocyte, immune response, lymphocyte, T cell, antigen, B cell, antibody, AIDS

1 Engage/Explore

Activating Prior Knowledge

Ask students whether they have ever remained healthy when a parent, brother, or sister came down with a cold. Ask them to suggest reasons why not everyone who is exposed to a pathogen develops the illness. Ask: **What are some factors that allow people to resist illness?** (*Samples: Getting enough rest, eating healthy foods, avoiding using utensils and other objects handled by a sick person.*)

••••••••• DISCOVER ••••••••••

Skills Focus inferring
Materials *sheets of paper, each cut into two matching jigsaw pieces*
Time 10 minutes
Tips Prepare matching sets of shapes by cutting sheets of paper in half with a zigzag or wavy pattern. Use a different pattern for each piece of paper. All paper should be the same color.
Expected Outcome Each student should find only one matching piece.
Think It Over Each defender cell recognizes only one type of invader.

READING STRATEGIES

Reading Tip As students preview *Exploring the Immune Response,* suggest that they also list questions they have about the information. Have students discuss their questions with partners. Encourage student pairs to predict answers to the questions. After they have read the section, have the partners meet again to discuss the answers to their questions and the meanings of the terms they listed during their preview.

Program Resources

♦ **Teaching Resources** 6-2 Lesson Plan, p. 149; 6-2 Section Summary, p. 150

Media and Technology

 Audiotapes English-Spanish Summary 6-2

2 Facilitate

Barriers That Keep Pathogens Out

Demonstration

Materials *disposable petri dish with nutrient agar, sterile cotton ball, tape*

ACTIVITY

Time 15 minutes for setup; 10 minutes each day over several days

This activity shows the presence of bacteria on a person's hand. Wipe a volunteer's hand with a cotton ball and then gently brush the cotton over the agar of the petri dish. Cover and label the dish. Tape it closed and place it upside down in a warm place. Allow students to observe the petri dish over the next few days. Do not open the dish. Ask students to describe the dish. (*The surface of the agar should be covered with dots or smudges, each consisting of millions of bacteria.*) Ask students to explain the results. (*Bacteria from the student's hand multiplied on the agar.*) Dispose of the petri dishes and all other materials according to the proper procedures. Be sure to check your district's and state's guidelines for the proper disposal of bacterial cultures. **learning modality: visual**

Addressing Naive Conceptions

Students may think that a cut or injury will lead to infection only if the skin is punctured by something that is contaminated with pathogens. Point out that the image in Figure 7 shows the bacteria that live on skin and that some of these bacteria can cause infection. **learning modality: verbal**

Figure 7 Skin is covered with bacteria. The dots in the photo are colonies of bacteria living on a person's hand.
Relating Cause and Effect How can a cut in the skin lead to an infection?

Barriers That Keep Pathogens Out

Your body has three lines of defense against pathogens. The first line consists of barriers that keep pathogens from getting into the body. You do not wear a sign that says "Pathogens Keep Out," but that doesn't matter. **Barriers such as the skin, breathing passages, mouth, and stomach trap and kill most pathogens with which you come into contact.**

The Skin When pathogens land on the skin, they are exposed to destructive chemicals in oil and sweat. Even if these chemicals don't kill them, the pathogens may fall off with dead skin cells. If the pathogens manage to stay on the skin, they must get through the tightly packed dead cells that form a barrier on top of living skin cells. Most pathogens get through the skin only when it is cut. Scabs form over cuts so rapidly that the period in which pathogens can enter the body in this way is very short.

The Breathing Passages As you know, you can inhale pathogens when you breathe in. The nose, pharynx, trachea, and bronchi, however, contain mucus and cilia. Together, the mucus and cilia trap and remove most of the pathogens that enter the respiratory system. In addition, irritation by pathogens may make you sneeze or cough. Both actions force the pathogens out of your body.

The Mouth and Stomach Some pathogens are found in foods, even if the foods are handled safely. The saliva in your mouth contains destructive chemicals and your stomach produces acid. Most pathogens that you swallow are destroyed by saliva or stomach acid.

General Defenses

In spite of barriers, pathogens sometimes get into your body and begin to damage cells. When body cells are damaged, they release chemicals that trigger the **inflammatory response,** which is the second line of defense. **In the inflammatory response, fluid and certain types of white blood cells leak from blood vessels into nearby tissues. The white blood cells then fight the pathogens.** Because the inflammatory response is the same no matter what the pathogen, it is sometimes called the body's general defense.

Background

Facts and Figures Malaria is a disease that occurs primarily in tropical regions of the world such as Africa, Central America, and Southeast Asia. It is estimated that there are more than 270 million new malaria infections worldwide each year and about 2 million deaths. *Malaria* means "bad air" in Italian, and in the nineteenth century it was thought to have been caused by gases from swampy regions. In 1880, however, Charles Laveran observed a protozoan parasite in the blood of an infected person. Later, it was discovered that the disease-causing parasite is transmitted through the bite of the *Anopheles* mosquito. Once in the bloodstream, the parasite travels to the liver, where it reproduces. The infected liver cells burst and release the parasites back into the bloodstream.

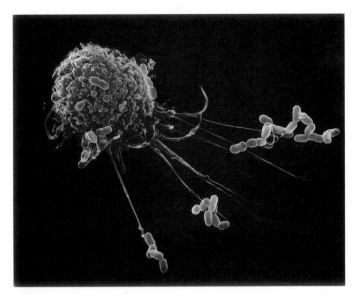

Figure 8 Caught! The bacteria, shown in green, don't stand a chance against the phagocyte, shown in red. Phagocytes are white blood cells that engulf and destroy bacteria.

All white blood cells are disease fighters, but there are different types, each with its own particular function. The kinds involved in the inflammatory response are called phagocytes. A **phagocyte** (FAG uh syt) is a white blood cell that engulfs pathogens and destroys them by breaking them down.

During the inflammatory response, blood vessels widen in the area affected by the pathogens. This enlargement increases the flow of blood to the area. The enlarged blood vessels—and the fluid that leaks out of them—make the affected area red and swollen. If you touch the swollen area, it will feel slightly warmer than normal. In fact, the term *inflammation* comes from a Latin word meaning "to set on fire."

In some cases, chemicals produced during the inflammatory response cause a fever, raising your body temperature above its normal temperature of 37° Celsius. Although fever makes you feel bad, it actually may help your body fight the infection. Some pathogens may not grow and reproduce well at higher temperatures.

☑ *Checkpoint* *What role do white blood cells play in the inflammatory response?*

Social Studies CONNECTION

Today the Panama Canal is an important shipping route that links the Atlantic and Pacific oceans. But because of two diseases that cause high fever—malaria and yellow fever—the Panama Canal almost didn't get built. Much of the canal, which links the Atlantic and Pacific oceans, passes through the mosquito-filled rain forests of Panama. Mosquitoes carry the pathogens that cause malaria and yellow fever.

In 1889 an attempt at digging a canal was abandoned, partly because so many workers became sick. In 1904, an American physician, Colonel William C. Gorgas, began a project in which swamps in the work area were drained. In addition, brush and grass were cut down. Gorgas's project destroyed the places where mosquitoes lived and reproduced. This action greatly reduced the mosquito population. The Panama Canal was completed in 1914.

Panama Canal

In Your Journal

Write a newspaper article about the construction of the Panama Canal. The article should focus on the problem of disease and the contribution of Colonel Gorgas.

General Defenses

Including All Students

Materials *modeling clay, large buttons*
Time 20 minutes

ACTIVITY

Visually impaired students may have difficulty in conceiving how a phagocyte destroys a pathogen. Have students with normal vision work with visually impaired students. To represent a phagocyte, the student with normal vision spreads a lump of clay on a flat surface in a roughly circular shape. The same student then positions the button, representing the pathogen, next to the phagocyte and has the visually impaired student touch both. The students then work together to peel up the "phagocyte" and wrap the clay around the button, representing the phagocyte engulfing the pathogen. The visually impaired student uses the sense of touch to determine that the "phagocyte" has completely surrounded the "pathogen" and destroyed it. **learning modality: kinesthetic**

Social Studies CONNECTION

On a globe, have volunteers locate the Panama Canal. Ask students to speculate what route was used for shipping before the canal was built. Point out that the trip from the east coast of the United States through the canal to the west coast is about 15,000 kilometers shorter than sailing around Cape Horn in South America.

In Your Journal Provide time and resources for students to research the building of the Panama Canal. Interested students may want to include illustrations with their articles. **learning modality: verbal**

Ongoing Assessment

Writing Ask students to briefly describe two ways in which the body defends itself against pathogens.

Answers to Self-Assessment

Caption Question

Figure 7 A cut provides an opening for bacteria to enter the body and cause an infection.

☑ *Checkpoint*

White blood cells called phagocytes engulf pathogens and destroy them by breaking them down.

The Immune System

Including All Students

Time 30 minutes

Some students may have difficulty remembering and distinguishing the terms associated with the immune system. Students can work in groups of three or more to create skits that dramatize the immune response. Group tasks can include research, writing, acting, and narrating, and any one student may take on more than one task. Students should identify components of the immune response in their skits, such as lymphocytes, T cells, B cells, antigens, antibodies, phagocytes, and pathogens. Students can present their skits to the class when finished. **limited English proficiency**

Integrating Chemistry

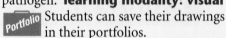

Challenge students to draw two or more pathogens with different antigens. *(Drawings may show a cell with differently patterned surfaces.)* Students should label their drawings and provide a caption that explains how a T cell recognizes a pathogen. **learning modality: visual**

Portfolio Students can save their drawings in their portfolios.

Inquiry Challenge

Materials *various materials, such as beads, pipe cleaners, paper clips*

Time 10 minutes

Explain to students that when active, antibodies take on a shape something like a Y. Each arm of the Y attaches and binds to an antigen. Challenge students to build models showing how specific antibodies attack specific antigens. **learning modality: kinesthetic**

The Immune System

If a pathogen infection is severe enough to cause a fever, it also triggers the third line of defense—the **immune response.** The immune response is controlled by the immune system, your body's disease fighting system. **The cells of the immune system can distinguish between different kinds of pathogens. The immune-system cells react to each kind of pathogen with a defense targeted specifically at that pathogen.** The white blood cells that do this are called **lymphocytes** (LIM fuh syts). There are two major kinds of lymphocytes—T lymphocytes and B lymphocytes, which are also called T cells and B cells. In *Exploring the Immune Response ,* you can see how T cells and B cells work together to destroy flu viruses.

T Cells A major function of **T cells** is to identify pathogens and distinguish one kind of pathogen from another. You have tens of millions of T cells circulating in your blood. Each kind of T cell recognizes a different kind of pathogen. What T cells actually recognize are marker molecules, called antigens, found on each pathogen. **Antigens** are molecules on cells that the immune system recognizes either as part of your body or as coming from outside your body. All cells have antigens, and each person's antigens are different from those of all other people.

You can think of antigens as something like the uniforms that athletes wear. When you watch a track meet, you can look at the runners' uniforms to tell which school each runner comes from. Like athletes from different schools, each different pathogen has its own kind of antigen. Antigens differ from one another because each kind of antigen has a different chemical structure.

Figure 9 By looking at the runners' uniforms, you can tell that they come from different schools. Similarly, the immune system recognizes a pathogen by its antigens—marker molecules on the pathogen. *Applying Concepts What is the name of the cell that distinguishes one pathogen from another?*

Facts and Figures Some serious human diseases occur when the human body attacks itself. In these diseases, known as auto-immune diseases, white blood cells produce antibodies against the body's healthy cells and tissues. *Lupus erythematosus* is the name given to two auto immune diseases. One affects only the skin, producing red patches covered with dark grayish scales.

The other form of lupus may affect any part of the body. Its forms vary from mild to fatal, mostly depending on what organs are affected. The antibodies produced by the immune system of people with systemic lupus attack the cells in the blood, proteins in the plasma, and other cells.

EXPLORING the Immune Response

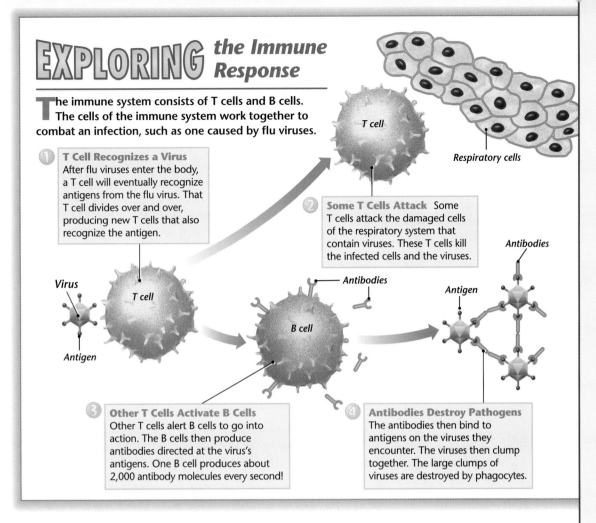

The immune system consists of T cells and B cells. The cells of the immune system work together to combat an infection, such as one caused by flu viruses.

① T Cell Recognizes a Virus After flu viruses enter the body, a T cell will eventually recognize antigens from the flu virus. That T cell divides over and over, producing new T cells that also recognize the antigen.

② Some T Cells Attack Some T cells attack the damaged cells of the respiratory system that contain viruses. These T cells kill the infected cells and the viruses.

③ Other T Cells Activate B Cells Other T cells alert B cells to go into action. The B cells then produce antibodies directed at the virus's antigens. One B cell produces about 2,000 antibody molecules every second!

④ Antibodies Destroy Pathogens The antibodies then bind to antigens on the viruses they encounter. The viruses then clump together. The large clumps of viruses are destroyed by phagocytes.

Labels: T cell · Respiratory cells · Virus · Antigen · T cell · B cell · Antibodies · Antibodies · Antigen

B Cells The lymphocytes called **B cells** produce chemicals that

 INTEGRATING CHEMISTRY help destroy each kind of pathogen. These chemicals are called **antibodies.** Antibodies lock onto antigens. Each kind of B cell produces only one kind of antibody. Each kind of antibody has a different structure. Antigen and antibody molecules fit together, like pieces of a puzzle. An antigen on a flu virus will only bind to one kind of antibody—the antibody that acts against that flu virus.

When antibodies bind to the antigens on a pathogen, they mark the pathogen for destruction. Some antibodies make pathogens clump together. Others keep pathogens from attaching to the body cells that they might damage. Still other antibodies make it easier for phagocytes to destroy the pathogens.

✓ *Checkpoint* *What is the function of an antibody?*

EXPLORING the Immune Response

To help students understand how the immune response functions, have volunteers read the captions aloud, as if they were telling a story. Point out that parts 2 and 3 occur at the same time. Also note that when T cells attack damaged cells, they destroy the infected cells as well as the viruses the cells contain. Ask students to identify the functions performed by T cells, B cells and phagocytes. (*T cells identify antigens, then alert B cells; they also attack infected cells. B cells produce antigens. Phagocytes destroy clumps of viruses.*) **learning modality: verbal**

Building Inquiry Skills: Applying Concepts

Challenge students to create analogies to explain the parts and functions of the immune response system. For example, a T cell might be compared to a computerized missile that moves in on a specific target. Encourage students to share their analogies. **learning modality: logical/mathematical**

Integrating Chemistry

Materials *different types and sizes of paperclips such as metal, plastic, coated, colored*

Explain to students that antibodies are complex, three-dimensional proteins. Like all proteins, antibodies are assembled from amino acids. Use the different types and sizes of paperclips to model how amino acids (paperclips) can be assembled into many different combinations. **learning modality: visual**

Media and Technology

 Transparencies "Exploring the Immune Response," Transparency 13

Program Resources

Science Explorer Series *Chemical Building Blocks,* Chapter 4, has additional information about the chemical compounds needed for life to exist.

Answers to Self-Assessment

Caption Question

Figure 9 T cell

✓ *Checkpoint*

An antibody recognizes and binds to a particular antigen. This enables the pathogen to be destroyed.

Ongoing Assessment

Organizing Information Have students make compare/contrast tables showing the similarities and differences between T cells and B cells.

The Immune System, continued

AIDS, a Disease of the Immune System

Stuck Together

In this activity, you will model one way in which an antibody prevents a pathogen from infecting a body cell.

1. Use a large ball to represent a body cell, and a smaller ball to represent a pathogen.
2. Press a lump of modeling clay onto the small ball. Then use the clay to stick the two balls together. This models how a pathogen attaches itself to a body cell.
3. Pull the two balls apart, keeping the clay on the small ball (the pathogen).
4. Put strips of tape over the clay, so that the clay is completely covered. The tape represents an antibody.
5. Now try to reattach the small ball to the larger one.

Making Models Use the model to explain how antibodies prevent pathogens from attaching to body cells.

AIDS, a Disease of the Immune System

Acquired immunodeficiency syndrome, or **AIDS,** is a disease caused by a virus that attacks the immune system. In the United States, AIDS is the leading cause of death in persons aged 25 to 44. The virus that causes AIDS is called human immunodeficiency virus, or HIV.

How HIV Affects the Body HIV is the only kind of virus known to attack the immune system directly. Once it invades the body, HIV enters T cells and reproduces inside them. People can be infected with HIV—that is, have the virus living in their body cells—for years before they become sick. More than 30 million people in the world may be infected with HIV.

Eventually HIV begins to destroy the T cells it has infected. Damage to the immune system is usually slow. But as the viruses destroy T cells, the body loses its ability to fight disease. Most persons infected with HIV eventually develop the disease AIDS.

Because their immune systems no longer function properly, people with AIDS become sick with diseases not normally found in people with healthy immune systems. Many people survive attack after attack of such diseases. But eventually their immune systems fail, ending in death. At this time, there is no cure for AIDS. However, new drug treatments allow people with the disease to survive much longer than in the past.

How HIV Is Spread Like all other viruses, HIV can only reproduce inside cells. In the case of HIV, the virus can only reproduce inside T cells. However, it can survive for a short time outside the human body in body fluids, such as blood and the fluids produced by the male and female reproductive systems.

HIV can spread from one person to another only if body fluids from an infected person come in contact with those of an uninfected person. Sexual contact is one way in which this can happen. HIV may also pass from an infected woman to her baby

Figure 10 The tiny red particles are HIV viruses emerging from a T cell. The viruses multiply inside the T cell and eventually cause the cell to die.
Relating Cause and Effect
Why does the death of T cells interfere with the body's ability to fight disease?

Figure 11 You cannot get HIV, the virus that causes AIDS, by hugging someone infected with the virus.

during pregnancy or childbirth or through breast milk. In addition, when drug users share needles, some infected blood may get into the needle and then infect the next person who uses it. A person can also get HIV through a transfusion of blood that contains the virus. But since 1985, all donated blood in the United States has been tested for signs of HIV, and infected blood is not used in transfusions.

It is important to know the many ways in which HIV is *not* spread. HIV does not live on skin, so you cannot be infected by hugging or shaking hands with an infected person. You can't get infected by using a toilet seat after it has been used by someone with HIV. And HIV is not spread when you bump into someone while playing sports.

Section 2 Review

1. Name four barriers that prevent pathogens from getting into the body. Explain how each barrier prevents infection.
2. Describe the inflammatory response.
3. What is the function of the immune system?
4. How is HIV different from other virus pathogens?
5. **Thinking Critically** **Applying Concepts** Explain why you can't contract HIV by touching a doorknob that someone infected with the virus has touched.

Check Your Progress CHAPTER PROJECT 6
At this point you should begin writing the newspaper articles or scripts for each of your broadcasts. Before you begin writing, outline the main ideas that you want to communicate. Work to make your descriptions sound like real news. (*Hint:* Make sure that your articles or scripts include information about each of the body's three lines of defense).

Chapter 6 **D ◆ 167**

The Skin as a Barrier

Preparing for Inquiry

Key Concept The skin of most organisms is a barrier to many pathogens.

Skills Objectives Students will be able to
♦ make models using apples to demonstrate how skin acts as a barrier;
♦ control variables by modifying the ability of apple skins to act as effective barriers to bacteria;
♦ draw conclusions about how effective apple skins and alcohol are at preventing bacterial growth.

Time 30 minutes

Advance Planning Provide a rotten apple to use as a source of bacteria, and thick, sturdy toothpicks for piercing apple skins.

Alternative Materials You can substitute disposable plastic knives for the toothpicks. Make sure students touch the rotten apple with the knife tips, then use the tips to make the new cuts.

Guiding Inquiry

Invitation Ask students to recall times they have fallen and perhaps cut and bruised themselves. Then ask: **Did you put an antibiotic cream and a bandage on the cut?** *(yes)* **On the bruise?** *(no)* **Why?** *(Students should explain that the cutting of the skin exposed the body to external pathogens, while the bruise was an internal wound protected by the skin.)*

Introducing the Procedure

You can let students practice the technique before they collect data. Watch students' technique of transferring bacteria to ensure proper results.

Troubleshooting the Experiment

♦ Students should take care not to break the apple skins when washing and drying the apples.
♦ In Step 4, the toothpick should touch but not break the apple skin. In Steps 5 and 6, the toothpick must break the skin.

THE SKIN AS A BARRIER

Bacteria are all around you. Many of those bacteria can cause disease, yet you usually remain free of disease. In this lab, you will investigate how the skin protects you from infectious disease.

Problem

How does skin act as a barrier to pathogens?

Skills Focus

making models, controlling variables, drawing conclusions

Materials

sealable plastic bags, 4   marking pen
fresh apples, 4   paper towels
rotting apple   toothpick
cotton swabs   rubbing alcohol

Procedure

1. Read over the entire procedure to see how you will treat each of four fresh apples. Write a prediction in your notebook about the change(s) you expect to see in each apple. Then copy the data table into your notebook.
2. Label four plastic bags *1, 2, 3,* and *4.*
3. Gently wash four fresh apples with water, then dry them carefully with paper towels. Place one apple in plastic bag 1, and seal the bag.
4. Insert a toothpick tip into a rotting apple and withdraw it. Lightly draw the tip of the toothpick down the side of the second apple without breaking the skin. Repeat these actions three more times, touching the toothpick to different parts of the apple without breaking the skin. Insert the apple in plastic bag 2, and seal the bag.

5. Insert the toothpick tip into the rotting apple and withdraw it. Use the tip to make a long, thin scratch down the side of the third apple. Be sure to pierce the apple's skin. Repeat these actions three more times, making additional scratches on different parts of the apple. Insert the apple into plastic bag 3, and seal the bag.
6. Repeat Step 5 to make four scratches in the fourth apple. However, before you place the apple in the bag, dip a cotton swab in rubbing alcohol, and swab the scratches. Then place the apple in plastic bag 4, and seal the bag. **CAUTION:** *Alcohol and its vapors are flammable. Work where there are no sparks, exposed flames, or other heat sources.*
7. Store the four bags in a warm, dark place. Wash your hands thoroughly with soap and water.
8. Every day for one week, remove the apples from their storage place, and observe them without opening the bags. Record your observations, then return the bags to their storage location. At the end of the activity, dispose of the unopened bags as directed by your teacher.

♦ Students should dip the toothpick in the rotting apple each time they touch the apple in Step 4, or cut the apple in Steps 5 and 6.

Expected Outcome

When the skin of the apple is cut or removed, two different processes take place. First, in a fairly short time, the white of the apple turns brown because oxidation takes place. This is a chemical reaction, which can be slowed down by adding an acid such as lemon or orange juice to the apple's surface. Second, bacteria begin

Safety

Remind students not to taste anything in the lab and to wash their hands immediately after handling the rotten apple. Review the safety guidelines in Appendix A.

Program Resources

♦ **Teaching Resources** Chapter 6 Real-World Lab, pp. 165–166

Analyze and Conclude

1. How did the appearance of the four apples compare? Explain your results.
2. In this activity, what condition in the human body is each of the four fresh apples supposed to model?
3. What is the control in this experiment?
4. What is the role of the rotting apple in this activity?

5. **Apply** How does this investigation show why routine cuts and scrapes should be cleaned and bandaged?

Design an Experiment

Using apples as you did in this activity, design an experiment to model how washing hands can prevent the spread of disease. Obtain your teacher's permission before carrying out your investigation.

DATA TABLE

Date	Apple 1 (no contact with decay)	Apple 2 (contact with decay, unbroken skin)	Apple 3 (contact with decay, scratched, untreated)	Apple 4 (contact with decay, scratched, treated with alcohol)

Sample Data Table

Date	Apple 1 (untouched)	Apple 2 (touched, unbroken skin)	Apple 3 (touched, scratched, untreated)	Apple 4 (touched, scratched, treated with alcohol)
1	no change	no change	scratched areas slightly dark	no change
2	no change	no change	scratched areas dark and soft	scratched areas slightly dark

the process of decay, a biological process resulting in the darkening and softening of the apple. This process takes longer to become visible than browning does. In this lab, decay—caused by bacteria— serves as the model for disease.

Analyze and Conclude

1. Apples 1 and 2 show little or no change because the skin prevented bacteria from entering the apple. Apple 3 shows significant decay; the breaks in the skin allowed bacteria to enter. Apple 4 may show less decay than Apple 3; bacteria were killed by alcohol.
2. The apple represents the human body, the apple skin represents the human skin. The decay-causing bacteria represent bacteria that can infect humans. Apple 1 shows that a person remains healthy when the skin is intact and no bacteria are present. If the skin is broken as in Apple 2, the person remains healthy even when bacteria are present. Apple 3 shows that bacteria can enter through a cut and cause infection. The infection may be lessened if a bacteria-killing agent (such as alcohol) is used, as in Apple 4.
3. The control is Apple 1.
4. The rotting apple is the source of decay-causing bacteria.
5. Cleaning cuts and scrapes may remove bacteria present at the time of the injury. Bandages keep bacteria from entering a cut that has not healed.

Extending the Inquiry

Design an Experiment Sample experiment: Use three washed, freshly cut apples to test for the presence and amount of bacteria. The first apple would serve as a control and would not be handled after being washed; the second would be handled by washed hands; and the third would be handled by unwashed hands. All three apples would be sealed in plastic bags for observation.

Objectives

After completing the lesson, students will be able to
◆ define and explain active immunity;
◆ define and explain passive immunity;
◆ identify some strategies for staying healthy.

Key Terms immunity, active immunity, vaccination, vaccine, passive immunity, antibiotic

1 Engage/Explore

Activating Prior Knowledge

Encourage students to discuss why people get immunizations. Ask students to list diseases for which they think vaccines do and do not exist.

········ DISCOVER ········

Skills Focus designing experiments
Materials *disinfectants and antibacterial products such as creams, mouthwashes, hand soaps, household cleaners, and spray disinfectants*
Time 15 minutes
Tips Use clean, empty containers or seal the tops of containers with tape. Caution students not to taste, smell, or touch any of the products. Have students list the product name, the pathogens it is supposed to kill, and the active ingredients for each. Active ingredients may include bacitracin, neomycin sulfate, benzalkonium chloride, hydrogen peroxide, iodine, isopropyl alcohol, and others.
Think It Over One possible experiment could involve using nutrient agar to grow bacteria from unwashed hands and from hands that have been washed with each soap. Tell students not to perform any experiments without first getting your approval for the procedure.

DISCOVER ·· ACTIVITY

What Substances Can Kill Pathogens?

1. Your teacher will give you a variety of products, such as disinfectant soaps and mouthwashes, that claim to kill pathogens. Read the labels to learn the pathogens that each product is supposed to destroy.

2. Also note the ingredients in each product that act against pathogens. These are labeled "active ingredients."

Think It Over
Designing Experiments How could you determine which of two different soaps is more effective at killing bacteria? Design an experiment to find out. Do not perform the experiment without obtaining your teacher's approval.

GUIDE FOR READING

◆ What is active immunity?
◆ What is passive immunity?

Reading Tip Before you read, rewrite the headings in the section as questions that begin with *how*, *why*, or *what*. As you read, write short answers to those questions.

Itch, itch, itch. That's probably what you remember about chicken pox, if you ever had it. But once you got better, you could be pretty sure that you would never get that disease again. As people recover from some diseases, they develop immunity to the diseases. **Immunity** is the body's ability to destroy pathogens before they can cause disease. There are two basic types of immunity—active and passive.

Active Immunity

If you've been sick with chicken pox, your body was invaded by chicken pox viruses. Your immune system responded to the virus antigens by producing antibodies against them. The next time that chicken pox viruses invade your body, your immune system will probably produce antibodies so quickly that you won't become sick. You now have **active immunity** to chicken pox, because your own body has produced the antibodies that fight the chicken pox pathogens. **Active immunity occurs when a person's own immune system produces antibodies in response to the presence of a pathogen.**

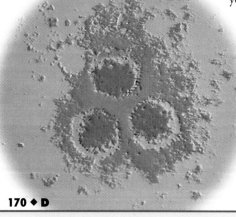

Figure 12 These virus particles cause chicken pox. Once you have had chicken pox you will probably never get that disease again.

READING STRATEGIES

Reading Tip After students rewrite the section headings as questions, have them preview the photographs and drawings and read the captions. Encourage them to write additional questions based on the pictures and captions. Instruct students to write short answers to their questions as they read.

Vocabulary Have students jot down the boldfaced terms in the section. Then ask them to use their own words to write definitions for each term. Have partners quiz each other on the terms.

Study and Comprehension Draw a sample Venn diagram on the board. Remind students that Venn diagrams are used for comparisons; refer students to the Skills Handbook, page 269. Have students use a Venn diagram to compare and contrast active and passive immunity.

Figure 13 Ouch! The injection may sting a bit, but it is a vaccination that will protect the little girl against disease. Vaccinations consist of dead or weakened pathogens that do not make you sick. *Classifying Why does a vaccination produce active immunity to a disease?*

How Active Immunity Is Produced Active immunity is produced by the cells of a person's immune system as part of the immune response. Remember that during the immune response, T cells and B cells help destroy the disease-causing pathogens. After the person recovers, some of the T cells and B cells keep the "memory" of the pathogen's antigen. If that kind of pathogen enters the body again, these memory cells recognize the pathogen's antigen. The memory cells start the immune response so quickly that the person usually doesn't get sick. Active immunity usually lasts for many years, and sometimes it lasts for life.

Vaccination One way in which you can gain active immunity is by coming down with the disease. Another way is by being vaccinated against the disease. **Vaccination** (vac suh NAY shun), or immunization, is the process by which harmless antigens are deliberately introduced into a person's body to produce active immunity. Vaccinations are given by injection or by mouth. Vaccinations can prevent polio, chicken pox, and other diseases.

The substance that is used in a vaccination is called a vaccine. A **vaccine** (vak SEEN) usually consists of pathogens that have been weakened or killed but can still trigger the immune system to go into action. The T cells and B cells still recognize and respond to the antigens of the weakened or dead pathogen. When you receive a vaccination, the weakened pathogens usually do not make you sick. However, your immune system responds by producing memory cells and active immunity to the disease.

✓ *Checkpoint* *What are two ways in which a person can gain active immunity?*

Answers to Self-Assessment

Caption Question

Figure 13 A vaccine triggers the immune system to create antibodies in response to the antigens of dead or weakened pathogens. As a result, memory cells are produced.

✓ *Checkpoint*

A person can gain active immunity as a result of infection or vaccination.

2 Facilitate

Active Immunity

Real-Life Learning

Tell students that a vaccine for chicken pox became available in the United States in 1995. Some students may have had chicken pox, but others may have received the vaccine. Encourage students to talk to the adults in their families about diseases and vaccinations. Point out that older generations may have been vaccinated against diseases that are no longer threats, such as smallpox. Ask students: **Do you think people will always have to be vaccinated against chicken pox?** *(Some students may think that vaccinations will always be necessary. Others may believe that the disease will disappear when enough people are immune so that it is no longer being spread by humans.)* **learning modality: verbal**

Building Inquiry Skills: Inferring

Ask students to describe how people gained immunity to the chicken pox virus before the vaccine was available. *(They had to get the disease to gain immunity.)* Explain that some people intentionally exposed themselves to the virus in order to gain active immunity. Have students brainstorm a list of the benefits and drawbacks of gaining immunity in this way. *(Samples: Benefits—immunity, getting the disease when young and healthy instead of when older or sick; drawbacks—you can spread the disease to others, you may experience complications.)* **learning modality: verbal**

Ongoing Assessment

Writing Have students explain how vaccination can produce active immunity. *(In vaccination, antigens are introduced into the body; usually they do not cause illness, but they make the immune system go into action. The T and B cells will be able to recognize and destroy that type of pathogen if it enters the body again.)*

Passive Immunity

Building Inquiry Skills: Inferring

Ask students to infer where the antibodies that produce passive immunity come from. (*Students should infer that the antibodies were made by cells from another person or animal that was infected with the virus.*) **learning modality: verbal**

Inquiry Challenge

Materials *common materials such as poster board, markers, colored marbles, modeling clay*

Time 20 minutes

Challenge small groups of students to work together to model the difference between the body's response to pathogens in active immunity and passive immunity. Tell students they can make diagrams, prepare a verbal presentation, or act out the body's response, as long as they show the pathogen entering the body and the body's response. Have groups present both representations to the class, and have the class guess which represents active and which represents passive immunity. **cooperative learning**

SCIENCE & History

Passive Immunity

Some diseases, such as rabies, are so uncommon that people rarely receive vaccinations against them. If a person is bitten by an animal that might have rabies, however, the person is usually given injections that contain antibodies to the rabies antigen. The protection that the person acquires this way is an example of passive immunity. This type of immunity is called **passive immunity** because the antibodies are given to the person—the person's own immune system did not make them.

Fighting Infectious Disease

From ancient times, people have practiced methods for preventing disease and caring for sick people. Ancient peoples, however, did not know what caused disease. About 200 years ago, people began to learn much more about the causes of infectious diseases and how to protect against them.

1854
Florence Nightingale

As an English nurse caring for British soldiers during the Crimean War, Florence Nightingale insisted that army hospitals be kept clean. By doing this, she saved many soldiers' lives. She is considered to be the founder of the modern nursing profession.

1800	1825	1850

1796
Edward Jenner

Edward Jenner, a country doctor in England, successfully vaccinated a child against smallpox, a deadly viral disease. Jenner used material from a sore of a person with cowpox, a mild but similar disorder. Although Jenner's procedure was successful, he did not understand why it worked.

1860s
Joseph Lister

Joseph Lister, an English surgeon, used carbolic acid to prevent infections in surgical patients. Because of Lister's techniques, far more people recovered from surgery than before.

172 ◆ D

Background

History of Science Smallpox was recorded as far back as the Roman Empire, when in A.D. 189 there were as many as 2,000 deaths per day throughout the empire. Even after the vaccine became available, epidemics continued to occur around the world.

In 1967, the World Health Organization (WHO) launched a worldwide vaccination campaign against smallpox. By 1975, most of the world's nations were free of smallpox.

The world's last known natural case of smallpox occurred in 1977. The only deaths reported thereafter occurred when the virus escaped from a laboratory in England.

In 1979, WHO declared the world to be free of the disease. This marks the first time in history that a naturally occurring disease has been completely eradicated from the human population.

Passive immunity occurs when the antibodies that fight the pathogen come from another source rather than from the person's own body. Unlike active immunity, which is long-lasting, passive immunity usually lasts no more than a few months.

A baby acquires passive immunity to some diseases before birth. This happens because antibodies from the mother's body pass into the baby's body. After birth, these antibodies protect the baby for a few months. After that time, the baby's own immune system has begun to function.

In Your Journal

Learn more about the work of one of these people. Then imagine that a new hospital is going to be dedicated to that person, and that you have been chosen to deliver the dedication speech. Write a speech that praises the person's contributions to fighting disease.

1882
Robert Koch

In Germany, Robert Koch identified one kind of microorganism in many samples of tissue taken from people with tuberculosis. Because he always found the same microorganism, Koch hypothesized that each infectious disease is caused by one specific pathogen.

| 1875 | 1900 | 1925 |

1868
Louis Pasteur

In France, Louis Pasteur showed that microorganisms were the cause of a disease in silkworms. Pasteur reasoned that he could control the spread of disease by killing microorganisms. He also proposed that infectious diseases in humans are caused by microorganisms.

1928
Alexander Fleming

In Britain, Alexander Fleming observed that bacteria growing on laboratory plates were killed when some kinds of fungi grew on the same plate. He discovered that one fungus produced a substance—penicillin—that killed bacteria. Penicillin became the first antibiotic.

Chapter 6 **D ◆ 173**

Challenge students to identify some of the effects of each discovery. For example, Jenner's discovery led to the effective control of smallpox and saved many lives.

Extend In 1999, the last smallpox viruses, stored in government health offices in Atlanta and Moscow, were scheduled to be destroyed. Challenge students to debate whether viruses that cause diseases that have been eradicated should be destroyed or saved for further scientific research. Students should form teams and debate the issue. *(The advantage of destroying the smallpox virus would be the prevention of another smallpox outbreak. The disadvantage consists of losing the ability to study the virus.)*

In Your Journal Encourage students to use both reference books and the Internet for their research. Remind students to imagine the audience as they write their speeches. **learning modality: verbal**

Ongoing Assessment

Writing Ask students to explain how passive immunity differs from active immunity. *(In active immunity, people's bodies produce antibodies to fight a specific pathogen. In passive immunity, the antibodies are given to the person.)*

Staying Healthy

Integrating Health

Students may confuse *antibodies* and *antibiotics*. Explain that, although their names sound similar, they are very different. Most antibiotics can kill several types of bacteria, but antibodies can only respond to the antigens of a particular pathogen. In addition, antibiotics cannot be used against viral infections, but antibody serums exist for both viral and bacterial infections, as well as for toxins such as the venom found in snake bites. **limited English proficiency**

3 Assess

Section 3 Review Answers

1. Active immunity is produced when a person's immune system produces antibodies in response to the presence of a pathogen.
2. Passive immunity is produced by transferring another organism's antibodies into the body. It usually lasts for a shorter time than active immunity.
3. Do not share items that may carry pathogens, keep clean, get plenty of rest and exercise, eat a balanced diet.
4. Since vaccination introduces antigens of pathogens into the body, the body responds as if the live pathogens themselves were present.

Performance Assessment

Writing Have students prepare lessons for younger students on ways of preventing infectious disease. **Portfolio** Students can save their lessons in their portfolios.

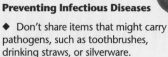

Preventing Infectious Diseases

◆ Don't share items that might carry pathogens, such as toothbrushes, drinking straws, or silverware.

◆ Keep clean. Wash your hands before eating and after using the bathroom.

◆ Cover your mouth when sneezing or coughing.

◆ Get eight hours of sleep every night.

◆ Eat a well-balanced diet.

◆ Get regular exercise.

Figure 14 Your actions can help prevent the spread of infectious diseases. *Applying Concepts How does keeping clean prevent the spread of disease?*

Staying Healthy

INTEGRATING HEALTH You almost certainly have immunity to some diseases, either because you have had the diseases or because you have been vaccinated against them. However, no one is immune to all diseases. But there are several steps you can take to decrease your risk of getting and spreading infectious diseases. Figure 14 summarizes these steps.

Unfortunately, you will probably become sick from time to time. When that happens, there are ways in which you can help yourself recover. Get plenty of rest. In addition, unless your stomach is upset, you should eat well-balanced meals. Drink plenty of fluids. These actions are all that you need to recover from most mild illnesses.

Sometimes when you are sick, medications can help you get better. If you have a disease that is caused by bacteria, you may be given an antibiotic. An **antibiotic** (an tih by AHT ik) is a chemical that kills bacteria or slows their growth without harming body cells. Unfortunately, there are no medications that cure viral illnesses, including the common cold. The best way to deal with most viral diseases is to get plenty of rest.

Some medicines don't kill pathogens but may help you feel more comfortable while you get better. Many of these are over-the-counter medications—drugs that can be purchased without a doctor's prescription. Such medications may reduce fever, clear your nose so you can breathe more easily, or stop a cough. Be sure you understand and follow the instructions for all types of medications. And if you don't start to feel better in a short time, you should see a doctor.

Section 3 Review

1. What is active immunity? How is it produced?
2. How is passive immunity produced? How does passive immunity differ from active immunity?
3. Identify four things that you can do that will help you avoid catching an infectious disease.
4. Thinking Critically Applying Concepts After receiving a vaccination, you may develop mild symptoms of the disease. Explain why.

Science at Home

With a family member, make a list of the vaccinations you have received. For each, note when you received the vaccination. Then, with your family member, learn about one of the diseases for which you were vaccinated. What kind of pathogen causes the disease? What are the symptoms of the disease? Is the disease still common in the United States?

Program Resources

◆ **Teaching Resources** 6-3 Review and Reinforce, p. 155; 6-3 Enrich, p. 156

Media and Technology

Interactive Student Tutorial CD-ROM D-6

Answers to Self-Assessment

Caption Question

Figure 14 By keeping clean, a person removes bacteria that might otherwise be able to enter the body and cause infection.

Noninfectious Disease

SECTION
4

Noninfectious Disease

DISCOVER

ACTIVITY

What Happens When Airflow Is Restricted?

1. Asthma is a disorder in which breathing passages become narrower than normal. This activity will help you understand how this condition affects breathing. Begin by breathing normally, first through your nose and then through your mouth. Observe how deeply you breathe.

2. Put one end of a drinking straw in your mouth. Then gently pinch your nostrils shut so that you cannot breathe through your nose.

3. With your nostrils pinched closed, breathe by inhaling air through the straw. Continue breathing this way for thirty seconds.

Think It Over

Observing Compare your normal breathing pattern to that when breathing through the straw. Which way were you able to take deeper breaths? Did you ever feel short of breath?

Americans are living longer today than ever before. A person who was born in 1990 can expect to live about 75 years. In contrast, a person born in 1950 could expect to live only about 68 years.

Progress against infectious disease is one reason why life spans have increased. However, as infectious diseases have become less common, noninfectious diseases have grown more prevalent. **Noninfectious diseases** are diseases that are not spread from person to person. Unlike infectious diseases, noninfectious diseases are not caused by microorganisms. A noninfectious disease, cardiovascular disease, is the leading cause of death in America. Allergies, diabetes, and cancer are other noninfectious diseases.

Allergies

Spring has arrived. Flowers are in bloom, and the songs of birds fill the air. Unfortunately for some people, sneezing is another sound that fills the air. People who sneeze and cough in the spring may not have colds. Instead, they may be suffering from an **allergy** to plant pollen in the air. **An allergy is a disorder in which the immune system is overly sensitive to a foreign substance—something not normally found in the body.**

GUIDE FOR READING

◆ What is an allergy?

◆ How does diabetes affect the body?

◆ What is cancer?

Reading Tip As you read, create a table in which you record the characteristics of each noninfectious disease.

▼ Plant pollen

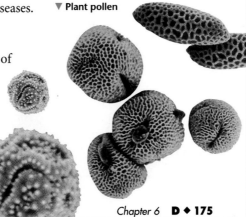

Chapter 6 **D ◆ 175**

Objectives

After completing the lesson, students will be able to
◆ define an allergy;
◆ explain how diabetes affects the body;
◆ explain how cancer affects the body.

Key Terms noninfectious disease, allergy, allergen, histamine, asthma, diabetes, tumor, carcinogen

1 Engage/Explore

Activating Prior Knowledge

Ask groups of students to brainstorm lists of diseases that cannot be spread from one person to another. Record all their responses on the board. Refer to the responses when students finish this section; at that point, help students add to the list and correct any misconceptions that they previously had.

DISCOVER

Skills Focus observing
Materials *plastic drinking straws*
Time 10 minutes
Tips Use narrow straws in this activity. Students with respiratory problems should not perform this activity if it will compromise their ability to breathe. Have them keep time and record observations.
Expected Outcome Students should not be able to breathe as deeply through the straws as they can through their noses.
Think It Over Students should be able to take deeper breaths without the straw. Some students may feel short of breath.

READING STRATEGIES

Reading Tip Have students work individually or in small groups to create their tables. Instruct students to create a framework for their tables before they begin reading. Column heads might be *Disease*, *Cause*, and *Characteristics*. As students read, they can complete the tables by writing in the characteristics of each noninfectious disease in their own words.

Program Resources

◆ **Teaching Resources** 6-4 Lesson Plan, p. 157; 6-4 Section Summary, p. 158
◆ **Interdisciplinary Exploration Series** "Fate of the Rain Forest," pp. 12–13

Media and Technology

 Audiotapes English-Spanish Summary 6-4

2 Facilitate

Allergies

Sharpen your Skills

Drawing Conclusions

Time 10 minutes

Tips Suggest that students list the ingredients side by side in a table to find those the desserts have in common.

Expected Outcome Because many ingredients are in both foods, there is not enough evidence to conclude an allergic reaction to strawberries. A more extensive record of foods eaten and reactions to foods is needed.

Extend Have students do research to learn about common allergies and their symptoms and how allergists determine which substances a person is allergic to. **learning modality: logical/mathematical**

Building Inquiry Skills: Making Models

Have students diagram what happens when a pathogen such as a virus invades the body and what happens when an allergen invades the body. Encourage students to label their drawings and write captions describing what happens at each stage. Ask: **What is the same in both drawings?** *(Both drawings show lymphocytes recognizing the foreign body and producing antibodies in response.)* **What is different?** *(In the immune response, the antibodies attach to the antigens on the pathogen. In the allergic response, the antibodies signal other cells to produce histamine.)* **learning modality: visual**

Sharpen your Skills

Drawing Conclusions

Two weeks ago, after you ate strawberry shortcake with whipped cream, you broke out in an itchy rash. Besides strawberries, the ingredients in the dessert were sugar, flour, butter, eggs, vanilla, baking powder, salt, and cream. Then last night, you ate a strawberry custard tart with whipped cream and again broke out in a rash. The tart's ingredients were strawberries, sugar, cornstarch, milk, eggs, flour, shortening, salt, and vanilla.

You think that you may be allergic to strawberries. Do you have enough evidence to support this conclusion? If so, why? If not, what additional evidence do you need?

Allergens An **allergen** is any substance that causes an allergy. In addition to different kinds of pollen, people may be allergic to dust, molds, some foods, and even some medicines. If you are lucky, you have no allergies at all. However, many people are allergic to one or more substances.

Reaction to Allergens Allergens may get into your body when you inhale them, eat them in food, or touch them with your skin. When lymphocytes encounter the allergen, they produce antibodies. These antibodies, unlike the ones made during the immune response, signal cells in the body to release a chemical called histamine. **Histamine** (HIS tuh meen) is a chemical that is responsible for the symptoms of an allergy, such as sneezing and watery eyes. Drugs that interfere with the action of histamine, called antihistamines, may lessen this reaction. However, if you have an allergy, the best strategy is to try to avoid the substance to which you are allergic.

Asthma If some people inhale a substance to which they are allergic, they may develop a condition called asthma. **Asthma** (AZ muh) is a disorder in which the respiratory passages narrow significantly. This narrowing causes the person to wheeze and become short of breath. Asthma attacks may be brought on by factors other than allergies, such as stress and exercise. People who have severe asthma attacks may require emergency care. If you have asthma, avoid the substances or activities that trigger asthma attacks and learn how to treat an attack.

Checkpoint *What is the effect of histamine on the body?*

Figure 15 Some people have allergic reactions to cats (left) or dust mites, tiny animals found in dust (below).

176 ◆ D

Background

Facts and Figures Researchers may have found a new vaccine to help people who are allergic to cats.

Traditional allergy treatment consists of months of injections made from the whole proteins of allergen. This treatment gradually sensitizes the body's immune response to the allergen, so that it no longer reacts by producing antibodies and histamines. The new vaccine blocks antigen receptors on T cells, preventing allergic reactions without repeated shots or exposure to the allergen. Because the new vaccine uses only the parts of the protein that stimulate the immune response, it works faster than the traditional treatment and may require only two injections each year. Researchers may have found a way to help people who are allergic to cats.

Diabetes

The pancreas produces a chemical called insulin. **Insulin** (IN suh lin) enables body cells to take in glucose from the blood and use it for energy. In the condition known as **diabetes** (dy uh BEE tis), either the pancreas fails to produce enough insulin or the body's cells can't use it properly. **As a result, a person with diabetes has high levels of glucose in the blood and excretes glucose in the urine. The person's body cells, however, do not have enough glucose.**

Effects of Diabetes People with diabetes may lose weight, feel weak, and be hungry all the time. These symptoms occur because the cells are unable to take in the glucose they need to function efficiently. In addition, these people may urinate frequently and feel thirsty as the kidneys work to eliminate the excess glucose from the body.

Diabetes is a serious condition that, if not treated properly, can result in death. Even with proper treatment, diabetes can have serious long-term effects. These effects can include blindness, kidney failure, and heart disease.

Forms of Diabetes There are two main forms of diabetes. Type I diabetes, the more serious form, usually begins in childhood or early adulthood. In Type I diabetes, the pancreas produces little or no insulin. People with this condition must get insulin injections.

Type II diabetes usually develops during adulthood. In this condition, either the pancreas doesn't make enough insulin or body cells do not respond normally to insulin. People with Type II diabetes may not need to take insulin. Instead, they may be able to control the symptoms of diabetes through proper diet, weight control, and exercise.

☑ *Checkpoint* *What are some symptoms of diabetes?*

Cancer

Under normal conditions, the body produces new cells at about the same rate that other cells die. In a condition known as cancer, however, the situation is quite different. **Cancer is a disease in which cells multiply uncontrollably, over and over, destroying healthy tissue in the process.** The word *cancer* is the Latin word for crab. Cancerous growths act something like a crab, pinching healthy tissues as they grow.

Figure 16 Many people with diabetes must test their blood frequently to determine the level of glucose in their blood. *Relating Cause and Effect What accounts for the high level of glucose in the blood of people with diabetes?*

Chapter 6 **D ◆ 177**

Answers to Self-Assessment

☑ *Checkpoints*

Histamine causes symptoms of an allergy.

Diabetes symptoms: Weight loss, excessive hunger or thirst, frequent urination, high glucose in blood

Caption Question
Figure 16 The body does not produce enough insulin or the cells cannot use it properly, so the body cells cannot take in glucose.

Diabetes

Building Inquiry Skills: Communicating

Materials *paper, colored pencils, markers*
Time 30 minutes

Tell students that although diabetes is recognizable by its warning signs, experts believe that about 8 million Americans are unaware that they have it. Have groups of students design information packets describing the warning signs and dangers of diabetes. Students should explain how symptoms, such as thirst and weight loss, are related to the causes of diabetes. You might contact the American Diabetes Association for additional information. Suggest that students use this information in producing their packets. **cooperative learning**

Cancer

Addressing Naive Conceptions

Some students may think that all cancer patients will die of cancer. Emphasize that advances in medical understanding and technology allow many people to survive cancer and go on to lead normal lives. Just as a healthy environment and good health habits can help protect people from developing cancer, factors such as diet and exercise can help people with cancer live longer and even recover from the disease. **learning modality: verbal**

Ongoing Assessment

Oral Presentation Ask students to choose a noninfectious disease and describe its causes and symptoms. (*Sample: Allergies are caused by an over-sensitive immune response to a foreign substance. Symptoms include burning eyes and sneezing.*)

Cancer, continued

Building Inquiry Skills: Applying Concepts

Point out to students that the text states that scientists do not know what causes cancer, but then goes on to state that carcinogens can cause cancer. Ask: **If scientists do not know what causes cancer, how can they say that tar in cigarette smoke or ultraviolet light can cause cancer?** *(Tar and ultraviolet light can cause cancer, but scientists do not know exactly what happens inside a cell to make it cancerous. In other words, scientists have identified certain substances that cause cancer, but they don't know what the substances actually do to cells.)* **learning modality: logical/ mathematical**

Integrating Physics

Tell students that radiation therapy may be applied to the body by implanting radioactive substances into tumors. Ask them to infer why this method would be better in some cases than using a machine like that shown in Figure 18. *(The radioactive substances could affect only the tumor, instead of affecting healthy cells as well.)* **learning modality: verbal**

Figure 17 The large orange mass in the X-ray is a cancerous tumor in the lung. The graph shows leading types of cancer that affect men and women in the United States. *Interpreting Graphs Do more women or men develop lung cancer each year?*

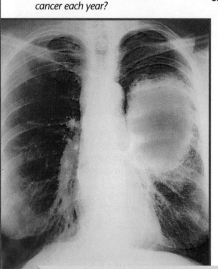

Tumor Formation As cancerous cells divide over and over, they often form abnormal tissue masses called **tumors.** Cancerous tumors invade the healthy tissue around them and destroy the tissue. Cancer cells can break away from a tumor and invade blood or lymph vessels. The blood or lymph then carries the cancer cells to other parts of the body, where they may begin to divide and form new tumors. Unless stopped by treatment, cancer progresses through the body.

Causes of Cancer Scientists do not know what causes cancer. Different factors may work together. One factor is the characteristics that people inherit from their parents. Because of their inherited characteristics, some people are more likely than others to develop certain kinds of cancer. For example, women whose mothers had breast cancer have a higher risk of developing breast cancer than do women with no family history of the disease.

Some substances or factors in the environment, called **carcinogens** (kahr SIN uh junz), can cause cancer. The tar in cigarette smoke is a carcinogen. Ultraviolet light, which is part of sunlight, can also be a carcinogen.

Cancer Treatment Surgery, drugs, and radiation are all used to treat cancer. If cancer is detected before it has spread, doctors remove the cancerous tumors through surgery. Sometimes, however, a surgeon can't remove all of the cancer. In these cases, drugs or radiation may be used to kill the cancer cells or slow their spread.

INTEGRATING PHYSICS Radiation treatment uses high-energy waves to kill cancer cells. X-rays and gamma rays are two types of radiation used in cancer treatment. These waves are similar to sunlight and the

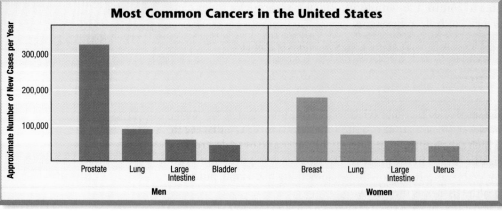

Most Common Cancers in the United States

Approximate Number of New Cases per Year

Men: Prostate, Lung, Large Intestine, Bladder
Women: Breast, Lung, Large Intestine, Uterus

Background

Facts and Figures Cancers are classified by the location in the body where they first develop or by the kind of tissue in which they originate. Carcinomas are tumors that begin in epithelial tissue. About 85 percent of malignant tumors are carcinomas. Sarcomas begin in connective tissue.

The treatment a patient receives is determined by the kind of the cancer and by how far the cancer has spread.

Treatment is considered to be successful only if every trace of the cancer is removed or destroyed. Surgery can only be completely successful if it is performed before the cancer has spread. Radiation can be used to deliver high energy rays to tissues that are deep inside the body, and chemotherapy can be used to destroy cancer cells that are spread throughout the body.

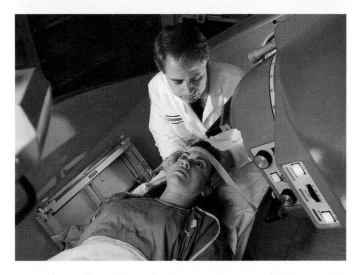

Figure 18 Radiation is one method that is used to treat cancer. The machine beams high-energy radiation at the tumor. This radiation kills cancer cells.

waves that make radios and microwave ovens work. However, X-rays and gamma rays have far more energy than sunlight, radio waves, or microwaves. When X-rays and gamma rays are aimed at tumors, they blast the cancer cells and kill them.

Cancer Prevention People can take steps to reduce their risk of developing cancer. For instance, they can avoid any form of tobacco, since tobacco and tobacco smoke contain carcinogens. Chewing tobacco and snuff contain carcinogens as well—they can cause cancers in the mouth. To prevent skin cancer, people can protect their skin from exposure to too much sunlight. A diet that is low in fat and includes plenty of fruits and vegetables can help people avoid some kinds of cancer, such as certain cancers of the digestive system.

Regular medical checkups are also important. Physicians or nurses may notice signs of cancer during a checkup. The earlier cancer is detected, the more likely it can be treated successfully.

Section 4 Review

1. What is an allergy? Describe how the body reacts to the presence of an allergen.
2. How does diabetes affect the level of glucose in the blood?
3. Describe how cancer cells harm the body.
4. **Thinking Critically Inferring** Doctors sometimes recommend that people with diabetes eat several small meals rather than three large ones. Why do you think doctors give this advice?

Science at Home

Explain to your family what allergies are and how allergens affect the body. Make a list of any substances your family members are allergic to. Use this list to determine whether certain allergies occur frequently in your family.

---

3 Assess

Section 4 Review Answers

1. An allergy is a disorder in which the immune system is overly sensitive to a foreign substance. When lymphocytes encounter allergens, they produce antibodies that signal the body's cells to release histamine, which causes symptoms such as sneezing.
2. The level of glucose is elevated either because the body does not produce enough insulin or because the cells cannot use it. Therefore, the cells do not take in glucose from the blood.
3. Cancer cells multiply uncontrollably and form tumors that invade and destroy healthy tissue.
4. Eating small meals rather than large ones prevents the glucose level in the blood from changing too rapidly. A diabetic's body can better process a steady level of glucose than a few rapid increases.

Science at Home

You may wish to have the class brainstorm a list of common allergens. Have students take the list home to use as a checklist. The list could include foods, pollen, animals, dust, and molds. Some students may discover that what they believed were seasonal colds might actually be allergies.

Program Resources

◆ **Teaching Resources** 6-4 Review and Reinforce, p. 159; 6-4 Enrich, p. 160

Media and Technology

 Interactive Student Tutorial CD-ROM D-6

Answers to Self-Assessment

Caption Question
Figure 17 More men

Performance Assessment

Organizing Information Have students create concept maps titled *Noninfectious Diseases*. Make sure students include symptoms, treatments, and preventive measures for each disease.

 Students can save their concept maps in their portfolios.

Causes of Death, Then and Now

Preparing for Inquiry

Key Concept The leading causes of death have changed over the past hundred years.

Skills Objectives Students will be able to
- interpret data about the leading causes of death;
- draw conclusions regarding the change in health threats since 1900;
- compare infectious to noninfectious diseases.

Time 20–30 minutes

Guiding Inquiry

Invitation Ask students what they think is the leading cause of death in the United States today. Have them consider news and television reports they have seen. Ask them to think about how household plumbing, safe commercial food handling, and improvements in general cleanliness have improved people's abilities to remain healthy.

Introducing the Procedure
- Refer to the Skills Handbook to teach or review how to make bar graphs and circle graphs.
- Remind students to round decimals to the nearest whole number in their calculations. However, students should make sure the percentages on their circle graphs add up to 100.

Troubleshooting the Experiment
Some students may need extra help with the math. Encourage students who are comfortable with the math to help others.

Expected Outcome
- Students should see that the leading causes of death a hundred years ago were caused by pathogens. They should also observe that heart disease has become a more common problem.
- If students do not make appropriate connections, have them try to identify the sources of their error. Some

---

Causes of DEATH, Then and Now

I In this lab you'll compare data on the leading causes of death in 1900 and today.

Problem

How do the leading causes of death today compare with those of a hundred years ago?

Materials

colored pencils	ruler
calculator (optional)	protractor
compass	

Procedure ✂

1. The data table on the next page shows the leading causes of death in the United States during two different years. Examine the data and note that two causes of death—accidents and suicides—are not diseases. The other causes are labeled either "I," indicating an infectious disease, or "NI," indicating a noninfectious disease.

Part 1 Comparing Specific Causes of Death

2. Look at the following causes of death in the data table: **(a)** pneumonia and influenza, **(b)** heart disease, **(c)** accidents, and **(d)** cancer. Construct a bar graph that compares the numbers of deaths from each of those causes in 1900 and today. Label the horizontal axis "Causes of Death." Label the vertical axis "Deaths per 100,000 People." Draw two bars side by side for each cause of death. Use a key to show which bars refer to 1900 and which refer to today.

Part 2 Comparing Infectious and Noninfectious Causes of Death

3. In this part of the lab, you will make two circle graphs showing three categories: infectious diseases, noninfectious diseases, and "other." You may want to review the information on creating circle graphs on page 272 of the Skills Handbook.

---

students may not be aware of the causes of pneumonia, tuberculosis, or most kinds of lethal diarrhea.

Analyze and Conclude

1. Students' answers should reflect that they could determine top causes of death in each year, as well as compare the total number of deaths to deaths attributed to particular causes.

2. Heart disease increased by 150 deaths per 100,000. Pneumonia/influenza decreased by 184 deaths per 100,000.

3. As a cause of death, infectious disease decreased the most—about 35%. Noninfectious disease increased the most—about 40%.

4. Sample: Since 1900, infectious diseases have been prevented by many factors including improvements in water treatment and sanitation, immunization, improved diets, medicines, and other disease treatment procedures.

Ten Leading Causes of Death in the United States, 1900 and Today

1900		Today	
Cause of Death	**Deaths per 100,000**	**Cause of Death**	**Deaths per 100,000**
Pneumonia, influenza (I)*	215	Heart disease (NI)	281
Tuberculosis (I)	185	Cancer (NI)	205
Diarrhea (I)	140	Stroke (NI)	59
Heart disease (NI)	130	Lung disease (NI)	39
Stroke (NI)	110	Accidents	35
Kidney disease (NI)	85	Pneumonia (I)	31
Accidents	75	Diabetes (NI)	22
Cancer (NI)	65	HIV Infection (I)	16
Senility (NI)	55	Suicide	12
Diphtheria (I)	40	Liver disease (NI)	10
Total	**1,100**	**Total**	**710**

*"I" indicates an infectious disease. "NI" indicates a noninfectious disease.

4. Start by grouping the data from 1900 into the three categories—infectious diseases, noninfectious diseases, and other causes. Find the total number of deaths for each category. Then find the size of the "pie slice" (the number of degrees) for each category, and construct your circle graph. To find the size of the infectious disease slice for 1900, for example, use the following formula:

$$\frac{\text{number of deaths from infectious diseases}}{1,100 \text{ deaths total}} = \frac{x}{360°}$$

5. Calculate the percentage represented by each category using this formula:

$$\frac{\text{number of degrees in a slice}}{360°} \times 100 = \underline{\ ?\ } \%$$

6. Repeat Steps 4 and 5 using the data from today to make the second circle graph. What part of the formula in Step 4 do you need to change?

Analyze and Conclude

1. What kind of information did you learn just from examining the data table in Step 1?
2. According to your bar graph, which cause of death showed the greatest increase between 1900 and today? The greatest decrease?
3. In your circle graphs, which category decreased the most from 1900 to today? Which increased the most?
4. Suggest an explanation for the change in the number of deaths due to infectious diseases from 1900 to today.
5. **Think About It** How do graphs help you identify patterns and other information in data that you might otherwise overlook?

More to Explore

Write a question related to the data table that you have not yet answered. Then create a graph or work with the data in other ways to answer your question.

5. Sample: When making graphs, data may be rearranged or reclassified in ways that show new information. For example, when the circle graphs were made, combining the data in new categories showed that infectious diseases have decreased dramatically.

Extending the Inquiry

More to Explore Students may find it helpful to work in small groups to list possible questions before they write their question. Sample: Among the ten top causes, how does the percentage of deaths from heart disease today compare with the percentage in 1900? *(Today, about 40% (281 ÷ 712) of these deaths are from heart disease; in 1900 about 12% (130 ÷ 1,100) were from heart disease.)* You might want to have students check each other's work before they share their questions and answers with the class.

Program Resources

◆ **Teaching Resources** Chapter 6 Skills Lab, pp. 167–169
◆ **Inquiry Skills Activity Book** Provides teaching and review of all inquiry skills

Safety

Make sure students exercise caution when working with sharp objects such as compasses. Review the safety guidelines in Appendix A.

Objective

After completing the lesson, students will be able to

◆ identify the environmental factors related to cancer.

1 Engage/Explore

Activating Prior Knowledge

Ask students to list environmental hazards they think might cause cancer. (*Samples: Cigarette smoke, pollution, excessive sunlight, chemicals in food*) For each, have students describe ways they can avoid exposing themselves to the danger. (*Samples: Don't smoke; try to avoid breathing second-hand smoke; wear sunscreen.*)

DISCOVER

Skills Focus developing hypotheses

Materials *pipe cleaners, ultraviolet-light detecting beads*

Time 10 minutes

Tips Ultraviolet detecting beads can be obtained from Educational Innovations, Inc., 151 River Road, Cos Cob, CT 06807. Make sure students' skins are protected from the sun.

Expected Outcome The beads will change colors when exposed to the ultraviolet light from the sun.

Think It Over Students' hypotheses may include keeping the beads out of sunlight, either by covering them with fabric or by coating them with sunscreen. Allow students to test their hypotheses after you have approved their plans.

SECTION 5 Cancer and the Environment

DISCOVER .... ACTIVITY

What Does Sunlight Do to the Beads?

1. Your teacher will give you beads that change color under certain conditions. Thread five beads on a pipe cleaner. Observe what the beads look like. Record your observations.

2. Wrap the pipe cleaner around your wrist. Go outdoors for one minute. Observe what happens to the beads.

Think It Over
Developing Hypotheses The ultraviolet light in sunlight causes the reaction you observed. Form a hypothesis about how you might prevent the beads from reacting as they did. How can you test your hypothesis?

GUIDE FOR READING

◆ How can people's environments affect their chances of developing cancer?

Reading Tip As you read, write short summaries of the information under each heading.

You are trapped in a place that is dark, tight, and so warm that it is hard to breathe. You climb upwards, carefully feeling for footholds as you inch along. The surfaces are so warm that your knees begin to feel hot as they scrape against the walls. Grimy dirt falls on your face, and you blink to keep it out of your eyes. This story sounds like a nightmare. But it was real life for the boys who worked as chimney sweeps.

Chimney Sweeps and Skin Cancer

In 1775, about one million people lived in London, England. Their homes were heated by coal fires. Because burning coal produces lots of grimy black soot, the soot had to be cleaned out of the chimneys regularly. Chimney sweeps did this job by crawling into the chimneys and scraping the soot off the walls.

READING STRATEGIES

Reading Tip Before students read, have them write the two main section headings on a sheet of paper, leaving enough space to write three or four sentences under each heading. Remind students that a summary presents the main idea and key details of a paragraph or passage. After students complete their summaries, invite volunteers to read them aloud.

Study and Comprehension After students read the section, have them write questions about the links between cancer and a person's environment. Direct students to write each question on a separate note card. Have them write answers to the questions on the backs of the note cards. Then have students work with partners or in small groups to answer each other's questions. After the activity, suggest that students keep their question cards to use as study guides.

Because chimney sweeps had to be small and thin enough to fit inside a chimney, most were boys. Since the work was dangerous, only boys who badly needed a job were willing to do it. Therefore, chimney sweeps were usually poor. Their homes did not have a water supply, and bathing was difficult. At the end of a hard day, chimney sweeps were covered with soot, but few washed it off.

A Link Between Soot and Cancer Percivall Pott, a London doctor, saw many chimney sweeps at his medical clinic. Pott noticed that the chimney sweeps often had soot ground deeply into their skin. He also observed that an alarmingly high number of chimney sweeps developed skin cancer. Pott hypothesized that something in soot caused the cancer. He recommended frequent bathing to reduce the risk of skin cancer. At first, people did not take Pott's advice. Many years later, scientists identified the carcinogens in soot. They are the same substances that make up the tar in cigarette smoke.

Carcinogens in the Environment Percivall Pott was one of the first scientists to understand that the environment can affect health. Cancer is one disease that can be caused by harmful environmental factors. **People's environments may contain carcinogens. To reduce the risk of cancer, the carcinogens need to be removed or people need to be protected from them.**

Pott's work led to present-day efforts to control environmental carcinogens. In the United States, the Environmental Protection Agency (EPA) is in charge of enforcing environmental laws. The EPA identifies environmental carcinogens and develops strategies for protecting people from them.

☑ *Checkpoint* *What did Pott recommend that chimney sweeps do in order to reduce their risk of skin cancer?*

Figure 19 Percivall Pott followed scientific procedure as he figured out the cause of skin cancer in chimney sweeps.

1770s — Observations
Percivall Pott notices that chimney sweeps have a high rate of cancer.

1775 — Formation of hypothesis
Pott hypothesizes that something in soot causes skin cancer.

1775 — Testing of hypothesis
Pott recommends that chimney sweeps bathe frequently, thus removing the cancer-causing soot.

1892 — Result of testing
Evidence shows that chimney sweeps who bathe regularly develop skin cancer at a lower rate than sweeps who rarely bathe.

Early 1900s — Confirmation of hypothesis
Certain substances in soot are found to cause skin cancer in laboratory animals.

Chimney Sweeps and Skin Cancer

Using the Visuals: Figure 19

Ask students: **What led Pott to hypothesize that something in soot caused skin cancer?** (*He observed that chimney sweeps had a high rate of skin cancer and that they were covered in soot.*) Ask: **How is Pott's recommendation to bathe frequently a test of his hypothesis?** (*If something in soot is causing the skin cancer, then removing the soot should decrease the incidence of skin cancer.*) Point out that the evidence to support Pott's hypothesis did not appear until 1892. Ask students why that might be. (*Samples: Not all chimney sweeps followed the recommendation; records of who did and did not bathe were not kept; skin cancer takes time to develop so records need to be kept over time.*) Lead students to discuss how scientific inquiry can cover periods longer than the life of a scientist, and how scientists build on each other's work. (*Students should notice that Pott's hypothesis was not confirmed until the early 1900s.*) **learning modality: verbal**

Social Studies CONNECTION

Suggest that interested students research the environmental and social conditions of cities such as London and Manchester, England, in the mid 1800s. Students can share their research with the class. **learning modality: verbal**

Program Resources

◆ **Teaching Resources** 6-5 Lesson Plan, p. 161; 6-5 Section Summary, p. 162

Media and Technology

 Audiotapes English-Spanish Summary 6-5

Answers to Self-Assessment

☑ *Checkpoint*

Pott recommended that chimney sweeps bathe frequently to reduce the risk of skin cancer.

Ongoing Assessment

Writing Ask students to explain why Pott's work led to present-day efforts to control environmental carcinogens. (*Pott's analysis of chimney sweeps showed that factors in the environment cause cancer and that people can be protected from such factors.*)

Environmental Carcinogens Today

Using the Visuals: Figure 20

Ask: **Why is the worker in the figure wearing safety equipment?** *(To protect against asbestos exposure)* Have students describe the different types of safety equipment being used and explain how they think each piece of equipment protects the worker. *(Samples: Mask— prevents breathing the fibers; goggles— keep eyes safe; gloves and suit—keep fibers off skin and cloth, where they might come in contact with mouth.)* **learning modality: visual**

3 Assess

Section 5 Review Answers

1. The environment may contain carcinogens, which cause cancer.
2. Pott observed more skin cancers in chimney sweeps, who were covered with soot, than in the rest of the population.
3. Asbestos can cause lung cancer when inhaled.
4. The number of skin cancers will probably increase because more ultraviolet light will reach Earth's surface.

Check Your Progress

Ask students to let you know about props or special lighting they need for their presentations. Set aside enough time for all presentations. Students may end their stories with the complete recovery or death of their patient, or they may announce that the disease is spreading to other people.

Performance Assessment

Writing Ask students to identify two environmental carcinogens and explain how they affect the body.

Figure 20 These asbestos ceiling panels were installed before people knew that asbestos can cause cancer. To protect the people who use the building, a worker is removing the panels.

Environmental Carcinogens Today

Scientists have identified many carcinogens found in the environment. Two important environmental carcinogens are asbestos and ultraviolet light.

Asbestos The mineral asbestos, which occurs in the form of fibers, is strong and does not burn. Because of these characteristics, asbestos was once widely used in materials such as roof shingles, brake linings, and insulation. However, scientists have since discovered that asbestos fibers can sometimes cause lung cancer when people inhale them repeatedly. Because of the dangers of asbestos, in 1989 the United States banned the manufacture and use of most asbestos products.

Ultraviolet Light As you learned in Chapter 2, skin cancer can result from overexposure to sunlight. Ultraviolet light is the part of sunlight that causes cancer. Fortunately, as sunlight travels from the sun to Earth, much of its ultraviolet light is absorbed high in the atmosphere, before it can reach Earth's surface. The gas ozone is the substance that absorbs most of the ultraviolet light.

In the 1970s and 1980s, scientists noticed that ozone levels in the upper atmosphere were decreasing. This decrease in ozone means that more ultraviolet light is reaching Earth's surface. At the same time, cases of skin cancer have been increasing. While the causes of the increase in skin cancer are complicated, some scientists believe that it is linked to the loss of ozone in the atmosphere.

Section 5 Review

1. How can the environment increase a person's risk for getting cancer?
2. What did Percivall Pott observe about the relationship between skin cancer and soot?
3. Why is asbestos dangerous?
4. **Thinking Critically** **Predicting** If ozone levels in the atmosphere decrease, what will probably happen to the number of skin cancers that develop each year? Explain.

Check Your Progress

Before your presentation, make your final revisions. If you are doing broadcasts, practice reading your scripts aloud. Experiment with different ways of bringing your series to a dramatic ending. Try to include answers to questions that might occur to your audience. For instance, are people around the patient at risk of invasion? If so, how can they defend themselves?

Background

Facts and Figures The Environmental Protection Agency estimates that 3,000 to 12,000 cases of cancer caused by asbestos exposure occur each year in the United States. The connection between asbestos and the development of cancer 20 or more years after exposure was first noted in a 1964 study of World War II shipyard workers. In 1971, the Occupational Safety and Health Administration began to regulate asbestos use.

Program Resources

◆ **Teaching Resources** 6-5 Review and Reinforce, p. 163; 6-5 Enrich, p. 164

Media and Technology

 Interactive Student Tutorial CD-ROM D-6

SECTION 1 Infectious Diseases

Key Ideas
◆ Infectious diseases are caused by pathogens: bacteria, viruses, fungi, and protists.
◆ Pathogens that infect humans can come from another person, a contaminated object, an animal bite, or the environment.

Key Terms
pathogen   infectious disease   toxin

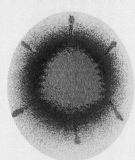

SECTION 2 The Body's Defenses

Key Ideas
◆ The body has three lines of defense against pathogens. The first consists of barriers such as the skin that keep pathogens out. The second line of defense consists of the inflammatory response.
◆ The immune system, which is the third line of defense, targets specific pathogens. T lymphocytes, or T cells, identify pathogens and distinguish one kind from another. B lymphocytes, or B cells, produce antibodies that destroy pathogens.
◆ AIDS is a disease of the immune system. HIV, the virus that causes AIDS, infects and destroys T cells, and therefore destroys the body's ability to fight disease.

Key Terms
inflammatory response   antigen
phagocyte   B cell
immune response   antibody
lymphocyte   AIDS
T cell

SECTION 3 Preventing Infectious Disease

Key Ideas
◆ In active immunity, a person's own immune system produces antibodies. A person can acquire active immunity by having the disease or by being vaccinated.
◆ In passive immunity, the antibodies come from a source other than the person's body.

Key Terms
immunity   vaccine
active immunity   passive immunity
vaccination   antibiotic

SECTION 4 Noninfectious Disease

Key Ideas
◆ An allergy is a disorder in which the immune system is overly sensitive to a foreign substance, called an allergen.
◆ In diabetes, the body does not produce enough insulin or can't use it properly.
◆ In cancer, cells multiply uncontrollably, destroying healthy tissues.

Key Terms
noninfectious disease   insulin
allergy   diabetes
allergen   tumor
histamine   carcinogen
asthma

SECTION 5 Cancer and the Environment
INTEGRATING ENVIRONMENTAL SCIENCE

Key Ideas
◆ In 1775, Percivall Pott hypothesized that soot caused cancer in chimney sweeps.
◆ Asbestos, which can cause lung cancer, and ultraviolet light, which can cause skin cancer, are environmental carcinogens.

USING THE INTERNET   ACTIVITY
www.science-explorer.phschool.com

Chapter 6 **D ◆ 185**

CHAPTER 6 REVIEW

Program Resources
◆ **Teaching Resources** Chapter 6 Project Scoring Rubric, p. 144; Chapter 6 Performance Assessment Teacher Notes, pp. 271–272; Chapter 6 Performance Assessment Student Worksheets, p. 273; Chapter 6 Test, pp. 274–277

Reviewing Content:
Multiple Choice
1. b 2. b 3. c 4. a 5. d

True or False
6. true 7. phagocyte 8. true 9. true
10. skin

Checking Concepts
11. The body has a natural system of barriers to keep pathogens out. The skin, breathing passages, mouth, and stomach trap and kill most pathogens.
12. Sharing a straw allows pathogens from one person's body to enter the body of another person.
13. B cells produce antibodies in response to specific antigens on pathogens; antibodies attach to antigens and prevent the pathogens from attacking cells.
14. Diabetes consists of insufficient insulin or the inability of cells to use insulin. This prevents the cells from properly absorbing and using glucose.
15. Inherited factors; exposure to environmental carcinogens.
16. Pott observed that a high number of chimney sweeps, who were usually covered with soot, developed skin cancer.
17. Students should explain that carbolic acid kills organisms that can get into surgical wounds and cause infection.

Thinking Visually
18. **a.** Some T cells attack pathogens.
b. Other T cells signal B cells to produce antibodies specific to the antigen.
c. Antibodies destroy the pathogenic bacteria.

Applying Skills
19. Students' graphs should show the temperature increasing to a peak in Week 1, remaining high in Week 2, then returning to normal in Weeks 3–5.
20. Week 3
21. Antibody levels rose during Week 2. As the antibody levels rise, the person's temperature returns to normal, and he or she begins to recover. This happens because of the effect the antibodies have on the bacteria that caused the illness.

Reviewing Content

For more review of key concepts, see the Interactive Student Tutorial CD-ROM.

Multiple Choice
Choose the letter of the best answer.

1. Some pathogenic bacteria produce poisons called
   a. histamines.
   b. toxins.
   c. phagocytes.
   d. pathogens.
2. Antibodies are produced by
   a. phagocytes.
   b. B cells.
   c. T cells.
   d. pathogens.
3. Which disease is caused by HIV?
   a. diabetes
   b. flu
   c. AIDS
   d. tetanus
4. A carcinogen causes
   a. cancer.
   b. colds.
   c. allergies.
   d. food poisoning.
5. Ozone in the atmosphere absorbs
   a. allergens.
   b. T cells.
   c. soot.
   d. ultraviolet light.

True or False
If a statement is true, write true. If it is false, change the underlined word or words to make the statement true.

6. People can get Lyme disease from <u>animal bites</u>.
7. A <u>T cell</u> engulfs pathogens and destroys them.
8. Vaccination produces <u>active immunity</u>.
9. A <u>tumor</u> is a mass of cancer cells.
10. Percivall Pott linked soot to <u>stomach</u> cancer.

Checking Concepts
11. Explain why it is difficult for pathogens to get to a part of the body in which they can cause disease.
12. Why is it important not to share a drinking straw with someone else?
13. What is the relationship between antigens and antibodies?
14. How does diabetes harm the body?
15. Identify three factors that can make a person likely to develop cancer.
16. What evidence led Percivall Pott to hypothesize that something in soot causes cancer?
17. **Writing to Learn** A patient of Joseph Lister is angry because Lister has covered her surgery wound with a bandage dipped in carbolic acid. The acid stings and the bandage is uncomfortable. Write a conversation between Lister and the patient in which Lister explains why she shouldn't take the bandage off.

Thinking Visually
18. **Flowchart** Complete the flowchart, which shows what happens after tuberculosis bacteria begin to multiply in the lungs. (For more information on flowcharts, see the Skills Handbook.)

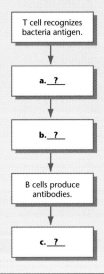

Thinking Critically
22. No. Colds are not caused by sitting in chilly drafts, but by viruses.
23. Some T cells recognize antigens and signal B cells to produce antibodies. Other T cells kill pathogens directly. B cells produce antibodies to prevent pathogens from infecting cells.
24. The immune system cannot fight HIV because the virus directly attacks T cells and weakens the body's immune response. When T cells are destroyed, the body is unable to produce antibodies or employ other immune defenses.
25. Pott believed that the soot ground into chimney sweep's skin was causing skin cancer, so bathing would remove the soot from the skin and reduce the risk of cancer.

Applying Skills

A person had an illness caused by bacteria. The table shows how the person's temperature and antibody level changed over the course of the disease. Use the table to answer Questions 19–21.

Week	Body Temperature (°C)	Antibody Level
0	37	low
1	39.8	low
2	39	medium
3	37	high
4	37	medium
5	37	low

19. Graphing Make a line graph of the temperature data. Label the horizontal axis "Week Number" and the vertical axis "Body Temperature."

20. Interpreting Data During what week did the person's temperature return to normal?

21. Drawing Conclusions When do antibody levels start to rise? What effect do antibodies have on the illness? Explain.

Thinking Critically

22. Applying Concepts Can you catch a cold by sitting in a chilly draft? Explain.

23. Comparing and Contrasting Compare the functions of T cells and B cells.

24. Relating Cause and Effect Why can the immune system successfully fight most pathogens, but not HIV?

25. Inferring Why did Pott think that frequent bathing would reduce chimney sweeps' risk of developing cancer?

Performance Assessment

CHAPTER PROJECT 6 — Wrap Up

Present Your Project Now you can share your news series and enjoy those prepared by your classmates. Before your presentation, make sure any sound effects and props support the story.

Reflect and Record In your notebook, reflect on what you learned by using your imagination to explore a science topic. Did it help you to better understand how the body fights disease? What new information did you learn from presentations made by other groups? If you had your project to do over, what would you do differently?

Getting Involved

In Your School Ask the school nurse to describe the signs of a serious allergic reaction. Find out what you should do if someone appears to be having such a reaction. Also ask what provisions the school makes for helping students who know that they have severe allergic reactions— for example, to bee stings. Then prepare a booklet on dealing with serious allergies. Have the nurse check your rough draft for accuracy. Put the finished booklet in the school library or nurse's office.

Chapter 6 **D ◆ 187**

Program Resources

◆ **Inquiry Skills Handbook** Provides teaching and review of all inquiry skills

Performance Assessment

Wrap Up — CHAPTER PROJECT 6

Present Your Project
If possible, allow students time to rehearse their presentations before presenting them to the class. You may want to have students perform their news reports for the class, or present written reports or audio or videotapes. Set aside enough time for all students to make their presentations.

Reflect and Record Encourage students to describe what parts of the project helped them to understand the body's defenses against disease. Some students may have had difficulty using the format of a news report, while others may have found that it helped them ask relevant questions and organize information. Have students identify questions they have after completing the project.

Getting Involved

In Your School Before the nurse talks to the class, have students write a list of questions to ask. Students may want to choose a particular allergen, one that affects them personally or one that has been the subject of legislation, such as perfume or peanut-based food products. Allow students to work in small groups to save time. When the booklets are completed, arrange to have them displayed in the library or student health center.

Nervous System

Sections	Time	Student Edition Activities	Other Activities	
CHAPTER PROJECT 7 **Tricks and Illusions** p. 189	Ongoing (2 weeks)	Check Your Progress, pp. 202, 211, 220 Wrap Up, p. 223	TE	Chapter 7 Project Notes, pp. 188–189
1 **How the Nervous System Works** pp. 190–195 ◆ Identify the functions of the nervous system. ◆ List the three types of neurons and tell how a nerve impulse travels.	3 periods/ 2½ blocks	**Discover** How Simple Is a Simple Task?, p. 190 **Skills Lab: Designing Experiments** Ready or Not, p. 195	TE TE	Building Inquiry Skills: Relating Cause and Effect, p. 191 Inquiry Challenge, p. 192
2 **Divisions of the Nervous System** pp. 196–203 ◆ Identify the function of the central nervous system, describe its parts, and explain how to keep it safe from injury. ◆ Identify the functions of the peripheral nervous system and its parts. ◆ Describe a reflex.	4 periods/ 2 blocks	**Discover** How Does Your Knee React?, p. 196 **Sharpen Your Skills** Controlling Variables, p. 198	TE TE ISLM	Inquiry Challenge, p. 197 Building Inquiry Skills: Making Models, p. 199 D-7, "Locating Touch Receptors"
3 **The Senses** pp. 204–211 ◆ Name the senses and state the overall function performed by the senses. ◆ Describe how eyes enable people to see. ◆ Describe how people hear sounds and maintain balance. ◆ Describe how people experience the senses of touch, taste, and smell.	4 periods/ 2 blocks	**Discover** What's in the Bag?, p. 204 **Try This** Why Do You Need Two Eyes?, p. 205 **Try This** Tick! Tick! Tick!, p. 208 **Sharpen Your Skills** Designing Experiments, p. 210	TE TE TE TE TE TE	Building Inquiry Skills: Observing, p. 205 Demonstration, p. 206 Integrating Physics, pp. 206, 208 Including All Students, p. 207 Building Inquiry Skills: Making Models, p. 209 Including All Students, p. 210
4 *INTEGRATING HEALTH* **Alcohol and Other Drugs** pp. 212–220 ◆ Name some commonly abused drugs and state how they affect the body. ◆ Explain how alcohol abuse harms the body.	4½ periods/ 2–3 blocks	**Discover** How Can You Best Say No?, p. 212 **Sharpen Your Skills** Communicating, p. 214 **Real-World Lab: You, the Consumer** With Caffeine or Without?, pp. 216–217	TE TE TE TE	Building Inquiry Skills: Communicating, p. 213 Demonstration, p. 214 Building Inquiry Skills: Measuring, p. 218 Building Inquiry Skills: Communicating, p. 219
Study Guide/Chapter Review pp. 221–223	1 period/ ½ block		ISAB	Provides teaching and review of all inquiry skills

For Standard or Block Schedule The Resource Pro® CD-ROM gives you maximum flexibility for planning your instruction for any type of schedule. Resource Pro® contains Planning Express®, an advanced scheduling program, as well as the entire contents of the Teaching Resources and the Computer Test Bank.

CHAPTER PLANNING GUIDE

Program Resources	Assessment Strategies	Media and Technology
TR Chapter 7 Project Teacher Notes, pp. 170–171 **TR** Chapter 7 Project Overview and Worksheets, pp. 172–175 **TR** Chapter 7 Project Scoring Rubric, p. 176	**SE** Performance Assessment: Chapter 7 Project Wrap Up, p. 223 **TE** Check Your Progress, pp. 202, 211, 220 **TE** Performance Assessment: Chapter 7 Project Wrap Up, p. 223 **TR** Chapter 7 Project Scoring Rubric, p. 176	
TR 7-1 Lesson Plan, p. 177 **TR** 7-1 Section Summary, p. 178 **TR** 7-1 Review and Reinforce, p. 179 **TR** 7-1 Enrich, p. 180 **TR** Chapter 7 Skills Lab, pp. 193–194	**SE** Section 1 Review, p. 194 **SE** Analyze and Conclude, p. 195 **TE** Ongoing Assessment, pp. 191, 193 **TE** Performance Assessment, p. 194 **TR** 7-1 Review and Reinforce, p. 179	Exploring Life Science Videodisc, Unit 4 Side 1, "Quick Reflexes" Audiotapes: English-Spanish Summary 7-1 Transparency 14, "Exploring the Path of a Nerve Message" Interactive Student Tutorial CD-ROM, D-7
TR 7-2 Lesson Plan, p. 181 **TR** 7-2 Section Summary, p. 182 **TR** 7-2 Review and Reinforce, p. 183 **TR** 7-2 Enrich, p. 184	**SE** Section 2 Review, p. 202 **TE** Ongoing Assessment, pp. 197, 199, 201 **TE** Performance Assessment, p. 202 **TR** 7-2 Review and Reinforce, p. 183	Exploring Life Science Videodisc, Unit 4 Side 1, "Quick Reflexes" Audiotapes: English-Spanish Summary 7-2 Transparency 15, "The Brain" Interactive Student Tutorial CD-ROM, D-7
TR 7-3 Lesson Plan, p. 185 **TR** 7-3 Section Summary, p. 186 **TR** 7-3 Review and Reinforce, p. 187 **TR** 7-3 Enrich, p. 188 **SES** Book O, *Sound and Light,* Chapters 2 and 4	**SE** Section 3 Review, p. 211 **TE** Ongoing Assessment, pp. 205, 207, 209 **TE** Performance Assessment, p. 211 **TR** 7-3 Review and Reinforce, p. 187	Audiotapes: English-Spanish Summary 7-3 Transparency 16, "The Eye" Transparency 17, "The Ear" Interactive Student Tutorial CD-ROM, D-7
TR 7-4 Lesson Plan, p. 189 **TR** 7-4 Section Summary, p. 190 **TR** 7-4 Review and Reinforce, p. 191 **TR** 7-4 Enrich, p. 192 **TR** Chapter 7 Real-World Lab, pp. 195–197	**SE** Section 4 Review, p. 220 **SE** Analyze and Conclude, p. 217 **TE** Ongoing Assessment, p. 213, 215, 219 **TE** Performance Assessment, p. 220 **TR** 7-4 Review and Reinforce, p. 191	Audiotapes: English-Spanish Summary 7-4 Interactive Student Tutorial CD-ROM, D-7
TR Chapter 7 Performance Assessment, pp. 278–280 **TR** Chapter 7 Test, pp. 281–284	**SE** Chapter Review, pp. 221–223 **TR** Chapter 7 Performance Assessment, pp. 278–280 **TR** Chapter 7 Test, pp. 281–284 **CTB** Test D-7	Computer Test Bank, Test D-7 Interactive Student Tutorial CD-ROM, D-7 Science Explorer Internet Site

Key: **SE** Student Edition   **TE** Teacher's Edition   **TR** Teaching Resources
     CTB Computer Test Bank   **SES** Science Explorer Series Text   **ISLM** Integrated Science Laboratory Manual
     ISAB Inquiry Skills Activity Book   **PTA** Product Testing Activities by *Consumer Reports*   **IES** Interdisciplinary Explorations Series

Meeting the National Science Education Standards and AAAS Benchmarks

National Science Education Standards	Benchmarks for Science Literacy	Unifying Themes
Science as Inquiry (Content Standard A) ◆ **Design and conduct a scientific investigation** Students design a test on people's responses to optical illusions. *(Chapter Project)* Students investigate how time of day affects reaction time. *(Skills Lab)* ◆ **Think critically and logically to make the relationships between evidence and explanations** Students draw conclusions about the effect of stimulants on water fleas. *(Real-World Lab)* **Life Science** (Content Standard C) ◆ **Structure and function in living systems** The nervous system has specialized cells that allow it to receive information, respond to information, and maintain homeostasis. *(Section 1)* ◆ **Regulation and behavior** The nervous system maintains stable body conditions. *(Section 1)* The nervous system uses senses to receive information about the environment. The brain processes this information to help humans survive. *(Sections 2, 3; Chapter Project)* **Science in Personal and Social Perspectives** (Content Standard F) ◆ **Personal health** Abusing drugs and alcohol can cause both short-term and long-term damage to a person's health. *(Section 4; Real-World Lab)* ◆ **Risks and benefits** Students debate whether bicycle helmet laws should be enacted to protect people from injury. *(Science and Society)*	**1C Scientific Inquiry** Students ensure that variables are controlled in experiments examining optical illusions, nervous system reaction time, and the effects of stimulants. *(Chapter Project; Skills Lab; Real-World Lab)* **5C Cells** Nerve cells have dendrites and axons, which are structures that differentiate them from other body cells. *(Section 1)* **6C Basic Functions** The central nervous system processes information that it receives from the peripheral nervous system. All body responses, including learning and thought, result from this function. *(Sections 2, 3; Chapter Project; Skills Lab)* **6D Learning** The brain is divided into three sections; of these, the cerebrum is responsible for the processes that allow humans to learn and remember. *(Section 2)* **6E Physical Health** Injury to the brain or spinal cord can cause severe damage or death; protecting your head with a helmet is one way to minimize the possibility of brain injury. *(Section 2; Science and Society)* Alcohol and other drugs are toxic substances that alter the responses of the nervous system and can cause permanent damage to body systems. *(Section 4; Real-World Lab)*	◆ **Scale and Structure** The nervous system is made up of two parts—the central and peripheral nervous systems. Neurons are the specialized cells of the nervous system. *(Sections 1, 2)* ◆ **Systems and Interactions** Sensory neurons, interneurons, and motor neurons respond to stimuli that affect the senses as well as stimuli within the body. The nervous system controls reaction time; reflexes; the processing of information, such as optical illusions; and the regulation of body systems. Alcohol and other drugs can interfere with the interaction of the nervous system. *(Sections 1, 2, 3, 4; Chapter Project; Skills Lab; Real-World Lab)* ◆ **Stability** The nervous system controls homeostasis of the body. Damage to the nervous system, through drug and alcohol use or injury, upsets the body's stability. *(Sections 1, 4; Real-World Lab; Science and Society)*

Media and Technology

Exploring Life Science Videodisc
◆ **Section 1** "Quick Reflexes" models how the parts of the nervous system work together to allow athletes to respond quickly when playing their sport.

Interactive Student Tutorial CD-ROM
◆ **Chapter Review** Interactive questions help students to self-assess their mastery of key chapter concepts.

Student Edition Connection Strategies

◆ **Section 2** Visual Arts Connection, p. 199
　　　　　　 Integrating Health, p. 202

◆ **Section 3** Integrating Physics, p. 206
　　　　　　 Integrating Physics, p. 208

◆ **Section 4** Integrating Health, p. 212

USING THE INTERNET **ACTIVITY**

www.science-explorer.phschool.com

Visit the Science Explorer Internet site to find an up-to-date activity for Chapter 7 of *Human Biology and Health*.

Student Edition Activities Planner

ACTIVITY	Time (minutes)	Materials — Quantities for one work group	Skills
Section 1			
Discover, p. 190	15	**Consumable** paper **Nonconsumable** pencil, penny	Inferring
Skills Lab, p. 195	50	**Nonconsumable** meter stick	Designing Experiments
Section 2			
Discover, p. 196	10	**Consumable** No special materials are required.	Inferring
Sharpen Your Skills, p. 198	45	**Nonconsumable** tape player, cassette tape of soft music	Controlling Variables
Section 3			
Discover, p. 204	20	**Nonconsumable** opaque paper bags; small objects, such as erasers, pens, paper clips, sponge, cotton balls, marbles, plastic spoons, bottle caps, coins, buttons	Observing
Try This, p. 205	15	**Nonconsumable** drinking straw, pipe cleaner	Inferring
Try This, p. 208	15	**Nonconsumable** ticking watch, metric ruler	Measuring
Sharpen Your Skills, p. 210	15	**Consumable** peeled pear, apple, and raw potato	Designing Experiments
Section 4			
Discover, p. 212	15	**Nonconsumable** pieces of wrapped candy	Inferring
Sharpen Your Skills, p. 214	45	**Consumable** paper **Nonconsumable** drawing materials	Communicating
Real-World Lab, pp. 216–217	40	**Consumable** drinking straw, toothpick, petroleum jelly, *Daphnia* culture, adrenaline solution (about 0.01%), beverages with and without caffeine **Nonconsumable** scissors, metric ruler, microscope slide, plastic dropper, clock or watch with second hand	Developing Hypotheses, Designing Experiments

A list of all materials required for the Student Edition activities can be found on pages T14–T15. You can order Materials Kits by calling 1-800-828-7777 or by accessing the Science Explorer Internet site at **www.science-explorer.phschool.com.**

188d

Tricks and Illusions

Sensory illusions, such as optical illusions, provide an opportunity to study how sensory information is interpreted by the brain. Note: If a person stares at the chapter opener long enough, a scallop shell seems to pop from the page.

Purpose In this project, students will observe their own responses to several illusions and choose at least one to investigate. During a science fair, they will record participants' responses to the illusion. Afterward, they will present their results to the class. This project will give students the opportunity to consider how their senses work and learn that, despite variations, people experience a shared sensory world.

Skills Focus After completing the project, students will be able to

◆ predict typical responses and observe their own responses and those of others to simple illusions;

◆ create a data table to record responses to a particular illusion;

◆ set up an illusion and present it to other students;

◆ create graphs or tables to interpret data and draw conclusions;

◆ communicate the results of their experiment to the class.

Project Time Line The entire project will require about two weeks. The first week will be devoted to trying out and selecting illusions. The second week will involve holding the science fair, gathering data, and presenting results. Class time will be needed for trying out the illusions, for the science fair, and for presentations. Before beginning the project, see Chapter 7 Project Teacher Notes on pages 170–171 in Teaching Resources for more details on carrying out the project. Also distribute the Chapter 7 Project Overview, Worksheets, and Scoring Rubric on pages 172–176 in Teaching Resources.

Suggested Shortcuts You can simplify the project by choosing a variety of illusions and setting them up in stations around the classroom. To save time, students could test these illusions on

---

The Nervous System

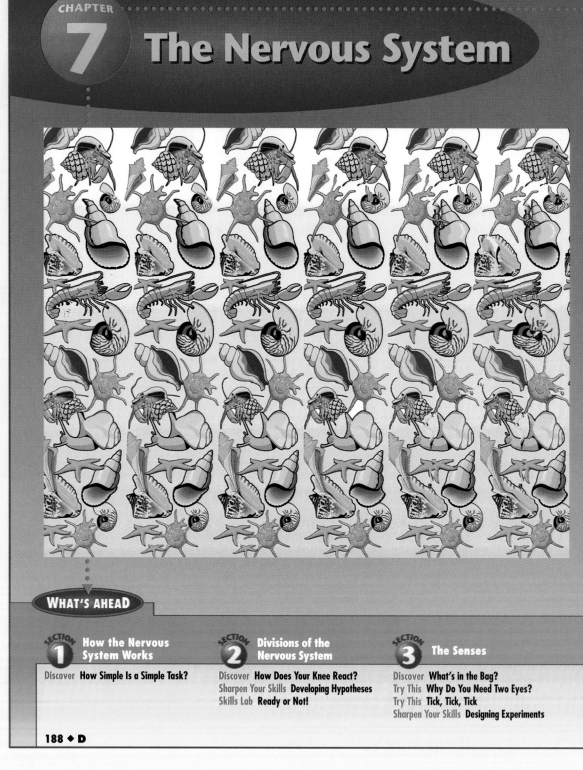

WHAT'S AHEAD

SECTION 1 How the Nervous System Works
Discover **How Simple Is a Simple Task?**

SECTION 2 Divisions of the Nervous System
Discover **How Does Your Knee React?**
Sharpen Your Skills **Developing Hypotheses**
Skills Lab **Ready or Not!**

SECTION 3 The Senses
Discover **What's in the Bag?**
Try This **Why Do You Need Two Eyes?**
Try This **Tick, Tick, Tick**
Sharpen Your Skills **Designing Experiments**

---

each other during one class period and report on their findings during another.

Possible Materials Materials will vary, depending on the illusions chosen. You can minimize the need for complicated materials by selecting simple illusions for students to use. Alternatively, you may wish to have students obtain materials as a requirement of successfully completing the project.

Some good reference books for this project include *You Won't Believe Your Eyes!* by Catherine O'Neill Grace; *Science, Art and Visual Illusions* by Robert Froman; *How to Really Fool Yourself: Illusions for All Your Senses* by Vicki Cobb; *Illusions: A Journey Into Perception* by Patricia Ann Rainey; and *Optricks* by Melinda Wentzell and D. K. Holland.

Launching the Project To introduce the project and to stimulate student interest, have students play the game of "gossip." Ask one student to start the gossip line by reading in a whisper the following message to a second student: "If a rabbit runs twice around the school, then puts butter on its ears, it will grow

Tricks and Illusions

Can you be sure of what you see, hear, smell, taste, or touch? In this chapter, you'll learn how you experience your environment through your senses. You'll see how the senses send information to your nervous system and how your brain interprets the messages.

But things aren't always what they seem. For example, an optical illusion is a picture or other visual effect that tricks you into seeing something incorrectly. In this project, you'll investigate how your senses can sometimes be fooled by illusions.

Your Goal To set up a science fair booth to demonstrate how different people respond to one or more illusions.

To complete this project, you must
- try out a variety of illusions, including some that involve the senses of hearing or touch as well as sight
- select one or more illusions, and set up an experiment to monitor people's responses to the illusions
- learn why the illusions fool the senses
- follow the safety guidelines in Appendix A

Get Started In a small group, discuss optical illusions or other illusions that you know about. Look in books to learn about others. Try them out. Which illusions would make an interesting experiment? How could you set up such an experiment at a science fair?

Check Your Progress You'll be working on this project as you study this chapter. To keep your project on track, look for Check Your Progress boxes at the following points.

Section 2 Review, page 202: Plan the experiment you will perform.
Section 3 Review, page 211: Carry out your experiment.
Section 4 Review, page 220: Explain why the illusions trick the senses.

Wrap Up At the end of the chapter (page 223), be prepared to share your findings with your classmates. Then explain how your illusions work.

Now you see it. Now you don't. Sometimes your eyes can play tricks on you. The picture shows rows of seashells and sea animals. Or does it?

Stare at the picture for several seconds, as if it were far away. The picture should look slightly out of focus. After a while, does anything seem to pop out from the picture?

SECTION 4

Integrating Health
Alcohol and Other Drugs

Discover **How Can You Best Say No?**
Sharpen Your Skills **Communicating**
Real-World Lab **With Caffeine or Without?**

D ◆ 189

Allow time for students to read the description of the project in their text and the Chapter Project Overview on pages 172–173 in Teaching Resources. Then discuss with students whether they must research their own illusions or whether you will provide them with a selection of illusions to choose from. Also, answer any initial questions that students may have. Pass out copies of the Chapter 7 Project Worksheets on pages 174–175 in Teaching Resources for students to review.

Performance Assessment

The Chapter 7 Project Scoring Rubric on page 176 of Teaching Resources will help you evaluate how well students complete the Chapter 7 Project. Students will be assessed on
- their research (if appropriate) and selection of an appropriate illusion;
- their design of data sheets to record responses;
- their participation in and gathering of data during the science fair;
- their class presentation of their results.

By sharing the Chapter 7 Scoring Rubric with students at the beginning of the project, you will make it clear to them what they are expected to do.

---

green fur." The second student should whisper what was heard to a third, and so on throughout the class. Have every fifth person quietly write down what the message sounded like so students can later see what changes occurred as the message was passed around the room. After the last student says the message aloud and it is compared with the original and with each written version, discuss with students how the mind uses information gathered by the senses and then "makes sense" of it.

Program Resources

- **Teaching Resources** Chapter 7 Project Teacher Notes, pp. 170–171; Chapter 7 Project Overview and Worksheets, pp. 172–175; Chapter 7 Project Scoring Rubric, p. 176

SECTION
1 How the Nervous System Works

Objectives

After completing the lesson, students will be able to

◆ identify the functions of the nervous system;

◆ list the three types of neurons and tell how a nerve impulse travels.

Key Terms stimulus, response, neuron, nerve impulse, dendrite, axon, nerve, sensory neuron, interneuron, motor neuron, synapse

1 Engage/Explore

Activating Prior Knowledge

Ask students: **What does it mean when someone says that something makes them nervous?** *(Students may say it means that a person is anxious or worried about something.)* Explain that anxiety and worry are different ways in which people react to their environment. Point out that the nervous system allows people to react to their environment.

⬤⬤⬤⬤⬤⬤ DISCOVER ⬤⬤⬤⬤⬤⬤

Skills Focus inferring
Materials *paper, pencil, penny*

Time 15 minutes
Tips Remind students to follow directions carefully as they complete the activity.
Think It Over Sample: Sense organs used include eyes and skin. Muscle movements include the muscles of the arms and hands holding the penny down, moving the penny from place to place, picking up the pencil, and tracing the circle. Thought processes involved include reading and understanding the instructions, choosing where to place the penny, and following the sequence of numbers.

DISCOVER

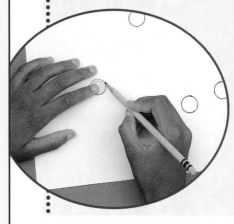

How Simple Is a Simple Task?

1. Trace the outline of a penny in twelve different places on a piece of paper.

2. Number the circles from 1 through 12. Write the numbers randomly, in no particular order.

3. Now pick up the penny again. Put it in each circle, one after another, in numerical order, beginning with 1 and ending with 12.

Think it Over

Inferring Make a list of all the sense organs, muscle movements, and thought processes in this activity. Compare your list with your classmates' lists. What organ system coordinated all the different processes involved in this task?

GUIDE FOR READING

◆ What are the functions of the nervous system?

◆ What are the three types of neurons and how do they interact?

Reading Tip Before you read, preview *Exploring the Path of a Nerve Impulse* on page 193. List any unfamiliar terms. Then, as you read, write a definition for each term.

The drums roll, and the crowd suddenly becomes silent. The people in the audience hold their breaths as the tightrope walker begins his long and dangerous journey across the wire. High above the circus floor, he inches along, slowly but steadily. One wrong movement could mean disaster.

To keep from slipping, tightrope performers need excellent coordination and a keen sense of balance. In addition, they must remember what they have learned from years of practice.

Even though you aren't a tightrope walker, you too need coordination, a sense of balance, memory, and the ability to learn. Your nervous system carries out all those functions. The nervous system consists of the brain, spinal cord, and nerves that run throughout the body. It also includes sense organs such as the eyes and ears.

190 ◆ D

READING STRATEGIES

Reading Tip As students preview *Exploring the Path of a Nerve Impulse* and list unfamiliar terms, encourage them to also list questions they have about receptors, nerve impulses, sensory neurons, interneurons, and motor neurons. As students read the section, have them write answers to their questions. Suggest students research to find information for any unanswered questions.

Study and Comprehension After students finish reading, have them review the section and jot down the main points and important details. Then have students use these notes to write summaries of the functions of the nervous system and the interaction among the three types of neurons. Remind students that in a summary, they should briefly state the main points and key details in their own words.

Jobs of the Nervous System

The Internet lets people gather information from anywhere in the world with the click of a button. Like the Internet, your nervous system is a communications network. Your nervous system is much more efficient, however.

The nervous system receives information about what is happening both inside and outside your body. It also directs the way in which your body responds to this information. In addition, your nervous system helps maintain homeostasis. Without your nervous system, you could not move, think, feel pain, or taste a spicy taco.

Receiving Information Because of your nervous system, you are aware of what is happening in the environment around you. For example, you know that a soccer ball is zooming toward you, that the wind is blowing, or that a friend is telling a funny joke. Your nervous system also checks conditions inside your body, such as the level of glucose in your blood.

Responding to Information Any change or signal in the environment that can make an organism react is a **stimulus** (STIM yoo lus)(plural *stimuli*). A zooming soccer ball is a stimulus. After your nervous system analyzes the stimulus, it causes a response. A **response** is what your body does in reaction to a stimulus—you kick the ball toward the goal.

Some nervous system responses, such as kicking a ball, are voluntary, or under your control. However, many processes necessary for life, such as heartbeat rate, are controlled by involuntary actions of the nervous system.

Maintaining Homeostasis The nervous system helps maintain homeostasis by directing the body to respond appropriately to the information it receives. For example, when you are hungry, your nervous system directs you to eat. This action maintains homeostasis by supplying your body with nutrients and energy it needs.

✓ *Checkpoint* *What is a stimulus?*

The Neuron—A Message-Carrying Cell

The cells that carry information through your nervous system are called **neurons** (NOO rahnz), or nerve cells. The message that a neuron carries is called a **nerve impulse.** The structure of a neuron enables it to carry nerve impulses.

Figure 1 The sparkling water is a stimulus. This toddler responds by thrusting her hands into the water and splashing.

Program Resources

◆ **Teaching Resources** 7-1 Lesson Plan, p. 177; 7-1 Section Summary, p. 178

Media and Technology

 Audiotapes English-Spanish Summary 7-1

Answers to Self-Assessment

✓ *Checkpoint*

A stimulus is a change or signal in the environment that can make an organism react.

---

2 Facilitate

Jobs of the Nervous System

Building Inquiry Skills: Relating Cause and Effect

Materials *lemon wedge, vinegar, rubber ball, assorted materials*
Time 10 minutes

Have students identify the stimuli and responses in several brief activities by recording what information the nervous system receives and how it responds. Make sure students wash their hands before and after tasting any food items. Some activities include:

◆ tasting a lemon wedge *(stimulus—sour taste, wet and cold feeling; response—mouth fills with saliva)*
◆ smelling vinegar *(stimulus—sour smell; response—nose wrinkles)*
◆ bouncing and then catching a ball *(stimulus—speed and direction of ball; response—catching the ball)*

learning modality: kinesthetic

The Neuron—A Message-Carrying Cell

Including All Students

Some students may be confused by the terms *nerve cell, nerve, neuron,* and *nerve fiber.* Emphasize that a nerve cell is the same as a neuron, but not the same as a nerve or a nerve fiber. Explain that a nerve fiber can be either an axon or a dendrite, and that a nerve is composed of many axons, dendrites, or both. **limited English proficiency**

Ongoing Assessment

Oral Presentation Have each student name the three jobs of the nervous system and give one example of each job.

D ◆ 191

The Neuron—A Message-Carrying Cell, continued

Using the Visuals: Figure 2

Help students understand the neuron. Point out that there are many dendrites, but only one axon, which splits into two branches. Explain that even though the dendrites in this illustration are shorter than the axon, this is not always the case. You might tell students that the sausage-shaped coverings of the axon are a material called myelin; also point out that not all axons are covered with this material. Finally, have students use their fingers to trace the path of a nerve impulse from dendrites to cell body to axon. **learning modality: visual**

Inquiry Challenge

Materials *notecards, markers*
Time 10 minutes

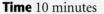

Organize the class into three groups. Assign each group to portray a type of neuron—sensory neurons, interneurons, and motor neurons. Challenge students to write notes to represent nerve impulses and model how nerve impulses are sent through the human body. *(Students in the role of sensory neurons should write notes describing stimuli to students representing interneurons. Interneurons should pass the notes to students playing motor neurons, who should write notes describing responses. Sample: Touching a hot stove. Sensory neurons—the stove is hot; interneurons pass this on; motor neurons—remove hand from stove.)* Make sure students understand the difference between the nerve impulse and the neurons, and can distinguish between different types of neurons. Have a reporter from each group share the group's results with the class. **cooperative learning**

192 ◆ D

The Structure of a Neuron A neuron has a large cell body that contains the nucleus. The cell body has threadlike extensions. One kind of extension, a **dendrite,** carries impulses toward the cell body. An **axon** carries impulses away from the cell body. Nerve impulses begin in a dendrite, move toward the cell body, and then move down the axon. A neuron can have many dendrites, but it has only one axon. An axon, however, can have more than one tip, so the impulse can go to more than one other cell.

Axons and dendrites are sometimes called nerve fibers. Nerve fibers are often arranged in parallel bundles covered with connective tissue, something like a package of uncooked spaghetti wrapped in cellophane. A bundle of nerve fibers is called a **nerve.**

Kinds of Neurons Different kinds of neurons perform different functions. **Three kinds of neurons are found in the body—sensory neurons, interneurons, and motor neurons. Together they make up a chain of nerve cells that carry an impulse through the nervous system.** *Exploring the Path of a Nerve Impulse* shows how these three kinds of neurons work together.

A **sensory neuron** picks up stimuli from the internal or external environment and converts each stimulus into a nerve impulse. The impulse travels along the sensory neuron until it reaches an interneuron, usually in the brain or spinal cord. An **interneuron** is a neuron that carries nerve impulses from one neuron to another. Some interneurons pass impulses from sensory neurons to motor neurons. A **motor neuron** sends an impulse to a muscle, and the muscle contracts in response.

☑ *Checkpoint* *What is the function of an axon?*

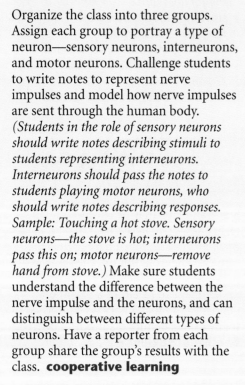

Figure 2 A neuron, or nerve cell, has one axon and many dendrites that extend from the cell body. The dendrites carry a nerve message toward the cell body, and the axon carries the message away from the cell body. *Applying Concepts How many axons can a neuron have?*

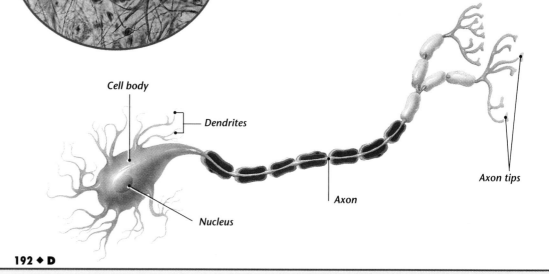

Cell body

Dendrites

Nucleus

Axon

Axon tips

Background

Facts and Figures Individual neurons vary in size. The smallest nerve cells may be as tiny as 0.004 mm in diameter. However, nerve cells can be extremely long; in an adult human, a single motor neuron that runs from the spine to the tip of the toe is over a meter in length. At the end of a neuron, the axon tips may form over 150 branches. This makes it possible for a single motor neuron to stimulate many different muscle cells.

All nerve impulses travel in the same direction within a neuron, from dendrite to axon. Thus sensory neurons, which carry impulses to the central nervous system, are arranged with their axons pointing towards the spinal cord and brain. Motor neurons, which carry impulses to muscles or glands, are arranged with their axons pointing away from the brain and central nervous system.

EXPLORING the Path of a Nerve Impulse

When you hear the phone ring, you pick it up to answer it. Many sensory neurons, interneurons, and motor neurons are involved in this action.

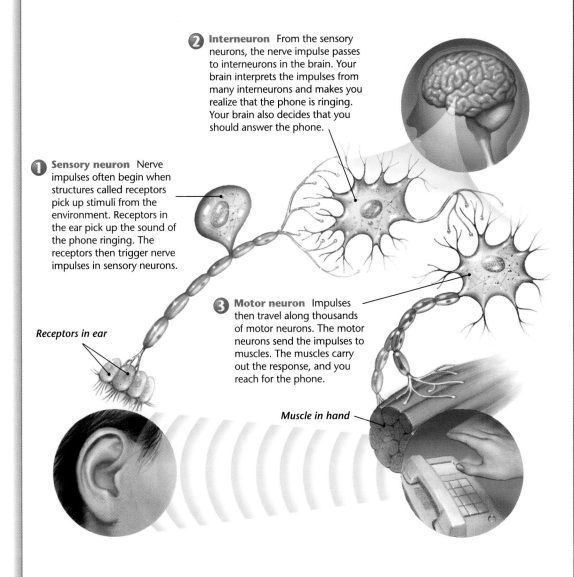

2 Interneuron From the sensory neurons, the nerve impulse passes to interneurons in the brain. Your brain interprets the impulses from many interneurons and makes you realize that the phone is ringing. Your brain also decides that you should answer the phone.

1 Sensory neuron Nerve impulses often begin when structures called receptors pick up stimuli from the environment. Receptors in the ear pick up the sound of the phone ringing. The receptors then trigger nerve impulses in sensory neurons.

3 Motor neuron Impulses then travel along thousands of motor neurons. The motor neurons send the impulses to muscles. The muscles carry out the response, and you reach for the phone.

Receptors in ear

Muscle in hand

Have students use the visual essay to study the path of a nerve impulse from a sensory neuron to a motor neuron. Ask: **Which kind of nerve fiber picks up the stimulus from the receptors?** *(dendrites)* Then ask: **Which kind of nerve fiber causes the muscles to contract?** *(axons)* Point out that there would be a tiny space between the motor neuron's axon tips and the muscle fibers. Have students trace the path of the nerve impulse, identifying the stimulus to which each kind of neuron responds. *(Sensory neurons respond to the ringing sound of the phone. Interneurons respond to impulses from sensory neurons. Motor neurons respond to impulses from interneurons.)*

Extend Have students measure on their bodies the distance the nerve impulse travels from the ear, to the brain, and to the hand. **learning modality: visual**

Media and Technology

 Transparencies "Exploring the Path of a Nerve Message," Transparency 14

 Exploring Life Science Videodisc
Unit 4, Side 1,
"Quick Reflexes"

Chapter 9

Answers to Self-Assessment

Caption Question

Figure 2 Each neuron has one axon.

☑ *Checkpoint*
An axon carries a nerve impulse away from the cell body.

Ongoing Assessment

Writing Have students make flowcharts that explain how a nerve impulse is transmitted through the body. *(Students' flowcharts should include a stimulus that is detected by receptors, which then trigger nerve impulses in sensory neurons. The sensory neuron passes the impulse to an interneuron, usually in the brain or spinal cord, which then sends the impulse to the motor neurons. Motor neurons carry the impulse to muscles, and the muscles carry out the response.)*

 Portfolio Students can save their flowcharts in their portfolios.

How a Nerve Impulse Travels

Using the Visuals: Figure 3

Have students trace the path of a nerve impulse down the axon to its tip, across the synapse, and to a dendrite of another cell. Ask: **How can nerve impulses travel from one cell to another if the cells are not touching?** (*Chemicals carry the impulses across the synapse.*) Point out that impulses also travel from axons to muscles or cells in other organs.
learning modality: visual

3 Assess

Section 1 Review Answers

1. Receive information about internal and external events, respond to this information, and maintain homeostasis.
2. Sensory neurons, interneurons, and motor neurons. A sensory neuron detects a stimulus and sends an impulse. The impulse travels to interneurons and then to motor neurons. The motor neuron sends the nerve impulse to a muscle.
3. Nerve impulses cross a synapse when chemicals are released by the axon.
4. The nerve impulse would not be able to cross the synapse, because the axon tips could not release the necessary chemicals.

Science at Home

Materials *salt and pepper shaker*
Make sure students define stimulus and response for their families. Students may realize that if they say "Thank you" when the salt and pepper are passed, the passing is a stimulus and the thanks is a response.

Performance Assessment

Oral Presentation Ask pairs of students to choose an everyday action and create posters that illustrate the path of the nerve impulses the action involves.

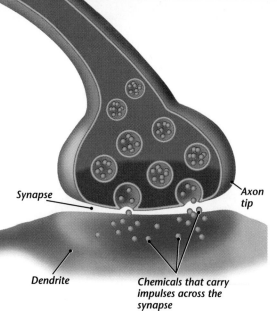

Synapse

Axon tip

Dendrite

Chemicals that carry impulses across the synapse

Figure 3 A synapse is the tiny space between the axon of one neuron and the dendrite of another neuron. When a nerve impulse reaches the end of an axon, chemicals are released into the synapse. These chemicals enable the nerve impulse to cross the synapse.

How a Nerve Impulse Travels

Every day of your life, millions of nerve impulses travel through your nervous system. Each of those nerve impulses begins in the dendrites of a neuron. The impulse moves rapidly toward the neuron's cell body and then down the axon until it reaches the axon tip. A nerve impulse travels along the neuron in the form of electrical and chemical signals. Nerve impulses can travel as fast as 120 meters per second!

There is a tiny space called a **synapse** (SIN aps) between each axon tip and the next structure. Sometimes this next structure is a dendrite of another neuron. Other times the next structure can be a muscle or a cell in another organ, such as a sweat gland. Figure 3 illustrates a synapse between the axon of one neuron and a dendrite of another neuron.

In order for a nerve impulse to be carried along, it must cross the gap between the axon and the next structure. The axon tips release chemicals that enable the impulse to cross the synapse. If that didn't happen, the impulse would stop at the end of the axon. The impulse would not be passed from sensory neuron, to interneuron, to motor neuron. Nerve impulses would never reach your brain or make your muscles contract.

You can think of a synapse as a river, and an axon as a road that leads up to the riverbank. The nerve impulse is like a car traveling on the road. To get to the other side, the car has to cross the river. The car gets on a ferry boat, which carries it across the river. The chemicals that the axon tips release are like a ferry that carries the nerve impulse across the synapse.

 ## Section 1 Review

1. Describe three functions of the nervous system.
2. Identify the three kinds of neurons that are found in the nervous system. Describe how they interact to carry nerve impulses.
3. How does a nerve impulse cross a synapse?
4. **Thinking Critically** **Predicting** What would happen to a nerve impulse carried by an interneuron if the tips of the interneuron's axon were damaged? Explain.

Science at Home

During dinner, ask a family member to pass the salt and pepper to you. Observe what your family member then does. Explain that the words you spoke were a stimulus and that the family member's reaction was a response. Discuss other examples of stimuli and responses with your family.

Program Resources

◆ **Teaching Resources** 7-1 Review and Reinforce, p. 155; 7-1 Enrich, p. 156

Media and Technology

Interactive Student Tutorial CD-ROM D-7

Ready or Not

D o people carry out tasks better at certain times of day? In this lab, you will design an experiment to answer this question.

Problem

Do people's reaction times vary at different times of day?

Materials

meter stick

Design a Plan

Part 1 Observing a Response to a Stimulus

1. Have your partner hold a meter stick with the zero end about 50 cm above a table.
2. Get ready to catch the meter stick by positioning the top of your thumb and forefinger just at the zero position as shown in the photograph.
3. Your partner should drop the meter stick without any warning. Using your thumb and forefinger only (no other part of your hand), catch the meter stick as soon as you can. Record the distance in centimeters that the meter stick fell. This distance is a measure of your reaction time.

Part 2 Design Your Experiment

4. With your partner, discuss how you can use the activity from Part 1 to find out whether people's reaction times vary at different times of day. Be sure to consider the questions below. Then write up your experimental plan.
   - What hypothesis will you test?
   - What variables do you need to control?
   - How many people will you test? How many times will you test each person?

5. Submit your plan for your teacher's review. Make any changes your teacher recommends. Create a data table to record your results. Then perform your experiment.

Analyze and Conclude

1. In this lab, what is the stimulus? What is the response? Is this response voluntary or involuntary? Explain.
2. Why can you use the distance on the meter stick as a measure of reaction time?
3. Based on your results, do people's reaction times vary at different times of day? Explain.
4. **Think About It** In Part 2, why is it important to control all variables except the time of day?

More to Explore

Do you think people can do arithmetic problems more quickly and accurately at certain times of the day? Design an experiment to investigate this question. Obtain your teacher's permission before trying your experiment.

Chapter 7 **D ◆ 195**

Ready or Not

Preparing for Inquiry

Key Concept Response time depends on a variety of factors.

Skills Objectives Students will be able to
- form hypotheses regarding whether people perform tasks better at certain times of day;
- design experiments to compare results for different people at different times;
- interpret data and draw conclusions about the effect of time of day on response time.

Time 50 minutes

Guiding Inquiry

Invitation

Ask students to name some situations when a quick reaction time would be advantageous. *(Samples: Applying the brakes to a car to avoid an accident; catching a falling object)*

Introducing the Procedure

Students should test each person at least five times, and then take the average of all trials.

Troubleshooting the Experiment

Students should hold the stick in the same position for every trial.

Analyze and Conclude

1. Stimulus—sight of the dropping stick; response—grabbing the stick. The response is voluntary; the person consciously chooses it.
2. Sample: If people's thumbs and forefingers are at zero at the time of the drop, the number of centimeters the stick drops will be directly proportional to the reaction time, because the stick always falls at the same rate.
3. Answers may vary. Research indicates that the reaction times of an individual do vary during the day.
4. All variables need to be controlled except the time of day so that any differences in reaction time can be directly attributed to the time of day.

Program Resources

- **Teaching Resources** Chapter 7 Skills Lab, pp. 193–194
- **Inquiry Skills Activity Book** Provides teaching and review of all inquiry skills

Safety

Remind students to take care while dropping or catching the meter stick. Review the safety guidelines in Appendix A.

Extending the Inquiry

Designing an Experiment Advise students to use simple arithmetic calculations rather than complex exercises, as it is easier to keep the simpler calculations consistent. Also, discuss why students cannot use the same calculations more than once with each person tested.

D ◆ 195

Objectives

After completing the lesson, students will be able to

◆ identify the function of the central nervous system, describe its parts, and explain how to keep it safe from injury;

◆ identify the functions of the peripheral nervous system and its parts;

◆ describe a reflex.

Key Terms central nervous system, peripheral nervous system, brain, spinal cord, cerebrum, cerebellum, brainstem, somatic nervous system, autonomic nervous system, reflex, concussion

1 Engage/Explore

Activating Prior Knowledge

Ask students: **What happens if you accidentally touch a hot frying pan handle?** (*You quickly move your hand.*) Ask: **Is that response automatic or do you have to think about it?** (*It's automatic.*) Tell the students that they will learn how the body controls this and other automatic responses.

DISCOVER

Skills Focus inferring
Materials *none*
Time 10 minutes
Tips Caution students not to engage in horseplay or rough-housing while carrying out the activity. Remind students that serious damage can be done if they strike one another too hard on the kneecap.
Expected Outcome Students' legs will swing forward.
Think It Over It might be an advantage in situations that could cause injury, such as touching a hot stove.

SECTION
2 Divisions of the Nervous System

DISCOVER ••ACTIVITY••••

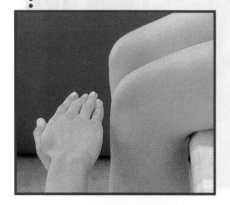

How Does Your Knee React?

1. Sit on a table or counter so that your legs dangle freely. Your feet should not touch the floor.

2. Have your partner use the side of his or her hand to *gently* tap one of your knees just below the kneecap. Observe what happens to your leg. Note whether you have any control over your reaction.

3. Change places with your partner. Repeat Steps 1 and 2.

Think It Over

Inferring When might it be an advantage for your body to react very quickly and without your conscious control?

GUIDE FOR READING

◆ What is the function of the central nervous system?

◆ What functions does the peripheral nervous system perform?

◆ What is a reflex?

Reading Tip As you read, make a list of main ideas and supporting details about the central and peripheral nervous systems.

A concert is about to begin. The conductor gives the signal, and the musicians begin to play. The sound of music, beautiful and stirring, fills the air.

To play music in harmony, an orchestra needs both musicians and a conductor. The musicians play the music, and the conductor directs the musicians and coordinates their playing.

Similarly, your nervous system has two divisions that work together—the central nervous system and the peripheral nervous system. The **central nervous system** consists of the brain and spinal cord. The **peripheral nervous system** consists of all the nerves located outside of the central nervous system. The central nervous system is like a conductor. The nerves of the peripheral nervous system are like the musicians.

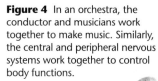
Figure 4 In an orchestra, the conductor and musicians work together to make music. Similarly, the central and peripheral nervous systems work together to control body functions.

Reading Tip Have students work with partners to list main ideas and supporting details for the information presented under each heading of the section. Suggest students take turns reading aloud and paraphrasing the information under a heading. Then have students work together to compose a list of the main ideas and supporting details presented under the heading.

Study and Comprehension List these terms on the board: *central nervous system, brain, spinal cord, cerebrum, cerebellum, brainstem, somatic nervous system, autonomic nervous system.* Then draw a chart on the board such as the one shown. Challenge students to list each term and describe its function.

What Is It?	What Does It Do?

The Central Nervous System

You can see the central and peripheral nervous systems in Figure 5. **The central nervous system is the control center of the body.** All information about what is happening in the world inside or outside your body is brought to the central nervous system. The **brain,** located in the skull, is the part of the central nervous system that controls most functions in the body. The **spinal cord** is the thick column of nerve tissue that links the brain to most of the nerves in the peripheral nervous system.

Most impulses from the peripheral nervous system travel through the spinal cord to get to the brain. Your brain then directs a response. The response usually travels from the brain, through the spinal cord, and then to the peripheral nervous system.

For example, here is what happens when you reach under the sofa to find a lost quarter. Your fingers move over the floor, searching for the quarter. When your fingers finally touch the quarter, the stimulus of the touch triggers nerve impulses in sensory neurons in your fingers. These impulses travel through nerves of the peripheral nervous system to your spinal cord. Then the impulses race up to your brain. Your brain interprets the impulses, telling you that you've found the quarter. Your brain starts nerve impulses that move down the spinal cord. From the spinal cord, the impulses travel through motor nerves in your arm and hand. The impulses in the motor neurons cause your fingers to grasp the quarter.

✓ *Checkpoint* *What does the spinal cord do?*

The Brain

Your brain contains about 100 billion neurons, all of which are interneurons. Each of those neurons may receive messages from up to 10,000 other neurons and may send messages to about 1,000 more! Three layers of connective tissue cover the brain. The space between the outermost layer and the middle layer is filled with a watery fluid. The skull, layers of connective tissue, and fluid all help protect the brain from injury.

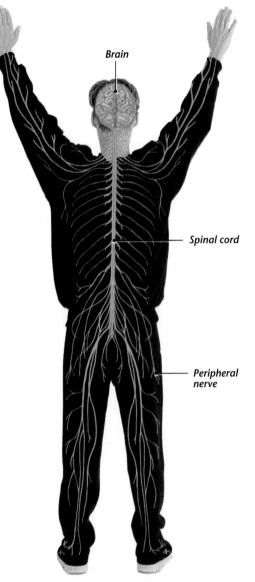

Brain

Spinal cord

Peripheral nerve

Figure 5 The central nervous system consists of the brain and spinal cord. The peripheral nervous system contains all the nerves that branch out from the brain and spinal cord.

Program Resources

◆ **Teaching Resources** 7-2 Lesson Plan, p. 181; 7-2 Section Summary, p. 182

Media and Technology

 Audiotapes English-Spanish Summary 7-2

Answers to Self-Assessment

✓ *Checkpoint*
The spinal cord links the brain to the nerves in the peripheral nervous system.

---

2 Facilitate

The Central Nervous System

Using the Visuals: Figure 5

Have students trace the path of the nerve impulses that originate in the hands of the figure. Ask: **What direction does the nerve impulse move?** *(From the hand to the brain)* **learning modality: visual**

Inquiry Challenge

Materials *coins of different sizes such as nickels, dimes, quarters, pennies*
Time 10 minutes

ACTIVITY

This activity will allow students to determine how the brain interprets impulses triggered by the senses. Challenge groups of students to design experiments to determine whether they can distinguish between similar objects by touching the objects without looking at them. Have students take on specific tasks, such as writing the hypothesis and experimental plan, testing subjects' ability to distinguish coins, and recording data from the experiment. Check students' plans and allow them to carry out their experiments.
cooperative learning

Ongoing Assessment

Organizing Information Have students make flowcharts to describe the path nerve impulses take from a peripheral nerve to the brain.
 Students can save their flowcharts in their portfolios.

The Brain

Using the Visuals: Figure 6

Direct students to study the relative locations of the cerebrum, the brainstem, and the cerebellum in the illustration. Have students point to their own spinal cord near the base of their skull and then move their fingers up toward their brainstem and cerebellum. Then have students contrast the structure of the cerebrum and cerebellum. *(The cerebrum is larger than the cerebellum, and the cerebrum's surface is creased by deep folds.)* Point out that the folds increase the surface area of the cerebrum in much the same way that villi increase the surface area of the small intestine.
learning modality: visual

Sharpen your Skills

Controlling Variables

Materials *tape player, cassette tape of soft music*
Time 15 minutes, plus 30 minutes to carry out the activity
Tips Caution students to play the tape softly. Remind students to control all variables except the presence or absence of music. Sample hypothesis: If soft music is playing in a room, then people will memorize words better. Sample experiment: Make up two lists of words having the same number, length, and familiarity of words. Test three or four people, first in a quiet room, then with music. Make sure the person looks at a different list each time you test him or her. Play the same music each time.
Extend Have students design a similar experiment to test whether the kind of music playing affects people's ability to remember words.

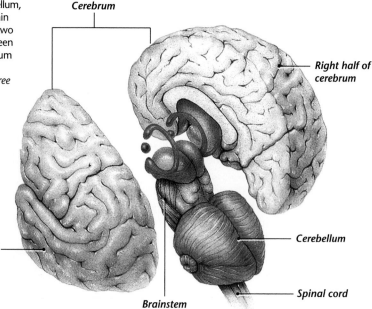

Figure 6 The cerebrum, cerebellum, and brainstem are the three main parts of the human brain. The two halves of the cerebrum have been separated to show the cerebellum and the brainstem. *Applying Concepts What are three functions of the cerebrum?*

Cerebrum

Right half of cerebrum

Left half of cerebrum

Cerebellum

Brainstem

Spinal cord

Sharpen your Skills

Controlling Variables

Are people better able to memorize a list of words in a quiet room or in a room where soft music is playing? First write a hypothesis. Then design an experiment to test your hypothesis. Make sure that all variables are controlled except the one you are testing—music versus quiet. Check your procedure with your teacher. Then perform your experiment. Analyze your results to see whether they support your hypothesis.

Cerebrum There are three main regions of the brain. These are the cerebrum, the cerebellum, and the brainstem. Find each in Figure 6. The largest part of the brain is called the cerebrum. The **cerebrum** (suh REE brum) interprets input from the senses, controls the movement of skeletal muscles, and carries out complex mental processes such as learning, remembering, and making judgments. Because of your cerebrum, you can find the comics in a newspaper and locate your favorite comic strip on the page. Your cerebrum also enables you to read the comic strip and laugh at its funny characters.

Notice in Figure 6 that the cerebrum is divided into a right and a left half. The two halves have somewhat different functions. The right half of the cerebrum contains the neurons that send impulses to the skeletal muscles on the left side of the body. In contrast, the left half of the cerebrum controls the right side of the body. When you reach with your right hand for a pencil, the messages that tell you to do so come from the left half of your cerebrum.

In addition, each half of the cerebrum controls slightly different kinds of mental activity. The right half of the cerebrum is usually associated with creativity and artistic ability. The left half, in contrast, is associated with mathematical skills, speech, writing, and logical thinking.

Background

History of Science Almost 2,400 years ago, Hippocrates, an ancient Greek anatomist, determined that the brain was the body's center of intelligence. In the next few centuries, other Greek scientists recognized that the body contained nerves and that nerve impulses traveling to the brain carry sensory information, while nerve impulses traveling away from the brain cause muscles to respond.

In the 1600s, British physician Thomas Willis showed where blood vessels and nerves entered the brain through the brainstem. Willis also distinguished gray and white areas of the cerebrum, as well as the folds in the outer layer of the cerebrum.

Later, scientists used microscopes to conclude that nerve cells and brain cells were similar in structure. This led to the idea that the brain and nerves formed a single system.

Cerebellum and Brainstem The second largest part of your brain is called the cerebellum. The **cerebellum** (sehr uh BEL um) coordinates the actions of your muscles and helps you keep your balance. When you put one foot in front of the other as you walk, the motor neuron impulses that tell your feet to move start in your cerebrum. However, your cerebellum gives you the muscular coordination and sense of balance that keep you from falling down.

The **brainstem,** which lies between the cerebellum and spinal cord, controls your body's involuntary actions—those that occur automatically. For example, the brainstem regulates your breathing and helps control your heartbeat.

☑ *Checkpoint* *What part of your brain coordinates the contractions of your muscles?*

The Spinal Cord

Run your fingers down the center of your back to feel the bones of the vertebral column. The vertebral column surrounds and protects the spinal cord. The spinal cord is the link between your brain and the peripheral nervous system. The layers of connective tissue that surround and protect the brain also cover the spinal cord. In addition, like the brain, the spinal cord is further protected by a watery fluid.

Figure 7 This illustration, by the Dutch artist M. C. Escher, is called "Day and Night." Escher created this picture in 1938.

Visual Arts CONNECTION

Some artists deliberately create works of art that can be interpreted by the brain in more than one way. The Dutch artist M. C. Escher (1898–1972) delighted in creating illustrations that played visual tricks on his viewers. Glance quickly at Escher's illustration in Figure 7. Then look at it again. Do you see the two different scenes in this single picture?

In Your Journal

Which scene did you see when you first looked at Figure 7? Did your brain interpret the picture differently the second time? Write a description of the visual trick that Escher has played in this illustration.

Answers to Self-Assessment

Caption Question

Figure 6 The cerebrum interprets input from the senses, controls the movement of skeletal muscles, and carries out complex mental processes.

☑ *Checkpoint*
The cerebellum

Building Inquiry Skills: Making Models

Materials *modeling clay of different colors*
Time 20 minutes

Have students create models of a cross-section of the brain. Each part of the brain should be labeled with a description of the processes it controls. Ask: **What part of your brain did you use to determine the size of each section of the model?** *(The cerebrum)* **learning modality: kinesthetic**

Visual Arts CONNECTION

Provide Escher drawings for students to examine. If they cannot interpret the image in the text, suggest they focus on one side of the scene, then the other.

In Your Journal Students should describe the visual trick by pointing out that there are two sets of birds, identical except for their colors, that are flying in opposite directions over two landscapes that are mirror images in every way except color. Challenge students to create their own drawing using similar techniques. **learning modality: verbal**

The Spinal Cord

Including All Students

Advanced students can do library research on spina bifida, which is a congenital medical condition that occurs when the vertebrae do not seal properly around the spinal cord before birth. The likelihood of this neural tube defect can be decreased if a pregnant woman ingests enough folic acid during the first three months of pregnancy. **learning modality: verbal**

Ongoing Assessment

Writing Have students choose a part of the brain and write a job description for it.

The term *peripheral* may be difficult for some students to spell and pronounce. Write the phonetic spelling *puh RIF er ul* on the board. Allow students to practice saying the word until they are comfortable pronouncing it. Help students remember the meaning of the term by explaining that the *peri-* means "around," and *-phery* comes from the Greek word meaning "to carry." Ask: **How does the peripheral nervous system carry impulses around the body?** *(The peripheral nervous system connects the rest of the body to the central nervous system.)* **limited English proficiency**

Building Inquiry Skills:
Comparing and Contrasting

Have students brainstorm lists of actions that are controlled by the somatic nervous system and by the autonomic nervous system. Some students may confuse involuntary actions with voluntary actions, because many voluntary actions seem to happen automatically. Explain that physical activities, such as walking or riding a bike, are controlled by the somatic nervous system even though we may be unaware that we are doing them.
learning modality: verbal

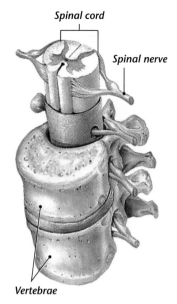

Spinal cord

Spinal nerve

Vertebrae

Figure 8 The spinal nerves, which connect to the spinal cord, emerge from spaces between the vertebrae. Each spinal nerve consists of both sensory and motor neurons.

The Peripheral Nervous System

The second division of the nervous system is the peripheral nervous system. **The peripheral nervous system consists of a network of nerves that branch out from the central nervous system and connect it to the rest of your body.** A total of 43 pairs of nerves make up the peripheral nervous system. Twelve pairs originate in the brain. The other 31 pairs—the spinal nerves—begin in the spinal cord. One nerve in each pair goes to the left side of the body, and the other goes to the right. As you can see in Figure 8, spinal nerves leave the spinal cord through spaces between the vertebrae.

Two-Way Traffic A spinal nerve is a little bit like a two-lane highway. Impulses travel on a spinal nerve in two directions—both to and from the central nervous system. Each spinal nerve contains axons of both sensory and motor neurons. The sensory neurons carry impulses from the body to the central nervous system. The motor neurons carry impulses in the opposite direction—from the central nervous system to the body.

Somatic and Autonomic Systems The nerves of the peripheral nervous system can be divided into two groups, called the somatic (soh MAT ik) and autonomic (awt uh NAHM ik) nervous systems. The nerves of the **somatic nervous system** control voluntary actions such as using a fork or tying your shoelaces. In contrast, nerves of the **autonomic nervous system** control involuntary actions. For example, the autonomic nervous system regulates the contractions of the smooth muscles that adjust the diameter of blood vessels.

Figure 9 The somatic nervous system controls voluntary actions. The girl's somatic nervous system is at work as she shapes the pot with her hands.
Classifying What part of the peripheral nervous system helps regulate the girl's heartbeat?

200 ◆ D

Background

Facts and Figures Short-term memory is thought of as electrical impulses that travel through nerves. This explains why people can hold a very limited amount of information in their short-term memory.

Unlike short-term memory, long-term memory seems to have infinite capacity. Long-term memories are created when information is somehow transferred or stored in the brain. Many scientists think that once information enters long-term memory, it stays there permanently. Long-term memories may include tastes, smells, and physical sensations. Some scientists speculate that long-term memory may be stored using a molecule, such as a protein. However, memories have been shown to last longer than individual molecules, so more research is required.

Reflexes

Imagine that you are watching an adventure movie. The movie is so thrilling that you don't notice a fly circling above your head. When the fly zooms right in front of your eyes, however, your eyelids immediately blink shut. You didn't decide to close your eyes. The blink, which is an example of a **reflex,** happened automatically. **A reflex is an automatic response that occurs very rapidly and without conscious control.** If you did the Discover activity, you saw another example of a reflex.

As you have learned, the contraction of skeletal muscles is usually controlled by the brain. However, in some reflex actions, skeletal muscles contract with the involvement of the spinal cord only—not the brain. Figure 10 shows the reflex action that occurs when you touch a sharp object, such as a cactus thorn. When your finger touches the object, sensory neurons send impulses to the spinal cord. The impulses then pass to interneurons in the spinal cord. From there the impulses pass directly to motor neurons in your arm and hand. The muscles then contract, and your hand jerks up and away from the sharp object. By removing your hand quickly, this reflex protects you from getting badly cut.

At the same time that some nerve impulses make your arm muscles contract, other nerve impulses travel up your spinal cord and to your brain. When these impulses reach your brain, your brain interprets them. You then feel a sharp pain in your finger.

Figure 10 If you touch a sharp object, your hand immediately jerks away. This action, which is known as a reflex, happens automatically. Nerve impulses begin in nerve endings (**1**) and then travel along sensory neurons (**2**) to interneurons in the spinal cord (**3**). From there, impulses travel through motor neurons (**4**) to muscles in your arm (**5**). The muscles contract to pull your hand away.

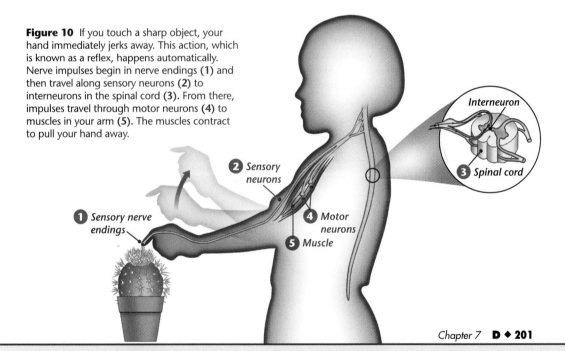

① Sensory nerve endings
② Sensory neurons
③ Spinal cord
④ Motor neurons
⑤ Muscle
Interneuron

Chapter 7 **D ◆ 201**

Answers to Self-Assessment
Caption Question
Figure 9 The autonomic nervous system

Reflexes

Using the Visuals: Figure 10
Direct students to trace the path of the impulse in the figure from the stimulus to its response. Ask: **How does it benefit people that the spinal cord is able to send an impulse to motor neurons in response to a stimulus without involving the brain?** *(It allows people to respond more quickly to danger than if the nerve impulses traveled all the way to and from the brain.)* **learning modality: visual**

Building Inquiry Skills: Applying Concepts
Remind students that a change in the environment that makes an organism react is called a stimulus. Ask: **What is the stimulus in the reflex mentioned in the text?** *(The fly zooming in front of your eyes)* Make sure students understand that although reflexes are automatic, they must involve stimuli, and are not always controlled by the autonomic nervous system. **learning modality: verbal**

Ongoing Assessment

Oral Presentation Have students give examples of voluntary, involuntary, and reflexive responses and explain how the impulses for each travel through the nervous system.

Safety and the Nervous System

Integrating Health

Ask students to infer how doctors could learn about the function of the nervous system by studying injuries to the brain. *(Sample: Damage to a particular part of the brain will result in the loss or change to the function controlled by that part.)* **learning modality: verbal**

3 Assess

Section 2 Review Answers

1. The central nervous system, which includes the brain and spinal cord, is the control center of the body.
2. A network of nerves that branch out from the central nervous system; carries nerve impulses between the central nervous system and the rest of the body.
3. An automatic response that occurs rapidly and without conscious control. Reflexes allow the body to respond quickly to danger.
4. Loss of balance; poor muscle coordination.

Check Your Progress **CHAPTER PROJECT 7**

Check students' plans for safety. Note that illusions do not necessarily affect all people the same way. Have students try out their illusions on a partner before others write lists of questions.

Figure 11 By wearing a helmet, this skateboarder is helping to prevent injury to his brain.

It takes longer for the pain impulses to get to the brain and be interpreted than it does for the reflex action to occur. By the time you feel the pain, you have already moved your hand away from the sharp object.

Safety and the Nervous System

INTEGRATING HEALTH Like other parts of the body, the nervous system can suffer injuries that interfere with its functioning. Concussions and spinal cord injuries are two ways in which the nervous system can be damaged.

A **concussion** is a bruiselike injury of the brain. A concussion occurs when soft tissue of the cerebrum bumps against the skull. Concussions can happen during a hard fall, an automobile accident, or contact sports such as football. With most concussions, you may have a headache for a short time, but the injured tissue heals by itself. However, if you black out, experience confusion, or feel drowsy after the injury, you should be checked by a doctor. To decrease your chances of getting a brain injury, wear a helmet when bicycling, skating, or performing other activities in which you risk bumping your head.

Spinal cord injuries occur when the spinal cord is cut or crushed. When the spinal cord is cut, all the nerve axons in that region are split, so impulses cannot pass through them. This type of injury results in paralysis, which is the loss of movement in some part of the body. Car crashes are the most common cause of spinal cord injuries. You can help protect yourself from a spinal cord injury by wearing a seatbelt when you travel in a car. Also, when you swim, make sure the water is deep enough before you dive in.

Section 2 Review

1. What is the function of the central nervous system? Which organs are part of this system?
2. What is the peripheral nervous system and what are its functions?
3. Explain what a reflex is. How do reflexes help protect the body from injury?
4. **Thinking Critically Relating Cause and Effect** What symptoms might indicate that a person's cerebellum has been injured?

Check Your Progress **CHAPTER PROJECT 7**

At this point, you should have chosen one or more illusions to investigate. Now write up the plan for your experiment. List some questions that you will ask to monitor people's responses to the illusions. (*Hint:* Try out your illusions and your questions on classmates to find out what responses to expect.) With your classmates, make plans for setting up the science fair.

Performance Assessment

Organizing Information Have students make concept maps that identify parts of the central nervous system and the peripheral nervous system.

 Students can save their concept maps in their portfolios.

Program Resources

◆ **Teaching Resources** 7-2 Review and Reinforce, p. 183; 7-2 Enrich, p. 184

Media and Technology

Interactive Student Tutorial CD-ROM D-7

SCIENCE AND SOCIETY

Should People Be Required to Wear Bicycle Helmets?

Bicycle riding is an enjoyable activity. But unfortunately, many bicycle riders become injured while riding. Each year about 150,000 children alone are treated in hospitals for head injuries that occur while bicycling. Head injuries can affect everything your brain does—thinking, remembering, seeing, and being able to move. Experts estimate that as many as 85 percent of bicycle-related head injuries could be prevented if all bicyclists wore helmets. But only about 18 percent of bicyclists wear helmets. What is the best way to get bicycle riders to protect themselves from head injury?

The Issues

Should Laws Require the Use of Bicycle Helmets? About 15 states have passed laws requiring bicycle riders to wear helmets. Nearly all of these laws, however, apply only to children. Some supporters of bicycle laws want to see the laws extended to all bicycle riders. Supporters point out that laws increase helmet use by 47 percent. In contrast, educational programs without laws to back them up increase bicycle helmet use by only 18 percent.

What Are the Drawbacks of Helmet Laws? Opponents of helmet laws believe it is up to the individual, not the government, to decide whether or not to wear a helmet. They say it is not the role of the government to stop people from taking risks. Rather than making people who don't

wear helmets pay fines, governments should educate people about the benefits of helmets. Car drivers should also be educated about safe driving procedures near bicycles.

Are There Alternatives to Helmet Laws? Instead of laws requiring people to wear helmets, some communities and organizations have set up educational programs that teach about the advantages of helmets. Effective programs teach about the dangers of head injuries and how helmets protect riders. In addition, they point out that safe helmets can be lightweight and comfortable. Effective education programs, though, can be expensive. They also need to reach a wide audience, including children, teens, and adults.

You Decide

1. Identify the Problem
In your own words, explain the issues concerning laws requiring people to wear bicycle helmets.

2. Analyze the Options
List two different plans for increasing helmet use by bicycle riders. List at least one advantage and one drawback of each plan.

3. Find a Solution
You are a member of the city government hoping to increase helmet use. Write a speech outlining your position for either a helmet law or an alternative plan. Support your position.

Background

Facts and Figures Even if people do wear bicycle helmets, they may not be protected from head injury if they do not wear the helmets properly. Therefore, educational programs that teach people about the advantages of helmets often emphasize how to wear a helmet properly. The front edge of the helmet should be positioned 2 to 3 cm above the rider's eyebrows, and the helmet and the chin strap should be snug, but not uncomfortable. Communities can also help to reduce bicycle head injuries by creating safer environments for people to ride their bikes. This might include setting aside special bicycle lanes on roads or making biking trails through parks.

SCIENCE AND SOCIETY

Should People Be Required to Wear Bicycle Helmets?

Purpose

Students will identify and analyze the difficulties involved in getting bicycle riders to protect themselves from head injury.

Role-Play

Time a day to prepare; 30 minutes for role-play

Divide students into four groups: (1) a group to represent state lawmakers, (2) a group to argue for the passage of a bicycle helmet law, (3) a group to argue against a helmet law, but for an education program paid for with taxes, and (4) a group to argue against any government regulation or tax-supported education programs. Tell the first group to work out rules and an agenda for a committee hearing on a proposed helmet law. Students in each of the other groups can work together to prepare a presentation to the committee during the hearing. Then hold the hearing, using the rules and agenda worked out by the committee members. Encourage students to act the way they think citizens would act in a real public hearing of this kind.

Extend Challenge students to find out whether your state or local government has passed a helmet law and, if so, whether it applies only to children or to bicycle riders of all ages. Suggest that students contact a member of a local law enforcement agency to ask what the penalties are for breaking such a law.

You Decide

Have students individually complete the first two steps before the role-play as a way of preparing themselves for their participation. After the role-play is concluded, students can complete the last step, using what they learned in the role-play to find a solution to the problem.

Objectives

After completing the lesson, students will be able to

◆ name the senses and state the overall function performed by the senses;

◆ describe how eyes enable people to see;

◆ describe how people hear sounds and maintain balance;

◆ describe how people experience the senses of touch, taste, and smell.

Key Terms cornea, pupil, iris, lens, retina, nearsightedness, farsightedness, eardrum, cochlea, semicircular canal

1 Engage/Explore

Activating Prior Knowledge

Challenge students to name the senses, then list them on the board. Have the class brainstorm a list of items or activities in the classroom that they perceive through each sense.

DISCOVER

Skills Focus observing
Materials *opaque paper bags; small objects, such as erasers, pens, paper clips, sponges, cotton balls, marbles, plastic spoons, bottle caps, coins, buttons*
Time 20 minutes
Tips Include objects of different sizes, shapes, and textures. Be certain to use objects that are not sharp. Encourage students to take notes about the objects they feel and record what objects they believe are in the bag.
Expected Outcome Students should be able to identify most of the objects using their sense of touch.
Think It Over Students could determine size, shape, texture, and weight. They could not determine color, scent, or taste.

SECTION 3 The Senses

DISCOVER ········· ACTIVITY

What's in the Bag?

1. Your teacher will give you a paper bag that contains several objects. Your challenge is to use only your sense of touch to identify each object. You will not look inside the bag.

2. Put your hand in the bag and carefully touch each object. Observe the shape of each object. Note whether its surface is rough or smooth. Also note other characteristics, such as its size, what it seems to be made of, and whether it can be bent.

3. After you have finished touching each object, write your observations on a sheet of paper. Then write your inference about what each object is.

Think It Over
Observing What could you determine about each object without looking at it? What could you not determine?

GUIDE FOR READING

◆ What overall function do the senses perform?

◆ How do your eyes enable you to see?

◆ How do you hear?

Reading Tip As you read, write an outline of this section. Use the headings in the section as the main topics in the outline.

You waited in line to get on the ride, and now it's about to begin. You grip the bars as the ride suddenly starts to move. Before you know it, you are lifted high above the ground and you feel the air whipping by. All you see is a dizzy blur.

You can thrill to the speed of amusement park rides because of your senses. **Each of your major senses—vision, hearing, balance, smell, taste, and touch—picks up a specific type of information about your environment. The sense organs change that information into nerve impulses and send the impulses to your brain.** Your brain then interprets the information. Because of the way in which your senses and brain work together, you learn a great deal about your environment.

Figure 12 Riders and bright lights whizzing by—that's what you see when you watch this amusement park ride.

READING STRATEGIES

Reading Tip Have students read the information under the first heading within the section. Work as a class to outline the information under the heading. Then have students work independently to complete the rest of the outline.

Study and Comprehension Before students begin reading, have them preview the section by reading the headings and subheadings. Then have students look at the pictures and read the captions. Discuss with students what they already know about the senses. Encourage students to ask questions about the function of the senses. Write the questions on the board and have students answer them after they have read the section.

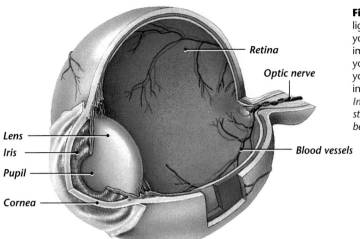

Retina

Optic nerve

Blood vessels

Lens

Iris

Pupil

Cornea

Figure 13 You see an object when light coming from the object enters your eye. The light produces an image on your retina. Receptors in your retina then send impulses to your cerebrum, and your cerebrum interprets these impulses. *Interpreting Diagrams What structures must light pass through before it reaches your retina?*

Vision

Your eyes are the sense organs that enable you to see the objects in your environment. They let you see this book in front of you, the window across the room, and the world outside the window. **Your eyes respond to the stimulus of light. They convert that stimulus into impulses that your brain interprets, enabling you to see.**

How Light Enters Your Eye When rays of light strike the eye, they pass through the structures shown in Figure 13. First, the light strikes the **cornea** (KAWR nee uh), the clear tissue that covers the front of the eye. The light then passes through a fluid-filled chamber behind the cornea and reaches the pupil. The **pupil** is the opening through which light enters the eye.

You may have noticed that people's pupils change size when they go from a dark room into bright sunshine. In bright light, the pupil becomes smaller. In dim light, the pupil becomes larger. The size of the pupil is adjusted by muscles in the iris. The **iris** is a circular structure that surrounds the pupil and regulates the amount of light entering the eye. The iris also gives the eye its color. If you have brown eyes, your irises are brown.

How Light Is Focused Light that passes through the pupil strikes the lens. The **lens** is a flexible structure that focuses light. The lens of your eye functions something like the lens of a camera, which focuses light on photographic film. Because of the way in which the lens of the eye bends the light rays, the image it produces is upside down. Muscles that attach to the lens adjust its shape. This adjustment produces an image that is clear and in focus.

TRY THIS

Why Do You Need Two Eyes? ACTIVITY

In this activity, you will investigate how your two eyes work together to allow you to see.

1. With your arms fully extended, hold a plastic drinking straw in one hand and a pipe cleaner in the other.
2. With both eyes open, try to insert the pipe cleaner into the straw.
3. Now close your right eye. Try to insert the pipe cleaner into the straw.
4. Repeat Step 3, but this time close your left eye instead of your right eye.

Inferring How does closing one eye affect your ability to judge distances?

Chapter 7 **D** ◆ 205

---

2 Facilitate

Vision

Building Inquiry Skills: Observing

Materials *mounted or hand mirror*
Time 15 minutes

Have students observe their own eyes in the mirror and compare the size of their pupils in bright light, dim light, and extremely dim light. Ask: **What happens to your pupils as the light darkens?** (*Pupils widen.*) Then ask: **What function is served when the pupil gets wider in dim light?** (*It allows more light to enter the eye so you can see better.*) **learning modality: kinesthetic**

TRY THIS

Skills Focus inferring
Materials *drinking straw, pipe cleaner*
Time 15 minutes
Tips Students will have more difficulty inserting the pipe cleaner when they have to close one eye than when they have both eyes open.
Inferring Closing one eye impairs a person's ability to judge distances.
Extend Challenge students to design a test that demonstrates how closing one eye reduces their total field of vision. (*Students can cover one eye and identify the objects on the edges of their vision, then cover the other eye and repeat. Students should then open both eyes and compare what they can see with both eyes open to what they saw through each eye.*)
learning modality: kinesthetic

Program Resources

◆ **Teaching Resources** 7-3 Lesson Plan, p. 185; 7-3 Section Summary, p. 186

Media and Technology

 Transparencies "The Eye," Transparency 16

 Audiotapes English-Spanish Summary 7-3

Answers to Self-Assessment

Caption Question

Figure 13 Light must pass through the cornea, pupil, and lens before it reaches the retina.

Ongoing Assessment

Writing Have students list the structures that make up the eye and identify the function of each.
 Students can save their lists in their portfolios.

Vision, continued

Demonstration

Materials *candle in holder, double-convex lens, white paper, optics bench (optional)*
Time 15 minutes

In a dark room, place the candle in the holder on a table and light the candle. CAUTION: *Use safety precautions with open flames. Do not allow students to light the candle or work too close to the flame.* Hold a converging or double-convex lens between the candle and a piece of white paper. Adjust the lens so that it reflects an image of the candle onto the paper. Ask: **What happens to the image of the candle?** *(It appears upside down.)* Extinguish the candle. Then ask: **Where in the eye is the upside-down image focused?** *(On the retina)* **learning modality: visual**

Correcting Vision Problems

 Integrating Physics

Materials *candle in holder, double-convex lens, white paper, optics bench (optional)*
Time 15 minutes

In a dark room, place the candle in the holder on a table and light the candle. Use caution with open flames, as noted above. Hold the lens securely between the candle and a piece of white paper. Adjust the lens so that it reflects a clear image of the candle onto the paper. Ask: **What part of the eye does the lens represent?** *(lens)* **The paper?** *(retina)* Ask: **How could you show near-sightedness?** *(Move the paper further away from the lens.)* Then ask: **How could you show farsightedness?** *(Move the lens closer to the paper.)* Point out to students that however the distance between the paper and the lens is changed, the image becomes unfocused. **learning modality: visual**

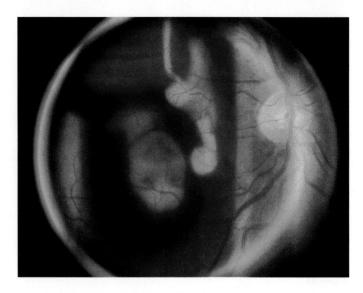

Figure 14 An upside-down image is focused on the retina. *Applying Concepts When you see an object, why does it appear right-side up?*

Figure 15 The retina of the eye contains light-sensitive cells. In this photograph, the rods have been colored pink, and the cones have been colored blue.

How You See an Image After passing through the lens, the focused light rays pass through a transparent, jellylike fluid. Then the light rays strike the **retina** (RET 'n uh), the layer of receptor cells that lines the back of the eye. The retina contains about 130 million receptor cells that respond to light. There are two types of receptors, rods and cones. Rod cells work best in dim light and enable you to see black, white, and shades of gray. In contrast, cone cells only work well in bright light and enable you to see colors. This difference between rods and cones explains why you see colors best in bright light, but you see only shadowy gray images in dim light.

When light strikes the rods and cones, nerve impulses begin. These nerve impulses travel to the cerebrum through the optic nerves. One optic nerve comes from the left eye and the other one comes from the right. In the cerebrum, two things happen. The brain turns the reversed image right-side up. In addition, the brain combines the images from each eye to produce a single image.

Correcting Vision Problems

INTEGRATING PHYSICS A lens—whether it is in your eye, in a camera, or in eyeglasses—is a curved, transparent object that bends light rays as they pass through it. If the lens of the eye does not focus light properly on the retina, vision problems result. The glass or plastic lenses in eyeglasses can help correct such vision problems.

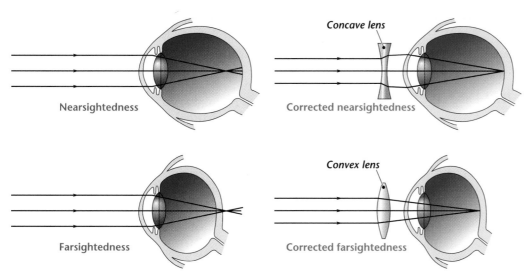

Nearsightedness

Corrected nearsightedness

Concave lens

Farsightedness

Corrected farsightedness

Convex lens

Nearsightedness People with **nearsightedness** can see nearby objects clearly. However, they have trouble seeing objects that are far away. Nearsightedness is caused by an eyeball that is too long. Because of the extra length that light must travel to reach the retina, distant objects do not focus sharply on the retina. Instead, the lens of the eye makes the image come into focus at a point in front of the retina, as shown in Figure 16.

To correct nearsightedness, a person needs to wear eyeglasses with concave lenses. A concave lens is a lens that is thicker at the edges than it is in the center. When light rays pass through a concave lens, they are bent away from the center of the lens. The concave lenses in glasses make light rays spread out before they reach the lens of the eye. Then, when these rays pass through the lens of the eye, they focus on the retina rather than in front of it.

Farsightedness People with **farsightedness** can see distant objects clearly. Nearby objects, however, look blurry. The eyeballs of people with farsightedness are too short. Because of this, the lens of the eye bends light from nearby objects so that the image does not focus properly on the retina. If light could pass through the retina, the image would come into sharp focus at a point behind the retina, as shown in Figure 16.

Convex lenses are used to help correct farsightedness. A convex lens is thicker in the middle than the edges. The convex lens makes the light rays bend toward each other before they reach the eye. Then the lens of the eye bends the rays even more. This bending makes the image focus exactly on the retina.

 Checkpoint *What type of lens is used to correct nearsightedness?*

Figure 16 Nearsightedness and farsightedness are conditions in which images do not focus properly on the retina. The diagrams on the left show where the images are focused in both of these conditions. The diagrams on the right show how lenses in eyeglasses can help correct these conditions.

Program Resources

🔵 **Science Explorer Series** *Sound and Light,* Chapter 4

Answers to Self-Assessment

Caption Question

Figure 14 The brain reverses the image from the retina so the image appears right-side up.

✓ *Checkpoint*
Concave

 ACTIVITY

Including All Students

Materials *convex and concave lenses*
Time 5 minutes

Allow students to feel each type of lens and compare the thickness of the lens at the edges and the center. Ask: **Which lens is thicker in the middle and thinner at the edges?** *(The convex lens)* Then ask students to describe the shape of a concave lens. *(Thinner in the middle; thicker on the edges)* If possible, invite a physical science teacher to demonstrate how convex and concave lenses bend light. **learning modality: kinesthetic**

Using the Visuals: Figure 16

Direct students to trace the path of light rays as they move through the nearsighted eye in Figure 16, then through the nearsighted glasses. Ask: **What do the nearsighted glasses do to the image? How does this correct vision?** *(The glasses bend the light rays outward so they are spread apart when they reach the lens of the eye. Then the lens of the eye can correctly focus the rays.)* Have students repeat the process for the farsighted glasses. *(The glasses bend the light rays inward so they are closer together when they reach the lens of the eye.)* **learning modality: visual**

Real-Life Learning

Many people wear contact lenses to correct their vision. Contact lenses are fitted to cover the cornea and curved to alter the path of light rays passing to the retina. Ask if any students currently wear contact lenses. Allow them to describe the advantages and disadvantages of wearing contact lenses instead of glasses. **learning modality: verbal**

Ongoing Assessment

Skills Check Tell students that people who are farsighted sometimes wear reading glasses to bring nearby objects into focus. Then ask students what kind of lenses are found in reading glasses. *(convex)*

Hearing

Tick! Tick! Tick!

In this activity, you will 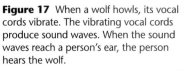 determine whether one of a person's ears hears better than the other one.

1. Work in teams of three. Hold a ticking watch next to the right ear of one team member.
2. Slowly move the watch away from the ear. Stop moving it at the point where the student can no longer hear the ticking.
3. At that point, have the third team member measure the distance between the watch and the student's right ear.
4. Repeat Steps 1 through 3 to test the student's left ear.

Measuring How did the two distances compare? Do you think this is an accurate way to evaluate someone's hearing? Why or why not?

Hearing

What wakes you up in the morning? Maybe an alarm clock buzzes, or perhaps your parent calls you. On a summer morning, you might hear birds singing. Whatever wakes you up, there's a good chance that it's a sound of some sort. **Your ears are the sense organs that respond to the stimulus of sound. The ears convert the sound to nerve impulses that your brain interprets.** So when you hear an alarm clock or other morning sound, your brain tells you that it's time to wake up.

How Sound Is Produced Sound is produced by vibrations. The material that is vibrating, or moving rapidly back and forth, may be almost anything—a guitar string, an insect's wings, or splashing water.

The vibrations create waves. The waves move outward from the source of the sound, something like ripples moving out from a stone dropped in water. The waves consist of moving particles, such as the molecules that make up air. When you hear a friend's voice, for example, sound waves have traveled from your friend's larynx to your ears. In addition to being able to travel through gases such as air, sound waves can also travel through liquids such as water and solids such as wood.

Sound Vibrations and the Ear The ear is structured to receive sound vibrations. As you can see in Figure 18, the ear consists of three parts—the outer ear, middle ear, and inner ear. The outer ear includes the part of the ear that you see. The visible part of the outer ear is shaped like a funnel.

Figure 17 When a wolf howls, its vocal cords vibrate. The vibrating vocal cords produce sound waves. When the sound waves reach a person's ear, the person hears the wolf.

This funnel-like shape enables the outer ear to gather sound waves. The sound waves then travel down the ear canal, which is also part of the outer ear.

At the end of the ear canal, sound waves reach the eardrum. The **eardrum,** which separates the outer ear from the middle ear, is a membrane that vibrates when sound waves strike it. Your eardrum vibrates in much the same way that the surface of a drum vibrates when it is struck. Vibrations from the eardrum pass to the middle ear, which contains the three smallest bones in the body—the hammer, anvil, and stirrup. The names of these bones are based on their shapes. The vibrating eardrum makes the hammer vibrate. The hammer passes the vibrations to the anvil, and the anvil passes them to the stirrup.

How You Hear The stirrup vibrates against a thin membrane that covers the opening of the inner ear. The membrane channels the vibrations into the fluid in the cochlea. The **cochlea** (KAHK le uh) is a snail-shaped tube that is lined with receptors that respond to sound. When the fluid in the cochlea vibrates, it stimulates these receptors. Sensory neurons then send nerve impulses to the cerebrum through the auditory nerve. These impulses are interpreted as sounds that you hear.

✓ *Checkpoint* *Where in the ear is the cochlea located?*

Your Sense of Balance

Your ear also controls your sense of balance. Above the cochlea in your inner ear are the **semicircular canals,** which are the structures in the ear that are responsible for your sense of balance.

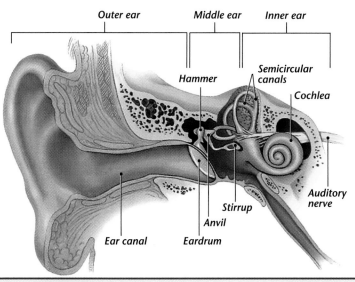

Outer ear   Middle ear   Inner ear

Hammer   Semicircular canals

Cochlea

Ear canal   Eardrum   Anvil   Stirrup   Auditory nerve

Figure 18 The ear has three regions—the outer ear, the middle ear, and the inner ear. Sound waves enter the outer ear and make structures in the middle ear vibrate. When the vibrations reach the inner ear, nerve impulses travel to the cerebrum through the auditory nerve. *Predicting What would happen if the bones of the middle ear were stuck together and could not move?*

Chapter 7 **D ◆ 209**

Answers to Self-Assessment

Caption Question

Figure 18 If the bones of the middle ear could not move, no vibrations would reach the inner ear and a person would be unable to hear.

✓ *Checkpoint*

The cochlea is in the inner ear.

Have students stretch the piece of balloon tightly over the narrow end of the funnel and fasten it with the rubber band. Ask: **What does the piece of balloon represent?** *(The eardrum)* Have students predict what will happen to the balloon if they place a vibrating tuning fork inside the funnel. Allow students to test their prediction. *(It vibrates.)* Ask: **How does this model what happens in the human ear?** *(Sound waves passing through the outer ear reach an eardrum that vibrates.)* **learning modality: kinesthetic**

Using the Visuals: Figure 18

Direct students to trace the path of a sound wave as it passes from the outer ear to the middle and inner ear. Ask: **What happens when the sound waves reach the eardrum?** *(They make the eardrum vibrate, which in turn passes the vibrations to the bones in the middle ear.)* Finally, ask students to locate where the auditory nerve connects to the ear. Point out the cochlea and ask: **What happens to vibrations in this structure?** *(The vibrations stimulate receptor cells to send impulses to the brain through the auditory nerve.)* **learning modality: visual**

Ongoing Assessment

Writing Ask students to describe how a sound is created and how it is heard. *(Vibrations create sound waves in air, water, or other matter. If the waves enter the ear, they cause the eardrum to vibrate. These vibrations pass to the middle ear and cause the hammer, anvil, and stirrup to vibrate. In the inner ear, the vibrations pass to fluid in the cochlea, where they stimulate receptors that send nerve impulses to the brain.)*

Your Sense of Balance

Including All Students

Materials *clear plastic jar with lid, water*
Time 5 minutes

Students who need an additional challenge can model how motion affects the semicircular canals. Have pairs of students fill a plastic jar halfway with water and seal it tightly. CAUTION: *Do not use glass containers for this activity. Make sure the outside of the jar is completely dry.* In an open area, have one partner hold the jar and spin quickly for about 10 seconds. The observing student should note the movement of the liquid in the jar. Have students switch roles. Ask: **What happened to the water in the jar?** *(It sloshed around.)* Then ask: **How does this model explain what happens inside the semicircular canals?** *(Like the water, the fluid in the semicircular canals is sloshed around when you move your head.)* **learning modality: kinesthetic**

Smell and Taste

Sharpen your Skills

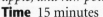

Designing Experiments

Materials *peeled pear, apple, and raw potato*
Time 15 minutes
Tips Students should wash hands before and after handling the food. Sample experiment: Blindfolded students taste and identify small pieces of food, then repeat the procedure holding their noses closed.
Extend Have students test whether a person can identify the food based on the food's scent, without tasting it.

Sharpen your Skills

Designing Experiments

Can people tell one food from another if they can taste the foods but not smell them? Design an experiment to find out. Use these foods: a peeled pear, a peeled apple, and a peeled raw potato. Be sure to control all variables except the one you are testing. Write your hypothesis and a description of your procedure. Show these to your teacher. Do not perform your experiment until your teacher approves your procedure.

Figure 19 The semicircular canals of the inner ear enable people to keep their balance—even in very tricky situations!

You can see how these structures got their name if you look at Figure 19. These canals, as well as two tiny sacs located behind them, are full of fluid. The canals and sacs are also lined with tiny cells that have hairlike extensions.

When your head moves, the fluid in the semicircular canals is set in motion. The moving fluid makes the cells' hairlike extensions bend. This bending produces nerve impulses in sensory neurons. The impulses travel to the cerebellum. The cerebellum then analyzes the impulses to determine the way your head is moving and the position of your body. If the cerebellum senses that you are losing your balance, it sends impulses to muscles that help you restore your balance.

Smell and Taste

You walk into the house and smell the aroma of freshly baked cookies. You bite into one and taste its rich chocolate flavor. When you smelled the cookies, receptors in your nose reacted to chemicals carried by the air from the cookies to your nose. When you took a bite of a cookie, taste buds on your tongue responded to chemicals in the food. These food chemicals were dissolved in saliva, which came in contact with your taste buds.

The senses of smell and taste work closely together, and both depend on chemicals. The chemicals trigger responses in receptors in the nose and mouth. Nerve impulses then travel to the brain, where they are interpreted as smells or tastes.

The nose can distinguish at least 50 basic odors. In contrast, there are only four main kinds of taste buds—sweet, sour, salty,

---

Background

Integrating Science Evidence suggests that the sense of touch actually covers the ability to sense five different types of stimuli. These five senses, collectively called the skin senses, enable people to sense two kinds of pressure (light and deep), two kinds of temperature (hot and cold), and pain. Scientists have tested the body's response to all five stimuli. Using tests with needles, very fine bristles, and tiny cylinders (hot or cold) to determine the degree of sensitivity to pain, pressure, and temperature, scientists have discovered that there are individual spots on the skin that detect each type of stimuli. The spots that respond to pain outnumber those that respond to touch. Even fewer spots respond to hot and cold temperatures.

and bitter. When you eat, however, you experience a much wider variety of tastes. The flavor of food is determined by both the the senses of smell and taste. When you have a cold, your favorite foods may not taste as good as they usually do. That is because a stuffy nose can decrease your ability to smell food.

Touch

Unlike vision, hearing, balance, smell, and taste, the sense of touch is not found in one specific place. Instead, the sense of touch is found in all areas of your skin. Your skin is your largest sense organ!

Your skin contains different kinds of touch receptors. Some of these receptors respond to light touch and others to heavy pressure. Still other receptors pick up sensations of pain and temperature change.

The receptors that respond to light touch are in the upper part of the dermis. They tell you when something brushes against your skin. These receptors also let you feel the textures of objects, such as smooth glass and rough sandpaper. Receptors deeper in the dermis pick up the feeling of pressure. Press down hard on the top of your desk, for example, and you will feel pressure in your fingers.

The dermis also contains receptors that respond to temperature and pain. Pain is unpleasant, but it can be one of the body's most important feelings, because it alerts the body to possible danger. Have you ever stepped into a bathtub of very hot water and then immediately pulled your foot out? If so, you can appreciate how pain can trigger an important response in your body.

Figure 20 Blind people use their sense of touch to read. To do this, they run their fingers over words written in Braille. Braille uses raised dots to represent letters and numbers. Here a teacher shows a blind child how to read Braille.

Section 3 Review

1. What overall role do the senses perform in the body?
2. Describe the process by which your eyes produce an image of your surroundings. Begin at the point at which light is focused by the lens.
3. How do sound vibrations affect structures in the ear to produce the sensation of hearing?
4. How are the senses of taste and smell similar? How are they different?
5. **Thinking Critically** **Relating Cause and Effect** Infections of the inner ear sometimes make people more likely to lose their balance and fall. Explain why this is so.

> **CHAPTER PROJECT 7**
>
> **Check Your Progress**
> By now, you should have submitted your plans for your experiment to your teacher. Make any necessary changes in the plan. Prepare all the materials for the fair, including the illusions and questionnaire. Have a data table ready so you can record all responses. (*Hint:* Be sure the people you test cannot see or hear each other's responses. Also, test a large enough number of individuals.)

Chapter 7 **D ◆ 211**

Program Resources

◆ **Teaching Resources** 7-3 Review and Reinforce, p. 187; 7-3 Enrich, p. 188

Media and Technology

Interactive Student Tutorial CD-ROM D-7

Touch

Addressing Naive Conceptions

Students may think that the sense of touch refers only to feeling things with their fingers. Point out that there are touch receptors throughout the skin.
learning modality: verbal

3 Assess

Section 3 Review Answers

1. The senses pick up specific information about the environment and change that information to nerve impulses that travel to the brain.
2. Focused light rays strike the retina. Receptor cells send nerve impulses to the brain, which turns the image right side up and combines the images from each eye into a single image.
3. Sound vibrations make the eardrum vibrate. These vibrations pass to the bones of the middle ear, which vibrate against a thin membrane that channels the vibrations to the cochlear fluid. The vibrating fluid stimulates receptor cells that send nerve impulses to the brain.
4. Taste and smell both respond to chemicals. Taste responds to chemicals in saliva, while smell responds to chemicals in air. There are about 50 basic odors, but only 4 basic tastes.
5. An infection may damage the semicircular canals and upset balance.

> **CHAPTER PROJECT 7**
>
> **Check Your Progress**
> If possible, set up a testing booth in which students can test each other or students from other classes.

Performance Assessment

Writing Have students write brief explanations of how each of the senses sends information to the brain when students eat a sandwich.

D ◆ 211

SECTION 4 Alcohol and Other Drugs

Objectives

After completing the lesson, students will be able to
◆ name some commonly abused drugs and state how they affect the body;
◆ explain how alcohol abuse harms the body.

Key Terms drug, drug abuse, tolerance, withdrawal, depressant, stimulant, anabolic steroid, alcoholism

1 Engage/Explore

Activating Prior Knowledge

Have a class discussion about drugs and drug abuse. Ask students questions such as these: **If I get sick, is it okay for me to take someone else's prescription medicine?** and **If a medicine makes me feel better, will taking twice as much make me feel better faster?** Encourage students to discuss similar issues. Explain that this section will give them information about the proper way to use medicine and other drugs.

 **DISCOVER**

Skills Focus inferring
Materials *pieces of wrapped candy*
Time 15 minutes
Tips After the activity, have students try to identify different kinds of arguments—for example, suggesting that drug use enhances popularity; insisting that drugs are harmless. Discard all candy after the activity.
Think It Over If peers encourage someone to do something, such as eat candy or use drugs, it may be difficult not to agree with them. Therefore, peer pressure can make it hard for people to say no to drugs.

SECTION 4 Alcohol and Other Drugs

DISCOVER •••••••••••••••••••••••••••• ACTIVITY

How Can You Best Say No?

1. In this activity, you will use candy to represent drugs. Your teacher will divide the class into groups of three students. In each group, your teacher will appoint two students to try to convince the other person to take the "drugs."

2. Depending on your role, you should think of arguments to get the person to accept the candy or arguments against accepting it. After everyone has had a chance to think of arguments, begin the discussion.

3. After a while, students in each group should exchange roles.

Think It Over

Inferring What role does peer pressure play in whether or not a person decides to abuse drugs?

GUIDE FOR READING

◆ How do commonly abused drugs affect the body?

◆ How does alcohol abuse harm the body?

Reading Tip Before you read, preview the table on page 215. List some ways in which drugs affect the central nervous system.

◀ Medicines in a drugstore

Drugs! You probably hear and see that word in a lot of places. Drugstores sell drugs to relieve headaches, soothe upset stomachs, and stop coughs. Radio and television programs and magazine articles explore drug-related problems. Your school probably has a program to educate students about drugs. When people talk about drugs, what do they mean? To a scientist, a **drug** is any chemical that causes changes in a person's body or behavior. Many drugs affect the functioning of the nervous system.

Medicines

Medicines are legal drugs that help the body fight disease and injury. Aspirin, for example, is a medicine that can relieve pain. To purchase some medicines, you need a doctor's prescription. Other medicines, however, can be bought in drugstores or supermarkets without a prescription. If medicines are used properly, they can help you stay healthy or speed your recovery from sickness. Whenever you take medicines of any kind, it is important to follow the directions for their proper use.

READING STRATEGIES

Reading Tip Help students interpret the column headings as they preview the table on effects of abused drugs. Have volunteers explain the difference between immediate effects and long-term effects. Then instruct students to list some of the ways in which drugs affect the central nervous system.

Study and Comprehension While students read the section, have them write a list of their questions about abused drugs. Encourage students to find answers to their questions in the chapter. After students have read the section, hold a question-and-answer session or panel discussion for the students to help each other answer their questions.

Drug Abuse

The deliberate misuse of drugs for purposes other than medical ones is called **drug abuse.** Medicines can be abused drugs if they are used in a way for which they were not intended. Many abused drugs, however, such as cocaine and heroin, are illegal under any circumstances. The use of these drugs is against the law because their effects on the body are almost always very dangerous.

Immediate Effects of Abused Drugs Abused drugs start to affect the body very shortly after they are taken. Different drugs have different effects. Some drugs cause nausea and a fast, irregular heartbeat. Others can cause sleepiness. Drug abusers may also experience headaches, dizziness, and trembling.

Most commonly abused drugs, such as marijuana, alcohol, and cocaine, are especially dangerous because they act on the brain and other parts of the nervous system. For example, alcohol can cause confusion, poor muscle coordination, and blurred vision. These effects are especially dangerous in situations in which an alert mind is essential, such as driving a car.

Most abused drugs can alter, or change, a person's mood and feelings. Because of this effect, these drugs are often called mood-altering drugs. For example, the mood of a person under the influence of marijuana may change from calm to anxious. Alcohol can sometimes make a person angry and even violent. Mood-altering drugs also affect patterns of thinking and the way in which the brain interprets information from the senses.

Tolerance If a person takes a drug regularly, the body may develop a tolerance to the drug. **Tolerance** is a state in which a drug user needs larger and larger amounts of the drug to produce the same effect on the body. Tolerance can cause people to take a very large amount of a drug, or an overdose. People who take an overdose may become unconscious or even die.

Figure 21 Abused drugs such as these can cause serious physical and emotional problems.
Applying Concepts List three ways in which drugs can affect the body.

Program Resources

◆ **Teaching Resources** 7-4 Lesson Plan, p. 191; 7-4 Section Summary, p. 192

Media and Technology

 Audiotapes English-Spanish Summary 7-4

Answers to Self-Assessment

Caption Question

Figure 21 Samples: They can act on the brain and nervous system to cause confusion, poor muscle coordination, altered mood, and blurred vision.

---

2 Facilitate

Medicines

Building Inquiry Skills: Communicating

Materials *empty boxes or labels from over-the-counter medications such as aspirin, cold and flu medicines, or skin ointments*
Time 20 minutes

Give each student a box or label. Have students find the symptoms that the medicine treats, the correct dosage, and any possible side effects. Students can summarize their findings from the class in a brief oral report. Ask: **Why is it important to read the label on over-the-counter medications?** *(You need to be sure that the medicine will treat your symptoms, that you take the right amount, and that you are prepared to recognize any dangerous side effects.)* **learning modality: verbal**

Drug Abuse

Addressing Naive Conceptions

Students may not realize that any substance that affects a person's body or behavior is a drug and may be abused. Point out that over-the-counter medications and herbs that are used as medicines can be very dangerous if not taken correctly. **learning modality: verbal**

Ongoing Assessment

Writing Have students list some typical effects of abused drugs.

Drug Abuse, continued

Communicating

Materials *paper, drawing* *materials*
Time 45 minutes
Tips Allow students to work in teams. After brainstorming ideas, some students can plan the narrative sequence of the commercial; others can create the storyboards; and others can write the script.
Extend Arrange to have students present their commercials to younger students or to another class.
cooperative learning

Other Effects of Drug Abuse

Demonstration

Materials *paper cup, red* *food coloring, water, plastic droppers*
Time 15 minutes

To show students how HIV and other infected blood can be passed through shared needles, give a volunteer a paper cup half full of water to which you have added 20 drops of food coloring. Have the volunteer draw up colored water in a dropper, then expel some of it into an empty cup. Then have the volunteer use the same dropper to draw up some clear water and expel the water in the dropper into another empty cup. The water in the second cup will be tinged with red. Ask: **What does the red liquid represent?** *(Infected blood)* **learning modality: visual**

Communicating

Plan a 30-second 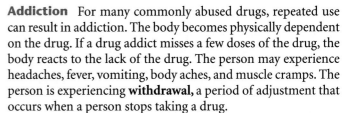 television commercial aimed at teenagers to help them avoid the pressure to try drugs. Your commercial should reveal some harmful effects of drugs and give strategies for avoiding drugs. Create several storyboards to show what the commercial will look like. Then write a script for your commercial.

Addiction For many commonly abused drugs, repeated use can result in addiction. The body becomes physically dependent on the drug. If a drug addict misses a few doses of the drug, the body reacts to the lack of the drug. The person may experience headaches, fever, vomiting, body aches, and muscle cramps. The person is experiencing **withdrawal,** a period of adjustment that occurs when a person stops taking a drug.

Some drugs may also cause a person to become emotionally dependent on them. The person becomes accustomed to the feelings and moods produced by the drug. Therefore, the person has a strong desire to continue using the drug.

☑ *Checkpoint* **What is meant by a tolerance to a drug?**

Other Effects of Drug Abuse

Drugs can also affect a person's health indirectly. Drug users sometimes share needles. When a person uses a needle to inject a drug, some of the person's blood remains in the needle after it is withdrawn. If the person has HIV or another pathogen in the blood, the next person to use the needle may become infected with the pathogen.

The abuse of drugs also has serious legal and social effects. A person who is caught using or selling an illegal drug may have to pay a fine or go to jail. Drug abuse can also make a person unable to get along with others. Drug abusers often have a hard time doing well in school or holding a job.

Kinds of Drugs

Figure 22 lists and describes the characteristics of some commonly abused drugs. Notice in the chart that some drugs are classified as depressants. **Depressants** are drugs that slow down the activity of the central nervous system. When people take depressants, their muscles relax and they may become sleepy. They may take longer than normal to respond to stimuli. For example, depressants may prevent people from reacting quickly to the danger of a car rushing toward them. Alcohol and narcotics, such as heroin, are depressants.

Stimulants, in contrast, speed up body processes. They make the heart beat faster and make the breathing rate increase. Cocaine and nicotine are stimulants, as are amphetamines. Amphetamines (am FET uh meenz) are prescription drugs that are sometimes sold illegally.

Background

Facts and Figures The most common drug tests require samples of blood, urine, or hair. Blood testing is often used after an accident or crime to determine the presence and amount of a drug in the body at the time of the incident. The results of a blood test can be used to estimate the time and amount of drug use that occurred up to twenty-four hours prior to the test. Urine tests can determine whether certain drugs have been used recently. The length of time a drug can be detected in urine varies from several hours to several weeks. Urine tests are often used to test athletes to determine whether there is a consistent pattern of drug use. Hair analysis can reveal chronic drug use that occurred at any point during the growth of the hair.

Some Effects of Commonly Abused Drugs

Drug Type	Short-Term Effects	Long-Term Effects	Addiction?	Emotional Dependence?
marijuana (including hashish)	anxiety, panic, excitement, sleepiness	difficulty with concentration and memory, respiratory disease and lung cancer	probably not	yes
nicotine (in cigarettes, cigars, chewing tobacco)	stimulant; nausea, loss of appetite, headache	heart and lung disease, difficulty breathing, heavy coughing	yes, strongly so	yes
alcohol	depressant; decreased alertness, poor reflexes, nausea, emotional depression	liver and brain damage, inadequate nutrition	yes	yes
inhalants (glue, nail polish remover, paint thinner)	sleepiness, nausea, headaches, emotional depression	damage to liver, kidneys, and brain; hallucinations	no	yes
cocaine (including crack)	stimulant; nervousness, disturbed sleep, loss of appetite	mental illness, damage to lining of nose, irregular heartbeat, heart or breathing failure, liver damage	yes	yes, strongly so
amphetamines	stimulant; restlessness, rapid speech, dizziness	restlessness, irritability, irregular heartbeat, liver damage	possible	yes
hallucinogens (LSD, mescaline, PCP)	hallucinations, anxiety, panic; thoughts and actions not connected to reality	mental illness; fearfulness; behavioral changes, including violence	no	yes
barbiturates (Phenobarbital, Nembutal, Seconal)	depressant; decreased alertness, slowed thought processes, poor muscle coordination	sleepiness, irritability, confusion	yes	yes
tranquilizers (Valium, Xanax)	depressant; blurred vision, sleepiness, unclear speech, headache, skin rash	blood and liver disease	yes	yes
narcotics (opium, codeine, morphine, heroin)	depressant; sleepiness, nausea, hallucinations	convulsion, coma, death	yes, very rapid development	yes, strongly so
anabolic steroids	mood swings	heart, liver, and kidney damage; hypertension; overgrowth of skull and facial bones	no	yes

Figure 22 Abused drugs can have many serious effects on the body. *Interpreting Charts What are the long-term effects of using inhalants?*

Kinds of Drugs

Building Inquiry Skills: Making Generalizations

As students examine the chart in Figure 22, have them make generalizations about the different categories of drugs and their effects. Ask questions such as the following: **What percent of the drugs listed may be physically addictive?** *(70 percent)* **What percent cause emotional dependency?** *(100 percent)* **learning modality: logical/mathematical**

Answers to Self-Assessment

Caption Question

Figure 22 The long term effects of using inhalants are damage to the liver, kidneys, and brain, as well as hallucinations.

✓ *Checkpoint*

Tolerance to a drug is the state in which a drug user needs larger and larger amounts of the drug to get the same effect.

Ongoing Assessment

Skills Check Have students use the table in Figure 22 to compare and contrast the short- and long-term effects of stimulants, depressants, and hallucinogens.

With Caffeine or Without

Preparing for Inquiry

Key Concept Stimulants such as caffeine cause body processes to speed up.

Skills Objectives Students will be able to
- develop hypotheses about the effect of caffeine on an organism;
- design experiments to test their hypotheses.

Time 40 minutes

Advance Planning Purchase *Daphnia* culture and adrenaline (epinephrine) from a biological supply company. To prepare the adrenaline solution (about 0.01%), dissolve 10 mg epinephrine hydrochloride in 100 mL distilled water. Have available all other materials, including beverages with caffeine and "decaffeinated" beverages.

Alternative Materials *Daphnia* may be also be obtained from aquarium stores or from lakes and ponds. Possible beverage choices include cola or coffee, citrus soda or juice, caffeine-free cola or decaffeinated coffee.

Guiding Inquiry

Invitation

Have students read through the lab. Ask students why adrenaline is used in Part 1 when the experiment is testing the effects of caffeine. *(It illustrates how a known stimulant will affect Daphnia.)* Ask students to describe the advantages and disadvantages of using *Daphnia* as the test subject. *(Samples: The transparent body allows easy observation of changes in heart rate. Effects of caffeine on water fleas may be different than effect on humans.)*

Introducing the Procedure
- Demonstrate the proper procedure for applying *Daphnia* to the microscope slide.
- Use the illustration of *Daphnia* to show students where the heart is located and demonstrate how to determine the heart rate.

Some substances, called inhalants, produce mood-altering effects when they are inhaled, or breathed in. Inhalants include paint thinner, nail polish remover, and some kinds of cleaning fluids. Hallucinogens, such as LSD and mescaline, can make people see or hear things that do not really exist.

Some athletes try to improve their performance by taking drugs known as steroids. **Anabolic steroids** (an uh BAH lik steer oydz) are synthetic chemicals that are similar to hormones produced in the body. You will learn more about hormones in Chapter 8.

Anabolic steroids may increase muscle size and strength. However, steroids can cause mood changes that lead to violence.

Real-World Lab

You, the Consumer

With Caffeine or Without?

Caffeine is a stimulant found in some beverages and foods, such as coffee and cola drinks. In this lab, you'll observe the effect that caffeine has on a nonhuman organism to help understand how caffeine may affect your own body.

Problem

What body changes does caffeine produce in water fleas (*Daphnia*)?

Skills Focus

developing hypotheses, designing experiments

Materials

drinking straw	scissors
metric ruler	toothpick
petroleum jelly	microscope slide
Daphnia culture	microscope
plastic dropper	
adrenaline solution (about 0.01%)	
clock or watch with second hand	
beverages with and without caffeine	

Procedure

Part 1 Observing Effects of a Known Stimulant

1. Cut off the tip of a drinking straw to form a tiny ring about 1 mm deep. With a toothpick, spread some petroleum jelly along the top rim of the ring.
2. Place the ring, jelly side down, on a microscope slide. This ring will be a chamber for your water fleas.
3. Using a plastic dropper, add a drop of *Daphnia* culture to the chamber. Then use the dropper to draw back most of the water. Leave the *Daphnia* and a small amount of water on the slide.
4. Use the low-power lens of a microscope to locate a water flea. Observe the heart, which you can see in the diagram.
5. Use a watch or clock with a second hand to count the number of heartbeats you observe in 1 minute. Record the heartbeat count in your notebook.

Troubleshooting the Experiment
- Students should use new *Daphnia* samples for Part 2 and for the Design an Experiment. Exposing a single *Daphnia* to many different substances in quick succession would stress the organism and lead to erroneous data. In addition, residual amounts of the various test substances could remain in the *Daphnia* as it is exposed to new test substances.
- Students should count heartbeats as soon as they are able to view the *Daphnia*. This avoids the chance that the *Daphnia* will become too hot on the slide and cause erroneous results.

Expected Outcome
- Normal heart rate for *Daphnia*, depending on the species, varies from 230 to 300 beats per minute.
- Adrenaline and caffeine are stimulants and should cause the heart rate to increase. Drinks without caffeine should not increase the heart rate.

In addition, steroid abuse can cause serious health problems, such as heart damage, liver damage, and increased blood pressure. Steroid use is especially dangerous for teenagers, whose growing bodies can be permanently damaged.

Alcohol

Alcohol is a drug found in many beverages, including beer, wine, cocktails, and hard liquor. Alcohol is a powerful depressant. In the United States, it is illegal for people under the age of 21 to buy or possess alcohol. In spite of this fact, alcohol is the most commonly abused drug in people aged 12 to 17.

---

6. Remove the slide from the microscope. Use a plastic dropper to add 1 drop of adrenaline solution to the water flea chamber. (Adrenaline is a substance that is produced by the human body that acts in a manner similar to a stimulant.)
7. Place the slide on the microscope. Using low power, locate a water flea. Count and record the number of heartbeats in a minute.

Part 2 Testing the Effects of Caffeine

8. Using the procedures you followed in Part 1, design an experiment that tests the effect of caffeine on *Daphnia's* heartbeat. You can use beverages with and without caffeine in your investigation. Be sure to write a hypothesis and control all necessary variables.
9. Submit your experimental plan to your teacher for review. After making any necessary changes, carry out your experiment.

Analyze and Conclude

1. What effect does a stimulant have on the body?

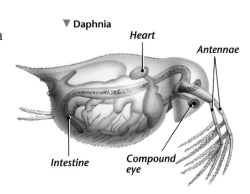

▼ Daphnia

Heart

Antennae

Intestine

Compound eye

2. In Part 1, how did you know that adrenaline acted as a stimulant?
3. In Part 2, did caffeine act as a stimulant?
4. **Apply** Based on your work in Part 2, how do you think your body would react to drinks with caffeine? To drinks without caffeine?

Design an Experiment

Do you think that "decaffeinated" products will act as a stimulant in *Daphnia*? Design a controlled experiment to find out. Obtain your teacher's approval before performing this experiment.

Analyze and Conclude

1. A stimulant causes the body of an organism to increase the rate of certain activities, such as heartbeat and breathing.
2. Because adrenaline caused an increase in the *Daphnia* heart rate.
3. Caffeine caused the heart rate to increase.
4. Some students may infer that drinks without caffeine will have no effect on humans, but drinks with caffeine will cause increased heart rates and related changes. Other students may say that since humans and *Daphnia* are so different, the effect of caffeine on humans cannot be predicted based on this evidence.

Extending the Inquiry

Design an Experiment Students should design an experiment similar to Part 2 of this lab, substituting a "decaffeinated" beverage for the beverage with caffeine. Results may vary depending on how completely the caffeine has been removed from the beverage.

Alcohol

Addressing Naive Conceptions

Many people believe that alcoholism only develops from drinking hard liquor. Explain that all forms of alcohol can be involved in alcohol abuse and alcoholism. A bottle of beer, a wine cooler, a glass of wine, and a shot glass of hard liquor all contain about the same amount of alcohol. Ask: **How can a person who drinks only wine coolers become an alcoholic?** *(If they become physically addicted and emotionally dependent on the alcohol in the wine coolers, they can develop alcoholism.)*
learning modality: verbal

Safety

Remind students to treat the *Daphnia* with as little stress as possible before the lab. They should handle glass microscope slides and scissors with care. Caution them not to taste any of the beverages. They should wash their hands thoroughly after the lab. Review the safety guidelines in Appendix A.

Program Resources

◆ **Teaching Resources** Chapter 7 Real-World Lab, pp. 195–197

Building Inquiry Skills: Measuring

Materials *1 L container, graduated cylinder marked in mL, dropper marked in mL, about 1 L of water, 1 mL of vegetable oil*

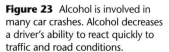

Time 15 minutes

Using water and oil to represent blood and alcohol, respectively, let pairs of students demonstrate the relative volumes of blood and alcohol present for a BAC value of 0.1 percent. Have them fill the 1 L container with 999 mL of water, then use the dropper to place 1 mL of oil on top of the water. Use this demonstration to show that even a small amount of alcohol in the bloodstream can have a serious impact on the body.
learning modality: visual

Including All Students

For students who need an additional challenge, have them calculate how many alcohol-related accidents take place in a 24-hour period. *(24 hours = 1,440 minutes. 1,440 minutes ÷ 2 minutes = 720 accidents)* Then challenge students to determine how many such accidents take place each year. *(365 × 720 = 262,800 accidents per year.)* **learning modality: logical/mathematical**

History
CONNECTION

Tell students that attitudes about drinking alcohol have varied among cultures and through history. Many countries have attempted to control alcohol consumption and alcoholism by prohibiting the sale of alcohol. In 1919, the Eighteenth Amendment to the Constitution of the United States was passed, prohibiting the sale of alcohol. In 1933, the Twenty-First Amendment was passed to repeal the Eighteenth. The years from 1919–1933 are known as Prohibition. Interested students may want to research alcohol-related social issues in the United States during the time leading up to Prohibition and the time following it. **learning modality: verbal**

How Alcohol Affects the Body Alcohol is absorbed by the digestive system quickly. If a person drinks alcohol on an empty stomach, the alcohol enters the blood and gets to the brain and other organs almost immediately. If alcohol is drunk with a meal, it takes longer to get into the blood.

To understand what alcohol does to the body, look at *Exploring the Effects of Alcohol.* The more alcohol in the blood, the more serious the effects. The amount of alcohol in the blood is usually expressed as blood alcohol concentration, or BAC. A BAC value of 0.1 percent means that one tenth of one percent of the fluid in the blood is alcohol. In some states, if car drivers have a BAC of 0.08 percent or more, they are legally drunk. In other states, drivers with a BAC of 0.1 are considered drunk.

Alcohol produces serious effects, including loss of normal judgment, at a BAC of less than 0.08 percent. This loss of judgment can have serious consequences. For example, people who have been drinking may not realize that they cannot drive a car safely. In the United States, alcohol is involved in about 40 percent of traffic-related deaths. About every two minutes, a person in the United States is injured in a car crash related to alcohol.

Long-Term Alcohol Abuse Many adults drink occasionally, and in moderation, without serious safety or health problems. However, heavy drinking, especially over a long period, can result in significant health problems. **The abuse of alcohol can cause the destruction of cells in the brain and liver, and it can also lead to addiction and emotional dependence.** Damage to the brain can cause mental disturbances, such as hallucinations and

Figure 23 Alcohol is involved in many car crashes. Alcohol decreases a driver's ability to react quickly to traffic and road conditions.

Background

Integrating Science Alcoholism involves both emotional dependence and physical addiction. Treatment for the emotional dependency includes psychotherapy and support groups. One treatment for the physical addiction to alcohol involves drugs that cause violent illness if alcohol is ingested while they are in the body. One such drug causes nausea, vomiting, a precipitous drop in blood pressure, heart pounding, and even a feeling of being on the verge of death. This drug blocks the metabolism of alcohol. When alcohol cannot be processed normally, it produces toxins that flood the patient's body. If a patient continues to take the drug, the fear of re-experiencing the symptoms helps them resist drinking. Other drugs allow the patient to drink small amounts of alcohol, but cause illness if too much alcohol is consumed.

loss of consciousness. The liver, which breaks down alcohol for elimination from the body, can become so scarred that it does not function properly. In addition, long-term alcohol abuse can increase the risk of getting certain kinds of cancer.

Abuse of alcohol can result in **alcoholism,** a disease in which a person is both physically addicted to and emotionally dependent on alcohol. To give up alcohol, alcoholics must go through withdrawal, as with any addictive drug. To give up drinking,

EXPLORING the Effects of Alcohol

Alcohol is a drug that affects every system of the body. It also impacts a person's thought processes and judgment.

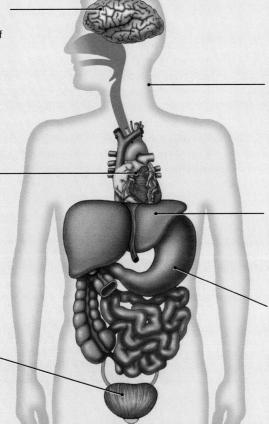

Nervous system Vision becomes blurred. Speech becomes unclear. Control of behavior is reduced. Judgment becomes poor.

Cardiovascular system At first, heartbeat rate and blood pressure increase. Later, with large amounts of alcohol, the heartbeat rate and blood pressure may decrease.

Excretory system Alcohol causes the kidneys to produce more urine. As a result, the drinker loses more water than usual.

Skin Blood flow to the skin increases, causing rapid loss of body heat.

Liver The liver breaks down alcohol. Over many years, liver damage can result.

Digestive system Alcohol is absorbed directly from the stomach and small intestine. The alcohol passes into the bloodstream quickly.

Chapter 7 **D ◆ 219**

EXPLORING
the Effects of Alcohol

As students study the visual essay, ask: **How does alcohol get to different parts of the body?** *(It is carried in the blood.)* Then ask about the short-term effects of alcohol. **Why shouldn't people drink alcohol to keep warm on a cold night?** *(Alcohol causes rapid loss of body heat, so people would get colder if they drank alcohol.)* **Why shouldn't people drink alcohol when they are thirsty?** *(When people are thirsty their bodies need water, and alcohol causes the body to lose water.)* **How does alcohol affect blood pressure and heart rate?** *(First blood pressure and heart rate rise; then they drop.)* **How does alcohol impair a person's ability to drive?** *(It blurs vision, keeps a person from making good judgments, and impairs coordination.)* **What is one long-term effect of alcohol abuse?** *(Liver damage)* **Extend** Invite a guest speaker from an organization such as Mothers Against Drunk Drivers to answer students' questions about alcohol and alcoholism. **learning modality: verbal**

Avoiding Drugs and Alcohol

Building Inquiry Skills: Communicating

Time 20 minutes

ACTIVITY

Have small groups of students role-play scenarios such as confronting a sibling who is using drugs or alcohol, helping a friend decide not to drink a beer at a party, and avoiding a drug pusher's threats. After students have taken turns in different roles, have them present one scenario for the class. **cooperative learning**

Ongoing Assessment

Writing Have students summarize how alcohol affects two different body systems.

3 Assess

Section 4 Review Answers

1. Some abused drugs cause confusion, poor muscle coordination, and blurred vision. These effects can be dangerous in situations where an alert mind, good judgment, and quick reaction time are essential. Other drugs can alter people's mood, which can make them have difficulties in social situations, or can even cause them to be violent.

2. Long-term alcohol abuse can cause destruction of cells in the brain and liver and increase a person's risk of getting certain kinds of cancer. It can also lead to addiction and emotional dependence.

3. Alcoholism is a disease in which a person is both physically addicted to and emotionally dependent on alcohol.

4. Depressants slow down the activity of the central nervous system. They relax the muscles and make people sleepy and slow to respond to stimuli. Stimulants speed up the body processes. They make the heart beat faster and make the breathing rate increase.

Check Your Progress
CHAPTER PROJECT 7

Encourage groups to work together to plan their presentations, and then divide the work. For example, one student or student pair could analyze the results, another describe the tests, and another explain how illusions trick the senses. Encourage students to prepare visual aids such as pie graphs to support their findings.

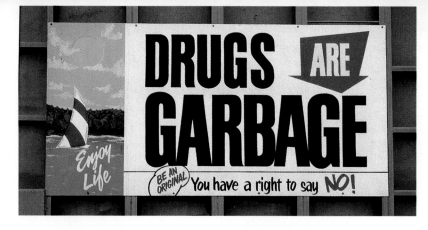

Figure 24 The message is clear: drugs are dangerous, and you have the right to refuse to take them.

alcoholics need both medical and emotional help. Medical professionals and organizations such as Alcoholics Anonymous can help a person stop drinking.

Avoiding Drugs and Alcohol

The best way to avoid depending on drugs and alcohol is not to start using them. Many teenagers who start do so because of peer pressure from people who are abusing drugs. Try to avoid situations in which there is a possibility that drugs may be used.

If you are faced with pressure to use drugs, give a simple but honest reason for your refusal. For example, you might say that you don't want to risk getting into trouble with the law. You do not need to apologize for your decision. And remember that people who don't respect your feelings aren't very good friends.

To stay away from drugs, it is important to find healthy things to do with friends. Become involved in sports and other school or community activities in which you and your friends can have fun together. Such activities help you feel good about yourself. By deciding not to use drugs, you are protecting your health.

Section 4 Review

1. How do abused drugs affect the nervous system? Why can these effects be dangerous?

2. What are the effects of long-term alcohol abuse?

3. What is alcoholism?

4. Thinking Critically **Comparing and Contrasting** Contrast the effects that stimulants and depressants have on the body.

Check Your Progress
CHAPTER PROJECT 7

By now you should have finished collecting your data and recording your observations. Now begin preparing a report about your findings. Think about the best way to communicate the procedures you followed and the results you obtained. Your report should explain how you think the illusions you chose trick the senses. Decide how to use graphs and other visuals in your report.

Performance Assessment

Drawing Have small groups of students choose one type of drug described in the section and create an informational display poster about its short-term and long-term effects on the body.

Program Resources

◆ **Teaching Resources** 7-4 Review and Reinforce, p. 191; 7-4 Enrich, p. 192

Media and Technology

Interactive Student Tutorial CD-ROM D-7

SECTION 1 How the Nervous System Works

Key Ideas
◆ The nervous system receives information about the external and internal environment, responds to this information, and helps maintain homeostasis.
◆ Neurons are the cells that carry nerve impulses. Sensory neurons pick up stimuli from the environment. Interneurons pass messages between neurons. Motor neurons send impulses that cause a response.
◆ To pass from the axon of a neuron to another structure, a nerve impulse must cross a space called a synapse.

Key Terms
stimulus	dendrite	interneuron
response	axon	motor neuron
neuron	nerve	synapse
nerve impulse	sensory neuron	

SECTION 2 Divisions of the Nervous System

Key Ideas
◆ The central nervous system, which consists of the brain and spinal cord, is the control center of the body.
◆ The cerebrum in the brain receives input from the senses, controls voluntary muscles, and controls complex mental processes. The cerebellum coordinates muscle action and balance. The brainstem controls involuntary actions necessary for life.
◆ The peripheral nervous system links the central nervous system to the rest of the body.

Key Terms
central nervous system	cerebellum
peripheral nervous system	brainstem
brain	somatic nervous system
spinal cord	autonomic nervous system
cerebrum	reflex
	concussion

SECTION 3 The Senses

Key Ideas
◆ The senses pick up information about the environment and change that information to nerve impulses.
◆ After light enters the eye, it passes through the lens, which focuses it on the retina. Impulses then travel to the brain.
◆ Sound waves start vibrations in structures in the ear. When the vibrations reach the cochlea, impulses are sent to the brain.
◆ The senses of smell and taste both respond to chemical stimuli.

Key Terms
cornea
pupil
iris
lens
retina
nearsightedness
farsightedness
cochlea
semicircular canals

SECTION 4 Alcohol and Other Drugs

INTEGRATING HEALTH

Key Ideas
◆ Abused drugs act on the nervous system. Depressants slow down the central nervous system. Stimulants speed up body processes. Marijuana, alcohol, amphetamines, and anabolic steroids are commonly abused drugs.
◆ The long-term abuse of alcohol can damage the liver and brain and lead to alcoholism.

Key Terms
drug	withdrawal	anabolic steroid
drug abuse	depressant	alcoholism
tolerance	stimulant	

USING THE INTERNET ACTIVITY
www.science-explorer.phschool.com

Program Resources
◆ **Teaching Resources** Chapter 7 Project Scoring Rubric, p. 176; Chapter 7 Performance Assessment Teacher Notes, p. 277; Chapter 7 Performance Assessment Student Worksheet, p. 279; Chapter 7 Test, pp. 280–283

Reviewing Content:
Multiple Choice
1. a **2.** b **3.** d **4.** d **5.** c

True or False
6. true **7.** true **8.** farsightedness
9. stirrup **10.** true

Checking Concepts

11. The axon carries the nerve impulse away from the cell body. The dendrites carry the nerve impulse to the cell body.
12. The autonomic nervous system controls involuntary actions.
13. When you ride a bicycle, the motor neuron impulses that tell your feet to peddle begin in the cerebrum. The cerebellum gives you the muscular coordination and a sense of balance that keep you from falling off the bicycle.
14. To protect your central nervous system, you should wear a helmet when bicycling, skating, or doing other activities where there is a risk of bumping your head. Wear a seatbelt in a motor vehicle. When swimming, make sure that the water is deep enough before diving into it.
15. For nearsightedness, the glasses bend the light rays away from each other so they are spread apart when they reach the lens of the eye. Then the lens of the eye can correctly focus the rays. For farsightedness, the glasses bend the light rays toward each other so they are closer together when they reach the lens of the eye.
16. Eardrum, hammer, anvil, stirrup, thin membrane, fluid in the cochlea
17. Anabolic steroids may increase strength and muscle size but they also cause mood changes, including violence.
18. Answers will vary. The plan should use the aliens' lack of a sense of touch to reveal who is an alien or to combat the aliens in some way.

Thinking Visually

19. a. Nerve cells **b.** Sensory neurons **c.** Motor neurons **d.** Other neurons **e.** Muscles

Applying Skills

20. Students' graphs should show a straight line pointing down and to the right.

Reviewing Content

 For more review of key concepts, see the Interactive Student Tutorial CD-ROM.

Multiple Choice
Choose the letter of the best answer.

1. A change or signal in the environment that makes the nervous system react is called a
  a. stimulus.   **b.** response.
  c. receptor.   **d.** synapse.
2. The structures that carry messages toward a neuron's cell body are
  a. axons.
  b. dendrites.
  c. nerves.
  d. impulses.
3. Which structure links the brain and the peripheral nervous system?
  a. the cerebrum
  b. the cerebellum
  c. the cochlea
  d. the spinal cord
4. Which structure adjusts the size of the pupil?
  a. the cornea
  b. the retina
  c. the lens
  d. the iris
5. Physical dependence on a drug is called
  a. withdrawal.
  b. response.
  c. addiction.
  d. tolerance.

True or False
If the statement is true, write true. If it is false, change the underlined word or words to make the statement true.

6. A nerve message is also called a <u>nerve impulse.</u>
7. The <u>brainstem</u> is the part of the brain that controls involuntary actions.
8. In <u>nearsightedness</u>, a person cannot see nearby objects clearly.
9. The hammer, anvil, and <u>wrench</u> are the three bones in the middle ear.
10. Alcohol is a <u>depressant.</u>

Checking Concepts

11. Compare the functions of axons and dendrites.
12. What is the function of the autonomic nervous system?
13. How do the cerebrum and cerebellum work together when you ride a bicycle?
14. What are some steps you can take to protect your central nervous system from injury?
15. Describe how lenses in eyeglasses correct nearsightedness and farsightedness.
16. List all the structures in your ear that must vibrate before you hear a sound. List them in the order in which they vibrate.
17. What are the effects of anabolic steroids on the body?
18. Writing to Learn Imagine that Earth has been invaded by space aliens who are exactly like humans except for the fact that they have no sense of touch. These aliens plan to take over Earth. Write a plan for fighting the aliens that makes use of the fact that they lack a sense of touch.

Thinking Visually

19. Concept Map Complete the following concept map about nerve cells and their functions. (For more on concept maps, see the Skills Handbook.)

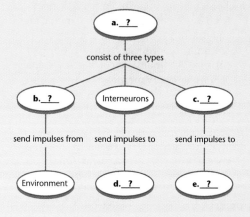

---

21. Manipulated variable—the distance from the eye chart; responding variable—the percentage of letters identified correctly
22. A farsighted person would probably not score well when they stood close to the chart.

Thinking Critically

23. The stroke occurred in the left side of the brain; the left side of the brain has control over the right side of the body.
24. This process is an example of a reflex. It protects the man by making him jerk his foot automatically up, before his foot pushes down further and causes any more damage or pain. The reflex action quickly prevents the man from doing any more harm to himself.
25. Answers will vary. Students should give simple but clear reasons such as not wanting to risk addiction, not wanting to get in trouble, and being afraid of the negative side effects of drugs.

Applying Skills

A person with normal vision stood at different distances from an eye chart and tried to identify the letters on the chart. The table gives the results. Use the table to answer Questions 20–22.

Distance from Eye Chart	Percent of Letters Identified Correctly
2 meters	100
4 meters	92
6 meters	80
8 meters	71
10 meters	60

20. **Graphing** Make a line graph of the data. Plot the distance from the chart on the horizontal axis. On the vertical axis, plot the percent of letters identified correctly.
21. **Controlling Variables** What was the manipulated variable in this experiment? What was the responding variable?
22. **Predicting** How would you expect the results to differ for a farsighted person? Explain.

Thinking Critically

23. **Relating Cause and Effect** When a person has a stroke, blood flow to part of the brain is reduced, and severe brain damage can result. Suppose that after a stroke, a woman is unable to move her right arm and right leg. In which side of her brain did the stroke occur? Explain.
24. **Applying Concepts** As a man walks barefoot along a beach, he steps on a sharp shell. His foot automatically jerks upward, even before he feels pain. What process is this an example of? How does it help protect the man?
25. **Making Judgments** If someone tried to convince you to take drugs, what arguments would you use as a way of refusing? Why do you think these arguments would be effective?

Performance Assessment

Wrap Up

Present Your Project Your report should include an explanation of how you did your research, what you were trying to find out, and how your results compared with your expected results. Also include information on how the nervous system was involved in your illusions. If you can, try to explain why the illusions work.

Reflect and Record In your journal, summarize what you learned from doing this project. Did the project go as you expected, or were you surprised by some results? If you had a chance to continue your investigations, what would you do next? Why?

Getting Involved

In Your School Find out what programs exist in your school to discourage students from abusing alcohol and drugs. Talk to the school nurse, the guidance counselor, or the principal about these programs. Ask them why they chose each approach. Use what you have learned to write an article about the school's anti-drug abuse program for the school newspaper.

Program Resources

◆ **Inquiry Skills Handbook** Provides teaching and review of all inquiry skills

Performance Assessment

Wrap Up

Present Your Project In addition to their data and explanations, allow students to demonstrate the illusions they studied. Help each presenter to explain the illusions in terms of the brain's influence on incoming sensory impulses or in terms of a general range of perceptions, depending on the experiment. Conclude the project presentation with a discussion of what students learned about the ways in which their nervous system interprets sensory nerve impulses. Ask the students to discuss how senses can deceive and to think about what kinds of eyewitness accounts they would believe after doing these experiments.

Reflect and Record Ask students to write specifically about what they have learned by doing their experiments. If they would do their experiments differently, have students write descriptions of their revised procedures.

Getting Involved

In Your School Encourage students to prepare a list of questions for the school staff, and help them set up appointments for interviews, if needed. You might want to ask students to compare the school's programs with their responses to Question 25 of Thinking Critically.

The Endocrine System & Reproduction

Sections	Time	Student Edition Activities	Other Activities
CHAPTER PROJECT 8 **A Precious Bundle** p. 225	Ongoing (2–3 weeks)	Check Your Progress, pp. 230, 236, 249 Wrap Up, p. 253	**TE** Chapter 8 Project Notes, pp. 224–225
1 The Endocrine System pp. 226–230 ◆ Identify the function of the endocrine system. ◆ Describe how negative feedback controls hormone levels. ◆ List and describe the glands of the endocrine system.	$2\frac{1}{2}$ periods/ 1–2 blocks	**Discover** What's the Signal?, p. 226	**TE** Integrating Chemistry, p. 227 **TE** Including All Students, p. 229
2 The Male and Female Reproductive Systems pp. 231–236 ◆ List the organs of the male and female reproductive systems and identify their function. ◆ Describe the events that occur during the menstrual cycle.	3 periods/ $1\frac{1}{2}$ blocks	**Discover** What's the Big Difference?, p. 231 **Sharpen Your Skills** Graphing, p. 235	
3 Pregnancy, Birth, and Childhood pp. 237–243 ◆ List the stages of human development that occur before birth. ◆ Describe what happens during childbirth. ◆ Describe the physical changes that occur during infancy and childhood.	$3\frac{1}{2}$ periods/ 1–2 blocks	**Discover** How Many Ways Does a Child Grow?, p. 237 **Try This** Way to Grow!, p. 239 **Sharpen Your Skills** Designing Experiments, p. 241	**TE** Including All Students, p. 240
4 INTEGRATING HEALTH **Adolescence–A Time of Change** pp. 244–250 ◆ Compare adolescence and puberty. ◆ Describe the mental and social changes associated with adolescence.	$3\frac{1}{2}$ periods/ 1–2 blocks	**Discover** How Do Ads Portray Teenagers?, p. 244 **Skills Lab: Interpreting Data** Growing Up, p. 250	**TE** Real-Life Learning, p. 246 **TE** Real-Life Learning, p. 248
Study Guide/Chapter Review pp. 251–253	1 period/ $\frac{1}{2}$ block		**ISAB** Provides teaching and review of all inquiry skills

 For Standard or Block Schedule The Resource Pro® CD-ROM gives you maximum flexibility for planning your instruction for any type of schedule. Resource Pro® contains Planning Express®, an advanced scheduling program, as well as the entire contents of the Teaching Resources and the Computer Test Bank.

CHAPTER PLANNING GUIDE

Program Resources	Assessment Strategies	Media and Technology
TR Chapter 8 Project Teacher Notes, pp. 198–199 **TR** Chapter 8 Project Overview and Worksheets, pp. 200–203 **TR** Chapter 8 Project Scoring Rubric, p. 204	**SE** Performance Assessment: Chapter 8 Project Wrap Up, p. 253 **TE** Check Your Progress, pp. 230, 236, 249 **TE** Performance Assessment: Chapter 8 Project Wrap Up, p. 253 **TR** Chapter 8 Project Scoring Rubric, p. 204	
TR 8-1 Lesson Plan, p. 205 **TR** 8-1 Section Summary, p. 206 **TR** 8-1 Review and Reinforce, p. 207 **TR** 8-1 Enrich, p. 208 **SES** Book L, *Chemical Interactions,* Chapter 1	**SE** Section 1 Review, p. 230 **TE** Ongoing Assessment, pp. 227, 229 **TE** Performance Assessment, p. 230 **TR** 8-1 Review and Reinforce, p. 207	🎧 Audiotapes: English-Spanish Summary 8-1 📽 Transparency 18, "Exploring the Endocrine System" 💿 Interactive Student Tutorial CD-ROM, D-8
TR 8-2 Lesson Plan, p. 209 **TR** 8-2 Section Summary, p. 210 **TR** 8-2 Review and Reinforce, p. 211 **TR** 8-2 Enrich, p. 212	**SE** Section 2 Review, p. 236 **TE** Ongoing Assessment, pp. 233, 235 **TE** Performance Assessment, p. 236 **TR** 8-2 Review and Reinforce, p. 211	🎧 Audiotapes: English-Spanish Summary 8-2 📽 Transparency 19, "The Male Reproductive System" 📽 Transparency 20, "The Female Reproductive System" 💿 Interactive Student Tutorial CD-ROM, D-8
TR 8-3 Lesson Plan, p. 213 **TR** 8-3 Section Summary, p. 214 **TR** 8-3 Review and Reinforce, p. 215 **TR** 8-3 Enrich, p. 216	**SE** Section 3 Review, p. 243 **TE** Ongoing Assessment, pp. 237, 239, 241 **TE** Performance Assessment, p. 243 **TR** 8-3 Review and Reinforce, p. 215	🎧 Audiotapes: English-Spanish Summary 8-3 💿 Interactive Student Tutorial CD-ROM, D-8
TR 8-4 Lesson Plan, p. 217 **TR** 8-4 Section Summary, p. 218 **TR** 8-4 Review and Reinforce, p. 219 **TR** 8-4 Enrich, p. 220 **TR** Chapter 8 Skills Lab, pp. 221–223	**SE** Section 4 Review, p. 249 **SE** Analyze and Conclude, p. 250 **TE** Ongoing Assessment, pp. 245, 247 **TE** Performance Assessment, p. 249 **TR** 8-4 Review and Reinforce, p. 220	💿 Exploring Physical Science Videodisc, Unit 4 Side 1, "Development is a Lifelong Process" 🎧 Audiotapes: English-Spanish Summary 8-4 💿 Interactive Student Tutorial CD-ROM, D-8
TR Chapter 8 Performance Assessment, pp. 285–287 **TR** Chapter 8 Test, pp. 288–291	**SE** Chapter Review, pp. 251–253 **TR** Chapter 8 Performance Assessment, pp. 285–287 **TR** Chapter 8 Test, pp. 288–291 **CTB** Test D-8	💾 Computer Test Bank, Test D-8 💿 Interactive Student Tutorial CD-ROM, D-8 🌐 Science Explorer Internet Site

Key: **SE** Student Edition   **TE** Teacher's Edition   **TR** Teaching Resources
     CTB Computer Test Bank   **SES** Science Explorer Series Text   **ISLM** Integrated Science Laboratory Manual
     ISAB Inquiry Skills Activity Book   **PTA** Product Testing Activities by *Consumer Reports*   **IES** Interdisciplinary Explorations Series

Meeting the National Science Education Standards and AAAS Benchmarks

National Science Education Standards	Benchmarks for Science Literacy	Unifying Themes
Science as Inquiry (Content Standard A) ◆ **Use mathematics in all aspects of scientific investigation** Students examine data to discover how the proportions of the human body change over time. *(Skills Lab)* **Life Science** (Content Standard C) ◆ **Reproduction and heredity** The female body produces eggs and the male body produces sperm. The egg and sperm unite to form a new individual. *(Section 2)* ◆ **Regulation and behavior** The endocrine system controls many of the body's daily activities as well as regulating developmental change. *(Section 1)* During the menstrual cycle, the body prepares itself to reproduce by releasing an egg and by thickening the uterine wall. *(Section 2)*	**2C The Nature of Mathematics** Students learn about how the levels of hormone change during the menstrual cycle. *(Section 2)* Students learn about the mass of the development of a baby during pregnancy. *(Section 3)* **6B Human Development** Fertilization occurs when male and female sex cells are united. Following fertilization, cells divide to produce an embryo. During the first three months of pregnancy, organs begin to form; during the second three months, all organs and body features develop; during the last three months, organs and features mature. The developing embryo is at risk to the mother's use of drugs and alcohol during pregnancy. Various body changes occur as adults age. *(Sections 1, 2, 3)*	◆ **Patterns of Change** The fertilized egg undergoes change and develops into an embryo. All stages of development follow the same pattern during the course of nine months. After birth, change occurs during the lifetime of the individual. *(Sections 3, 4)* ◆ **Stability** Hormones produced by the human endocrine system help the body maintain stability. Hormones are produced throughout the lifetime of the male and female and play an important role in the development of sexual characteristics. *(Sections 1, 2,)* ◆ **Unity and Diversity** The male and female reproductive systems differ in structure, but the primary function is to produce new individuals. *(Sections 1, 2)* ◆ **Systems and Interactions** The male and female reproductive systems produce sex cells needed for reproduction and hormones that regulate body activities. The interaction of the male and female reproductive systems can produce a new human being. *(Sections 1, 2)*

Media and Technology

Exploring Life Science Videodisc
◆ **Section 4** "Development is a Lifelong Process" gives a high-speed peek at human development from fertilization through the senior years.

Interactive Student Tutorial CD-ROM
◆ **Chapter Review** Interactive questions help students to self-assess their mastery of key chapter concepts.

Student Edition Connection Strategies

◆ **Section 1** Integrating Chemistry, p. 227

◆ **Section 3** Integrating Health, p. 238

◆ **Section 4** Integrating Health, p. 244
   Social Studies Connection, p. 247

www.science-explorer.phschool.com

Visit the Science Explorer Internet site to find an up-to-date activity for Chapter 8 of *Human Biology and Health*.

ACTIVITY	Time (minutes)	Materials *Quantities for one work group*	Skills
Section 1			
Discover, p. 226	15	**Consumable** No special materials are required.	Inferring
Section 2			
Discover, p. 231	20	**Nonconsumable** slides of human egg and sperm cells, microscope	Observing
Sharpen Your Skills, p. 235	20	**Consumable** graph paper **Nonconsumable** ruler	Graphing
Section 3			
Discover, p. 237	15	**Consumable** No special materials are required.	Observing
Try This, p. 239	25	**Nonconsumable** balance, objects of various masses	Making Models
Sharpen Your Skills, p. 241	40	**Consumable** No special materials are required.	Designing Experiments
Section 4			
Discover, p. 244	15	**Nonconsumable** magazine or newspaper ads directed at teenagers	Drawing Conclusions
Skills Lab, p. 250	30	**Consumable** No special materials are required.	Interpreting Data

A list of all materials required for the Student Edition activities can be found on pages T14–T15. You can order Materials Kits by calling 1-800-828-7777 or by accessing the Science Explorer Internet site at **www.science-explorer.phschool.com.**

A Precious Bundle

Caring for an infant is a full-time responsibility. Students may not realize how much having a small child would disrupt their everyday lives until they attempt to model the day-to-day activities of a parent.

Purpose In this project, students will model parenting behavior and consider how the presence of a baby could change their lives.

Skills Focus After completing the Chapter 8 project, students will be able to
♦ observe behavior and use their observations to develop a list of tasks involved in caring for an infant;
♦ model behavior and solve problems in terms of the model;
♦ make generalizations based on their feelings and reactions;
♦ communicate their responses.

Project Time Line The project should take at least a week. The first day can be used to explain the project, hand out the materials, and discuss the responsibilities and expectations of the project. The last day could be devoted to a discussion of students' experiences and journal entries. Three days are devoted to the actual modeling phase of the experiment. Provide students with a day or two to reflect on their journal entries and complete the Chapter 8 Project Worksheets. Before beginning the project, see Chapter 8 Project Teacher Notes on pages 198–199 in Teaching Resources for more details on carrying out the project. Also distribute the Students' Chapter 8 Project Overview and Worksheets and Scoring Rubric on pages 200–204 in Teaching Resources.

Possible Materials Provide each student with a bag of flour, and allow him or her to cover the bags with plastic bags. Students may want to wrap their bags in blankets or provide other accessories. Encourage students to suggest and use other materials as well.
♦ 5-lb bags of flour or suitable substitutes
♦ plastic bags to cover flour bags
♦ twist ties
♦ writing materials

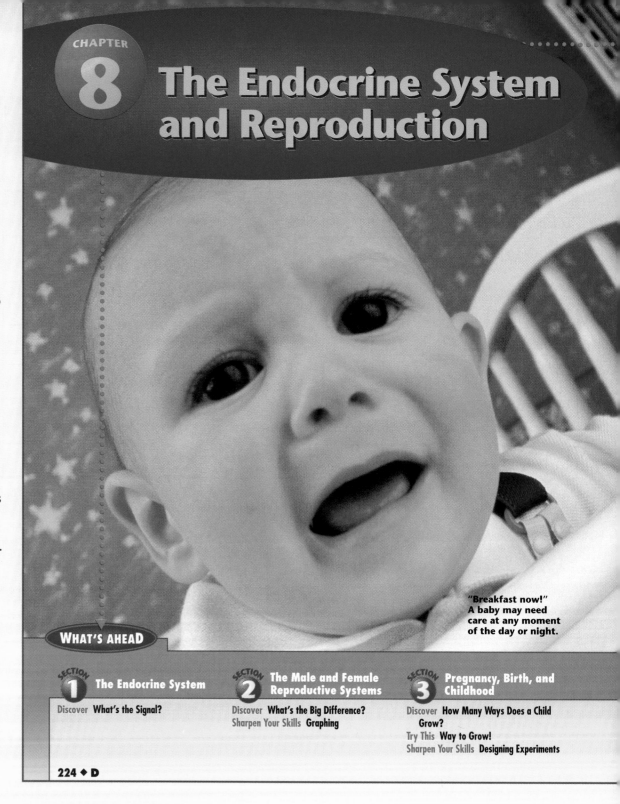

CHAPTER

8 The Endocrine System and Reproduction

"Breakfast now!" A baby may need care at any moment of the day or night.

WHAT'S AHEAD

SECTION 1 The Endocrine System
Discover What's the Signal?

SECTION 2 The Male and Female Reproductive Systems
Discover What's the Big Difference?
Sharpen Your Skills Graphing

SECTION 3 Pregnancy, Birth, and Childhood
Discover How Many Ways Does a Child Grow?
Try This Way to Grow!
Sharpen Your Skills Designing Experiments

224 ◆ D

Launching the Project Babies often communicate by crying. To introduce the project and to stimulate student interest, ask: "Why do babies cry?" (*Samples: Because they're hungry, or when they feel pain.*)

Allow time for students to read the description of the project in their text and the Chapter Project Overview on pages 200–201 in Teaching Resources. Then encourage discussions on infant care, materials that could be used, and any initial questions students may have. Pass out copies of the Chapter 8 Project Worksheets on pages 202–203 in Teaching Resources for students to review.

Have students brainstorm a list of daily childcare activities as a class or in small groups. Remind students to include considerations for preparation of baby food, changing diapers, bathing, dressing, and medical check-ups. Students should also include childcare activities that meet infants' need to learn, to feel loved, to observe and interact with their surroundings, and to gain confidence that needs will be met.

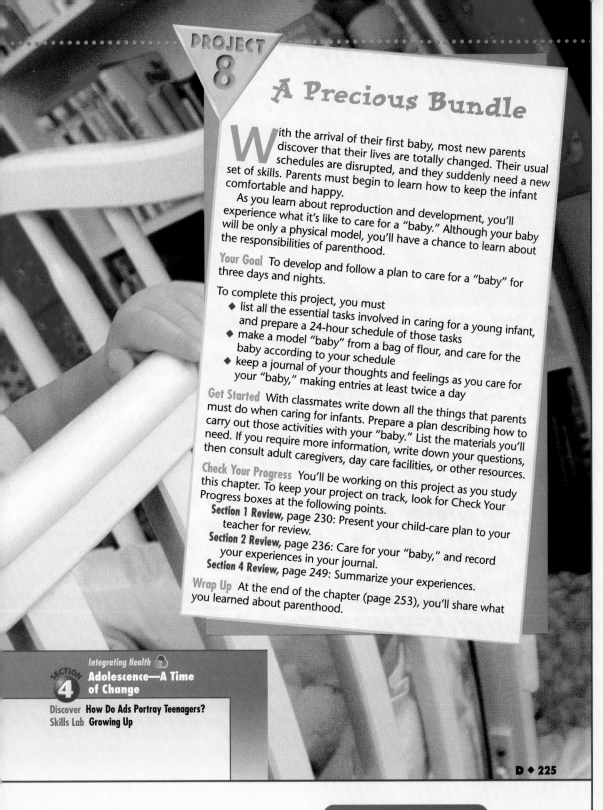

A Precious Bundle

With the arrival of their first baby, most new parents discover that their lives are totally changed. Their usual schedules are disrupted, and they suddenly need a new set of skills. Parents must begin to learn how to keep the infant comfortable and happy.

As you learn about reproduction and development, you'll experience what it's like to care for a "baby." Although your baby will be only a physical model, you'll have a chance to learn about the responsibilities of parenthood.

Your Goal To develop and follow a plan to care for a "baby" for three days and nights.

To complete this project, you must
- list all the essential tasks involved in caring for a young infant, and prepare a 24-hour schedule of those tasks
- make a model "baby" from a bag of flour, and care for the baby according to your schedule
- keep a journal of your thoughts and feelings as you care for your "baby," making entries at least twice a day

Get Started With classmates write down all the things that parents must do when caring for infants. Prepare a plan describing how to carry out those activities with your "baby." List the materials you'll need. If you require more information, write down your questions, then consult adult caregivers, day care facilities, or other resources.

Check Your Progress You'll be working on this project as you study this chapter. To keep your project on track, look for Check Your Progress boxes at the following points.

Section 1 Review, page 230: Present your child-care plan to your teacher for review.
Section 2 Review, page 236: Care for your "baby," and record your experiences in your journal.
Section 4 Review, page 249: Summarize your experiences.

Wrap Up At the end of the chapter (page 253), you'll share what you learned about parenthood.

SECTION
4
Integrating Health
Adolescence—A Time of Change

Discover How Do Ads Portray Teenagers?
Skills Lab Growing Up

After completing a reasonable list of daily activities, have the students work with each other to translate real child care into facsimiles that use the bag of flour as a surrogate. Tell students that this process of modeling an event is a scientific way of testing a hypothesis or discovering behaviors. Emphasize that the most accurate and valuable information will come from following the routines as accurately as possible.

Performance Assessment

The Chapter 8 Project Scoring Rubric on page 204 of Teaching Resources will help you evaluate how well students complete the Chapter 8 Project. Students will be assessed on
- how well they plan their daily tasks and prepare themselves to take care of the model baby;
- how thoroughly they complete the task chart;
- their willingness to take the role seriously, indicated by the completeness of writing and discussion responses that show evidence of child care practices and issues;
- their communication in class discussions and written work.

By sharing the Chapter 8 Scoring Rubric with students at the beginning of the project, you will make it clear to them what they are expected to do.

Program Resources

- **Teaching Resources** Chapter 8 Project Teacher's Notes, pp. 198–199; Chapter 8 Project Overview and Worksheets, pp. 200–203; Chapter 8 Project Scoring Rubric, p. 204

SECTION ① The Endocrine System

Objectives

After completing the lesson, students will be able to
◆ identify the organs of the endocrine system and their functions;
◆ describe how negative feedback controls hormone levels.

Key Terms endocrine gland, hormone, target cell, hypothalamus, pituitary gland, negative feedback

1 Engage/Explore

Activating Prior Knowledge

Tell students you are going to give them a "pop" quiz on what they learned in a previous chapter. Ask: **What is the name for the reaction when you feel panic or fear?** *(Students should remember the "fight or flight" response from Chapter 1.)* Inform students the same body system that regulates the "fight or flight" response controls their bodies' daily activities and many long-term changes.

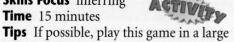
DISCOVER

Skills Focus inferring
Time 15 minutes
Tips If possible, play this game in a large open area such as in a gym or outdoors.
Expected Outcome Players will be eliminated from the game when they do not immediately respond to the "Freeze!" signal.
Think It Over Winning the game depends on responding quickly to the "Freeze!" signal; one mistake or delayed response will put a player out of the game. The body uses nerve impulses as signals. Tell students they will learn about another type of signal in this chapter.

SECTION ① The Endocrine System

SECTION ① The Endocrine System

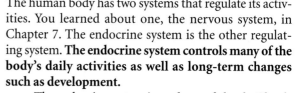
DISCOVER ....ACTIVITY....

What's the Signal?

1. Stand up and move around the room until your teacher says "Freeze!" Then stop moving immediately. Stay perfectly still until your teacher says "Start!" Then begin moving again.

2. Anyone who moves between the "Freeze!" command and the "Start!" command has to leave the game.

3. Play until only one person is left in the game. That person is the winner.

Think It Over
Inferring Why is it important for players in this game to respond to signals? What types of signals does the human body use?

GUIDE FOR READING

◆ What is the function of the endocrine system?
◆ How does negative feedback control hormone levels?

Reading Tip Before you read, preview *Exploring the Endocrine System* on pages 228–229. List the terms in the diagram that are new to you. Look for their meanings as you read.

226 ◆ D

You're playing softball on a hot afternoon. Without warning, thick, dark clouds form. Suddenly, there's a flash of lightning. Thunder cracks overhead. Someone screams, you jump, and everyone runs for cover. Your heart is pounding, your palms are sweaty, and your muscles are tight.

Your body's reaction to the sudden storm was caused mainly by your body's endocrine system. In this section, you will learn about the role of the endocrine system in many body processes—from the quick response to a thunder clap, to the slower body changes that turn a child into an adult.

The Role of the Endocrine System

The human body has two systems that regulate its activities. You learned about one, the nervous system, in Chapter 7. The endocrine system is the other regulating system. **The endocrine system controls many of the body's daily activities as well as long-term changes such as development.**

The endocrine system is made up of glands. Glands are organs that produce chemicals. You already know about some glands, such as those that produce saliva or sweat. Those glands release their chemicals into tiny tubes. The tubes deliver the chemicals to a specific location within the body or to the skin's surface.

The endocrine system does not have delivery tubes. **Endocrine glands** (EN duh krin) produce and release their chemical products directly into the bloodstream. The blood then carries those chemicals throughout the body.

READING STRATEGIES

Reading Tip Before students preview *Exploring the Endocrine System*, provide them with note cards on which to write unfamiliar terms from the diagram, one term per card. Have students write definitions for the terms on the back of the cards as they read. Then direct student pairs to quiz each other on the terms, using the cards as flashcards.

Study and Comprehension Have students write brief summaries of the information under each heading. They may choose to construct a diagram or map to organize the information visually. Remind students to include only main ideas and key details in their summaries. Students can then use the summaries as study guides for the section.

Hormones

The chemical product of an endocrine gland is called a **hormone.** Hormones turn on, turn off, speed up, or slow down the activities of different organs and tissues. You can think of a hormone as a chemical messenger. Because hormones are carried by blood, they can regulate activities in tissues and organs far from the glands that produced them.

Hormone Production What causes the release of hormones? In situations such as a sudden storm, nerve impulses from the senses travel to the brain. There, information, such as the sound of thunder, is interpreted. The brain then sends a nerve impulse to a specific endocrine gland. That gland, in turn, releases the hormone adrenaline into the bloodstream. As you read in Chapter 1, adrenaline causes your heart rate to increase, makes you breathe faster and deeper, and releases sugars that power your muscles.

In contrast to the body's response to a nerve impulse, hormones cause a slower, but longer-lasting, response. For example, the brain sends a quick signal to an endocrine gland to release adrenaline into the bloodstream. When the adrenaline reaches the heart, it makes the heart beat more rapidly. The heart continues to race until the amount of adrenaline in the blood drops to a normal level.

Target Cells When a hormone enters the bloodstream, why **INTEGRATING CHEMISTRY** does it affect some organs but not others? The answer lies in its chemical structure. A hormone interacts only with certain **target cells,** cells that recognize the hormone's chemical structure. A hormone and its target cell fit together the way a key fits into a lock. Hormones not meant for a particular organ will travel through the bloodstream until they find the "lock" that they fit.

Figure 1 The endocrine system controls the body's response to an exciting situation (left) as well as the changes that occur as a child grows (right).
Applying Concepts What substances produced by endocrine glands control these body processes?

Answers to Self-Assessment

Caption Question
Figure 1 Hormones

2 Facilitate

The Role of the Endocrine System

Using the Visuals: Figure 1

Point out the images in Figure 1 and ask: **What is the same about these two photos?** *(Both show body processes regulated by the endocrine system.)* **How are the body processes different?** *(Excitement is a short-term response to a situation, while growth is a long-term process.)* **learning modality: verbal**

Hormones

Addressing Naive Conceptions

Students may believe that all hormones first become active during puberty. Explain that the human body relies on many different types of hormones throughout life. Some hormones regulate blood levels of substances, such as calcium, sugar, and salt. Tell students that insulin, which they learned about in Chapter 6, is a hormone. **learning modality: verbal**

 **Integrating Chemistry**

Materials *construction paper, scissors* **ACTIVITY**

To promote understanding of the "key and lock" concept of hormones and target cells, have student pairs construct a model of a hormone and target cell that fit together. Invite students to exchange the hormone models only and then ask why hormones and target cells no longer fit. *(The hormone "key" no longer fits into the target cell "lock" because each hormone/target unit has a unique design.)* **limited English proficiency**

Ongoing Assessment

Writing Ask students to describe the relationship between the endocrine system and hormones.

The Hypothalamus

Building Inquiry Skills: Inferring

Ask students: **How does the hypothalamus link the nervous system and the endocrine system?** (*The hypothalamus releases hormones and also sends nerve messages.*) Explain that the hypothalamus uses both nerve messages and hormones to control endocrine glands such as the pituitary. Ask: **Do the endocrine glands only respond to hormones? Explain.** (*No, the endocrine glands also respond to nerve messages.*) **learning modality: verbal**

EXPLORING
the Endocrine System

As students read the captions, ask: **Do the same glands control the same processes in both males and females?** (*No*) Then ask: **Which endocrine glands are found only in females?** (*ovaries*) **Which are only found in males?** (*testes*) Finally, have students make a table with three columns. In the first, list the names of all of the endocrine glands. In the second column, state the function of that gland in females, and in the third column, state the function of that gland in males. (*All will be the same except for the ovaries and testes.*)

Extend Have students predict the symptoms of a malfunction in various endocrine glands. For example, ask: **What do you think would happen to a person whose thymus was not functioning properly?** (*The immune system would be impaired.*) Encourage interested students to use reference books or an electronic resource in the school library to find out whether their predictions are correct. **learning modality: logical/mathematical**

Each endocrine gland releases different hormones and thus controls different processes. *Exploring the Endocrine System* shows the locations of the endocrine glands and describes some activities they control.

The Hypothalamus

The nervous system and the endocrine system work together. The **hypothalamus** (hy poh THAL uh mus), a tiny part of the brain near the middle of your head, is the link between the two systems. Nerve messages controlling sleep, hunger, and other conditions come from the hypothalamus. The hypothalamus also produces hormones that control other endocrine glands and organs. Through its nerve impulses and hormones, the hypothalamus plays a major role in maintaining homeostasis.

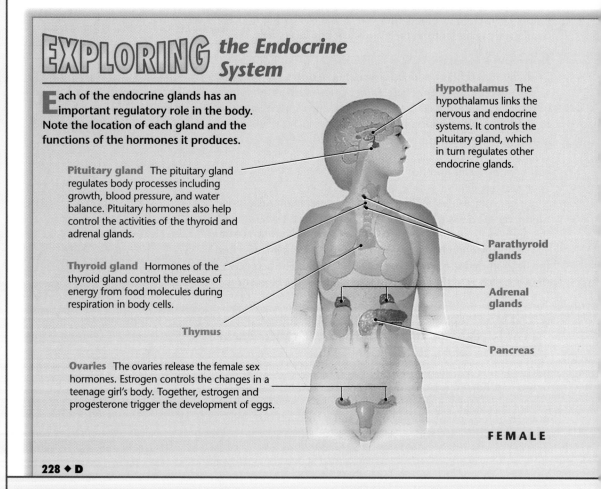

EXPLORING the Endocrine System

Each of the endocrine glands has an important regulatory role in the body. Note the location of each gland and the functions of the hormones it produces.

Pituitary gland The pituitary gland regulates body processes including growth, blood pressure, and water balance. Pituitary hormones also help control the activities of the thyroid and adrenal glands.

Thyroid gland Hormones of the thyroid gland control the release of energy from food molecules during respiration in body cells.

Thymus

Ovaries The ovaries release the female sex hormones. Estrogen controls the changes in a teenage girl's body. Together, estrogen and progesterone trigger the development of eggs.

Hypothalamus The hypothalamus links the nervous and endocrine systems. It controls the pituitary gland, which in turn regulates other endocrine glands.

Parathyroid glands

Adrenal glands

Pancreas

FEMALE

Background

Facts and Figures Human Growth Hormone (HGH) is produced in the pituitary gland and is secreted throughout a person's entire life. HGH is absolutely necessary for growth in children who are lacking HGH and do not reach normal heights. Boys of 18 with HGH deficiency may only be 135 cm tall. In contrast, the average height of normal 18-year-old boys is 170 cm.

Scientists can now produce synthetic HGH with genetic engineering techniques. Synthetic HGH has the same effect as natural HGH, so it can be used to treat children with HGH deficiency. When synthetic HGH is injected, children begin to metabolize fat and grow very quickly. The earlier treatment is started, the closer to a normal height a child will grow.

The Pituitary Gland

Just below the hypothalamus is an endocrine gland about the size of a pea. The **pituitary gland** (pih TOO ih tehr ee) communicates with the hypothalamus to control many body activities. In response to nerve impulses or hormone signals from the hypothalamus, the pituitary gland releases its hormones. Some of those hormones act as an "on" switch for other endocrine glands. For example, one pituitary hormone signals the thyroid gland to produce hormones. Other pituitary hormones control body activities directly. Growth hormone regulates growth from infancy to adulthood. Another pituitary hormone directs the kidneys to regulate the amount of water in the blood.

☑ *Checkpoint* *What causes the pituitary gland to release hormones?*

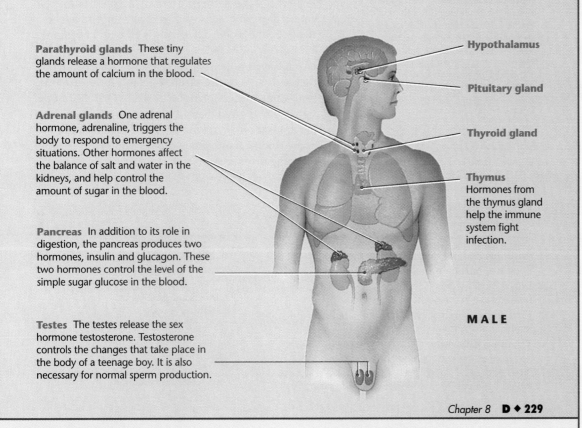

Parathyroid glands These tiny glands release a hormone that regulates the amount of calcium in the blood.

Adrenal glands One adrenal hormone, adrenaline, triggers the body to respond to emergency situations. Other hormones affect the balance of salt and water in the kidneys, and help control the amount of sugar in the blood.

Pancreas In addition to its role in digestion, the pancreas produces two hormones, insulin and glucagon. These two hormones control the level of the simple sugar glucose in the blood.

Testes The testes release the sex hormone testosterone. Testosterone controls the changes that take place in the body of a teenage boy. It is also necessary for normal sperm production.

Hypothalamus

Pituitary gland

Thyroid gland

Thymus Hormones from the thymus gland help the immune system fight infection.

MALE

Chapter 8 **D ◆ 229**

Program Resources

 Science Explorer Series *Chemical Interactions*, Chapter 1

Media and Technology

Transparencies "Exploring the Endocrine System," Transparency 18

Answers to Self-Assessment

☑ *Checkpoint*
The pituitary gland responds to nerve impulses or hormone signals from the hypothalamus.

The Pituitary Gland

Including All Students

To help students pronounce the scientific **ACTIVITY** terms in this section and to identify the endocrine glands and their functions, have students work in small groups. Each group can make note cards with the name of an endocrine gland on one side and its function on the other. Prepare several large outlines of the human body. Have each group use their note cards to label an outline with the name of each gland. Students can pronounce the name of the gland aloud as they locate it on the outline. Then have groups write captions for the glands using the function side of their note cards. **cooperative learning**

Building Inquiry Skills: Organizing Information

Have students locate the pituitary glands in the figures shown in the Exploring. On the board, write *Hypothalamus*. Beneath that, write *Pituitary*, and *Thyroid* and *Adrenal* below. Ask students: **How can this list help you remember both the locations and the functions of these glands?** *(The glands are placed in the body in the same order as the list, from top to bottom. Also, the hypothalamus controls the pituitary, and the pituitary controls the thyroid and adrenal glands.)* **learning modality: visual**

Ongoing Assessment

Writing Have students list the glands in the endocrine system and describe one function of each gland. Students can save their lists in their portfolios.

Negative Feedback

Using the Visuals: Figure 2

Ask students: **What sequence of events makes the thyroid stop producing thyroxine?** *(The hypothalamus signals the pituitary to stop producing TSH, and the thyroid stops producing thyroxine.)* Ask students to explain why this is called "negative" feedback. *(Because it results in a reduction in the activity of the thyroid and pituitary.)* Make sure students understand that "negative feedback" in this context does not refer to criticism.
learning modality: verbal

3 Assess

Section 1 Review Answers

1. Controls many of the body's daily activities as well as long-term changes; endocrine glands
2. When the amount of a hormone in the blood reaches the right level, the endocrine system signals the gland to stop producing that hormone.
3. The pituitary gland produces hormones in response to nerve impulses or hormones sent out by the hypothalamus.
4. Sample: The hypothalamus. It controls the function of the pituitary gland, which regulates many other glands of the endocrine system.

Check Your Progress

As you review students' schedules, make sure each student has included all essential child care tasks. Encourage students to be realistic. Remind them that babies need to eat several times a day, and that real babies will often disrupt scheduled events by crying or being ill. Make sure students arrange for alternative childcare when they need to meet other obligations.

Performance Assessment

Writing Have students write short paragraphs describing how the endocrine system helps the body maintain homeostasis.

Hypothalamus senses cells need more energy

Thyroid stops producing thyroxine

Pituitary releases TSH

STOP

START

Pituitary stops producing TSH

Thyroid produces thyroxine

Hypothalamus senses cells have enough energy

Figure 2 The release of the hormone thyroxine is controlled through negative feedback. When enough thyroxine is present, the system signals the thyroid gland to stop releasing the hormone. *Predicting What happens when the amount of thyroxine becomes too low?*

Section 1 Review

1. What role does the endocrine system play in the body? What are the organs of the endocrine system called?
2. Explain how negative feedback helps to maintain homeostasis in the body.
3. How do the hypothalamus and the pituitary gland interact?
4. **Thinking Critically** **Making Judgments** Years ago, one of the endocrine glands was called the "master gland." Which part of the endocrine system would you consider the master gland? Explain.

230 ◆ D

Program Resources

◆ **Teaching Resources** 8-1 Review and Reinforce, p. 207; 8-1 Enrich, p. 208

Media and Technology

 Interactive Student Tutorial CD-ROM D-8

Negative Feedback

One way that the endocrine system maintains homeostasis may remind you of the way a heating system works. Suppose you set a thermostat at 20°C. If the temperature falls below 20°, the thermostat signals the furnace to turn on. When the furnace heats the area to the proper temperature, information about the warm conditions "feeds back" to the thermostat. The thermostat then gives the furnace a negative signal that means "no more heat." That signal turns the furnace off.

The type of signal used in a heating system is called **negative feedback** because the system is turned off by the condition it produces. The endocrine system often works in this way. Through negative feedback, when the amount of a particular hormone in the blood reaches a certain level, the endocrine system sends signals that stop the release of that hormone. **Negative feedback is an important way that the body maintains homeostasis.**

You can see an example of negative feedback in Figure 2. Like a thermostat in a cool room, the endocrine system senses when there's not enough thyroxine in the blood. Thyroxine is a thyroid hormone. It controls how much energy is available to cells. When there's not enough energy available, the hypothalamus signals the pituitary gland to release thyroid-stimulating hormone (TSH). That hormone signals the thyroid gland to release thyroxine. When the amount of thyroxine reaches the right level, the endocrine system signals the thyroid gland to stop releasing thyroxine.

Check Your Progress

You should now be ready to turn in your plan for your teacher's review. Your plan should include your daily schedule and a list of the materials you'll need. Be sure to describe the kind of journal you plan to keep. (*Hint:* Discuss with your teacher any problems you foresee in caring for the "baby" for three full days and nights.)

Answers to Self-Assessment

Caption Question

Figure 2 When the amount of thyroxine becomes too low, the endocrine system will signal the thyroid gland to produce more thyroxine. (The hypothalamus signals the pituitary to release TSH. TSH stimulates the thyroid to produce thyroxine.)

SECTION 2 The Male and Female Reproductive Systems

SECTION 2 The Male and Female Reproductive Systems

DISCOVER · ACTIVITY

What's the Big Difference?

1. Your teacher will provide prepared slides of eggs and sperm.

2. Examine each slide under the microscope, first under low power, then under high power. Be sure you view at least one sample of egg and sperm from the same species.

3. Sketch and label each sample.

Think It Over

Observing What differences did you observe between sperm cells and egg cells? What general statement can you make about eggs and sperm?

Many differences between an adult animal and its young are controlled by the endocrine system. In humans, two endocrine glands—the ovaries in girls and the testes in boys—control many of the changes that occur as a child matures. These glands release hormones that cause the body to develop as a person grows older.

Sex Cells

You may find it hard to believe that you began life as a single cell. That single cell was produced by the joining of two other cells, an egg and a sperm. An **egg** is the female sex cell. A **sperm** is the male sex cell.

The joining of a sperm and an egg is called **fertilization.** Fertilization is an important part of **reproduction,** the process by which living things produce new individuals of the same type. When fertilization occurs, a fertilized egg, or **zygote,** is produced. Every one of the trillions of cells in your body is descended from the single cell that formed during fertilization.

GUIDE FOR READING

◆ What are the organs of the male and female reproductive systems?

◆ What events occur during the menstrual cycle?

Reading Tip As you read, create a table comparing the male and female reproductive systems. Include the type of sex cells and primary reproductive organs of each.

Figure 3 This gosling began its life as a single cell. When it is fully grown, it will be made up of millions of cells.

READING STRATEGIES

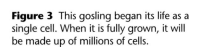

Reading Tip As students read, have them list differences between the male and female reproductive systems in a table such as the one shown.

Characteristic	Male	Female
Sex cell	sperm	egg
Organs	testes	ovaries
Hormones	testosterone	estrogen

Program Resources

◆ **Teaching Resources** 8-2 Lesson Plan, p. 209; 8-2 Section Summary, p. 210

Media and Technology

Audiotapes English-Spanish Summary 8-2

SECTION 2 The Male and Female Reproductive Systems

Objectives

After completing the lesson, students will be able to

◆ list the organs of the male and female reproductive systems and identify their function;

◆ describe the events that occur during the menstrual cycle.

Key Terms egg, sperm, fertilization, reproduction, zygote, chromosome, testis, testosterone, scrotum, semen, penis, ovary, estrogen, oviduct, uterus, vagina, menstrual cycle, ovulation, menstruation

1 Engage/Explore

Activating Prior Knowledge

Organize students in small discussion groups and have them brainstorm lists of things they think they already know about the male and female reproductive systems. Use these lists to address any naive conceptions students may have.

· · · · · · · · DISCOVER · · · · · · ·

Skills Focus observing
Materials *slides of human egg and sperm cells, microscope*
Time 20 minutes
Tips Students may need help focusing the microscope and finding the egg and sperm cells. Encourage them to begin at low power before switching to high power.
Expected Outcome Students should be able to view both types of cells.
Think It Over Sperm cells are much smaller than egg cells, and have long tail-like parts. Eggs are round, usually much larger than sperm from the same species, and do not have tails.

2 Facilitate

Sex Cells

Building Inquiry Skills: Inferring

Point out that both a sperm and an egg are single-celled. Ask: **How many cells does a zygote have?** *(one)* Then ask students to infer how the two sex cells can join to form only one zygote. *(Students should infer that each sex cell contributes only part of a complete zygote cell.)* **learning modality: logical/mathematical**

Addressing Naive Conceptions

Students may think that when a sperm cell joins with an egg cell, the entire sperm enters the egg. Explain that only the nucleus of the sperm enters the egg, and does so through a passageway formed by a membrane on the tip of the sperm's head. Inform students that after the sperm nucleus enters an egg, a membrane forms that prevents the entrance of any more sperm. **learning modality: verbal**

The Male Reproductive System

Real-Life Learning

Tell students that high fevers, or even hot summer weather, can cause temporary infertility in men by raising the temperature of the testes. Although it is important for the testes to be protected against heat, point out that they are also protected against cold by the muscle that lines the skin of the scrotum. In cold temperatures and under other conditions, this muscle contracts so that the testes are held closer to the body. **learning modality: verbal**

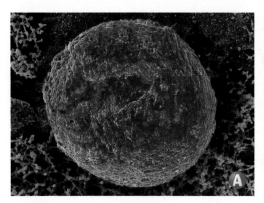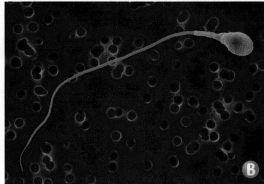

Figure 4 The human reproductive system produces either eggs or sperm. **A.** An egg is one of the largest cells in the body. **B.** A sperm, which is much smaller than an egg, has a tail that allows it to move.

Like other cells in the body, sex cells contain rod-shaped structures called chromosomes. **Chromosomes** (KROH muh sohmz) carry the information that controls inherited characteristics, such as eye color and blood type. Every cell in the human body, except the sex cells, contains 46 chromosomes. Each sex cell contains half that number, or 23 chromosomes. During fertilization, the 23 chromosomes in a sperm join the 23 chromosomes in an egg. The result is a zygote with 46 chromosomes. The zygote contains all of the information needed to produce a new human being.

☑ *Checkpoint* *What happens to the number of chromosomes when a male sex cell and a female sex cell join?*

The Male Reproductive System

The male reproductive system is shown in Figure 5. **The male reproductive system is specialized to produce sperm and the hormone testosterone.**

The Testes The oval-shaped **testes** (tes teez) (singular *testis*), are the organs of the male reproductive system in which sperm are produced. The testes are actually clusters of hundreds of tiny coiled tubes. Sperm are formed inside the tubes.

The testes also produce the hormone **testosterone** (tes TAHS tuh rohn). Testosterone controls the development of physical characteristics in men. Some of those characteristics include facial hair, a deep voice, broad shoulders, and the ability to produce sperm.

Notice in Figure 5 that the testes are located in an external pouch of skin called the **scrotum** (SKROH tum). That external location keeps the testes about 2° to 3°C below the usual body temperature of 37°C. That temperature difference is important. Sperm need the slightly cooler conditions to develop normally.

Background

Facts and Figures Some men choose a vasectomy as a means of contraception. In this fairly simple procedure, which can be performed in a doctor's office under local anesthesia, the vas deferens—the tube through which sperm pass from the testes to the urethra—is severed and a short section is removed. This prevents the sperm from being able to travel from the testes.

A vasectomy does not affect the production of testosterone. Males therefore can continue normal sexual functions and retain male characteristics such as facial hair and a deep voice.

Sperm can remain in the reproductive tract, however, for up to six weeks. Other forms of contraception must be used during this period. After approximately six weeks, the male is sterile.

Sperm Production The production of sperm cells begins in males at some point during the teenage years. Each sperm is composed of a head that contains chromosomes and a long, whiplike tail. Basically, a sperm cell is a tiny package of chromosomes that can swim.

The Path of Sperm Cells Once sperm cells form in the testes, they travel through other structures in the male reproductive system. During this passage, sperm mix with fluids produced by nearby glands. This mix of sperm cells and fluids is called **semen** (SEE mun). Semen contains a huge number of sperm—about 5 to 10 million per drop! The fluids in semen provide an environment in which sperm can swim. Semen also contains nutrients that the moving sperm use as a source of energy.

Semen leaves the body through an organ called the **penis.** The male urethra runs through the penis. The urethra is the tube through which the semen travels as it leaves the body.

Urine also leaves the body through the urethra, as you learned in Chapter 5. When semen passes through the urethra, however, muscles near the bladder contract. Those muscles prevent urine and semen from mixing.

 Checkpoint **What is a sperm composed of?**

Figure 5 In the male reproductive system, the testes produce sperm and the hormone testosterone. *Interpreting Diagrams What pathway do sperm follow to reach the urethra?*

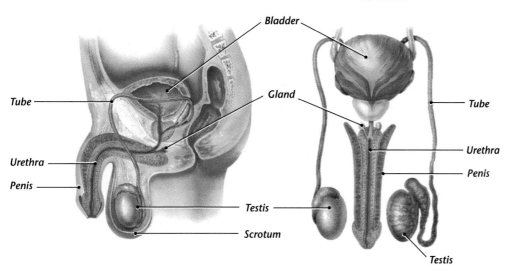

Bladder

Tube

Gland

Tube

Urethra

Urethra

Penis

Penis

Testis

Testis

Scrotum

Media and Technology

Transparencies "The Male Reproductive System," Transparency 19

Answers to Self-Assessment

Caption Question

Figure 5 The sperm travel from the testes, through the tubes, and into the urethra.

 Checkpoint

The number of chromosomes doubles.

Checkpoint

Each sperm cell is composed of a head that contains chromosomes and a long tail.

Including All Students

Some students may have difficulty remembering the terms associated with the male reproductive system. Encourage students to use the text and Figure 5 to create a list of terms and definitions they may have trouble recalling. Pair students after they complete their lists to quiz each other. Students can then revise their lists by adding any terms they missed or by correcting erroneous definitions. **limited English proficiency**

Portfolio Students can save their definitions in their portfolios.

Language Arts
CONNECTION

Tell students that the word *semen* is a Latin word meaning *seed.* Some other words that come from the same root are *seminar* and *seminal.* Have students look these words up in the dictionary and discuss how the idea of seeds is relevant to the meaning of each word. **learning modality: verbal**

Addressing Naive Conceptions

Students may think that testosterone is not produced until puberty. In fact, testosterone production begins in the fetal stage. If it is not produced at exactly the right time during the fetus' development in the womb, male reproductive organs will not develop. Small amounts of testosterone are produced until puberty, when production increases dramatically. **learning modality: verbal**

Ongoing Assessment

Organizing Information Have students draw concept maps describing the production and path of sperm.

Portfolio Students can save their concept maps in their portfolios.

The Female Reproductive System

Using the Visuals: Figure 6

Have students trace the path of the egg as they study the structures in the figure. Ask students to describe the path of the egg after it matures. *(The mature egg is released by an ovary and passes through an oviduct into the uterus.)* **Where does fertilization take place?** *(The oviduct)* **limited English proficiency**

Building Inquiry Skills: Comparing and Contrasting

Explain that the ovaries perform functions similar to those performed by the testes. One difference between them is that, while the testes do not begin producing sperm until puberty, the ovaries produce undeveloped egg cells, called *oocytes*, before the female is born. In fact, by the time a female child is born, her ovaries already contain, in the form of oocytes, all the eggs that she will ever produce. Challenge students to use both the text and additional research to gather information on the similarities and differences between the ovaries and testes. Students can then use the information to develop compare and contrast tables. Invite students to share their tables or diagrams with the class.
learning modality: visual

 Students can save their tables or diagrams in their portfolios.

Addressing Naive Conceptions

Students may not realize that fertilization can occur whenever viable sperm cells and viable egg cells are present. Point out that sperm cells can live for 4 to 6 days inside the female body and that egg cells can live for about 2 days after they are released. **learning modality: verbal**

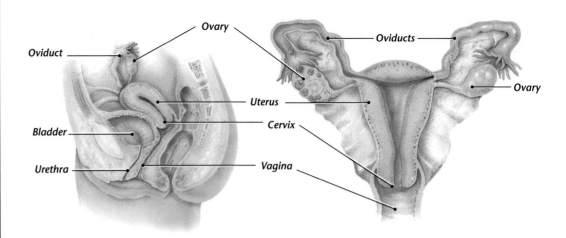

Ovary — Oviduct — Oviducts — Ovary — Uterus — Cervix — Bladder — Vagina — Urethra

Figure 6 In the female reproductive system, the two ovaries produce eggs and hormones such as estrogen. From an ovary, an egg travels through an oviduct to the uterus. *Interpreting Diagrams Through what opening does an unfertilized egg pass when leaving the uterus?*

The Female Reproductive System

Unlike the male reproductive system, almost all of the female reproductive system is inside the body. **The role of the female reproductive system is to produce eggs and, if an egg is fertilized, to nourish a developing baby until birth.** The organs of the female reproductive system are shown in Figure 6.

The Ovaries Find the two ovaries in Figure 6. The **ovaries** (OH vuh reez) are located slightly below the waist, one on each side of the body. The name for these organs comes from the word *ova*, meaning "egg." One major role of the ovaries is to produce egg cells.

Like the testes in males, the ovaries also are endocrine glands that produce hormones. One hormone, **estrogen** (ES truh jun), triggers the development of some adult female characteristics. For example, estrogen causes the hips to widen and the breasts to develop. Estrogen also plays a role in the process by which egg cells develop.

The Path of the Egg Cell As you can see in Figure 6, each ovary is located near an **oviduct** (OH vih duct). The two oviducts are passageways for eggs. They are also the places where fertilization usually occurs. Each month, one of the ovaries releases a mature egg, which enters the nearest oviduct. The egg moves through the oviduct, which leads to the uterus, or womb. The **uterus** (YOO tur us) is a hollow muscular organ about the size of a pear. If the egg has been fertilized, it remains in the uterus and begins to develop.

Integrating Science Biologists have identified many animal and insect pheromones, which are chemicals released by animals that trigger behavior in animals of the same species. Insects use pheromones to attract mates and to warn of danger. In 1998, researchers at the University of Chicago identified one human pheromone by proving that chemicals released by women could cause changes in the menstrual cycles of other women. Dr. Martha McClintock, the lead investigator on the new study, has been studying this effect since 1971. In the 1998 study, researchers used cotton pads to collect the underarm secretions of women at different times of their cycles. When these pads were treated with alcohol and rubbed under the noses of other women for 30 days, 68 percent of these women found their menstrual cycles changed.

An egg that has not been fertilized starts to break down as it enters the uterus. It leaves the uterus through an opening at its base called the cervix. The egg then enters the vagina. The **vagina** (vuh JY nuh) is a muscular passageway leading to the outside of the body. The vagina is also called the birth canal. It is the passageway through which a baby leaves the mother's body during the birth process.

☑ *Checkpoint* *What is one of the roles of the ovaries?*

The Menstrual Cycle

When the female reproductive system becomes mature during the teenage years, there are about 400,000 undeveloped eggs in a woman's ovaries. However, only about 500 of those eggs will actually leave the ovaries and reach the uterus. An egg is released about once a month in a mature female's body. The monthly cycle of changes that occurs in the female reproductive system is called the **menstrual cycle** (MEN stroo ul).

During the menstrual cycle, an egg develops in an ovary. At the same time, the uterus prepares for the arrival of a fertilized egg. In this way, the menstrual cycle prepares the female's body for pregnancy, the condition that begins after fertilization has taken place.

Stages of the Cycle The menstrual cycle begins when an egg starts to mature in one of the ovaries. At the same time, the lining of the uterus begins to thicken. About halfway through a typical cycle, the mature egg is released from the ovary into an oviduct. This process is called **ovulation** (OH vyuh lay shun).

Sharpen your Skills

Graphing ACTIVITY

A woman's hormone levels change throughout the menstrual cycle. The table below shows the levels of one female hormone, known as LH, during the menstrual cycle.

Day	Level of LH
1	12
5	14
9	14
13	70
17	12
21	12
25	8

Construct a line graph using the information in the table. Label the horizontal axis *Day.* Label the vertical axis *Hormone Level.* What event takes place about the same time that LH reaches its highest level?

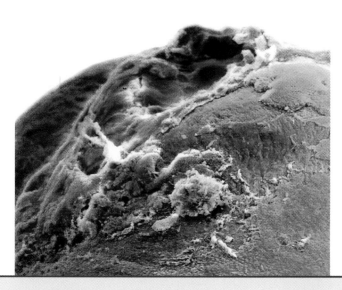

Figure 7 During ovulation an egg bursts from the side of an ovary. In this photograph, the egg is the round red structure on the right.

Chapter 8 **D ◆ 235**

Answers to Self-Assessment

Caption Question

Figure 6 The cervix

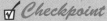 ☑ *Checkpoint*

Either one: produce eggs, produce hormones

The Menstrual Cycle

Sharpen your Skills

Graphing

Materials *graph paper, ruler*

Time 20 minutes

Tips Students should be able to infer from their graphs that ovulation takes place at about the time LH reaches its highest levels.

Extend Tell students that another hormone called estrogen is responsible for the buildup of the uterine lining. Ask students to draw a line that might show the level of estrogen in the body during a 25-day cycle. (*The graph line would look very similar to the one for LH.*) **learning modality: logical/mathematical**

Addressing Naive Conceptions

Students may confuse the menstrual cycle with menstruation. The menstrual cycle includes the maturation of the egg, the thickening of the uterine lining, the release of the egg, and the breakdown of the uterine lining, as well as menstruation. Menstruation describes the process by which the blood and tissue of the lining exit the body. **learning modality: verbal**

Ongoing Assessment

Writing Have students explain the processes that take place during the menstrual cycle.

 Students can save their explanations in their portfolios.

Using the Visuals: Figure 8

Draw the outline of a cycle diagram on the board, with space for five captions. Tell students they will use information in Figure 8 to fill in the cycle diagram on the board. Have student volunteers read each caption aloud, while another volunteer fills in the caption on the board. After students finish the diagram, ask students to infer what would prevent the cycle from beginning again. *(If the egg is fertilized, the cycle will be interrupted.)* **limited English proficiency**

3 Assess

Section 2 Review Answers

1. Male—sperm cells; female—egg cells
2. The lining of the uterus thickens during the beginning of the cycle. If the egg is not fertilized after its release, the lining of the uterus breaks down and menstruation begins.
3. The head of the sperm cell is a package of chromosomes. The tail helps the sperm swim toward the egg.
4. Ovulation consists of the release of a mature egg from an ovary. It occurs about once a month.
5. Similar—both produce sex cells and hormones. Different—testes produce sperm and testosterone, while ovaries produce eggs and estrogen.

CHAPTER PROJECT 8

Check Your Progress

Some students may be more thoughtful and responsive if they are allowed to complete the project alone. Others may benefit from role-playing discussions in which they compare child-care experiences and give each other pointers. Assess the mood of the class to determine the best way to approach the project.

Performance Assessment

Organizing Information Have students create flowcharts of the path traveled by the sperm or the path of the egg through the appropriate reproductive system.

DAY 28
DAY 2
DAY 4
DAY 6
DAY 8
DAY 10
DAY 12
DAY 14
DAY 16
DAY 18
DAY 20
DAY 22
DAY 24
DAY 26
Days 1–4 Menstrual discharge
Days 5–13 Developing egg
Days 14–15 Ovulation occurs
Days 16–22 Egg moves through oviduct
Days 23–28 Egg enters uterus

Figure 8 During the menstrual cycle, the lining of the uterus builds up with extra blood and tissue. About halfway through a typical cycle, ovulation takes place. If the egg is not fertilized, menstruation occurs.

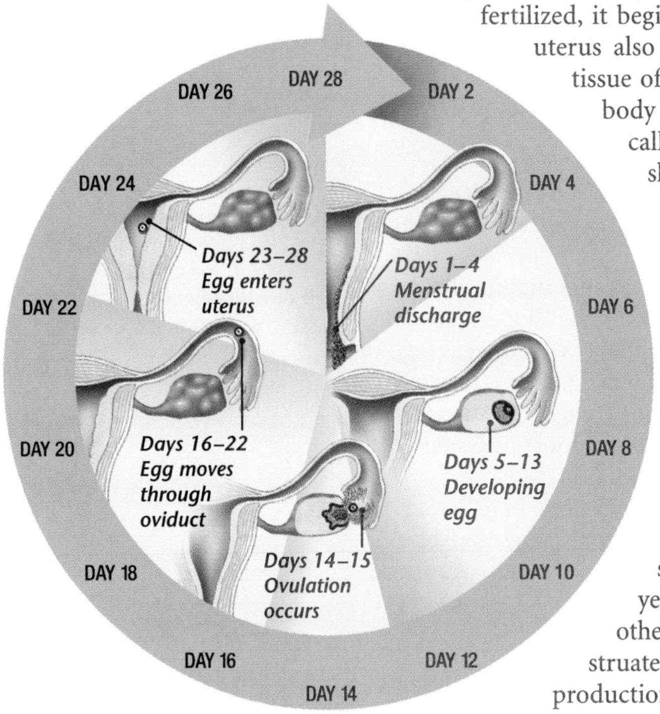

Once the egg is released, it can be fertilized for the next few days if sperm are present in the oviduct. If the egg is not fertilized, it begins to break down. The lining of the uterus also breaks down. The extra blood and tissue of the thickened lining pass out of the body through the vagina. This process is called **menstruation** (men stroo AY shun). On average, menstruation lasts about 4 to 6 days. At the same time that menstruation occurs, a new egg begins to mature in the ovary, and the cycle continues. You can follow the main steps in the cycle in Figure 8.

Endocrine Control The menstrual cycle is controlled by hormones of the endocrine system. Hormones also trigger a girl's first menstruation. Many girls begin menstruation between the ages of 10 and 14 years. Some girls start earlier, while others start later. Women continue to menstruate until about age 50. At around that age, production of sex hormones drops. As a result, the ovaries stop releasing mature egg cells.

Section 2 Review

1. What specialized cells are produced in the male and female reproductive systems?
2. How does the uterus change during the menstrual cycle?
3. How does a sperm's structure help it function?
4. What is ovulation? How often does it occur?
5. **Thinking Critically Comparing and Contrasting** In what ways are the functions of the ovaries and the testes similar? How do their functions differ?

CHAPTER PROJECT 8

Check Your Progress

You should now be caring for your "baby," taking it with you everywhere or arranging for a responsible person to care for it. You or your substitute must continue to perform all the child-care tasks, such as feeding the baby, changing diapers, and playing with the baby. Whenever you travel, you must have a safe method for transporting the baby. Don't forget to make at least two journal entries each day.

Background

Facts and Figures Premenstrual syndrome (PMS) can occur during the last 7 to 10 days of the menstrual cycle. PMS produces physical symptoms such as cramping, headaches, breast tenderness, and fluid retention. It also leads to behavioral symptoms such as anxiety, crying spells, and appetite changes. Although the exact cause of PMS is unknown, it is thought to be due to changing hormonal levels.

Program Resources

- **Teaching Resources** 8-2 Review and Reinforce, p. 211; 8-2 Enrich, p. 212

Media and Technology

Interactive Student Tutorial CD-ROM D-8

3 Pregnancy, Birth, and Childhood

SECTION 3
Pregnancy, Birth, and Childhood

DISCOVER · ACTIVITY · · · ·

How Many Ways Does a Child Grow?

1. Compare the two photographs at the left. One shows a baby girl. The other shows the same girl at the age of five.

2. Make two lists—one of the similarities and the other of the differences you see.

3. Compare your lists with those of your classmates.

Think It Over
Observing Based on your observations, list three physical changes that occur in early childhood.

An egg can be fertilized during the first few days after ovulation. If fertilization occurs, the amazing process of human development begins.

A fertilized egg, or zygote, is no larger than the period at the end of this sentence. Yet after fertilization, the zygote undergoes changes that result in the formation of a new human. **The zygote develops first into an embryo and then into a fetus.** About nine months after fertilization, a baby is born.

The Zygote

After an egg cell and sperm cell join, the zygote moves down the oviduct toward the uterus. During this trip, which takes about four days, the zygote begins to divide. The original cell divides to make two cells, these two cells divide to make four, and so on. Eventually, the growing mass of hundreds of cells forms a hollow ball. The ball attaches to the lining of the uterus. For the next eight weeks or so, the developing human is called an **embryo** (EM bree oh).

> ### GUIDE FOR READING
> ◆ What are the stages of human development that occur before birth?
> ◆ What happens during childbirth?
>
> *Reading Tip* As you read, use the headings to outline the events that occur during pregnancy, birth, and childhood.

Figure 9 Only one sperm can fertilize an egg. Once fertilization occurs, the process of human development begins.

Chapter 8 **D** ◆ 237

SECTION 3 Pregnancy, Birth, and Childhood

Objectives
After completing the lesson, students will be able to
◆ list the stages of human development that occur before birth;
◆ describe what happens during childbirth;
◆ describe the physical changes that occur during infancy and childhood.

Key Terms embryo, amniotic sac, placenta, umbilical cord, fetus

1 Engage/Explore

Activating Prior Knowledge

Show students several pictures of a variety of baby mammals, including human beings. Encourage students to brainstorm a list of characteristics that they all have in common. *(Sample: Feed on mother's milk, depend on parents for food, are smaller than parents but have similar characteristics.)*

· · · · · · · · DISCOVER · · · · · · · ·

Skills Focus observing
Time 15 minutes
Tips Bring in additional photographs showing individuals as babies and as children.
Think It Over Students should note several major differences between the two photos. Overall, the child has grown to be taller and heavier than the baby. The proportions of her body have also changed—the child's head is smaller in proportion to the rest of her body, and the child's limbs are longer in proportion to the rest of her body. The child's features have become less rounded.

D ◆ 237

2 Facilitate

The Zygote

Building Inquiry Skills: Calculating

Remind students that every zygote starts out as a single cell. Tell students that when cells divide, the number continually doubles. Ask them to predict how many divisions of the single-celled zygote will be necessary to produce more than 1,000 cells. *(11 cell divisions equals 1,024 cells)* Ask: **If cell division occurs every 26 hours, how long would it take for the embryo to have over 1,000 cells?** *(286 hours or 12 days)* **learning modality: logical/mathematical**

The Development of the Embryo

Using the Visuals: Figure 10

Refer students to Figure 10. Draw their attention to the uterus. Tell students to examine the uterus and the uterine wall. Ask: **Which membranes develop from the uterine wall?** *(The amniotic sac and the placenta)* Point out the enlargement. Explain to students that the enlargement shows details of the placenta shown in the main diagram. Ask: **Is the embryo connected directly to a part of the mother's reproductive system? Explain.** *(No. It is connected to the placenta.)* **learning modality: visual**

Integrating Health

Inform students that women who drink during pregnancy have an increased risk of giving birth to children with fetal alcohol syndrome (FAS). FAS consists of a variety of birth defects including low birth weight and an abnormally small head, facial deformities, and mild to moderate mental retardation. As FAS children develop, they often exhibit behavioral and cognitive problems. **learning modality: verbal**

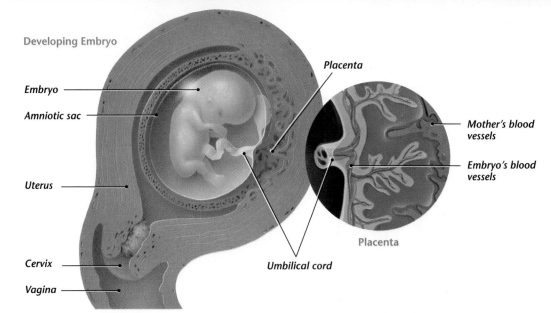

Developing Embryo

Embryo
Amniotic sac
Uterus
Cervix
Vagina
Placenta
Umbilical cord
Mother's blood vessels
Embryo's blood vessels
Placenta

Figure 10 The placenta connects the mother and the developing embryo. But the mother's and the embryo's blood vessels remain separate, as you can see in the closeup of the placenta. *Interpreting Diagrams What structure carries nutrients and oxygen from the placenta to the embryo?*

The Development of the Embryo

Soon after the embryo attaches to the uterus, many changes take place. The hollow ball of cells grows inward. New membranes form. One membrane surrounds the embryo and develops into a fluid-filled sac called the **amniotic sac** (am nee AHT ik). Locate the amniotic sac in Figure 10. The fluid in the amniotic sac cushions and protects the developing baby.

Another membrane that forms is the **placenta** (pluh SEN tuh). The placenta becomes the link between the developing embryo and the mother. In the placenta, the embryo's blood vessels flow next to the mother's blood vessels. Blood from the two systems does not mix, but many substances are exchanged. The embryo receives nutrients, oxygen, and other substances from the mother. It gives off carbon dioxide and other wastes.

The embryo soon moves a short distance from the placenta. A ropelike structure called the **umbilical cord** forms between the embryo and the placenta. It contains blood vessels that link the embryo to the mother, but the two circulatory systems remain separated by a thin barrier.

INTEGRATING HEALTH The barrier that separates the embryo's and mother's blood prevents some diseases from spreading from the mother to the embryo. However, substances such as chemicals in tobacco smoke, alcohol, and some other drugs can pass through the barrier to the embryo. For this reason, pregnant women should not smoke tobacco, drink alcohol, or take any drug without a doctor's approval.

Checkpoint How does an embryo obtain oxygen?

Background

Facts and Figures In-vitro fertilization (IVF) involves the fertilization of mature egg cells by sperm cells in a petri dish or test tube. The term *in vitro* comes from the Latin words meaning "in glass." After the eggs are fertilized, the potential embryos are transferred into a petri dish containing a suitable growth medium and allowed to divide until they form hollow balls of cells (blastocysts). During this time, hormone treatments are being used to prepare the mother's uterus to accept the embryos. When the embryos are ready, they are introduced through the cervix into the mother's uterus. The first successful birth of a child by means of IVF occurred in England in 1978. The IVF procedure was carried out by Patrick Steptoe and R. G. Edwards.

The Development of the Fetus

From the ninth week of development until birth, the embryo is called a **fetus** (FEE tus). Although the fetus starts out about as small as a walnut shell, it now looks more like a baby. Many internal organs have developed. The head is about half the body's total size. The fetus's brain is developing rapidly. It also has dark eye patches, fingers, and toes. By the end of the third month, the fetus is about 9 centimeters long and has a mass of about 26 grams.

Between the fourth and sixth months, the tissues of the fetus continue to develop into more recognizable shapes. Bones become distinct. A heartbeat can be heard with a stethoscope. A layer of soft hair grows over the skin. The arms and legs develop more completely. The fetus begins to move and kick, a sign that its muscles are growing. At the end of the sixth month, the mass of the fetus is approaching 700 grams. Its body is about 20 centimeters long.

The final 3 months prepare the fetus to survive outside the mother's body. The brain surface develops grooves and ridges. The lungs become developed enough to carry out the exchange of oxygen and carbon dioxide. The eyelids can open. Eyelashes and eyebrows grow. The fetus doubles in length. Its mass may reach 3 kilograms or more.

Figure 11 At the beginning of the fourth month of development, a fetus has developed internal organs, dark eye patches, fingers, and toes. Later, its eyes will open, and fingernails and toenails will form.

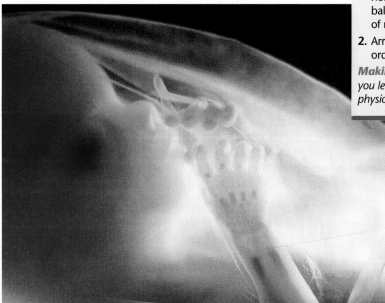

TRY THIS

Way to Grow!

The table lists the average mass of a developing baby at different months of pregnancy.

ACTIVITY

Month of Pregnancy	Mass (grams)
1	0.02
2	2.0
3	26
4	150
5	460
6	640
7	1,500
8	2,300
9	3,200

1. Use a balance to identify an everyday object with a mass equal to each mass listed in the table. You may need to use different balances to cover the range of masses listed.

2. Arrange the objects in order by month.

Making Models What did you learn by gathering these physical models?

The Development of the Fetus

TRY THIS

Skills Focus making models

ACTIVITY

Materials *balance, objects of various masses*

Time 25 minutes

Provide balances that can handle the listed range of masses. If necessary, shorten the list. Students can combine objects to reach the higher masses.

Extend Challenge students to create graphs showing the relative gain in mass of the developing fetus. **learning modality: kinesthetic**

Social Studies
CONNECTION

Ask students if they have ever heard of the drug thalidomide. Explain that in the late 1950s, this drug was given to pregnant women in Europe to treat nausea and vomiting. In 1961, the drug was found to be associated with a number of birth defects, including severely shortened arms and legs. Women who took this drug during the first three months of their pregnancies sometimes had babies with these birth defects, though those who took the drug during the last three months had normal babies. Thalidomide was never approved for use in the United States. The head of the Food and Drug Administration, Dr. Frances Kelsey, delayed approval of the drug because of concerns with numbness in some of the users. It was during this interim that the dangers of using thalidomide during pregnancy became known. **learning modality: verbal**

Ongoing Assessment

Writing Ask students to choose a stage in the development of the embryo or fetus and describe what happens at that stage. *(Sample: During the 1st to 3rd month, the fetus develops internal organs, the head is half the size of the body, the brain develops rapidly. The fetus has dark eye patches, fingers, and toes.)*

 Students can save their descriptions in their portfolios.

Answers to Self-Assessment

Caption Question

Figure 10 The umbilical cord

✓ *Checkpoint*

The embryo obtains oxygen from the mother. Substances such as nutrients, oxygen, carbon dioxide, and other wastes are exchanged in the placenta.

Birth

Real-Life Learning

Students have probably heard descriptions of childbirth from their family members, on television, or in movies. Encourage students to think about some of the terms they have heard used in these descriptions. Use the text to help explain what the terms mean. For example, a television doctor may use the term *dilating*. Explain that this refers to the cervix enlarging to allow the baby to pass through, and that this is the main activity during the labor stage. Students may have other questions, or may use words other than those in the text to describe births they have heard or read about. Help them relate each stage to the stages described in the text. **limited English proficiency**

Including All Students

Divide students into groups of three or four and then challenge them to present the material on birth and the fetus in a creative form. Suggest that students may want to present the material as a play, as a poster, or as an interview or news announcement. Each student in the group should participate in the planning stages of the presentation. If students choose to make a poster, then all students should help in drawing the poster. Students who plan role-playing activities should divide tasks such that some students do the writing and some the acting. Allow students to present their creative projects to the class. **cooperative learning**

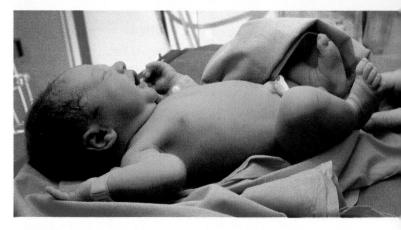

Figure 12 After about 9 months of growth and development inside the uterus, a baby is born. You can see where the umbilical cord of this newborn was tied and cut.

Birth

After about 9 months of development inside the uterus, the baby is ready to be born. **The birth of a baby takes place in three stages—labor, delivery, and afterbirth.**

Labor During the first stage of birth, strong muscular contractions of the uterus begin. These contractions are called labor. The contractions cause the cervix to enlarge, eventually allowing the baby to fit through the opening. As labor progresses, the contractions become stronger and more frequent. Labor may last from about 2 hours to more than 20 hours.

Delivery The second stage of birth is called delivery. During delivery, the baby is pushed completely out of the uterus, through the vagina, and out of the mother's body. The head usually comes out first. At this time, the baby is still connected to the placenta by the umbilical cord. Delivery usually takes less time than labor does—from several minutes to a few hours.

Shortly after delivery, the umbilical cord is tied, then cut about five centimeters from the baby's abdomen. Cutting the umbilical cord does not cause the baby any pain. Within 7 to 10 days, the remainder of the umbilical cord dries up and falls off, leaving a scar called the navel, or belly button.

Afterbirth About 15 minutes after delivery, the third stage of the birth process begins. Contractions push the placenta and other membranes out of the uterus through the vagina. This stage, called afterbirth, is usually completed in less than an hour.

Birth and the Fetus The birth process is stressful for both the fetus and the mother. The fetus is pushed and squeezed as it travels out of the mother's body. Contractions put pressure on the placenta and umbilical cord, briefly cutting off the fetus's supply of oxygen.

Background

History of Science Up until the early nineteenth century, women who had to go to maternity hospitals faced a mortality rate as high as 30 percent. Most deaths resulted from an infection called puerperal fever. In 1844, a Hungarian doctor named Ignaz Semmelweiss worked at an obstetric clinic in Vienna. Semmelweiss observed that in one part of the clinic, where medical students were taught, mortality rates were two to three times higher than in another part, which was managed by midwives. Semmelweiss concluded that the medical students were carrying infection. When he directed the students to sterilize their hands after dissecting, the mortality rate in that part of the clinic dropped to around 1 percent. Unfortunately, his work was resisted by medical authorities throughout Europe.

In response to the changes, the fetus's endocrine system releases adrenaline. The fetus's heart rate increases. Within a few seconds of delivery, a baby may cry or cough. This action helps rid the lungs of fluid and fills them with air. The newborn's heart rate then slows to a steady pace. Blood travels to the lungs and picks up oxygen from the air that the baby breathes in. The newborn's cry helps it adjust to the changes in its surroundings.

☑ *Checkpoint* **What events occur during labor?**

Multiple Births

The delivery of more than one baby from a single pregnancy is called a multiple birth. In the United States, a set of twins is born in about one out of every 100 births. Triplets are born in about one out of every 8,000 births.

There are two types of twins: identical twins and fraternal twins. Identical twins develop from a single fertilized egg. The fertilized egg, or zygote, splits into two identical zygotes. The two zygotes have identical inherited traits and will develop into babies of the same sex. Fraternal twins develop when two eggs are released from the ovary and are fertilized by two different sperm. Fraternal twins are no more alike than any other brothers or sisters. Fraternal twins may or may not be the same sex.

Triplets and other multiple births can occur when three or more eggs are produced and fertilized by different sperm. Such births can also occur when a zygote splits into three or more parts.

Figure 13 Identical twins (left) develop from the same zygote; they share identical characteristics. Fraternal twins (right) develop from two different fertilized eggs. *Applying Concepts Why can fraternal twins be different sexes while identical twins cannot?*

Chapter 8 **D ◆ 241**

Designing Experiments

How does the frequency of **ACTIVITY** twins in your school compare to the frequency given in the text? Develop a plan to find out. With your teacher's permission, carry out your plan. Then collect and analyze your data. Of the total number of students, how many are twins? Are your results close to 1 out of 100?

Multiple Births

Sharpen your **Skills**

Designing Experiments

Time 40 minutes

Tips Explain that a set of **ACTIVITY** twins counts as one birth, not two separate births. For students to compare their results with the frequencies in the text, they need to count sets of twins as only one birth. For example, to match the U.S. average for 100 pregnancies, there should be 99 single births and one birth of twins.

Extend Challenge students to use their data to graph comparisons of national and school statistics on twin births.

learning modality: logical/ mathematical

Addressing Naive Conceptions

Students may have heard that the tendency to have twins runs in families. Explain that this is only true for fraternal twins. The tendency for a woman's ovaries to release more than one mature egg cell during a cycle seems to be inherited. On the other hand, identical twins are not produced by an inherited trait, so they do not run in families. An increasing number of multiple births are the results of treatments for infertility, including in-vitro fertilization and drugs that cause the ovaries to release several mature eggs at once. The birth of fraternal twins under these circumstances does not indicate that the family has the tendency to produce twins.

learning modality: verbal

Answers to Self-Assessment

☑ *Checkpoint*

During labor, strong muscular contractions of the uterus cause the cervix to enlarge. As labor progresses, the contractions become stronger and more frequent.

Answers to Self-Assessment

Caption Question

Figure 13 Fraternal twins develop from two different fertilized eggs, so the chances that they are the same sex is the same as for any other brothers or sisters. Identical twins develop from the same fertilized egg, so they must be the same sex.

Writing Have students create flowcharts for the events in the three stages of childbirth.

 Students can save their flowcharts in their portfolios.

Infancy

Real-Life Learning

Students who have siblings in the infant stage may wish to share their experiences with the rest of the class. Ask students to tell the age of their siblings and describe for the class their physical characteristics such as weight and length. Students may also describe motor skills the infants demonstrate, as well as other infant behavior such as crying, feeding, and sleeping habits. Ask students whether their family's infant recognizes family members and whether they note any facial expressions indicating emotions.
learning modality: verbal

Childhood

Language Arts
CONNECTION

Students may be interested to learn that the beginning of childhood is defined as the time when children acquire language. Many infants can say one or two words by the time they are a little over one year old. By the time children are three years old, they learn more than two new words a day, and their working vocabulary contains about 1,000 words. Although there is slight variation from child to child, most humans develop language at about the same rate. This is even true for deaf children whose families communicate using sign language. Ask students: **Why is language acquisition a good determination of the stages of life for children?** (*Because it happens at the same ages for almost all children.*)
learning modality: verbal

Figure 14 During infancy, many physical and mental skills develop. Babies can usually crawl by about seven months of age (left). By the age of two (right), most babies are coordinated enough to feed themselves. *Making Generalizations What other skills develop during infancy?*

Infancy

What can a newborn baby do? You might say "Not much!" A newborn can perform only simple actions, such as crying, sucking, yawning, and blinking. But during infancy—the first two years of life—babies undergo many changes and learn to do many things.

Physical Changes A baby's shape and size change greatly during infancy. When a baby is born, its head makes up about one fourth of its body length. As the infant develops, its head grows more slowly, and its body, legs, and arms begin to catch up. Its nervous and muscular systems become better coordinated. The baby then starts to develop new physical skills.

The exact ages at which physical skills develop vary from baby to baby. A newborn cannot lift its head. But after about 3 months, it can hold its head up and reach for objects. Within the next 2 months or so, the infant can grasp objects. At about 7 months, most infants can move around by crawling. Somewhere between 10 and 16 months, most infants begin to walk by themselves.

Other Changes How does an infant communicate? You may think that babies display feelings mostly by crying. But young infants can show pleasure by smiling and laughing. They can turn their heads or spit out food they don't like. Babies also begin to make babbling sounds. Sometime between the ages of one and three years, many children speak their first word. By the end of infancy, children can do many things for themselves, such as understand simple directions, feed themselves, and play with toys. However, infants are too young to know when something can hurt them. They must be watched carefully at all times.

Background

Facts and Figures The terms used for newborns relate to their inability to use language. *Infant* comes from the Latin for "nonspeaker," and *baby* comes from a Middle English word for "babble." The capacity for language emerges soon after the first birthday, although children understand words before they speak.

Some components of language acquisition appear to be inherited. When learning grammatical rules, all children follow a characteristic sequence, regardless of what language they are learning. The American linguist Noam Chomsky based his theory of generative grammar on this remarkable fact. In this theory, children are born with an understanding of the logical rules that determine the grammatical structure of all languages.

Childhood

Infancy ends and childhood begins at about two years of age. Childhood continues until about the age of 13 years. Children gradually become more active and independent, and experience many physical and mental changes.

Physical Changes Throughout childhood, children continue to grow. They become taller and heavier as their bones and muscles increase in size. They become more coordinated as they practice skills such as walking, holding a fork, using a pencil, and playing games. Over a period of several years, baby teeth fall out and are replaced by permanent teeth. Toward the end of childhood, the bones, especially the legs, begin to grow faster. An increased appetite signals that the body needs more nutrients for its next stage of growth and development.

Other Changes As they develop, children show a growing curiosity and increasing mental abilities. Their curiosity helps them learn about their surroundings. With the help of family members and teachers, children learn to read and to solve problems. Language skills improve rapidly. For example, most four-year-olds can express themselves clearly and can carry on conversations.

Over time, children learn to make friends, care about others, and behave responsibly. Between the ages of 3 and 6, they learn to share and play with others. As children think about and care more for others, friends become more important. About the age of 10, children develop a strong wish to fit in with others of their age group. As their independence increases, children take on more responsibilities at home and school.

Figure 15 During childhood, children learn to get along with others. Their physical activities and games help them become stronger and more coordinated.

 Section 3 Review

1. What three stages of development does a fertilized egg go through before birth?
2. Briefly describe what happens during each of the three stages of birth.
3. What is the function of the amniotic sac? What is the function of the placenta?
4. List two physical changes that occur during infancy.
5. **Thinking Critically** Relating Cause and Effect Why is it dangerous for a pregnant woman to drink alcohol or to smoke?

Science at Home

Discuss with a family member some of the physical and other changes that take place during infancy and childhood. If possible, find out about some of your own milestones—when you first smiled, walked, or talked, for example. Discuss how these milestones relate to the physical changes that occur at each stage.

Program Resources

◆ **Teaching Resources** 8-3 Review and Reinforce, p. 215; 8-3 Enrich, p. 216

Media and Technology

 Interactive Student Tutorial CD-ROM D-8

Answers to Self-Assessment

Caption Question

Figure 14 During infancy, babies develop the ability to hold their heads up, to reach for and grasp objects, and to walk. They also learn to play with toys, understand simple directions, and communicate.

---

3 Assess

Section 3 Review Answers

1. Zygote, embryo, and fetus.
2. During labor, uterine contractions cause the cervix to enlarge. During delivery, the baby is pushed out of the uterus through the vagina and out of the mother's body. In afterbirth, contractions push the placenta out of the uterus through the vagina.
3. The fluid in the amniotic sac cushions and protects the developing baby. The placenta allows the exchange of materials between the mother and fetus.
4. During infancy, the baby's body, arms, and legs grow faster than its head, and the baby's nervous and muscular systems become better coordinated.
5. Because alcohol and substances in tobacco smoke can pass from the mother to the developing embryo through the placenta.

Science at Home

Encourage students to create a scrapbook of their childhood milestones. Students who are unable to learn about events that occurred early in their lives can focus on their development during later childhood. Encourage them to think about milestones such as when they learned to tie their shoes, or when they first spent the night away from home.

Performance Assessment

Writing Have students create time lines of events that begin with a zygote and end at childhood. Students should write at least one characteristic to describe each stage of development. Students can save their time lines in their portfolios.

D ◆ 243

SECTION 4 Adolescence —A Time of Change

Objectives

After completing the lesson, students will be able to
◆ compare adolescence and puberty;
◆ describe the mental and social changes associated with adolescence.

Key Terms adolescence, puberty

1 Engage/Explore

Activating Prior Knowledge

Ask students to think of a favorite TV show that features teenage characters. Ask them how the characters are portrayed and whether they think the characters are realistic. Encourage students to give reasons for their answers.

•••••• DISCOVER ••••••

Skills Focus drawing conclusions **ACTIVITY**
Materials *magazine or newspaper ads directed at teenagers*
Time 15 minutes
Tips Show ads for a variety of products—cosmetics, clothing, food, and entertainment, for example. Ads for unhealthy products such as snacks or sugary beverages, or ads that use teenage celebrities to promote a product, are also good choices.
Think It Over Students should identify specific methods used by ads to try to persuade consumers to buy products or services. For example, an ad may imply that the product is used by, or helps to create, popular, or "perfect" teens.

SECTION 4 Adolescence—A Time of Change

DISCOVER •••••••••••••••••••••••• ACTIVITY

How Do Ads Portray Teenagers?

1. Carefully examine an advertisement taken from a teen magazine. The ad should show one or more teenagers. Be sure to read the text and examine the picture.

2. Think about how the ad portrays the teenagers. How do they look and act? Do you think they are typical teens? How accurate is this "picture" of teenagers? Write down your thoughts.

Think It Over
Drawing Conclusions How does the ad use teenagers to try to influence people your age? Explain your opinion. Do you think the ad is effective?

GUIDE FOR READING

◆ What is the difference between adolescence and puberty?

◆ What mental and social changes are associated with adolescence?

Reading Tip As you read, make a list of the changes that take place during adolescence.

I f you compared a current photo of yourself with one taken three years ago, you would notice many changes. Starting at about the age of 12, you gradually begin to change from a child to an adult. Although many changes happen during infancy and childhood, some of the most significant changes occur during adolescence. **Adolescence** (ad ul ES uns) is the stage of development when children become adults physically and mentally.

By the end of adolescence, you will be able to do things you could not do during childhood. You will become eligible for privileges such as a driver's license and the right to vote. Along

Figure 16 During adolescence, teens mature both physically and mentally. It's a time when many teens try new experiences and take on more responsibilities. Working in the community is one way that teens can explore their interests while helping others.

READING STRATEGIES

Reading Tip After students list changes that take place during adolescence, encourage them to analyze the information based on their own experiences. Make sure students understand that these changes happen for different people at different times.

Study and Comprehension After students read the section, have them list main ideas and supporting details for each major heading. Then have them copy each main idea and detail separately on strips of paper. Ask students to fold the paper strips and exchange them with partners. Then have partners arrange the strips so that details appear under the appropriate main headings. Instruct partners to check each other's work for accuracy.

with these privileges, you will be expected to take on adult responsibilities, such as driving safely. Adolescence is the time to work to become the healthy adult you want to be.

Physical Changes

Adolescence is a time of rapid physical growth. A person grows taller and heavier, and begins to look like an adult. However, some of the most important physical changes take place inside the body. These physical changes are controlled by the hormones of the endocrine system.

Puberty Sometime between the ages of about 9 and 14 years, a child enters puberty. **Puberty** (PYOO bur tee) is the period of sexual development in which the body becomes able to reproduce. Some people think that the term *puberty* is another word for adolescence, but that is not correct. **Adolescence includes more than just the physical changes of puberty. Many important mental and social changes take place as well.**

In girls, hormones produced by the pituitary gland and the ovaries control the physical changes of puberty. The sex organs develop. Ovulation and menstruation begin. The breasts begin to enlarge, and the hips start to widen. The skin begins to produce more oils, and body odor increases.

In boys, hormones from the testes and the pituitary gland govern the changes. The sex organs develop, and sperm production begins. The voice deepens. Hair appears on the face and sometimes on the chest. As with girls, more skin oils are produced, and body odor increases.

Physical Changes

Building Inquiry Skills: Applying Concepts

Ask students to look at Figure 16. Ask: **Can you tell just by looking at these photographs whether the people have gone through puberty? Explain.** *(No, puberty has to do with physical changes that make a male or female capable of reproduction.)* Then ask students to name the physical changes that allow males and females to reproduce. *(Males—produce sperm; females—ovulation begins)* **learning modality: visual**

Addressing Naive Conceptions

Some students may think that, once they begin puberty, the physical changes associated with that stage of development should occur at a steady pace over a relatively brief period of time. Some may be worried that they have begun to change but have not progressed further. Reassure these students that on average, puberty lasts about four years and can proceed at varying rates. **learning modality: verbal**

Program Resources

◆ **Teaching Resources** 8-4 Lesson Plan, p. 217; 8-4 Section Summary, p. 218

Media and Technology

 Audiotapes English-Spanish Summary 8-4

Ongoing Assessment

Writing Ask students to list the physical changes that take place during puberty in males and females.

Physical Changes, continued

Real-Life Learning

Stress the fact that teens need to eat well-balanced and nutritious diets because their bodies are growing and changing so rapidly. Point out that the recommended amounts of nutrients and calories listed on food labels are calculated for adults, not growing adolescents. Adolescents often need more calories and larger amounts of certain nutrients than adults. Provide reference materials and have students work in groups to create tables that summarize the various nutritional requirements for growing teens. Students should note that boys and girls do not have the same nutritional requirements. Specifically, girls need to consume more iron and calcium than boys do. Encourage students to plan a healthful diet for adolescence based on their tables. **cooperative learning**

Addressing Naive Conceptions

Many adolescent students believe that the changes in their bodies indicate a need to eat restricted diets in order to manage their weight. Emphasize that dieting during puberty can be very dangerous. Research has shown that students who fail to eat adequate amounts of calories or nutrients during this time may not develop fully, may never reach their full height, and may experience serious health problems. **learning modality: verbal**

Building Inquiry Skills: Communicating

Encourage students to talk to their older relatives about the relative's personal development and how it affected them, but make sure students know that everyone develops at his or her own pace. **limited English proficiency**

Figure 17 Despite their different sizes, each of these teens is developing normally. *Relating Cause and Effect What body system controls the rate at which changes occur during puberty?*

Bone and Muscle Growth Just as infants and children experience growth spurts, or periods of rapid growth, so do adolescents. Girls tend to experience their growth spurt slightly younger than boys do. Thus, during early adolescence girls tend to be taller than boys. Later in adolescence boys display rapid growth. Overall, boys tend to reach taller adult heights than girls.

Have you ever heard the phrase "growing pains"? Some adolescents grow so rapidly that they experience aches in their arms and legs. A sudden change in height or weight can cause a teen to feel clumsy or awkward at times. It takes time to adjust to a new body size and shape. Regular exercise can help a teen adjust more quickly. Teens should not over-exercise, however, as growing bones and muscles can be injured if overworked.

Another effect rapid growth can produce is hunger. It's normal for teens to go through periods when they eat huge amounts of food. The extra food provides the raw materials and energy required by the growing body. Nutritious meals and snacks can supply the body with the nutrients it needs.

When Puberty Begins As adolescents mature, they may compare their physical development with that of their peers. Teens of the same age can be at different stages of growth. This is because the age at which puberty begins varies from person to person.

These different rates of physical development may lead to misunderstandings. Adolescents whose bodies mature at a younger age may be expected to have adult judgment and take on more responsibilities than other teens. Those whose bodies develop later may face different challenges. They may be treated like children because of their young appearance.

✓ *Checkpoint* What is a growth spurt?

Background

Facts and Figures The mental and social changes that occur during adolescence can be traced to hormones and other biological factors. In boys, the production of larger quantities of testosterone has been associated with strong emotions and moodiness, especially aggressiveness. Estrogen has been associated with moodiness and strong emotions in girls, who are more prone to depression.

Studies have shown that adolescents report feeling happier and less prone to moodiness in highly structured activities including adults, as opposed to spending time alone or with friends. Taking classes, having a job, or being involved in church or civic activities may help students deal more effectively with the stresses and changes of adolescence.

Mental and Social Changes

Adolescents may notice changes in the way they think, feel, and get along with others. Many teenagers have mixed feelings about the changes they are experiencing. They may feel excited and happy about them one day, and shy and confused the next day. **Adolescents undergo many mental and social changes as they become more mature.**

Mental Changes Between about the ages of 13 and 15, a teenager gradually becomes able to think and reason like an adult. Teens can think in ways that they could not as children. For example, young children think of hunger only when their stomachs are empty, or of pain only when they are hurt. They don't think beyond what's happening at the moment. Teenagers' thoughts are no longer limited to their immediate experiences. They begin to consider the consequences of their actions and make thoughtful judgments. Memory and problem-solving skills also improve. These and other mental abilities are often developed at school or through interests such as music or theater.

Adolescence is a time when individuals begin to question things that they accepted as children. Adolescents may wonder about the opinions and actions of friends and family members. They may also begin to ask themselves questions such as "Who am I?" and "What will I do with my life?" Often teens find answers by talking with parents, religious leaders, and other adults. Other times teens try out new experiences—from new hairstyles and clothes to volunteering their time to help others.

Figure 18 In the ceremony being celebrated here, tribal members help this 14-year-old Apache girl mark her passage to adulthood.

Social Studies CONNECTION

In many cultures, adolescence is seen as a passage from childhood to adulthood. In the Apache culture, girls who have entered puberty and begun their menstrual cycles undergo the Changing Woman ceremony. Often the whole community enjoys the feasting, dancing, and performances that are part of the ceremony. The girl dresses in a decorated buckskin dress and is sprinkled with cattail pollen. Other parts of the ceremony include fasting followed by special meals and prayer. After the ceremony, the girl is considered a woman by tribal members.

In Your Journal

Imagine you have just witnessed the Changing Woman ceremony. Write a short letter to a friend describing the event. Include information about the significance of the ceremony. Relate the experience to events with which you are familiar.

Chapter 8 **D ◆ 247**

Mental and Social Changes

Social Studies CONNECTION

In the traditional Apache culture, the Changing Woman ceremony not only introduces the pubescent girl to adult life, it also serves the community in many ways. The celebration and its elaborate preparations bring the entire community together and remind them of four cultural values: physical strength, good disposition, prosperity, and a long life of good health.

In Your Journal More information about the Changing Woman ceremony is available on the Internet. Consult the Science Explorer website for current references. Students can research the eight phases of the ceremony and identify familiar events in their own experience that have similar meanings.
www.science-explorer.phschool.com

Media and Technology

Exploring Life Science Videodisc
Unit 4, Side 1,
"Development is
a Lifelong Process"

Chapter 10

Answers to Self-Assessment

Caption Question

Figure 17 The endocrine system controls the changes that occur at puberty.

☑ *Checkpoint*

A growth spurt is a period of rapid growth.

Ongoing Assessment

Organizing Information Have students create a concept map showing the physical or mental changes that occur during adolescence.

 Students can save their concept maps in their portfolios.

Mental and Social Changes, continued

Real-Life Learning

Write the words *peer pressure* on the board and ask students to brainstorm what the term means to them. Then organize students into small groups to create lists of situations in which teens may experience peer pressure in both negative and positive ways. Invite students to think of ways to avoid negative peer pressure, then to role-play how they could react and respond in certain situations. For example, ask: **If a group of peers are trying to encourage you to try smoking with them, how might you refuse?** *(Students' answers will vary. Practice saying "no" will often strengthen students' ability to refuse in a real encounter.)* Finally, students can role-play how to support a friend who is experiencing peer pressure. **cooperative learning**

Life as an Adult

Building Inquiry Skills: Communicating

Ask students to write about what they expect their lives to be like when they are adults. Have them describe how they think their lives will change from the period of adolescence to adulthood. Ask them to think about at what age they expect themselves to be adults and to give explanations for their thinking. Encourage them to think about how decisions they make today might affect their adult life. **learning modality: verbal**

Figure 19 During the adolescent years, teens place a high value on friendships. *Making Judgments How can friends help each other develop skills that will be important throughout life?*

Social Changes It is common for adolescents to experience changes in their relationships with others. As they become more independent, teens spend more time with their friends. Because friends' opinions are very important, teens may worry whether friends approve of their clothing, looks, personality, and interests. Some teens may also become interested in members of the opposite sex.

As you learned in Chapter 1, peer pressure may influence the decisions and actions of teenagers. Peer pressure can produce both negative and positive results. Negative peer pressure can lead teens to do things that go against their values. The support of friends, on the other hand, can encourage teens to work toward their goals or develop new interests and skills.

☑️ *Checkpoint* *What social changes occur during adolescence?*

Life as an Adult

At what point does adolescence end and adulthood begin? On a certain birthday? When people are physically mature? When people start to live on their own? If you look up the word *adult* in the dictionary, it is defined as being grown up, or mature. Legally, Americans are considered to be adults at the age of 16 or 18 for some activities and at the age of 21 for others. From a physical and mental standpoint, however, it is difficult to say when adulthood begins.

Background

Integrating Science Life in industrialized societies often cuts off adolescents from their elders, isolating them and prolonging adolescence. Anthropologists note that in less technologically developed cultures, adolescence is not always the stormy and stressful transition it seems to be in the Western world.

However, the popular view of adolescents as rebellious individuals who care more about what their peers think than their parents think may not be completely true. Studies indicate that adolescents are greatly influenced by their families, and that most have relatively few disagreements with their parents. When choosing peers, adolescents tend to look for people whose values and attitudes are consistent with those of their parents.

Physical changes continue to occur throughout adulthood. After about the age of 30, a process known as aging begins. Aging becomes more noticeable between the ages of 40 and 65. The skin starts to become wrinkled, the eyes lose their ability to focus on close objects, the hair may lose its coloring, and muscle strength decreases. During this period, females stop menstruating and ovulating. Males usually continue to produce sperm throughout their lives, although the number of sperm they produce decreases with age.

After age 65, aging intensifies, often leading to less efficient heart and lung action. But the effects of aging can be slowed if people follow sensible diets and good exercise plans. With the help of such healthy behaviors, more and more adults remain active throughout their lives.

Responsibilities—as well as opportunities, rights, and privileges—arrive with adulthood. During adolescence you learn to take care of yourself. Eventually, no one will tell you how to spend your money or what to eat. As an adult, you may need to make decisions that affect not just yourself, but your spouse and your children as well. You will need know what values are important to you, and make decisions that match those values.

Figure 20 Adulthood is a time when opportunities and choices expand. Adults can also share their knowledge and experience with younger people.

Section 4 Review

1. What is the difference between puberty and adolescence? Describe three physical changes that occur in boys and girls during puberty.
2. Name two mental changes and one social change that adolescents experience.
3. Why do adolescents sometimes feel clumsy or awkward?
4. What behaviors can adults practice to slow down the effects of aging?
5. **Thinking Critically** **Making Judgments** "Developing a sense of who you are is the most important part of adolescence." What does this statement mean? Do you agree with it? Explain.

Check Your Progress CHAPTER PROJECT 8

By now, you should be preparing a summary of what you learned about being a parent. What skills do parents need? What are some of the rewards of parenthood? What are some of the challenges? How would you feel if you had to continue caring for the "baby" past the project deadline? Write answers to these questions as your final journal entry.

Chapter 8 **D ◆ 249**

Program Resources

◆ **Teaching Resources** 8-4 Review and Reinforce, p. 219; 8-4 Enrich, p. 220

Media and Technology

 Interactive Student Tutorial CD-ROM D-8

Answers to Self-Assessment

Caption Question

Figure 19 Friends can encourage teens to work toward goals or develop new interests and skills.

☑ *Checkpoint*

Adolescents experience changes in their relationships with others, spend more time with friends, and become more influenced by peer pressure.

3 Assess

Section 4 Review Answers

1. Puberty is the period in which the body becomes physically able to reproduce. Adolescence includes social and mental changes as well. In boys and girls, the sex organs develop rapidly, body odor increases, and the skin produces more oils.
2. Mental changes (accept any two): Adolescents are able to think and reason as adults; they can question the opinions and actions of others, consider consequences, and make judgments. Social changes (accept any): They begin to spend more time with friends, respond to peer pressure, and may become interested in the opposite sex.
3. Adolescents often experience rapid growth of bones and other physical changes. Sudden changes in height or weight can cause awkwardness.
4. Sensible diet and exercise plans.
5. Sample answer: The statement means that adolescence is a time for asking questions such as "Who am I?" and "What will I do with my life?" I agree. Unless you know yourself, you can't make important decisions that match your values.

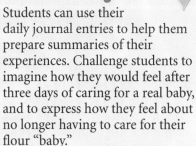

Check Your Progress CHAPTER PROJECT 8

Students can use their daily journal entries to help them prepare summaries of their experiences. Challenge students to imagine how they would feel after three days of caring for a real baby, and to express how they feel about no longer having to care for their flour "baby."

Performance Assessment

Writing Ask students to imagine they are going to talk to a younger sibling about what to expect during adolescence. To prepare, students can write brief descriptions of physical and mental changes the child will go through.

 Students can save their descriptions in their portfolios.

D ◆ 249

Growing Up

Preparing for Inquiry

Key Concept As the human body develops and grows, it not only increases in size, but its proportions change in a regular way from conception to adulthood.

Skills Objectives Students will be able to
- organize information about the proportions of the human body during development;
- calculate percentages;
- interpret data to make inferences about the rates at which different body parts grow;
- design experiments to test their predictions about the relationship between the circumference of the head compared to body height.

Time 30 minutes

Guiding Inquiry

Invitation

Obtain illustrations from magazines showing people of various ages. If possible, use pictures taken from different distances or perspectives so that the total image height is similar, even though the pictures show people of different heights. Invite students to compare the images and describe general differences between people of different ages.

Introducing the Procedure

Have students find the lines on the diagram that represent 50% and 100%. Ask them what height measurements would correspond to those figures for their own height, and for familiar animals such as horses, birds, dogs, and cats. Make sure students understand that the diagram compares the whole height at each stage without comparing the heights directly.

Troubleshooting the Experiment

Students may have trouble estimating between the lines. Copy the diagram onto the board or photocopy the diagram so students can add and label additional marks.

Growing Up

Problem

How do the proportions of the human body change during development?

Procedure

1. Examine the diagram below. Notice that the figures are drawn against a graph showing percents. You can use this diagram to determine how the lengths of major body parts compare to each figure's height. Make a data table in which to record information about each figure's head size and leg length.

2. Look at Figure D. You can use the graph to estimate that the head is about 15% of the figure's full height. Record that number in your data table.

3. Examine Figures A through C. Determine the percent of the total height that the head makes up. Record your results. (*Hint:* Figure A shows the legs folded. You will need to estimate the data for that figure.)

4. Now compare the length of the legs to the total body height for Figures A through D. Record your results.

Analyze and Conclude

1. How do the percents for head size and leg length change from infancy to adulthood?

2. What can you infer about the rate at which different parts of the body grow? Explain.

3. **Think About It** If you made a line graph using the data in the diagram, what would be on the horizontal axis? On the vertical axis? What additional information could you gain from this line graph?

Design an Experiment

Make a prediction about the relationship between the circumference of the head compared to body height. Then design an experiment to test your prediction, using people for test subjects. Obtain your teacher's permission before carrying out the experiment.

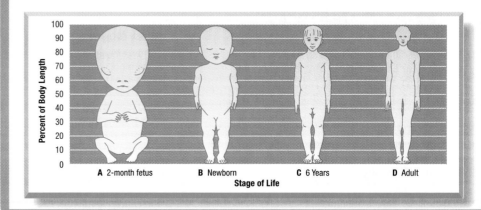

Program Resources

- **Teaching Resources** Chapter 8 Skills Lab, pp. 221–223
- **Inquiry Skills Activity Book** Provides teaching and review of all inquiry skills

Sample Data Table

Comparison of Selected Body Parts to Height

Figure	Head Size	Leg Length
A	about 45%	about 15%
B	about 25%	about 35%
C	about 20%	about 40%
D	about 15%	about 50%

SECTION 1 The Endocrine System

Key Ideas
◆ The endocrine system controls many of the body's daily activities, as well as the body's overall development.
◆ The endocrine system releases chemical messages called hormones. Hormones travel through the bloodstream to their target organs.
◆ Homeostasis in the body is maintained partly through negative feedback: the right amount of a particular hormone signals the body to stop producing that hormone.

Key Terms
endocrine gland	hypothalamus
hormone	pituitary gland
target cell	negative feedback

SECTION 2 The Male and Female Reproductive Systems

Key Ideas
◆ The male reproductive system is specialized to produce sperm and the hormone testosterone.
◆ The role of the female reproductive system is to produce eggs and to nourish a developing baby until birth.
◆ Eggs are produced in the ovaries of the female. During the menstrual cycle, an egg develops, and the uterus prepares for the arrival of a fertilized egg.

Key Terms
egg	testosterone	oviduct
sperm	scrotum	uterus
fertilization	semen	vagina
reproduction	penis	menstrual cycle
zygote	ovary	ovulation
chromosome	estrogen	menstruation
testis		

SECTION 3 Pregnancy, Birth, and Childhood

Key Ideas
◆ If an egg is fertilized, pregnancy begins. The zygote develops into an embryo and then a fetus.
◆ A baby develops inside the mother's uterus for about 9 months before it is born. Birth takes place in three stages—labor, delivery, and afterbirth.
◆ Infancy is a time of rapid physical growth and mastery of basic skills. During child-hood, children become more independent.

Key Terms
embryo	placenta	fetus
amniotic sac	umbilical cord	

SECTION 4 Adolescence— A Time of Change
INTEGRATING HEALTH

Key Ideas
◆ Adolescence includes the physical changes of puberty as well as mental and social changes.
◆ Puberty is the period of sexual development in which the body becomes able to reproduce. Males and females develop the physical characteristics of adult men and women.

Key Terms
adolescence	puberty

USING THE INTERNET

ACTIVITY

www.science-explorer.phschool.com

CHAPTER 8 REVIEW

Analyze and Conclude
1. In the newborn, the head makes up about 30% of body length; by adulthood, it makes up about 15%. For infants, leg length is only about 15% of the total body height; it increases throughout life to about 50% of total height.
2. Different parts of the body grow at different rates. For example, the legs grow much more throughout life than the head.
3. Horizontal axis—age in years; vertical axis—body length. Graphing the data would enable you to find new information by estimating values between the ages given in the diagram.

Extending the Inquiry
Design an Experiment Students' predictions will vary. Make sure that plans are safe, that students explain the predictions they want to test, and that they obtain permission from possible subjects before conducting their investigations.

Program Resources

◆ **Teaching Resources** Chapter 8 Project Scoring Rubric, p. 204; Chapter 8 Performance Assessment Teacher Notes, pp. 198–199; Chapter 8 Performance Assessment Student Worksheet, p. 287; Chapter 8 Test, pp. 288–291

Reviewing Content: Multiple Choice

1. d 2. b 3. a 4. c 5. c

True or False

6. adrenal 7. true 8. true 9. true
10. endocrine

Checking Concepts

11. The hypothalamus is the link between the nervous system and the endocrine system. It also controls the pituitary gland, which in turn regulates other endocrine glands in the body.

12. The signal to stop secreting thyroxine. It is sent through negative feedback. After the hypothalamus senses that cells have enough energy, it signals the pituitary to stop producing TSH, which then makes the thyroid stop producing thyroxine.

13. At the beginning of the cycle, the uterine lining builds up in preparation for a fertilized egg. If the egg is unfertilized, the uterus sheds its lining.

14. A zygote forms from the fertilization of an egg by a sperm. During the first four days, the zygote moves down the oviduct and rapidly divides to become a hollow ball of cells. After about four days, it reaches the uterus and attaches to the uterine lining.

15. A fetus receives food and oxygen and gets rid of wastes through the placenta, which provides a connection between the developing fetus and the mother. The umbilical cord connects the fetus to the placenta. The umbilical cord contains blood vessels that carry oxygen and nutrients from the placenta to the embryo. It also contains other blood vessels that carry carbon dioxide and other waste products from the embryo to the placenta.

16. An infant grows rapidly. Its nervous and muscular systems become better coordinated. The baby gradually masters basic physical skills such as sitting up, crawling, and walking.

17. Sample: Physical—sex organs develop, bones grow rapidly; mental—begin to question the consequences of his actions, try out new experiences; social—become more independent, become influenced by peer pressure.

Reviewing Content

 For more review of key concepts, see the Interactive Student Tutorial CD-ROM.

Multiple Choice
Choose the letter of the best answer.

1. Which structure links the nervous system and the endocrine system?
   a. pituitary gland
   b. adrenal gland
   c. parathyroid gland
   d. hypothalamus
2. What is the male sex cell called?
   a. testis
   b. sperm
   c. egg
   d. ovary
3. The release of an egg from an ovary is known as
   a. ovulation.
   b. fertilization.
   c. menstruation.
   d. afterbirth.
4. Two individuals that develop from the same zygote are called
   a. embryos.
   b. fraternal twins.
   c. identical twins.
   d. triplets.
5. Sex organs develop rapidly during
   a. infancy.
   b. childhood.
   c. puberty.
   d. adulthood.

True or False
If the statement is true, write true. If it is false, change the underlined word or words to make the statement true.

6. The <u>pituitary</u> gland produces adrenaline.
7. The female reproductive glands are the <u>ovaries</u>.
8. The joining of a sperm and an egg is called <u>fertilization</u>.
9. An <u>oviduct</u> is the passageway through which an egg travels from the ovary to the uterus.
10. The physical changes of adolescence are controlled by the <u>nervous</u> system.

Checking Concepts

11. What is the function of the hypothalamus?
12. When enough thyroxine has been released into the blood, what signal is sent to the thyroid gland? How is that signal sent?
13. What changes occur in the uterus during the menstrual cycle?
14. How does a zygote form? What happens to the zygote about four days after it forms?
15. Describe how a fetus receives food and oxygen and gets rid of wastes.
16. Summarize the physical changes that take place during infancy.
17. List six changes a ten-year-old boy should expect to occur in the next five years. Include physical, mental, and social changes.
18. Writing to Learn Imagine you're a skeleton in the body of a sixteen-year-old person. Write about the changes you've experienced since infancy.

Thinking Visually

19. Flowchart Copy this flowchart and fill in the main stages that occur between fertilization and birth. (For more on flowcharts, see the Skills Handbook.)

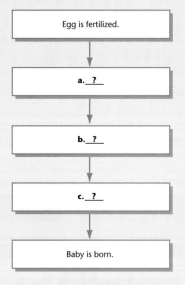

---

18. Students may refer to bone formation in the fetus, changes in bone proportions from infancy to childhood, then the spurts of growth that usually occur during adolescence.

Thinking Visually

19. a. Zygote is formed. **b.** Embryo develops. **c.** Fetus develops.

Applying Skills

20. During weeks 12 through 16
21. Graphs should show length increasing as

time increases. The slope of the line should change until it becomes a fairly straight diagonal line after 20 weeks.

22. The fetus has grown to four times that length by week 24, and six times that length by week 36.

Thinking Critically

23. These two hormones work together to maintain homeostasis in the body by regulating the amount of sugar in the blood. When the sugar levels are high, the pancreas produces

Applying Skills

The data table below shows how the length of a developing baby changes during pregnancy. Use the table to answer Questions 20–22.

Week of Pregnancy	Average Length (mm)	Week of Pregnancy	Average Length (mm)
4	7	24	300
8	30	28	350
12	75	32	410
16	180	36	450
20	250	38	500

20. **Measuring** Use a metric ruler to mark each length on a piece of paper. During which four-week period did the greatest increase in length occur?

21. **Graphing** Graph the data by plotting time on the horizontal axis and length on the vertical axis.

22. **Interpreting Data** At the twelfth week, a developing baby measures about 75 mm. By which week has the fetus grown to four times that length? Six times that length?

Thinking Critically

23. **Applying Concepts** The pancreas produces insulin, a hormone that lowers the level of sugar in the blood. Glucagon, another hormone of the pancreas, increases the level of sugar in the blood. Suggest how these two hormones might work together to maintain homeostasis in the body.

24. **Relating Cause and Effect** How can playing games help children develop important skills?

25. **Comparing and Contrasting** In what way is development during adolescence similar to development before birth? How are the two stages different?

CHAPTER 8 REVIEW

Performance Assessment

CHAPTER PROJECT 8
Wrap Up

Present Your Project You now have the chance to discuss what you learned as you cared for your "baby." What do you now know about parenting that you didn't know before? Consider reading passages from your journal to the class, including the summary you wrote.

Reflect and Record In your journal, describe how well you carried out this project. Did you care for the baby for three complete days? Did you do each task as carefully as you would have for a real infant? How do you think this project was similar to caring for a real baby? How was it different?

Getting Involved

In Your Community Find out from your teachers or from your school nurse whether baby-sitting courses are offered in your community. With your classmates, discuss what skills and information a baby-sitting course should teach. If possible, contact the organization that offers baby-sitting courses. Does your description match what the course offers?

Chapter 8 **D ◆ 253**

---

insulin to lower the blood sugar levels. When the sugar in the blood is low, the pancreas produces glucagon to increase the blood sugar levels.

24. Playing games can help children learn to get along with others and become stronger and more coordinated. Some games also help them develop important mental skills.

25. Development during adolescence is similar to development before birth because during both of these stages, development occurs very rapidly. They are different in that adolescence

Program Resources

◆ **Inquiry Skills Handbook** Provides teaching and review of all inquiry skills.

---

includes mental and social changes as well as physical changes.

Performance Assessment

Wrap Up
CHAPTER PROJECT 8
Present Your Project Have a class discussion in which volunteers can read selections from their journals. To start the discussion, refer to the list of tasks the class developed at the beginning of the project. Ask students to describe how they addressed these tasks in their projects and to explain how they feel after the project. Encourage students to talk about their experiences and how their attitudes have changed.

Reflect and Record Encourage students to write honest reflections of their experiences doing this project. Make sure students know that, although they are being evaluated on how well they carried out the procedures, a greater value can be obtained by reflecting honestly on their experiences and using their assessments as a basis for future behaviors.

Getting Involved

In Your Community Schools, public libraries, and community organizations may offer baby-sitting courses. Have students work in groups to develop lists of what should be taught in baby-sitting courses. Encourage students to consider whether courses should be geared for the requirements of specific ages of children. If students' descriptions do not match the actual course descriptions, have students question whether they should revise their lists. Encourage interested students to talk to their parents about taking one of the courses.

D ◆ 253

The Olympic Games

This interdisciplinary feature presents the central theme of the Olympics by connecting four different disciplines: science, social studies, mathematics, and language arts. The four explorations are designed to capture students' interest and help them see how the content they are studying in science relates to other school subjects and to real-world events. The unit is particularly suitable for team teaching.

1 Engage/Explore

Activating Prior Knowledge

Have students volunteer information they already know about the Olympics. Ask: **What are the Olympic Games?** *(An inter-national sports competition)* **How often are they held?** *(The Summer and Winter Games alternate every two years.)* **What are some of the events in the Olympics?** *(Samples: Basketball, gymnastics, ice skating)* Ask students how many of them dream about being in the Olympics and what sport they imagine themselves competing in.

Introducing the Unit

Help students recall what they learned in Chapter 2, Section 3, The Muscular System, by asking questions such as these: **What are the three types of muscles in the body?** *(Skeletal, smooth, and cardiac)* **Which muscles does an athlete strengthen during training for the Olympics?** *(Athletes strengthen skeletal muscles. They also strengthen cardiac muscle, since vigorous exercise strengthens the heart.)* **Why do you think a study of the Olympics has been included in a book on human biology and health?** *(Only athletes who are at the peak of fitness have a chance to compete in the Olympics.)*

The Olympic flame is a symbol of the spirit of the Olympic Games.

THE OLYMPIC GAMES

WHAT EVENT —

◆ *began in the spirit of competition and fair play?*

◆ *has the motto "faster, higher, stronger"?*

◆ *supports amateur sports?*

◆ *is the dream of young athletes around the world?*

The Olympic Games began more than 2,500 years ago in Olympia, Greece. For one day every four years, the best athletes in Greece gathered to compete. The games honored the Greek god Zeus. The ancient Greeks valued both physical and intellectual achievement. A winning athlete at the Olympic Games was rewarded with a lifetime of honor and fame.

For more than a thousand years, the Greeks held the games at Olympia every four years. This four-year period was called an Olympiad. The games were discontinued in A.D. 394, when the Romans ruled Greece.

Centuries later, in the 1880s, Pierre de Coubertin, a Frenchman, convinced the United States and other nations to bring back the Olympic games. Coubertin hoped that the modern Olympics would promote world peace by bringing together athletes from all nations. The modern Olympics began in Athens in 1896.

Today the Summer and Winter Olympics alternate every two years. For several weeks, athletes from all around the world experience the excitement of competing. Only a few know the joy of winning. But all who participate learn about fair play, striving toward a goal, and becoming a little bit faster and stronger through training.

This ancient marble statue is called *Discobolus*, ancient Greek for "discus thrower." The statue is a Roman copy of a statue made in Greece about 2,500 years ago.

254 ◆ D

Program Resources

◆ **Teaching Resources** Interdisciplinary Explorations, Social Studies, pp. 224–226; Language Arts, pp. 227–229; Mathematics, pp. 230–232; Science, pp. 233–235

Sports in Ancient Greece

The ancient Greeks valued physical fitness as much as an educated mind. Men and boys exercised regularly by wrestling, sprinting, throwing the discus, and tossing the javelin. Greek philosophy taught that a sound mind and body created a well-balanced person. Greek art glorified the muscles and movement of the human body in magnificent sculptures and paintings.

The first recorded Olympic Games were held in 776 B.C. That year a cook named Coroebus from Elis, Greece, won the only event in the games—a sprint of about 192 meters. The prize was a wreath of olive leaves. In ancient Greece an olive wreath was the highest mark of honor.

Over the next 130 years, other events were added to the games, including longer running events, wrestling, chariot racing, boxing, and the

Chariot racing became a popular sport in the ancient Olympics. This scene is painted on a Greek amphora, a pottery jar for olive oil or wine.

pentathlon. *Pent-* comes from the Greek word meaning "five." A pentathlon included five competitions: long jump, javelin toss, discus throw, foot race, and wrestling. Early records indicate that women were not allowed to compete in the games.

Ancient Greece

MACEDONIA
Pella •
• Amphipolis
Olynthos •
Mt. Olympus ▲
Larissa •
• Dodona
GREECE
AEGEAN SEA
• Mytilene
Delphi •
• Thebes
Marathon •
Corinth • Athens
■ Olympia
ASIA MINOR
Ephesus •
• Miletus
• Sparta
Halicarnassus •
Knidos •
Lindos •

N W E S

0   50   100 mi
0   50   100 km

MEDITERRANEAN SEA   *CRETE*

Ancient Greece was a land of many rival city-states, such as Athens and Sparta. Each city-state sent its best athletes to the games at Olympia.

Social Studies Activity

The Olympics encourage peaceful competition among athletes from many nations. But political conflicts sometimes have disrupted or canceled the games. For example, the 1916 games were canceled because of World War I. Other Olympics are remembered for the achievements of certain athletes, such as Babe Didrikson in 1932. Find out what political events affected particular Olympics during the twentieth century. Or find out who were the outstanding athletes at different games. Report your findings to the class.

D ◆ 255

2 Facilitate

- Help students see the relationship between the three maps.
- Explain that a city-state is an independent state surrounding a city. Some students might research to learn more about ancient Greek city-states, such as Athens, Sparta, and Thebes.
- Ask students to find out what sports have recently been added to the Olympics. *(Samples: Mountain biking and lightweight rowing, both in 1996)* Have them learn whether any sports have been discontinued. *(Samples: Croquet in 1900 and tug-of-war in 1920)*

Social Studies Activity

Political events that have affected the Olympics include the rise of the Nazi party in Germany, which dominated the 1936 Berlin games; WWII, which led to the cancellation of the 1940 and 1944 games; and the boycott of the 1980 games in protest of the Soviet Union's invasion of Afghanistan. Books containing information on politics and the Olympics include *Jesse, the Man Who Outran Hitler,* by Jesse Owens, and *More Than a Game: Sports and Politics,* by Martin B. Vinokur.

Teaching Resources The following worksheets correlate with this page: Babe Didrikson, page 224; and Olympic Torch Relay, pages 225–226.

3 Assess

Activity Assessment

Evaluate students' research methods and note taking. Make sure students demonstrate that they have learned more than just the most basic facts about an athlete or a political event.

Background

History The first modern Olympic Games were held in 1896. During that first event, 300 athletes from fewer than 15 countries competed in 9 sports. In the 1996 Atlanta Summer Olympics, more than 10,000 athletes from over 190 countries competed in 29 sports.

At first, only summer Olympic sports were featured. However, in 1924 the Winter Olympics were started. At first, both summer and winter events were held in the same year. Since 1994, the summer and winter games have alternated every two years.

The Olympic flag was flown for the first time in 1920. The five interlocking rings represent the unity of all countries in Africa, the Americas, Asia, Australia, and Europe.

2 Facilitate

- Point out that an autobiography is the life story of a person written by that person. In contrast, a biography is a life story of a person written by someone else.
- Ask: **In the last paragraph, Jackie says she developed booster rockets. What does this mean?** *(She suddenly got a lot faster.)* Explain that this is an example of a metaphor, which is an implied comparison between two things. Ask students what two things are being compared in this metaphor. *(Her speed is being compared to the speed supplied by rockets.)*
- Ask: **The passage ends with Jackie saying "the last was—at long last—first." What does this imply?** *(When she first began training, she came last in races, but now she has won a race.)*

Language Arts Activity

Have students make notes about the event they worked toward and how much they had improved by the time of the event. Ask students whether they felt that the end result justified the work they did. Instead of writing about a specific event, some students might prefer to write about a task or project on which they needed to work hard.

Teaching Resources The following worksheets correlate with this page: Working Hard to Improve, page 227; Words from the Olympics, page 228; and Write a News Report, page 229.

3 Assess

Activity Assessment

Students should describe both the event and their preparation for it as well what they learned in the process.

Language Arts

Modern Olympic Games

At the 1988 Olympic games in Seoul, South Korea, Jackie Joyner-Kersee was one of the star athletes. She won two gold medals there. In total, between 1984 and 1996, she won six Olympic medals (three of them gold), making her one of the world's greatest athletes.

Jackie grew up in East St. Louis, Illinois, where she started running and jumping at age ten. Although she was a natural at the long jump, she wasn't a fast runner. But her coach, Mr. Fennoy, encouraged her. After her final Olympics, Jackie wrote an autobiography—a story of her life. Here is an excerpt from her book *A Kind of Grace.*

Jackie Joyner-Kersee throws the javelin, one of seven events in the Olympic heptathlon. She won the heptathlon twice, in 1988 and 1992.

After school the boys' and girls' teams jogged to Lincoln Park's irregular-shaped track and makeshift long-jump pit. The track was a 36-inch-wide strip of black cinders sprinkled amid the rest of the dirt and grass. We called it the bridle path because that's what it looked like. We ran over, around and through the potholes, rocks, glass and tree limbs that littered the track. . . . After practice, we jogged another two or three miles around the neighborhood to complete our workout.

In winter, when it was too cold to practice outside, we trained inside the Lincoln High building. Every afternoon after school and at 9:00 every Saturday morning, the team of twenty-five girls split into groups on the two floors and ran along the brown concrete corridors. When it was time for hurdling drills, Mr. Fennoy set up hurdles in the center of the hallway on the second floor, and put us through our paces. We sprinted and leaped past the doors to the math and science classrooms. We ran to the end of the hall, turned around and repeated the drill in the opposite direction. . . .

The running drills, exhausting as they were, eventually paid off. In 1977, between the ninth and tenth grade, I developed booster rockets and cut an astonishing four seconds off my 440 time. I surged to the front of the pack in practice heats. By the time we entered Lincoln High as tenth-graders, I was the fastest 440 runner on the team. The last was—at long last—first.

Language Arts Activity

What does Jackie mean by "the last was—at long last—first"? How did she get to be first? Some people say that Jackie was just a natural athlete. Jackie herself says, "I think it was my reward for all those hours of work on the bridle path, the neighborhood sidewalks and the schoolhouse corridors."

Think about a period in your life when you had to prepare for a math competition, a recital, a performance, a sports event, or other event. Write a short autobiographical sketch describing how you worked to improve your performance.

Background

Facts and Figures Jackie Joyner-Kersee was born in Illinois, in 1962. At 14, she won the U.S. junior national title in the pentathlon. She won this title three more times in the next three years.

After high school, she went to the University of California at Los Angeles on a basketball scholarship. There she met her coach Bob Kersee, who would later become her husband.

At the 1984 Los Angeles Olympics, Jackie entered the heptathlon, which consisted of 100-meter hurdles, high jump, shot put, 200-meter dash, long jump, javelin, and 800-meter race. She won a silver medal. In the 1988 Olympics, she won a gold medal in the heptathlon and broke the heptathlon world record. She also won a gold medal for the long jump.

Olympic Records

To prepare for the Olympic Games, top athletes train for years. Sometimes they even move to climates that will help them prepare to compete in their sports. Skiers, for example, might move to a mountain region where they can train year-round. Athletes also use the most advanced equipment available in their sport. This scientific approach to training has helped athletes set new records for speed, height, and distance. In addition, measurement tools such as timing clocks have become more precise. Sprinters and other athletes can now break records by just a few hundredths of a second.

The table and graph below show how the winning height in the women's high jump has changed over many Olympic Games. Notice that the high jump measures height in inches.

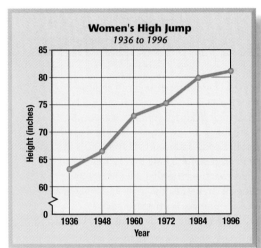

Women's High Jump (height in inches)	
1936	63
1948	$66\frac{1}{8}$
1960	$72\frac{3}{4}$
1972	75
1984	$79\frac{1}{2}$
1996	$80\frac{3}{4}$

Stefka Kostadinova of Bulgaria won the women's high jump at the 1996 Olympics in Atlanta, Georgia. How much higher did she jump than the 1936 winner?

Men's 400-Meter Run (time in seconds)	
1936	46.5
1948	46.2
1960	44.9
1972	44.66
1984	44.27
1996	43.49

Math Activity

The line graph above shows how the heights in the Olympic women's high jump have changed since 1936. Use the table showing times for the men's 400-meter run to create your own line graph.

How did the winning performance in the men's 400-meter run change over time? How does your graph differ from that of the women's high jump? Why do the graphs differ?

D ◆ 257

Background

History The high jump was not part of the ancient Greek games. One of the earliest rules stated that a jumper had to leave the ground one foot at a time instead of taking off with both feet simultaneously. That rule still stands today.

In 1874, Marshall Brooks first cleared 6 feet (1.83 meters). Athletes started exploring different techniques for clearing the bar, although until 1936, the rules stated that athletes had to clear the bar feet first.

Changes in the high jump helped players develop different techniques. The supports were altered so that the bar would fall if touched. More cushioning was added to the landing pads. In 1968, Dick Fosbury took advantage of this when he jumped with his back to the bar, head and shoulders first. This technique, the Fosbury Flop, is now used by all top jumpers.

2 Facilitate

◆ Assign some students to measure the heights for the high jump listed in the table against the classroom wall and to mark these heights with masking tape labels.

◆ Ask: **Why has the high jump record changed so much since 1936?** (*Samples: There is a larger pool of athletic women competing today than there was in 1936; training has improved.*)

◆ As an extension, explain that speed can be calculated by dividing distance by time, and have students calculate the rate for the men's 400-meter run for each year in the table. Do a sample calculation for students. For 1936, $\frac{400 \text{ m}}{46.5 \text{ s}} = 8.6$ m/s.
Then have students prepare a graph of these rates.

Math Activity

Remind students to plot the year on the horizontal axis and the time on the vertical axis. Point out the break in the vertical axis between 0 and 60 inches. The zigzag symbol indicates the break. Suggest that students do the same on their graphs between 0 and 40 seconds.

Teaching Resources The following worksheets correlate with this page: Where's the Starting Line?, page 230; Interpreting Data in a Table, page 231; and Predict Using a Graph, page 232.

3 Assess

Activity Assessment

Check students' graphs for appropriate titles and accurate labeling of axes. Answers: The winning time decreased over time. The graph slopes downward instead of upward because the winning time is getting smaller.

2 Facilitate

- ◆ Ask a physical-education teacher to explain to the class what happens inside muscles as people exercise. Ask him or her to explain why people need to warm up and cool down after exercise, and why the muscles sometimes ache the day after exercise. If a speaker is not available, challenge interested students to research the questions and present their findings to the class. Other students can research what a "stitch" is and what causes muscle cramps.
- ◆ Point out that some athletes are fast sprinters. Other athletes are not fast but have excellent endurance; they are more suited for activities such as cross-country running.
- ◆ Point out that once people improve their fitness, their heart rates increase less as their level of activity increases. The heart also returns faster to its resting rate once the exertion is over.

Science Activity

Stress that students should be calm, quiet, and relaxed when measuring their resting heart rate. Caffeine, some prescribed medications, or even just thinking about exciting or annoying things can raise the heart rate significantly.

Teaching Resources The following worksheets correlate with this page: Science Olympiad, pages 233–234, and Technology in the Olympics, page 235. Note that the Science Olympiad worksheet requires two students, one of whom should not see the worksheet on page 234 before the activity is performed.

Getting Fit, Staying Fit

If you could be an Olympic athlete, would you be a runner, an ice skater, a gymnast, or some other athlete? Whatever their sport, Olympic athletes need to be physically fit to compete at their best. Physical fitness is the ability of the heart, blood vessels, lungs, and muscles to work together to meet the body's needs. Most people never compete in the Olympics. But if you are physically fit, you can reach your personal best.

The best way to boost your fitness is to exercise regularly. When you exercise, your heart, lungs, and muscles benefit. Team sports are good exercise, but so are activities such as walking, riding a bicycle, skating, swimming, and dancing. For the most benefit, people should exercise at least three times a week. Before you start an exercise program, have a physical examination to make sure that you do not have any health problems that rule out vigorous exercise.

A good exercise routine consists of stages, as shown in the flowchart below. Begin by warming up for five to ten minutes. To warm up, do your workout activity, but at a slower pace. If you plan to run, you can warm up by walking. You also should do exercises that gently stretch the muscles that you will use in your workout.

For the workout itself, you can choose exercises that will develop your heart and lungs, your muscular fitness, or both. A person whose heart and lungs function easily during vigorous exercise has good endurance. Endurance is the ability to exercise for a long time without getting tired. Walking, running, swimming, and bicycling all strengthen the heart and lungs and increase endurance. Team sports such as basketball and soccer also build endurance.

Stages in a Fitness Workout

Warm-up	Stretch	Workout	Cool-down	Stretch
Slowly move muscles to be used in workout.	Stretch muscles to be used in workout.	Do an activity such as walking, running, swimming, gymnastics, or riding a bicycle.	Move muscles used in workout at a reduced pace.	Stretch muscles used in workout.
5–10 minutes	5–10 minutes	20–45 minutes	5–10 minutes	5–10 minutes

Background

Facts and Figures Regular exercise has numerous benefits. Research shows that exercise reduces the risk of death from heart disease or stroke. Exercise also helps in weight loss, strengthens bones, improves the functioning of the immune system, and helps prevent one form of diabetes.

Some scientists believe that neurotransmitters released during exercise improve a person's mood. A neurotransmitter is a chemical that transmits nerve impulses between synapses. Research shows that exercise has positive psychological benefits.

There is no conclusive evidence yet that intense prolonged exercise (such as running several kilometers each day) leads to a longer life than milder frequent exercise (such as 30 minutes each day of swimming, jogging, or dance aerobics).

These cross-country runners are about to test their physical fitness.

To improve muscular fitness, activities such as gymnastics and weight training are good choices. But many activities that are good for your heart and lungs contribute to muscular fitness too.

After you exercise vigorously, you should cool down by doing a gentler exercise. Stretching is also important for cooling down.

Science Activity

Your target heart rate is the approximate heart rate you need to maintain during a workout in order to increase your endurance. Target heart rate is usually expressed as a range—for example, 145 to 170 beats per minute.

1. To calculate your target heart rate, first take your pulse when you are at rest. Refer to page 112 for instructions on taking your pulse. Determine the number of times that your heart beats in one minute. This number is called your resting heart rate.

2. Subtract your resting heart rate from 210, which is about the maximum number of times your heart can beat in a minute.

3. To find the lower limit of your target heart rate, multiply the number you obtained in Step 2 by 0.6. Then add this number to your resting heart rate.

4. To get the upper limit of your target heart rate, multiply the number you obtained in Step 2 by 0.8. Then add this number to your resting heart rate.

Tie It Together

Plan an Olympic Day!

Design a competition that can be held at your school. Decide the time, place, and kind of contests to hold. Remember that the ancient Greeks honored intellect as well as athletics. So you could include games that test the mind as well as the body.

Research the decathlon, pentathlon, heptathlon, and marathon in the ancient and modern Olympics. You could design your own pentathlon that includes athletic and nonathletic events.

To organize the Olympic Day, you should:

◆ Set up the sports contests by measuring and marking the ground for each event.

◆ Find stopwatches, meter sticks, tape measures, and any necessary equipment.

◆ Locate or make prizes for first, second, and third place in each event.

◆ Enlist volunteers to compete in the events.

◆ Assign someone to take notes and to write a newspaper story on your Olympic Day.

D ◆ 259

READING STRATEGIES

Further Reading

◆ **Books** *Chronicle of the Olympics.* DK Publishing, 1998.
Siddons, Larry. *The Olympics at 100: A Celebration in Pictures.* Macmillan Publishing Company, 1995.
Wallechinsky, David. *The Complete Book of the Winter Olympics: 1998 Edition.* Overlook Press, 1998.

3 Assess

Activity Assessment

The target heart rate of most students will be in the range of 150 to 190. Watch for students who skipped steps.

Tie It Together

Time 5 days (2 days to research the events in the Olympics; 1 day to make a list of events for school; 1 day to gather materials and volunteers; 1 day to hold the events)

Tips Group students in fives. Once students have suggested activities, make a final list from their suggestions of events. Events should include tests of mental as well as physical ability. Events should vary widely in the kinds of skills required, so that most students in the class have a chance to perform well in at least one event. Make sure events vary enough so that no student in the class feels excluded from the games.

◆ Try to include some events that require teamwork to succeed. Not all students value or enjoy competitiveness.

◆ Assign students who are less interested in sports and competition to record results, judge events, take photographs, or write up newspaper-style articles on the day.

◆ Before the events, stress that the original spirit of the Olympics valued unity among nations and good sportsmanship. Discuss with students what good sportsmanship means. Ask them to give examples of the types of behavior associated with good and bad sportsmanship.

◆ Consider disqualifying students who display poor sportsmanship.

Developing scientific thinking in students is important for a solid science education. To learn how to think scientifically, students need frequent opportunities to practice science process skills, critical thinking skills, as well as other skills that support scientific inquiry. The *Science Explorer* Skills Handbook introduces the following key science skills:

◆ Science Process Skills
◆ SI Measuring Skills
◆ Skills for Conducting a Scientific Investigation
◆ Critical Thinking Skills
◆ Information Organizing Skills
◆ Data Table and Graphing Skills

The Skills Handbook is designed as a reference for students to use whenever they need to review a science skill. You can use the activities provided in the Skills Handbook to teach or reinforce the skills.

Think Like a Scientist

Observing

ACTIVITY

Before students look at the photograph, remind them that an observation is only what they can see, hear, smell, taste, or feel. Ask: **Which senses will you use to make observations from this photograph?** *(Sight is the only sense that can be used to make observations from the photograph.)* **What are some observations you can make from the photograph?** *(Answers may vary. Sample answers: The boy is wearing sneakers, sport socks, shorts, and a tee shirt; the boy is sitting in the grass holding something blue against his knee; the boy is looking at his knee; there is a soccer ball laying beside the boy.)* List the observations on the chalkboard. If students make any inferences or predictions about the boy at this point, ask: **Can you be sure your statement is factual and accurate from just observing the photograph?** Help students understand how observations differ from inferences and predictions.

Inferring

ACTIVITY

Review students' observations from the photograph. Then ask: **What inferences can you**

Think Like a Scientist

Although you may not know it, you think like a scientist every day. Whenever you ask a question and explore possible answers, you use many of the same skills that scientists do. Some of these skills are described on this page.

Observing

When you use one or more of your five senses to gather information about the world, you are **observing.** Hearing a dog bark, counting twelve green seeds, and smelling smoke are all observations. To increase the power of their senses, scientists sometimes use microscopes, telescopes, or other instruments that help them make more detailed observations.

An observation must be factual and accurate—an exact report of what your senses detect. It is important to keep careful records of your observations in science class by writing or drawing in a notebook. The information collected through observations is called evidence, or data.

Inferring

When you explain or interpret an observation, you are **inferring,** or making an inference. For example, if you hear your dog barking, you may infer that someone is at your front door. To make this inference, you combine the evidence—the barking dog—and your experience or knowledge—you know that your dog barks when strangers approach—to reach a logical conclusion.

Notice that an inference is not a fact; it is only one of many possible explanations for an observation. For example, your dog may be barking because it wants to go for a walk. An inference may turn out to be incorrect even if it is based on accurate observations and logical reasoning. The only way to find out if an inference is correct is to investigate further.

Predicting

When you listen to the weather forecast, you hear many predictions about the next day's weather—what the temperature will be, whether it will rain, and how windy it will be. Weather forecasters use observations and knowledge of weather patterns to predict the weather. The skill of **predicting** involves making an inference about a future event based on current evidence or past experience.

Because a prediction is an inference, it may prove to be false. In science class, you can test some of your predictions by doing experiments. For example, suppose you predict that larger paper airplanes can fly farther than smaller airplanes. How could you test your prediction?

ACTIVITY Use the photograph to answer the questions below.

Observing Look closely at the photograph. List at least three observations.

Inferring Use your observations to make an inference about what has happened. What experience or knowledge did you use to make the inference?

Predicting Predict what will happen next. On what evidence or experience do you base your prediction?

---

make from your observations? *(Students may say that the boy hurt his knee playing soccer and is holding a coldpack against his injured knee.)* **What experience or knowledge helped you make this inference?** *(Students may have experienced knee injuries from playing soccer, and they may be familiar with coldpacks like the one the boy is using.)* **Can anyone suggest another possible explanation for these observations?** *(Answers may vary. Sample answer: The boy hurt his knee jogging, and he just happened to sit beside a soccer ball his sister*

left in the yard.)* **How can you find out whether an inference is correct?** *(by further investigation)*

Predicting

ACTIVITY

After coming to some consensus about the inference that the boy hurt his knee, encourage students to make predictions about what will happen next. *(Students' predictions may vary. Sample answers: The boy will go to the doctor. A friend will help the boy home. The boy will get up and continue playing soccer.)*

Classifying

Could you imagine searching for a book in the library if the books were shelved in no particular order? Your trip to the library would be an all-day event! Luckily, librarians group together books on similar topics or by the same author. Grouping together items that are alike in some way is called **classifying.** You can classify items in many ways: by size, by shape, by use, and by other important characteristics.

Like librarians, scientists use the skill of classifying to organize information and objects. When things are sorted into groups, the relationships among them become easier to understand.

Classify the objects in the photograph into two groups based on any characteristic you choose. Then use another characteristic to classify the objects into three groups.

ACTIVITY

Making Models

This student is using a model to demonstrate what causes day and night on Earth. What do the flashlight and the tennis ball in the model represent?

ACTIVITY

Have you ever drawn a picture to help someone understand what you were saying? Such a drawing is one type of model. A model is a picture, diagram, computer image, or other representation of a complex object or process. **Making models** helps people understand things that they cannot observe directly.

Scientists often use models to represent things that are either very large or very small, such as the planets in the solar system, or the parts of a cell. Such models are physical models—drawings or three-dimensional structures that look like the real thing. Other models are mental models—mathematical equations or words that describe how something works.

Communicating

Whenever you talk on the phone, write a letter, or listen to your teacher at school, you are communicating. **Communicating** is the process of sharing ideas and information with other people. Communicating effectively requires many skills, including writing, reading, speaking, listening, and making models.

Scientists communicate to share results, information, and opinions. Scientists often communicate about their work in journals, over the telephone, in letters, and on the Internet. They also attend scientific meetings where they share their ideas with one another in person.

On a sheet of paper, write out clear, detailed directions for tying your shoe. Then exchange directions with a partner. Follow your partner's directions exactly. How successful were you at tying your shoe? How could your partner have communicated more clearly?

ACTIVITY

Classifying

ACTIVITY

Encourage students to think of other common things that are classified. Then ask: **What things at home are classified?** *(Clothing might be classified by placing it in different dresser drawers; glasses, plates, and silverware are grouped in different parts of the kitchen; screws, nuts, bolts, washers, and nails might be separated into small containers.)* **What are some things that scientists classify?** *(Scientists classify many things they study, including organisms, geological features and processes, and kinds of machines.)* After students have classified the different fruits in the photograph, have them share their criteria for classifying them. *(Some characteristics students might use include shape, color, size, and where they are grown.)*

Making Models

ACTIVITY

Ask students: **What are some models you have used to study science?** *(Students may have used human anatomical models, solar system models, maps, stream tables.)* **How did these models help you?** *(Models can help you learn about things that are difficult to study, either because they are too big, too small, or complex.)* Be sure students understand that a model does not have to be three-dimensional. For example, a map in a textbook is a model. Ask: **What do the flashlight and tennis ball represent?** *(The flashlight represents the sun, and the ball represents Earth.)* **What quality of each item makes this a good model?** *(The flashlight gives off light, and the ball is round and can be rotated by the student.)*

Communicating

ACTIVITY

Challenge students to identify the methods of communication they've used today. Then ask: **How is the way you communicate with a friend similar to and different from the way scientists communicate about their work to other scientists?** *(Both may communicate using various methods, but scientists must be very detailed and precise, whereas communication between friends may be less detailed and precise.)* Encourage students to communicate like a scientist as they carry out the activity. *(Students' directions should be detailed and precise enough for another person to successfully follow.)*

On what did you base your prediction? *(Scientific predictions are based on knowledge and experience.)* Point out that in science, predictions can often be tested with experiments.

Making Measurements

Measuring in SI

Review SI units in class with students. Begin by providing metric rulers, graduated cylinders, balances, and Celsius thermometers. Use these tools to reinforce that the meter is the unit of length, the liter is the unit of volume, the gram is the unit of mass, and the degree Celsius is the unit for temperature. Ask: **If you want to measure the area of the floor in this classroom, which SI unit would you use?** *(meter)* **Which unit would you use to measure the amount of matter in your textbook?** *(gram)* **Which would you use to measure how much water a drinking glass holds?** *(liter)* **When would you use the Celsius scale?** *(To measure the temperature of something)* Then use the measuring equipment to review SI prefixes. For example, ask: **What are the smallest units on the metric ruler?** *(millimeters)* **How many millimeters are there in 1 cm?** *(10 mm)* **How many in 10 cm?** *(100 mm)* **How many centimeters are there in 1 m?** *(100 cm)* **What does 1,000 m equal?** *(1 km)*

Length (Students
should state that the shell **ACTIVITY**
is 4.6 centimeters, or 46 millimeters, long.) If students need more practice measuring length, have them use meter sticks and metric rulers to measure various objects in the classroom.

Liquid Volume **ACTIVITY**
(Students should state that the volume of water in the graduated cylinder is 62 milliliters.) If students need more practice measuring liquid volume, have them use a graduated cylinder to measure different volumes of water.

Making Measurements

When scientists make observations, it is not sufficient to say that something is "big" or "heavy." Instead, scientists use instruments to measure just how big or heavy an object is. By measuring, scientists can express their observations more precisely and communicate more information about what they observe.

Measuring in SI

The standard system of measurement used by scientists around the world is known as the International System of Units, which is abbreviated as SI (in French, *Système International d'Unités*). SI units are easy to use because they are based on multiples of 10. Each unit is ten times larger than the next smallest unit and one tenth the size of the next largest unit. The table lists the prefixes used to name the most common SI units.

Common SI Prefixes		
Prefix	**Symbol**	**Meaning**
kilo-	k	1,000
hecto-	h	100
deka-	da	10
deci-	d	0.1 (one tenth)
centi-	c	0.01 (one hundredth)
milli-	m	0.001 (one thousandth)

Length To measure length, or the distance between two points, the unit of measure is the **meter (m)**. One meter is the approximate distance from the floor to a doorknob. Long distances, such as the distance between two cities, are measured in kilometers (km). Small lengths are measured in centimeters (cm) or millimeters (mm). Scientists use metric rulers and meter sticks to measure length.

Common Conversions
1 km = 1,000 m
1 m = 100 cm
1 m = 1,000 mm
1 cm = 10 mm

The larger lines on the metric ruler in the picture show centimeter divisions, while the smaller, unnumbered lines show millimeter divisions. How many centimeters long is the shell? How many millimeters long is it? **ACTIVITY**

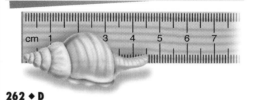

Liquid Volume To measure the volume of a liquid, or the amount of space it takes up, you will use a unit of measure known as the **liter (L).** One liter is the approximate volume of a medium-sized carton of milk. Smaller volumes are measured in milliliters (mL). Scientists use graduated cylinders to measure liquid volume.

Common Conversion
1 L = 1,000 mL

The graduated cylinder in the picture is marked in milliliter divisions. Notice that the water in the cylinder has a curved surface. This curved surface is called the *meniscus.* To measure the volume, you must read the level at the lowest point of the meniscus. What is the volume of water in this graduated cylinder? **ACTIVITY**

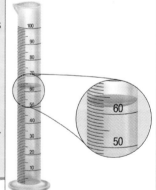

Mass To measure mass, or the amount of matter in an object, you will use a unit of measure known as the **gram** (**g**). One gram is approximately the mass of a paper clip. Larger masses are measured in kilograms (kg). Scientists use a balance to find the mass of an object.

Common Conversion

1 kg = 1,000 g

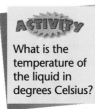

The electronic balance is measuring the mass of an apple in kilograms.
ACTIVITY
What is the mass of the apple? Suppose a recipe for applesauce called for one kilogram of apples. About how many apples would you need?

Temperature
To measure the temperature of a substance, you will use the **Celsius scale**. Temperature is measured in degrees Celsius (°C) using a Celsius thermometer. Water freezes at 0°C and boils at 100°C.

ACTIVITY
What is the temperature of the liquid in degrees Celsius?

Converting SI Units

To use the SI system, you must know how to convert between units. Converting from one unit to another involves the skill of **calculating**, or using mathematical operations. Converting between SI units is similar to converting between dollars and dimes because both systems are based on multiples of ten.

Suppose you want to convert a length of 80 centimeters to meters. Follow these steps to convert between units.
1. Begin by writing down the measurement you want to convert—in this example, 80 centimeters.
2. Write a conversion factor that represents the relationship between the two units you are converting. In this example, the relationship is *1 meter = 100 centimeters*. Write this conversion factor as a fraction, making sure to place the units you are converting from (centimeters, in this example) in the denominator.

3. Multiply the measurement you want to convert by the fraction. When you do this, the units in the first measurement will cancel out with the units in the denominator. Your answer will be in the units you are converting to (meters, in this example).

Example

80 centimeters = ___?___ meters

$$80 \text{ centimeters} \times \frac{1 \text{ meter}}{100 \text{ centimeters}} = \frac{80 \text{ meters}}{100}$$

$$= 0.8 \text{ meters}$$

Convert between the following units.
ACTIVITY
1. 600 millimeters = _?_ meters
2. 0.35 liters = _?_ milliliters
3. 1,050 grams = _?_ kilograms

Mass (*Students should state that the mass of the apple is 0.1 kilograms. They would need 10 apples to make 1 kilogram.*) If students need practice measuring mass, have them use a balance to measure the mass of various common objects, such as coins, paper clips, and books.

Temperature (*Students should state that the temperature of the liquid is 35°C.*) If students need practice measuring temperature, have them use a Celsius thermometer to measure the temperature of various water samples.

Converting SI Units

Review the steps for converting SI units and work through the example with students. Then ask: **How many millimeters are in 80 centimeters?** (*Students should follow the steps to calculate that 80 centimeters is equal to 800 millimeters.*)

Have students do the conversion problems in the activity. (*1. 600 millimeters = 0.6 meters; 2. 0.35 liters = 350 milliliters; 3. 1,050 grams = 1.05 kilograms*) If students need more practice converting SI units, have students make up conversion problems and trade with a partner.

Conducting a Scientific Investigation

Posing Questions

Before students do the activity on the next page, walk them through the steps of a typical scientific investigation. Begin by asking: **Why is a scientific question important to a scientific investigation?** *(It is the reason for conducting a scientific investigation and how every investigation begins.)* **What is the scientific question in the activity at the bottom of the next page?** *(Is a ball's bounce affected by the height from which it is dropped?)*

Developing a Hypothesis

Emphasize that a hypothesis is a prediction about the outcome of a scientific investigation, but it is *not* a guess. Ask: **On what information do scientists base their hypotheses?** *(Their observations and previous knowledge or experience)* Point out that a hypothesis does not always turn out to be correct. Ask: **In that case, do you think the scientist wasted his or her time? Explain your answer.** *(No, because the scientist probably learned from the investigation and maybe could develop another hypothesis that could be supported.)*

Designing an Experiment

Have a volunteer read the Experimental Procedure in the box. Then call on students to identify the manipulated variable *(amount of salt added to water)*, the variables that are kept constant *(amount and starting temperature of water, placing containers in freezer)*, the responding variable *(time it takes water to freeze)*, and the control *(Container 3)*.

Ask: **How might the experiment be affected if Container 1 had only 100 mL of water?** *(It wouldn't be a fair comparison with the containers that have more water.)* **What if Container 3 was not included in the experiment?** *(You wouldn't have anything to compare the other two containers to know if their freezing times were faster or slower than normal.)* Help students understand the importance of

Conducting a Scientific Investigation

In some ways, scientists are like detectives, piecing together clues to learn about a process or event. One way that scientists gather clues is by carrying out experiments. An experiment tests an idea in a careful, orderly manner. Although all experiments do not follow the same steps in the same order, many follow a pattern similar to the one described here.

Posing Questions

Experiments begin by asking a scientific question. A scientific question is one that can be answered by gathering evidence. For example, the question "Which freezes faster—fresh water or salt water?" is a scientific question because you can carry out an investigation and gather information to answer the question.

Developing a Hypothesis

The next step is to form a hypothesis. A **hypothesis** is a prediction about the outcome of the experiment. Like all predictions, hypotheses are based on your observations and previous knowledge or experience. But, unlike many predictions, a hypothesis must be something that can be tested. A properly worded hypothesis should take the form of an *If... then...* statement. For example, a hypothesis might be *"If I add salt to fresh water, then the water will take longer to freeze."* A hypothesis worded this way serves as a rough outline of the experiment you should perform.

264 ◆ D

keeping all variables constant except the manipulated variable. Also be sure they understand the role of the control. Then ask: **What operational definition is used in this experiment?** *("Frozen" means the time at which a wooden stick can no longer move in a container.)*

Designing an Experiment

Next you need to plan a way to test your hypothesis. Your plan should be written out as a step-by-step procedure and should describe the observations or measurements you will make.

Two important steps involved in designing an experiment are controlling variables and forming operational definitions.

Controlling Variables In a well-designed experiment, you need to keep all variables the same except for one. A **variable** is any factor that can change in an experiment. The factor that you change is called the **manipulated variable.** In this experiment, the manipulated variable is the amount of salt added to the water. Other factors, such as the amount of water or the starting temperature, are kept constant.

The factor that changes as a result of the manipulated variable is called the responding variable. The **responding variable** is what you measure or observe to obtain your results. In this experiment, the responding variable is how long the water takes to freeze.

An experiment in which all factors except one are kept constant is a **controlled experiment.** Most controlled experiments include a test called the control. In this experiment, Container 3 is the control. Because no salt is added to Container 3, you can compare the results from the other containers to it. Any difference in results must be due to the addition of salt alone.

Forming Operational Definitions
Another important aspect of a well-designed experiment is having clear operational definitions. An **operational definition** is a statement that describes how a particular variable is to be measured or how a term is to be defined. For example, in this experiment, how will you determine if the water has frozen? You might decide to insert a stick in each container at the start of the experiment. Your operational definition of "frozen" would be the time at which the stick can no longer move.

EXPERIMENTAL PROCEDURE

1. Fill 3 containers with 300 milliliters of cold tap water.

2. Add 10 grams of salt to Container 1; stir. Add 20 grams of salt to Container 2; stir. Add no salt to Container 3.

3. Place the 3 containers in a freezer.

4. Check the containers every 15 minutes. Record your observations.

Interpreting Data

The observations and measurements you make in an experiment are called data. At the end of an experiment, you need to analyze the data to look for any patterns or trends. Patterns often become clear if you organize your data in a data table or graph. Then think through what the data reveal. Do they support your hypothesis? Do they point out a flaw in your experiment? Do you need to collect more data?

Drawing Conclusions

A conclusion is a statement that sums up what you have learned from an experiment. When you draw a conclusion, you need to decide whether the data you collected support your hypothesis or not. You may need to repeat an experiment several times before you can draw any conclusions from it. Conclusions often lead you to pose new questions and plan new experiments to answer them.

Is a ball's bounce affected by the height from which it is dropped? Using the steps just described, plan a controlled experiment to investigate this problem. **ACTIVITY**

D ◆ 265

Interpreting Data

Emphasize the importance of collecting accurate and detailed data in a scientific investigation. Ask: **What if the students forgot to record the times that they made their observations in the experiment?** (*They wouldn't be able to completely analyze their data to draw valid conclusions.*) Then ask: **Why are data tables and graphs a good way to organize data?** (*It often makes it easier to compare and analyze data.*) You may wish to have students review the Skills Handbook pages on Creating Data Tables and Graphs at this point.

Drawing Conclusions

Help students understand that a conclusion is not necessarily the end of a scientific investigation. A conclusion about one experiment may lead right into another experiment. Point out that in scientific investigations, a conclusion is a summary and explanation of the results of an experiment.

Tell students to suppose that for the Experimental Procedure described on this page, they obtained the following results: Container 1 froze in 45 minutes, Container 2 in 80 minutes, and Container 3 in 25 minutes. Ask: **What conclusions can you draw about this experiment?** (*Students might conclude that the more salt that is added to fresh water, the longer it takes the water to freeze. The hypothesis is supported, and the question of which freezes faster is answered—fresh water.*)

You might wish to have students work in pairs to plan the controlled experiment. **ACTIVITY** (*Students should develop a hypothesis, such as "If I increase the height from which a ball is dropped, then the height of its bounce will increase." They can test the hypothesis by dropping balls from varying heights (the manipulated variable). All trials should be done with the same kind of ball and on the same surface (constant variables). For each trial, they should measure the height of the bounce (responding variable).*) After students have designed the experiment, provide rubber balls and invite them to carry out the experiment so they can collect and interpret data and draw conclusions.

Thinking Critically

Comparing and Contrasting

Emphasize that the skill of comparing and contrasting often relies on good observation skills, as in this activity. *(Students' answers may vary. Sample answer: Similarities—both are dogs and have four legs, two eyes, two ears, brown and white fur, black noses, pink tongues; Differences—smooth coat vs. rough coat, more white fur vs. more brown fur, shorter vs. taller, long ears vs. short ears.)*

Applying Concepts

Point out to students that they apply concepts that they learn in school in their daily lives. For example, they learn to add, subtract, multiply, and divide in school. If they get a paper route or some other part-time job, they can apply those concepts. Challenge students to practice applying concepts by doing the activity. *(People add antifreeze to the water in their car's radiator to lower the temperature at which the solution will freeze, and thus keep the water in the radiator from freezing.)*

Interpreting Illustrations

Again, point out the need for good observation skills. Ask: **What is the difference between "interpreting illustrations" and "looking at the pictures"?** *("Interpreting illustrations" requires thorough examination of the illustration, caption, and labels, while "looking at the pictures" implies less thorough examination.)* Encourage students to thoroughly examine the diagram as they do the activity. *(Students' paragraphs may vary, but should describe the internal anatomy of an earthworm, including some of the organs in the earthworm.)*

Thinking Critically

Has a friend ever asked for your advice about a problem? If so, you may have helped your friend think through the problem in a logical way. Without knowing it, you used critical-thinking skills to help your friend. Critical thinking involves the use of reasoning and logic to solve problems or make decisions. Some critical-thinking skills are described below.

Comparing and Contrasting

When you examine two objects for similarities and differences, you are using the skill of **comparing and contrasting.** Comparing involves identifying similarities, or common characteristics. Contrasting involves identifying differences. Analyzing objects in this way can help you discover details that you might otherwise overlook.

Compare and contrast the two animals in the photo. First list all the similarities that you see. Then list all the differences.

Applying Concepts

When you use your knowledge about one situation to make sense of a similar situation, you are using the skill of **applying concepts.** Being able to transfer your knowledge from one situation to another shows that you truly understand a concept. You may use this skill in answering test questions that present different problems from the ones you've reviewed in class.

You have just learned that water takes longer to freeze when other substances are mixed into it. Use this knowledge to explain why people add a substance called antifreeze to their car's radiator in the winter.

Interpreting Illustrations

Diagrams, photographs, and maps are included in textbooks to help clarify what you read. These illustrations show processes, places, and ideas in a visual manner. The skill called **interpreting illustrations** can help you learn from these visual elements. To understand an illustration, take the time to study the illustration along with all the written information that accompanies it. Captions identify the key concepts shown in the illustration. Labels point out the important parts of a diagram or map, while keys identify the symbols used in a map.

Blood vessels
Reproductive organs
Hearts
Brain
Mouth
Bristles
Digestive tract
Nerve cord
Waste-removal organs
Intestine

▲ Internal anatomy of an earthworm

Study the diagram above. Then write a short paragraph explaining what you have learned.

Relating Cause and Effect

If one event causes another event to occur, the two events are said to have a cause-and-effect relationship. When you determine that such a relationship exists between two events, you use a skill called **relating cause and effect.** For example, if you notice an itchy, red bump on your skin, you might infer that a mosquito bit you. The mosquito bite is the cause, and the bump is the effect.

It is important to note that two events do not necessarily have a cause-and-effect relationship just because they occur together. Scientists carry out experiments or use past experience to determine whether a cause-and-effect relationship exists.

ACTIVITY
You are on a camping trip and your flashlight has stopped working. List some possible causes for the flashlight malfunction. How could you determine which cause-and-effect relationship has left you in the dark?

Making Generalizations

When you draw a conclusion about an entire group based on information about only some of the group's members, you are using a skill called **making generalizations.** For a generalization to be valid, the sample you choose must be large enough and representative of the entire group. You might, for example, put this skill to work at a farm stand if you see a sign that says, "Sample some grapes before you buy." If you sample a few sweet grapes, you may conclude that all the grapes are sweet—and purchase a large bunch.

ACTIVITY
A team of scientists needs to determine whether the water in a large reservoir is safe to drink. How could they use the skill of making generalizations to help them? What should they do?

Making Judgments

When you evaluate something to decide whether it is good or bad, or right or wrong, you are using a skill called **making judgments.** For example, you make judgments when you decide to eat healthful foods or to pick up litter in a park. Before you make a judgment, you need to think through the pros and cons of a situation, and identify the values or standards that you hold.

ACTIVITY
Should children and teens be required to wear helmets when bicycling? Explain why you feel the way you do.

Problem Solving

When you use critical-thinking skills to resolve an issue or decide on a course of action, you are using a skill called **problem solving.** Some problems, such as how to convert a fraction into a decimal, are straightforward. Other problems, such as figuring out why your computer has stopped working, are complex. Some complex problems can be solved using the trial and error method—try out one solution first, and if that doesn't work, try another. Other useful problem-solving strategies include making models and brainstorming possible solutions with a partner.

Relating Cause and Effect

Emphasize that not all events that occur together have a cause-and-effect relationship. For example, tell students that you went to the grocery and your car stalled. Ask: **Is there a cause-and-effect relationship in this situation? Explain your answer.** *(No, because going to the grocery could not cause a car to stall. There must be another cause to make the car stall.)* Have students do the activity to practice relating cause and effect. *(Students should identify that the flashlight not working is the effect. Some possible causes include dead batteries, a burned-out light bulb, or a loose part.)*

Making Generalizations

Point out the importance of having a large, representative sample before making a generalization. Ask: **If you went fishing at a lake and caught three catfish, could you make the generalization that all fish in the lake are catfish? Why or why not?** *(No, because there might be other kinds of fish you didn't catch because they didn't like the bait or they may be in other parts of the lake.)* **How could you make a generalization about the kinds of fish in the lake?** *(By having a larger sample)* Have students do the activity to practice making generalizations. *(The scientists should collect and test water samples from a number of different parts of the reservoir.)*

Making Judgments

Remind students that they make a judgment almost every time they make a decision. Ask: **What steps should you follow to make a judgment?** *(Gather information, list pros and cons, analyze values, make judgment)* Invite students to do the activity, and then to share and discuss the judgments they made. *(Students' judgments will vary, but should be supported by valid reasoning. Sample answer: Children and teens should be required to wear helmets when bicycling because helmets have been proven to save lives and reduce head injuries.)*

Problem Solving

ACTIVITY

Challenge student pairs to solve a problem about a soapbox derby. Explain that their younger brother is building a car to enter in the race. The brother wants to know how to make his soapbox car go faster. After student pairs have considered the problem, have them share their ideas about solutions with the class. *(Most will probably suggest using trial and error by making small changes to the car and testing the car after each change. Some students may suggest making and manipulating a model.)*

Organizing Information

Concept Maps

Challenge students to make a concept map with at least three levels of concepts to organize information about types of transportation. All students should start with the phrase *types of transportation* at the top of the concept map. After that point, their concept maps may vary. *(For example, some students might place* private transportation *and* public transportation *at the next level, while other students might have* human-powered *and* gas-powered. *Make sure students connect the concepts with linking words. Challenge students to include cross-linkages as well.)*

Compare/ Contrast Tables

Have students make their own compare/contrast tables using two or more different sports or other activities, such as playing musical instruments. Emphasize that students should select characteristics that highlight the similarities and differences between the activities. *(Students' compare/contrast tables should include several appropriate characteristics and list information about each activity for every characteristic.)*

Organizing Information

As you read this textbook, how can you make sense of all the information it contains? Some useful tools to help you organize information are shown on this page. These tools are called *graphic organizers* because they give you a visual picture of a topic, showing at a glance how key concepts are related.

Concept Maps

Concept maps are useful tools for organizing information on broad topics. A concept map begins with a general concept and shows how it can be broken down into more specific concepts. In that way, relationships between concepts become easier to understand.

A concept map is constructed by placing concept words (usually nouns) in ovals and connecting them with linking words. Often, the most general concept word is placed at the top, and the words become more specific as you move downward. Often the linking words, which are written on a line extending between two ovals, describe the relationship between the two concepts they connect. If you follow any string of concepts and linking words down the map, it should read like a sentence.

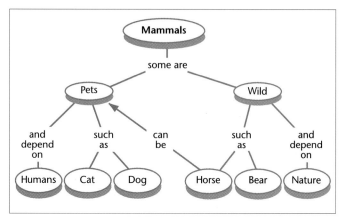

Some concept maps include linking words that connect a concept on one branch of the map to a concept on another branch. These linking words, called cross-linkages, show more complex interrelationships among concepts.

Compare/Contrast Tables

Compare/contrast tables are useful tools for sorting out the similarities and differences between two or more items. A table provides an organized framework in which to compare items based on specific characteristics that you identify.

To create a compare/contrast table, list the items to be compared across the top of a table. Then list the characteristics that will form the basis of your comparison in the left-hand

Characteristic	Baseball	Basketball
Number of Players	9	5
Playing Field	Baseball diamond	Basketball court
Equipment	Bat, baseball, mitts	Basket, basketball

column. Complete the table by filling in information about each characteristic, first for one item and then for the other.

Venn Diagrams

Another way to show similarities and differences between items is with a Venn diagram. A Venn diagram consists of two or more circles that partially overlap. Each circle represents a particular concept or idea. Common characteristics, or similarities, are written within the area of overlap between the two circles. Unique characteristics, or differences, are written in the parts of the circles outside the area of overlap.

To create a Venn diagram, draw two overlapping circles. Label the circles with the names of the items being compared. Write the

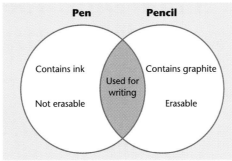

Pen   **Pencil**

Contains ink

Contains graphite

Used for writing

Not erasable

Erasable

unique characteristics in each circle outside the area of overlap. Then write the shared characteristics within the area of overlap.

Flowcharts

A flowchart can help you understand the order in which certain events have occurred or should occur. Flowcharts are useful for outlining the stages in a process or the steps in a procedure.

To make a flowchart, write a brief description of each event in a box. Place the first event at the top of the page, followed by the second event, the third event, and so on. Then draw an arrow to connect each event to the one that occurs next.

Preparing Pasta

Boil water

↓

Cook pasta

↓

Drain water

↓

Add sauce

Cycle Diagrams

A cycle diagram can be used to show a sequence of events that is continuous, or cyclical. A continuous sequence does not have an end because, when the final event is over, the first event begins again. Like a flowchart, a cycle diagram can help you understand the order of events.

To create a cycle diagram, write a brief description of each event in a box. Place one event at the top of the page in the center. Then, moving in a clockwise direction around an imaginary circle, write each event in its proper sequence. Draw arrows that connect each event to the one that occurs next, forming a continuous circle.

Steps in a Science Experiment

Pose a question

Develop a hypothesis

Design an experiment

Interpret data

Draw conclusions

D ◆ 269

Venn Diagrams
ACTIVITY

Students can use the same information from their compare/contrast tables to create a Venn diagram. Make sure students understand that the overlapping area of the circles is used to list similarities and the parts of the circles outside the overlap area are used to show differences. If students want to list similarities and differences among three activities, show them how to add a third circle that overlaps each of the other two circles and has an area of overlap for all three circles. *(Students' Venn diagrams will vary. Make sure they have accurately listed similarities in the overlap area and differences in the parts of the circles that do not overlap.)*

Flowcharts
ACTIVITY

Encourage students to create a flowchart to show the things they did this morning as they got ready for school. Remind students that a flowchart should show the correct order in which events occurred or should occur. *(Students' flowcharts will vary somewhat. A typical flowchart might include: got up → ate breakfast → took a shower → brushed teeth → got dressed → gathered books and homework → put on jacket.)*

Cycle Diagrams
ACTIVITY

Review that a cycle diagram shows a sequence of events that is continuous. Then challenge students to create a cycle diagram that shows how the weather changes with the seasons where they live. *(Students' cycle diagrams may vary, though most will include four steps, one for each season.)*

Creating Data Tables and Graphs

Data Tables

Have students create a data table to show how much time they spend on different activities during one week. Suggest that students first list the main activities they do every week. Then they should determine the amount of time they spend on each activity each day. Remind students to give this data table a title. *(Students' data tables will vary. A sample data table is shown below.)*

Bar Graphs

Students can use the data from their data table above to make a bar graph showing how much time they spend on different activities during a week. Help students understand that on this particular graph, the time spent on each activity is the responding variable, because it is the result being measured. Therefore, the vertical axis should be divided into units of time, such as hours. Remind students to label both axes and give their graph a title. *(Students' bar graphs will vary. A sample bar graph is shown below.)*

Creating Data Tables and Graphs

How can you make sense of the data in a science experiment? The first step is to organize the data to help you understand them. Data tables and graphs are helpful tools for organizing data.

Data Tables

You have gathered your materials and set up your experiment. But before you start, you need to plan a way to record what happens during the experiment. By creating a data table, you can record your observations and measurements in an orderly way.

Suppose, for example, that a scientist conducted an experiment to find out how many Calories people of different body weights burn while doing various activities. The data table shows the results.

Notice in this data table that the manipulated variable (body weight) is the heading of one column. The responding variable (for Experiment 1, the number of Calories burned while bicycling) is the heading of the next column. Additional columns were added for related experiments.

CALORIES BURNED IN 30 MINUTES OF ACTIVITY			
Body Weight	Experiment 1 Bicycling	Experiment 2 Playing Basketball	Experiment 3 Watching Television
30 kg	60 Calories	120 Calories	21 Calories
40 kg	77 Calories	164 Calories	27 Calories
50 kg	95 Calories	206 Calories	33 Calories
60 kg	114 Calories	248 Calories	38 Calories

Bar Graphs

To compare how many Calories a person burns doing various activities, you could create a bar graph. A bar graph is used to display data in a number of separate, or distinct, categories. In this example, bicycling, playing basketball, and watching television are three separate categories.

To create a bar graph, follow these steps.

1. On graph paper, draw a horizontal, or *x*-, axis and a vertical, or *y*-, axis.
2. Write the names of the categories to be graphed along the horizontal axis. Include an overall label for the axis as well.
3. Label the vertical axis with the name of the responding variable. Include units of measurement. Then create a scale along the axis by marking off equally spaced numbers that cover the range of the data collected.
4. For each category, draw a solid bar using the scale on the vertical axis to determine the

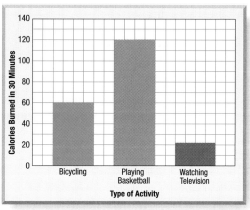

Calories Burned by a 30-kilogram Person in Various Activities

appropriate height. For example, for bicycling, draw the bar as high as the 60 mark on the vertical axis. Make all the bars the same width and leave equal spaces between them.
5. Add a title that describes the graph.

Time Spent on Different Activities in a Week				
	Going to Classes	Eating Meals	Playing Soccer	Watching Television
Monday	6	2	2	0.5
Tuesday	6	1.5	1.5	1.5
Wednesday	6	2	1	2
Thursday	6	2	2	1.5
Friday	6	2	2	0.5
Saturday	0	2.5	2.5	1
Sunday	0	3	1	2

Time Spent on Different Activities in a Week

Line Graphs

To see whether a relationship exists between body weight and the number of Calories burned while bicycling, you could create a line graph. A line graph is used to display data that show how one variable (the responding variable) changes in response to another variable (the manipulated variable). You can use a line graph when your manipulated variable is *continuous*, that is, when there are other points between the ones that you tested. In this example, body weight is a continuous variable because there are other body weights between 30 and 40 kilograms (for example, 31 kilograms). Time is another example of a continuous variable.

Line graphs are powerful tools because they allow you to estimate values for conditions that you did not test in the experiment. For example, you can use the line graph to estimate that a 35-kilogram person would burn 68 Calories while bicycling.

To create a line graph, follow these steps.

1. On graph paper, draw a horizontal, or *x*-, axis and a vertical, or *y*-, axis.
2. Label the horizontal axis with the name of the manipulated variable. Label the vertical axis with the name of the responding variable. Include units of measurement.
3. Create a scale on each axis by marking off equally spaced numbers that cover the range of the data collected.
4. Plot a point on the graph for each piece of data. In the line graph above, the dotted lines show how to plot the first data point (30 kilograms and 60 Calories). Draw an imaginary vertical line extending up from the horizontal axis at the 30-kilogram mark. Then draw an imaginary horizontal line extending across from the vertical axis at the 60-Calorie mark. Plot the point where the two lines intersect.

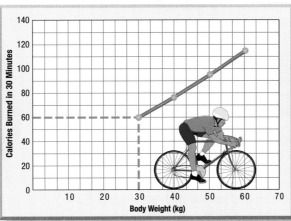

Effect of Body Weight on Calories Burned While Bicycling

5. Connect the plotted points with a solid line. (In some cases, it may be more appropriate to draw a line that shows the general trend of the plotted points. In those cases, some of the points may fall above or below the line.)
6. Add a title that identifies the variables or relationship in the graph.

> **ACTIVITY**
> Create line graphs to display the data from Experiment 2 and Experiment 3 in the data table.

> **ACTIVITY**
> You read in the newspaper that a total of 4 centimeters of rain fell in your area in June, 2.5 centimeters fell in July, and 1.5 centimeters fell in August. What type of graph would you use to display these data? Use graph paper to create the graph.

Line Graphs

Walk students through the steps involved in creating a line graph using the example illustrated on the page. For example, ask: **What is the label on the horizontal axis? On the vertical axis?** *(Body Weight (kg); Calories Burned in 30 Minutes)* **What scales are used on each axis?** *(10 kg on the x-axis and 20 calories on the y-axis)* **What does the second data point represent?** *(77 Calories burned for a body weight of 40 kg)* **What trend or pattern does the graph show?** *(The number of Calories burned in 30 minutes of cycling increases with body weight.)*

Have students follow the steps to carry out the first **ACTIVITY**. *(Students should make a different graph for each experiment with different y-axis scales to practice making scales appropriate for data. See sample graphs below.)*

Have students carry out the second **ACTIVITY**. *(Students should conclude that a bar graph would be best to display the data. A sample bar graph for these data is shown below.)*

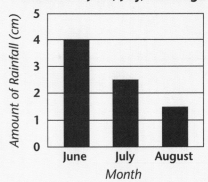

Rainfall in June, July, and August

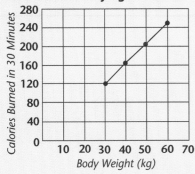

Effect of Body Weight on Calories Burned While Playing Basketball

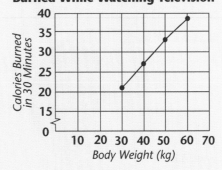

Effect of Body Weight on Calories Burned While Watching Television

Circle Graphs

Emphasize that a circle graph has to include 100 percent of the categories for the topic being graphed. For example, ask: **Could the data in the bar graph titled "Calories Burned by a 30-kilogram Person in Various Activities" (on the previous page) be shown in a circle graph? Why or why not?** *(No, because it does not include all the possible ways a 30-kilogram person can burn Calories.)* Then walk students through the steps for making a circle graph. Help students to use a compass and a protractor. Use the protractor to illustrate that a circle has 360 degrees. Make sure students understand the mathematical calculations involved in making a circle graph.

You might wish to have students work in pairs to complete the activity. *(Students' circle graphs should look like the graph below.)*

Circle Graphs

Like bar graphs, circle graphs can be used to display data in a number of separate categories. Unlike bar graphs, however, circle graphs can only be used when you have data for *all* the categories that make up a given topic. A circle graph is sometimes called a pie chart because it resembles a pie cut into slices. The pie represents the entire topic, while the slices represent the individual categories. The size of a slice indicates what percentage of the whole a particular category makes up.

The data table below shows the results of a survey in which 24 teenagers were asked to identify their favorite sport. The data were then used to create the circle graph at the right.

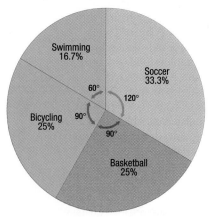

Sports That Teens Prefer

FAVORITE SPORTS

Sport	Number of Students
Soccer	8
Basketball	6
Bicycling	6
Swimming	4

To create a circle graph, follow these steps.

1. Use a compass to draw a circle. Mark the center of the circle with a point. Then draw a line from the center point to the top of the circle.
2. Determine the size of each "slice" by setting up a proportion where x equals the number of degrees in a slice. (NOTE: A circle contains 360 degrees.) For example, to find the number of degrees in the "soccer" slice, set up the following proportion:

$$\frac{\text{students who prefer soccer}}{\text{total number of students}} = \frac{x}{\text{total number of degrees in a circle}}$$

$$\frac{8}{24} = \frac{x}{360}$$

Cross-multiply and solve for x.

$$24x = 8 \times 360$$
$$x = 120$$

The "soccer" slice should contain 120 degrees.

3. Use a protractor to measure the angle of the first slice, using the line you drew to the top of the circle as the 0° line. Draw a line from the center of the circle to the edge for the angle you measured.
4. Continue around the circle by measuring the size of each slice with the protractor. Start measuring from the edge of the previous slice so the wedges do not overlap. When you are done, the entire circle should be filled in.
5. Determine the percentage of the whole circle that each slice represents. To do this, divide the number of degrees in a slice by the total number of degrees in a circle (360), and multiply by 100%. For the "soccer" slice, you can find the percentage as follows:

$$\frac{120}{360} \times 100\% = 33.3\%$$

6. Use a different color to shade in each slice. Label each slice with the name of the category and with the percentage of the whole it represents.
7. Add a title to the circle graph.

In a class of 28 students, 12 students **ACTIVITY** take the bus to school, 10 students walk, and 6 students ride their bicycles. Create a circle graph to display these data.

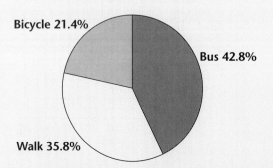

Ways Students Get to School

Bicycle 21.4%

Bus 42.8%

Walk 35.8%

Laboratory Safety

Safety Symbols

These symbols alert you to possible dangers in the laboratory and remind you to work carefully.

Safety Goggles Always wear safety goggles to protect your eyes in any activity involving chemicals, flames or heating, or the possibility of broken glassware.

Lab Apron Wear a laboratory apron to protect your skin and clothing from damage.

Breakage You are working with materials that may be breakable, such as glass containers, glass tubing, thermometers, or funnels. Handle breakable materials with care. Do not touch broken glassware.

Heat-resistant Gloves Use an oven mitt or other hand protection when handling hot materials. Hot plates, hot glassware, or hot water can cause burns. Do not touch hot objects with your bare hands.

Heating Use a clamp or tongs to pick up hot glassware. Do not touch hot objects with your bare hands.

Sharp Object Pointed-tip scissors, scalpels, knives, needles, pins, or tacks are sharp. They can cut or puncture your skin. Always direct a sharp edge or point away from yourself and others. Use sharp instruments only as instructed.

Electric Shock Avoid the possibility of electric shock. Never use electrical equipment around water, or when the equipment is wet or your hands are wet. Be sure cords are untangled and cannot trip anyone. Disconnect the equipment when it is not in use.

Corrosive Chemical You are working with an acid or another corrosive chemical. Avoid getting it on your skin or clothing, or in your eyes. Do not inhale the vapors. Wash your hands when you are finished with the activity.

Poison Do not let any poisonous chemical come in contact with your skin, and do not inhale its vapors. Wash your hands when you are finished with the activity.

Physical Safety When an experiment involves physical activity, take precautions to avoid injuring yourself or others. Follow instructions from your teacher. Alert your teacher if there is any reason you should not participate in the activity.

Animal Safety Treat live animals with care to avoid harming the animals or yourself. Working with animal parts or preserved animals also may require caution. Wash your hands when you are finished with the activity.

Plant Safety Handle plants in the laboratory or during field work only as directed by your teacher. If you are allergic to certain plants, tell your teacher before doing an activity in which those plants are used. Avoid touching harmful plants such as poison ivy, poison oak, or poison sumac, or plants with thorns. Wash your hands when you are finished with the activity.

Flames You may be working with flames from a lab burner, candle, or matches. Tie back loose hair and clothing. Follow instructions from your teacher about lighting and extinguishing flames.

No Flames Flammable materials may be present. Make sure there are no flames, sparks, or other exposed heat sources present.

Fumes When poisonous or unpleasant vapors may be involved, work in a ventilated area. Avoid inhaling vapors directly. Only test an odor when directed to do so by your teacher, and use a wafting motion to direct the vapor toward your nose.

Disposal Chemicals and other laboratory materials used in the activity must be disposed of safely. Follow the instructions from your teacher.

Hand Washing Wash your hands thoroughly when finished with the activity. Use antibacterial soap and warm water. Lather both sides of your hands and between your fingers. Rinse well.

General Safety Awareness You may see this symbol when none of the symbols described earlier appears. In this case, follow the specific instructions provided. You may also see this symbol when you are asked to develop your own procedure in a lab. Have your teacher approve your plan before you go further.

D ◆ 273

Laboratory Safety

Laboratory safety is an essential element of a successful science class. It is important for you to emphasize laboratory safety to students. Students need to understand exactly what is safe and unsafe behavior, and what the rationale is behind each safety rule.

Review with students the Safety Symbols and Science Safety Rules listed on this and the next two pages. Then follow the safety guidelines below to ensure that your classroom will be a safe place for students to learn science.

◆ Post safety rules in the classroom and review them regularly with students.
◆ Familiarize yourself with the safety procedures for each activity before introducing it to your students.
◆ Review specific safety precautions with students before beginning every science activity.
◆ Always act as an exemplary role model by displaying safe behavior.
◆ Know how to use safety equipment, such as fire extinguishers and fire blankets, and always have it accessible.
◆ Have students practice leaving the classroom quickly and orderly to prepare them for emergencies.
◆ Explain to students how to use the intercom or other available means of communication to get help during an emergency.
◆ Never leave students unattended while they are engaged in science activities.
◆ Provide enough space for students to safely carry out science activities.
◆ Keep your classroom and all science materials in proper condition. Replace worn or broken items.
◆ Instruct students to report all accidents and injuries to you immediately.

Laboratory Safety

Additional tips are listed below for the Science Safety Rules discussed on these two pages. Please keep these tips in mind when you carry out science activities in your classroom.

General Precautions

♦ For open-ended activities like Chapter Projects, go over general safety guidelines with students. Have students submit their procedures or design plans in writing and check them for safety considerations.
♦ In an activity where students are directed to taste something, be sure to store the material in clean, *nonscience* containers. Distribute the material to students in *new* plastic or paper dispensables, which should be discarded after the tasting. Tasting or eating should never be done in a lab classroom.
♦ During physical activity, make sure students do not overexert themselves.
♦ Remind students to handle microscopes and telescopes with care to avoid breakage.

Heating and Fire Safety

♦ No flammable substances should be in use around hot plates, light bulbs, or open flames.
♦ Test tubes should be heated only in water baths.
♦ Students should be permitted to strike matches to light candles or burners *only* with strict supervision. When possible, you should light the flames, especially when working with sixth graders.
♦ Be sure to have proper ventilation when fumes are produced during a procedure.
♦ All electrical equipment used in the lab should have GFI switches.

Using Chemicals Safely

♦ When students use both chemicals and microscopes in one activity, microscopes should be in a separate part of the room from the chemicals so that when students remove their goggles to use the microscopes, their eyes are not at risk.

Science Safety Rules

To prepare yourself to work safely in the laboratory, read over the following safety rules. Then read them a second time. Make sure you understand and follow each rule. Ask your teacher to explain any rules you do not understand.

Dress Code

1. To protect yourself from injuring your eyes, wear safety goggles whenever you work with chemicals, burners, glassware, or any substance that might get into your eyes. If you wear contact lenses, notify your teacher.
2. Wear a lab apron or coat whenever you work with corrosive chemicals or substances that can stain.
3. Tie back long hair to keep it away from any chemicals, flames, or equipment.
4. Remove or tie back any article of clothing or jewelry that can hang down and touch chemicals, flames, or equipment. Roll up or secure long sleeves.
5. Never wear open shoes or sandals.

General Precautions

6. Read all directions for an experiment several times before beginning the activity. Carefully follow all written and oral instructions. If you are in doubt about any part of the experiment, ask your teacher for assistance.
7. Never perform activities that are not assigned or authorized by your teacher. Obtain permission before "experimenting" on your own. Never handle any equipment unless you have specific permission.
8. Never perform lab activities without direct supervision.
9. Never eat or drink in the laboratory.
10. Keep work areas clean and tidy at all times. Bring only notebooks and lab manuals or written lab procedures to the work area. All other items, such as purses and backpacks, should be left in a designated area.
11. Do not engage in horseplay.

First Aid

12. Always report all accidents or injuries to your teacher, no matter how minor. Notify your teacher immediately about any fires.
13. Learn what to do in case of specific accidents, such as getting acid in your eyes or on your skin. (Rinse acids from your body with lots of water.)
14. Be aware of the location of the first-aid kit, but do not use it unless instructed by your teacher. In case of injury, your teacher should administer first aid. Your teacher may also send you to the school nurse or call a physician.
15. Know the location of emergency equipment, such as the fire extinguisher and fire blanket, and know how to use it.
16. Know the location of the nearest telephone and whom to contact in an emergency.

Heating and Fire Safety

17. Never use a heat source, such as a candle, burner, or hot plate, without wearing safety goggles.
18. Never heat anything unless instructed to do so. A chemical that is harmless when cool may be dangerous when heated.
19. Keep all combustible materials away from flames. Never use a flame or spark near a combustible chemical.
20. Never reach across a flame.
21. Before using a laboratory burner, make sure you know proper procedures for lighting and adjusting the burner, as demonstrated by your teacher. Do not touch the burner. It may be hot. And never leave a lighted burner unattended!
22. Chemicals can splash or boil out of a heated test tube. When heating a substance in a test tube, make sure that the mouth of the tube is not pointed at you or anyone else.
23. Never heat a liquid in a closed container. The expanding gases produced may blow the container apart.
24. Before picking up a container that has been heated, hold the back of your hand near it. If you can feel heat on the back of your hand, the container is too hot to handle. Use an oven mitt to pick up a container that has been heated.

Using Glassware Safely

♦ Use plastic containers, graduated cylinders, and beakers whenever possible. If using glass, students should wear safety goggles.
♦ Use only nonmercury thermometers with anti-roll protectors.
♦ Check all glassware periodically for chips and scratches, which can cause cuts and breakage.

Using Chemicals Safely

25. Never mix chemicals "for the fun of it." You might produce a dangerous, possibly explosive substance.

26. Never put your face near the mouth of a container that holds chemicals. Never touch, taste, or smell a chemical unless you are instructed by your teacher to do so. Many chemicals are poisonous.

27. Use only those chemicals needed in the activity. Read and double-check labels on supply bottles before removing any chemicals. Take only as much as you need. Keep all containers closed when chemicals are not being used.

28. Dispose of all chemicals as instructed by your teacher. To avoid contamination, never return chemicals to their original containers. Never simply pour chemicals or other substances into the sink or trash containers.

29. Be extra careful when working with acids or bases. Pour all chemicals over the sink or a container, not over your work surface.

30. If you are instructed to test for odors, use a wafting motion to direct the odors to your nose. Do not inhale the fumes directly from the container.

31. When mixing an acid and water, always pour the water into the container first and then add the acid to the water. Never pour water into an acid.

32. Take extreme care not to spill any material in the laboratory. Wash chemical spills and splashes immediately with plenty of water. Immediately begin rinsing with water any acids that get on your skin or clothing, and notify your teacher of any acid spill at the same time.

Using Glassware Safely

33. Never force glass tubing or thermometers into a rubber stopper or rubber tubing. Have your teacher insert the glass tubing or thermometer if required for an activity.

34. If you are using a laboratory burner, use a wire screen to protect glassware from any flame. Never heat glassware that is not thoroughly dry on the outside.

35. Keep in mind that hot glassware looks cool. Never pick up glassware without first checking to see if it is hot. Use an oven mitt. See rule 24.

36. Never use broken or chipped glassware. If glassware breaks, notify your teacher and dispose of the glassware in the proper broken-glassware container. Never handle broken glass with your bare hands.

37. Never eat or drink from lab glassware.

38. Thoroughly clean glassware before putting it away.

Using Sharp Instruments

39. Handle scalpels or other sharp instruments with extreme care. Never cut material toward you; cut away from you.

40. Immediately notify your teacher if you cut your skin when working in the laboratory.

Animal and Plant Safety

41. Never perform experiments that cause pain, discomfort, or harm to mammals, birds, reptiles, fishes, or amphibians. This rule applies at home as well as in the classroom.

42. Animals should be handled only if absolutely necessary. Your teacher will instruct you as to how to handle each animal species brought into the classroom.

43. If you know that you are allergic to certain plants, molds, or animals, tell your teacher before doing an activity in which these are used.

44. During field work, protect your skin by wearing long pants, long sleeves, socks, and closed shoes. Know how to recognize the poisonous plants and fungi in your area, as well as plants with thorns, and avoid contact with them.

45. Never eat any part of an unidentified plant or fungus.

46. Wash your hands thoroughly after handling animals or the cage containing animals. Wash your hands when you are finished with any activity involving animal parts, plants, or soil.

End-of-Experiment Rules

47. After an experiment has been completed, clean up your work area and return all equipment to its proper place.

48. Dispose of waste materials as instructed by your teacher.

49. Wash your hands after every experiment.

50. Always turn off all burners or hot plates when they are not in use. Unplug hot plates and other electrical equipment. If you used a burner, check that the gas-line valve to the burner is off as well.

Using Sharp Instruments

◆ Always use blunt-tip safety scissors, except when pointed-tip scissors are required.

Animal and Plant Safety

◆ When working with live animals or plants, check ahead of time for students who may have allergies to the specimens.

◆ When growing bacteria cultures, use only disposable petri dishes. After streaking, the dishes should be sealed and not opened again by students. After the lab, students should return the unopened dishes to you. Students should wash their hands with antibacterial soap.

◆ Two methods are recommended for the safe disposal of bacteria cultures. *First method:* Autoclave the petri dishes and discard without opening. *Second method:* If no autoclave is available, carefully open the dishes (never have a student do this) and pour full-strength bleach into the dishes and let stand for a day. Then pour the bleach from the petri dishes down a drain and flush the drain with lots of water. Tape the petri dishes back together and place in a sealed plastic bag. Wrap the plastic bag with a brown paper bag or newspaper and tape securely. Throw the sealed package in the trash. Thoroughly disinfect the work area with bleach.

◆ To grow mold, use a new, sealable plastic bag that is two to three times larger than the material to be placed inside. Seal the bag and tape it shut. After the bag is sealed, students should not open it. To dispose of the bag and mold culture, make a small cut near an edge of the bag and cook in a microwave oven on high setting for at least 1 minute. Discard the bag according to local ordinance, usually in the trash.

◆ Students should wear disposable nitrile, latex, or food-handling gloves when handling live animals or nonliving specimens.

End-of-Experiment Rules

◆ Always have students use antibacterial soap for washing their hands.

A

absorption The process by which nutrient molecules pass through the wall of the digestive system into the blood. (p. 83)

acne A bacterial infection of the skin in which the oil glands become blocked and swollen. (p. 62)

active immunity Immunity that occurs when a person's own immune system produces antibodies in response to the presence of a pathogen. (p. 170)

addiction A physical dependence on a substance; an intense need by the body for a substance. (p. 141)

adolescence The stage of development between childhood and adulthood when children become adults physically and mentally. (p. 244)

adrenaline A chemical that gives a burst of energy and causes changes in the body to prepare a person for quick action. (p. 26)

AIDS (acquired immunodeficiency syndrome) A disease caused by a virus that attacks the immune system. (p. 166)

alcoholism A disease in which a person is both physically addicted to and emotionally dependent on alcohol. (p. 219)

allergen A substance that causes an allergy. (p. 176)

allergy A disorder in which the immune system is overly sensitive to a foreign substance. (p. 175)

alveoli Tiny sacs of lung tissue specialized for the movement of gases between the air and the blood. (p. 134)

amino acids Small units that are linked together chemically to form large protein molecules. (p. 72)

amniotic sac A fluid-filled sac that cushions and protects a developing fetus in the uterus. (p. 238)

anabolic steroids Synthetic chemicals that are similar to hormones produced in the body and that may increase muscle size and cause mood swings. (p. 216)

antibiotic A chemical that kills bacteria or slows their growth without harming the body cells of humans. (p. 174)

antibody A chemical produced by a B cell of the immune system that destroys a specific kind of pathogen. (p.165)

antigen A molecule on a cell that the immune syst can recognize either as part of the body or as coming from outside the body. (p. 164)

anus A muscular opening at the end of the rectum through which digestive waste material is elimir from the body. (p. 93)

aorta The largest artery in the body. (p. 106)

artery A blood vessel that carries blood away from heart. (p. 104)

asthma A disorder in which the respiratory passag narrow significantly. (p. 176)

atherosclerosis A condition in which an artery wa thickens as a result of the buildup of fatty mater (p. 121)

atrium Each of the two upper chambers of the hear that receives blood that comes into the heart. (p.

autonomic nervous system The group of nerves t controls involuntary actions. (p. 200)

axon A threadlike extension of a neuron that carri nerve impulses away from the cell body. (p. 192

B

B cell A lymphocyte that produces chemicals that destroy a specific kind of pathogen. (p. 165)

bile A substance produced by the liver that breaks fat particles. (p. 91)

blood pressure The pressure that is exerted by the blood against the walls of blood vessels. (p. 111)

blood transfusion The transference of blood from person to another. (p. 116)

brain The part of the central nervous system that i located in the skull and controls most functions the body. (p. 197)

brainstem The part of the brain that controls man body functions that occur automatically. (p. 19)

bronchi The passages that branch from the trachea and direct air into the lungs. (p. 134)

bronchitis An irritation of the breathing passages which the small passages become narrower than normal and may be clogged with mucus. (p. 14)

C

calorie The amount of energy needed to raise the temperature of one gram of water by one Celsiu degree. (p. 69)

cancer A disease in which some body cells divide uncontrollably. (p. 61)

capillary A tiny blood vessel where substances are exchanged between the blood and the body cell (p. 104)

ohydrates Nutrients composed of carbon, oxygen, d hydrogen that are a major source of energy and ovide the raw materials to make parts of cells. . 69)

on monoxide A colorless, odorless gas produced en substances—including tobacco—are burned. . 141)

nogen A substance or a factor in the environment at can cause cancer. (p. 178)

iac muscle Muscle tissue found only in the heart. . 53)

iovascular system The body system that consists the heart, blood vessels, and blood, and that rries needed substances to cells and carries waste oducts away from cells. (p. 100)

lage A connective tissue that is more flexible than ne and that gives support to some parts of the dy. (p. 42)

membrane The outside boundary of a cell. (p. 18) he basic unit of structure and function in a living ing. (p. 18)

ral nervous system The brain and spinal cord; the ntrol center of the body. (p. 196)

bellum The part of the brain that coordinates the tions of the muscles and helps maintain balance. . 199)

rum The part of the brain that interprets input m the senses, controls the movement of skeletal uscles, and carries out complex mental processes. . 198)

esterol A waxy, fatlike substance, found only in imal products, that is an important part of your dy's cells; can build up on artery walls. (p. 71)

mosomes Rod-shaped structures in cells that carry e information that controls inherited characteristics ch as eye color and blood type. (p. 231) Tiny hairlike extensions of cells that can move gether like whips. (p. 132)

lea A snail-shaped tube in the inner ear lined with und receptors; nerve impulses are sent from the chlea to the brain. (p. 209)

ussion A bruiselike injury of the brain that occurs en the soft tissue of the cerebrum bumps against e skull. (p. 202)

ective tissue A body tissue that provides support r the body and connects all of its parts. (p. 19)

inuum A gradual progression through many ages between one extreme and another, as in the ness-wellness continuum. (p. 30)

rolled experiment An experiment in which all ctors are identical except one. (p. 265)

ea The clear tissue that covers the front of the eye. 205)

coronary artery An artery that supplies blood to the heart itself. (p. 107)

cytoplasm The area in a cell between the cell membrane and the nucleus; contains a clear, jellylike substance in which cell structures are found. (p. 18)

delivery The second stage of birth, in which the baby is pushed completely out of the uterus, through the vagina, and out of the mother's body. (p. 240)

dendrite A threadlike extension of a neuron that carries nerve impulses toward the cell body. (p. 192)

depressant A drug that slows down the activity of the central nervous system. (p. 214)

dermis The lower layer of the skin. (p. 59)

diabetes A condition in which either the pancreas fails to produce enough insulin, or the body's cells can't use it properly. (p. 177)

diaphragm A large, dome-shaped muscle that plays an important role in breathing. (p. 136)

diffusion The process by which molecules move from an area in which they are highly concentrated to an area in which they are less concentrated. (p. 109)

digestion The process by which the body breaks down food into small nutrient molecules. (p. 82)

dislocation An injury in which a bone comes out of its joint. (p. 46)

drug abuse The deliberate misuse of drugs for purposes other than appropriate medical ones. (p. 213)

drug Any chemical that causes changes in a person's body or behavior. (p. 212)

eardrum The membrane that separates the outer ear from the middle ear, and that vibrates when sound waves strike it. (p. 209)

egg A female sex cell. (p. 231)

embryo A developing human during the first eight weeks after fertilization has occurred. (p. 237)

emphysema A serious disease that destroys lung tissue and causes difficulty in breathing. (p. 142)

endocrine gland An organ of the endocrine system which produces and releases its chemical products directly into the bloodstream. (p. 226)

enzyme A protein that speeds up chemical reactions in the body. (p. 84)

epidermis The outermost layer of the skin. (p. 58)

epiglottis A flap of tissue that seals off the windpipe and prevents food from entering. (p. 85)

epithelial tissue A body tissue that covers the surfaces of the body, inside and out. (p. 19)

esophagus A muscular tube that connects the mouth to the stomach. (p. 85)

estrogen A hormone produced by the ovaries that controls the development of adult female characteristics. (p. 234)

excretion The process by which wastes are removed from the body. (p. 145)

farsightedness The condition in which distant objects can be seen clearly but nearby objects look blurry. (p. 207)

fats High-energy nutrients that are composed of carbon, oxygen, and hydrogen and contain more than twice as much energy as an equal amount of carbohydrates. (p. 71)

fertilization The joining of a sperm and an egg. (p. 231)

fetus A developing human from the ninth week of development until birth. (p. 239)

fiber A complex carbohydrate, found in plant foods, that cannot be broken down into sugar molecules by the body. (p. 70)

fibrin A chemical that is important in blood clotting because it forms a fiber net that traps red blood cells. (p. 116)

follicle Structure in the dermis of the skin from which a strand of hair grows. (p. 59)

Food Guide Pyramid A chart that classifies foods into six groups to help people plan a healthy diet. (p. 78)

force A push or a pull. (p.106)

fracture A break in a bone. (p. 46)

gallbladder The organ that stores bile after it is produced by the liver. (p. 91)

glucose A sugar that is the major source of energy for the body's cells. (p. 70)

heart A hollow, muscular organ that pumps blood throughout the body. (p. 102)

heart attack A condition in which blood flow to a part of the heart muscle is blocked, which causes heart cells to die. (p. 121)

hemoglobin An iron-containing protein that binds chemically to oxygen molecules and makes up most of red blood cells. (p. 114)

histamine A chemical that is responsible for the symptoms of an allergy. (p. 176)

homeostasis The process by which an organism's internal environment is kept stable in spite of changes in the external environment. (p. 24)

hormone The chemical product of an endocrine gland that speeds up or slows down the activities of an organ or tissue. (p. 227)

hypertension A disorder in which a person's blood pressure is consistently higher than normal. (p.)

hypothalamus A tiny part of the brain that links the nervous system and the endocrine system. (p. 22)

hypothesis A prediction about the outcome of an experiment. (p. 264)

immune response Part of the body's defense against pathogens in which cells of the immune system react to each kind of pathogen with a defense targeted specifically at that pathogen. (p. 164)

immunity The ability of the immune system to des pathogens before they can cause disease. (p. 170)

infectious disease A disease that can pass from one organism to another. (p. 157)

inflammatory response Part of the body's defense against pathogens, in which fluid and white bloo cells leak from blood vessels into tissues; the whi blood cells destroy pathogens by breaking them down. (p. 162)

insulin A chemical produced in the pancreas that enables the body's cells to take in glucose from th blood and use it for energy. (p. 177)

interneuron A neuron that carries nerve impulses from one neuron to another. (p. 192)

involuntary muscle A muscle that is not under conscious control. (p. 50)

iris The circular structure that surrounds the pupil an regulates the amount of light entering the eye. (p.)

joint A place where two bones come together. (p. 4

kidney A major organ of the excretory system; eliminates urea, excess water, and other waste materials from the body. (p. 145)

labor The first stage of birth, in which strong musc contractions of the uterus occur. (p. 240)

large intestine The last section of the digestive system where water is absorbed from food and the remain material is eliminated from the body. (p. 93)

larynx The voice box, located in the top part of the trachea, underneath the epiglottis. (p. 137)

lens The flexible structure that focuses light that ha entered the eye. (p. 205)

ligament Strong connective tissue that holds togeth the bones in a movable joint. (p.44)

liver The largest and heaviest organ in the body; it breaks down substances and eliminates nitrogen from the body. (p. 91)

lungs The main organs of the respiratory system. (p. 134)

lymph node A small knob of tissue in the lymphatic system that filters lymph. (p. 118)

lymph The fluid that the lymphatic system collects and returns to the bloodstream. (p. 118)

lymphatic system A network of veinlike vessels that returns the fluid that leaks out of blood vessels to the bloodstream. (p. 118)

lymphocyte White blood cell that reacts to each kind of pathogen with a defense targeted specifically at that pathogen. (p. 164)

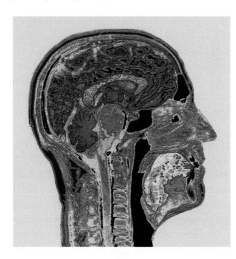

magnetic resonance imaging A method for taking clear images of both the bones and soft tissues of the body. (p. 47)

manipulated variable The one factor that a scientist changes during an experiment. (p. 265)

marrow The soft tissue that fills the internal spaces in bone. (p. 42)

melanin A pigment that gives the skin its color (p. 59)

menstrual cycle The monthly cycle of changes that occurs in the female reproductive system, during which an egg develops and the uterus prepares for the arrival of a fertilized egg. (p. 235)

menstruation The process that occurs if fertilization does not take place, in which the thickened lining of the uterus breaks down and blood and tissue then pass out of the female body through the vagina. (p. 236)

mental health A component of wellness that involves a person's feelings, or emotions. (p. 29)

minerals Nutrients that are needed by the body in small amounts and are not made by living things. (p. 74)

motor neuron A neuron that sends an impulse to a muscle, causing the muscle to contract. (p. 192)

mucus A thick, slippery substance produced by the body. (p. 85)

muscle tissue A body tissue that contracts or shortens, making body parts move. (p. 18)

nearsightedness The condition in which nearby objects can be seen clearly but distant objects look blurry. (p. 207)

negative feedback A process in which a system is turned off by the condition it produces; examples of negative feedback systems include regulation of temperature by a thermostat and the regulation of the levels of many hormones in the blood. (p. 230)

nephron One of a million tiny, filtering structures found in the kidneys that removes wastes from blood and produces urine. (p. 146)

nerve A bundle of nerve fibers. (p. 192)

nerve impulse The message carried by a neuron. (p. 191)

nerve tissue A body tissue that carries messages back and forth between the brain and every other part of the body. (p. 19)

neuron A cell that carries messages through the nervous system. (p. 191)

nicotine A drug in tobacco that speeds up the activities of the nervous system, heart, and other organs. (p. 141)

noninfectious disease A disease that is not spread from person to person. (p. 175)

nucleus The control center of a cell that directs the cell's activities and contains information that determines the cell's characteristics. (p. 18)

nutrients Substances in food that provide the raw materials and energy the body needs to carry out all the essential life processes. (p. 68)

operational definition A statement that describes how a particular variable is to be measured or a term is to be defined. (p. 265)

organ A structure in the body that is composed of different kinds of tissue. (p. 20)

organ system A group of organs that work together to perform a major function in the body. (p. 20)

osteoporosis A condition in which the body's bones become weak and break easily. (p. 45)

ovary Organ of the female reproductive system in which eggs and estrogen are produced. (p. 234)

oviduct A passageway for eggs from an ovary to the uterus; the place where fertilization usually occurs. (p. 234)

ovulation The process in which a mature egg is released from the ovary into an oviduct; occurs about halfway through a typical menstrual cycle. (p. 235)

pacemaker A group of cells located in the right atrium that sends out signals that make the heart muscle contract and that regulates heartbeat rate. (p. 104)

pancreas A triangular organ that produces enzymes that flow into the small intestine. (p. 92)

passive immunity Immunity in which the antibodies that fight a pathogen come from another organism rather than from the person's own body. (p. 172)

passive smoking The involuntary inhalation of smoke from other people's cigarettes, cigars, or pipes. (p. 143)

pathogen An organism that causes disease. (p. 157)

peer pressure The pressure from friends and classmates to behave in certain ways. (p. 29)

penis The organ through which both semen and urine leave the male body. (p. 233)

Percent Daily Value An indication of how the nutritional content of a food fits into the diet of a person who consumes a total of 2,000 Calories a day. (p. 80)

peripheral nervous system All the nerves located outside the central nervous system; connects the central nervous system to all parts of the body. (p. 196)

peristalsis Involuntary waves of muscle contraction that keep food moving along in one direction through the digestive system. (p. 85)

phagocyte A white blood cell that destroys pathogens by engulfing them and breaking them down. (p. 163)

pharynx The throat; part of both the respiratory and digestive systems. (p. 132)

physical health A component of wellness that consists of how well the body functions. (p. 28)

pituitary gland An endocrine gland just below the hypothalamus that communicates with the hypothalamus to control many body activities. (p. 229)

placenta A membrane that becomes the link between the developing embryo or fetus and the mother. (p. 238)

plasma The liquid part of blood. (p. 113)

platelet A cell fragment that plays an important part in forming blood clots. (p. 116)

pore An opening through which sweat reaches the surface of the skin. (p. 59)

pressure The force that something exerts over a given area. (p. 110)

proteins Nutrients that contain nitrogen as well as carbon, hydrogen, and oxygen; they are needed for tissue growth and repair and play a part in chemical reactions within cells. (p. 72)

puberty The period of sexual development during the teenage years in which the body becomes able to reproduce. (p. 245)

pupil The opening through which light enters the eye. (p. 205)

rectum A short tube at the end of the large intestine where waste material is compressed into a solid form before being eliminated. (p. 93)

red blood cell A cell in the blood that takes up oxyge in the lungs and delivers it to cells elsewhere in the body. (p. 114)

reflex An automatic response that occurs very rapidl and without conscious control. (p. 201)

reproduction The process by which living things produce new individuals of the same type. (p. 231

respiration The process in which oxygen and glucos undergo a complex series of chemical reactions inside cells. (p. 131)

response What the body does in reaction to a stimul (p. 191)

retina The layer of receptor cells at the back of the e on which an image is focused; nerve impulses are sent from the retina to the brain. (p. 206)

saliva The fluid released when the mouth waters tha plays an important role in both mechanical and chemical digestion. (p. 84)

saturated fats Fats, such as butter, that are usually sc at room temperature. (p. 71)

scrotum An external pouch of skin in which the test are located. (p. 232)

semen A mixture of sperm cells and fluids. (p. 233)

semicircular canals Structures in the inner ear that a responsible for the sense of balance. (p. 209)

sensory neuron A neuron that picks up stimuli from the internal or external environment and convert each stimulus into a nerve impulse. (p. 192)

skeletal muscle A muscle that is attached to the bon of the skeleton. (p. 51)

small intestine The part of the digestive system in which most chemical digestion takes place. (p. 90)

smooth muscle Involuntary muscle found inside ma internal organs of the body. (p. 52)

social health A component of wellness that consists how well a person gets along with others. (p. 29)

somatic nervous system The group of nerves that controls voluntary actions. (p. 200)

sperm A male sex cell. (p. 231)

sphygmomanometer An instrument that measures blood pressure. (p. 111)

spinal cord The thick column of nerve tissue that is enclosed by the vertebrae and that links the brain most of the nerves in the peripheral nervous syst (p. 197)

sprain An injury in which the ligaments holding bo together are stretched too far and tear. (p. 46)

stimulant A drug that speeds up body processes. (p. 214)

stimulus Any change or signal in the environment that can make an organism react in some way. (p. 191)

stomach A J-shaped, muscular pouch located in the abdomen that expands to hold all of the food that is swallowed. (p. 86)

stress The reaction of a person's body and mind to threatening, challenging, or disturbing events. (p. 25)

synapse The tiny space between the tip of an axon and the next structure (p. 194)

T cell A lymphocyte that identifies pathogens and distinguishes one pathogen from the other. (p. 164)

tar A dark, sticky substance produced when tobacco burns. (p. 140)

target cell A cell in the body that recognizes a hormone's chemical structure; a cell to which a hormone binds chemically. (p. 227)

tendon Strong connective tissue that attaches a muscle to a bone. (p. 52)

testis Organ of the male reproductive system in which sperm and testosterone are produced. (p. 232)

testosterone A hormone produced by the testes that controls the development of physical characteristics in men. (p. 232)

tissue A group of similar cells that perform the same function. (p. 18)

tolerance A state in which a drug user, after repeatedly taking a drug, needs larger and larger doses of the drug to produce the same effect. (p. 213)

toxin A poison that is produced by bacterial pathogens and that damages cells. (p. 158)

trachea The windpipe; a passage through which air moves in the respiratory system. (p. 133)

tumor An abnormal tissue mass that results from the rapid division of cancerous cells. (p. 178)

umbilical cord A ropelike structure that forms in the uterus between the embryo and the placenta. (p. 238)

unsaturated fats Fats, such as olive oil and canola oil, that are usually liquid at room temperature. (p. 71)

urea A poisonous chemical that comes from the breakdown of proteins and that is removed from the body by the kidneys. (p. 145)

ureter A narrow tube that carries urine from one of the kidneys to the urinary bladder. (p. 145)

urethra A small tube through which urine flows from the body. (p. 146)

urinary bladder A sacklike muscular organ that stores urine until it is eliminated from the body. (p. 146)

urine A watery fluid produced by the kidneys that contains urea and other waste materials. (p. 145)

uterus The hollow muscular organ of the female reproductive system in which a baby develops. (p. 234)

vaccination The process by which harmless antigens are deliberately introduced into a person's body to produce active immunity. (p. 171)

vaccine A substance used in a vaccination that consists of pathogens that have been weakened or killed but can still trigger the immune system into action. (p. 171)

vagina A muscular passageway through which a baby leaves the mother's body. (p. 235)

valve A flap of tissue in the heart or a vein that prevents blood from flowing backward. (p. 102)

variable Any factor that can change in an experiment. (p. 265)

vein A blood vessel that carries blood back to the heart. (p. 104)

ventricle Each of the two lower chambers of the heart that pumps blood out of the heart. (p. 102)

vertebrae The 26 small bones that make up the backbone. (p. 39)

villi Tiny finger-shaped structures that cover the inner surface of the small intestine and provide a large surface area through which digested food is absorbed. (p. 92)

vitamins Molecules that act as helpers in a variety of chemical reactions within the body. (p. 73)

vocal cords Folds of connective tissue that stretch across the opening of the larynx and produce a person's voice. (p. 137)

voluntary muscle A muscle that is under conscious control. (p. 50)

wellness The state of being at the best possible level of health—in the body, the mind, and relationships with others. (p. 28)

white blood cell A blood cell that fights disease. (p. 115)

withdrawal A period of adjustment that occurs when a drug-dependent person stops taking the drug. (p. 214)

X-ray A form of energy that travels in waves that can pass through some living tissue, but not through bone. (p. 47)

zygote A fertilized egg, produced by the joining of a sperm and an egg. (p. 231)

D ◆ 283

platelets 115, 116
Plato 255
polio 171
pores 59
posing questions, skill of 264
Pott, Percivall 183
poultry 79
predicting, skill of 260
pregnancy 237–239
  embryo 237–238
  fetus 237–238, 239, 240
  zygote 231, 232, 237, 241
premolars 84
prescription drugs 212
pressure 110. *See also* blood pressure;
    peer pressure.
problem solving, skill of 267
proteins 72
  complete 72
  digestion of 88–89
  incomplete 72
  in urine 148
protists 159, 160
puberty 245–246
pulse rate 104, 108, 112
pupil 205
pyridoxine 73

radiation
  for cancer treatment 178–179
  X-rays 47
reaction times 195
rectum 93
red blood cells 99, 113, 114–115, 135, 141
red marrow 42
reflex 201–202
relating cause and effect, skill of 267
reproduction 231–241
  defined 231
reproductive system 21, 231–236
  female 234–236
  male 232–233
  sex cells 231–232
respiration
  defined 131
  smoking-related disorders 141–144
respiratory health
  smoking and 140–144, 151
respiratory system 21, 129–144, 151
  and air 131
  alveoli 134–135
  breathing process 136–137
  bronchi 133, 134
  defenses against pathogens 162
  gas exchange 135
  lungs 133, 134
  nose 132, 133
  oxygen 130–131
  path of air 132–135
  pharynx 132, 133
  trachea 133–134
responding variable 265
response 191, 195
resting heart rate 259
retina 206, 207

riboflavin 73
rice 79
rickets 72
ringworm 158
Rocky Mountain spotted fever 160
rods 206

safety
  in the laboratory 273–275
  and nervous system 202
  and skeletal system 48–49
safety in the laboratory 273–275
saliva 84, 162
salivary amylase 86
salivary glands 83
saturated fats 12, 71
scabs 116, 162
scientific investigations 183, 264–265
scientific method. *See* scientific
    investigations.
scrotum 232
scurvy 72–73
secretions
  digestive 86, 91–92
semen 233
semicircular canals 209–210
senses 204–11, 221
  balance 209–210
  functions of 204
  hearing 208–209
  smell 210–211
  taste 210–211
  touch 211
  vision 205–207
sensory neurons 192, 193, 200, 201
septum 103
serving size
  food label listings 80
sex cells 231–232. *See also* egg and sperm.
simple carbohydrates 12, 70
SI units of measurement 262–263
skeletal muscles 51–52
  caring for 54
  reflex action of 201–202
skeletal system 17, 21, 38–45
  bone care 44–45
  bone growth 41, 42
  bone strength 40–41
  bone structure 41–42
  common injuries 46
  function of 38–40
  joints 42–44
  number of bones in 38
  preventing injuries 48–49
skills, science process 260–272
skin 56–62
  as barrier against infection 168–169
  care of 60
  cleanliness of 62
  defenses against pathogens 162
  dermis 58, 59
  diet and 60
  epidermis 58–59
  as excretory organ 150
  functions of 56–57

sense of touch 211
sun exposure 60–62
skin cancer 61–62, 179, 182–183, 184
small intestine 83, 86, 90–93
  absorption in 92–93
  functions of 90–91
smell 210–211
smoking 140–144. *See also* tobacco.
  antismoking ads 129
  cancer and 142, 178, 179
  cardiovascular health and 124, 143
  choosing not to smoke 144
  passive 143
  respiratory health and 141–142, 151
smooth muscle 51, 52–53
snack foods 77
Snow, John 159
social development 248
social health 28, 29, 30
sodium 74
  hypertension and 123
somatic nervous system 200
soot
  skin cancer and 182–183
sound 208–209
sperm 231, 232, 249
  path of 233
  production of 233
sphygmomanometer 111
spinal cord 190, 196, 197, 199, 200, 201
  injuries 202
spinal nerves 200
spongy bone 41
sprain 46
starch 70
startle reaction 23
steroids, anabolic 215, 216–217
stimulant 214–215
stimulus 191, 195
stirrup 209
stomach 86–87
  defenses against pathogens 162
stress
  dealing with 27
  defined 25
  homeostasis and 25–26
  long-term 27
  mental health and 29
  physical response to 25–26
sugars 12, 70, 79
sunlight
  cancer and 61–62, 178, 179, 182, 184
  melanin and 59
  skin exposure to 60–62
  vitamin D and 57, 72
sweat glands 59
sweets 79
"swollen glands" 118
synapse 194

T cells
  (T lymphocytes) 164–165, 166, 171
tar in tobacco smoke 140
target cells 227–228
target heart rate 259

Acknowledgments

Illustration

Carmella Clifford: 91, 205, 209
Bruce Day: 26
John Edwards and Associates: 40–41 **(Henry Hill)**, 193 **(Dave Fischer)**
Function thru Form: 79
GeoSystems Global Corporation: 255
Floyd E. Hosmer: 192
Keith Kasnot: 85, 87, 146–147, 228, 229, 238
Martucci Design: 35, 80, 127, 146, 159, 178
Matt Mayerchak: 34, 64, 96, 152, 186, 222
Fran Milner: 17, 53, 83, 92, 108–109, 114–115, 134–135, 233, 234
Morgan Cain & Associates: 18, 30, 58, 86, 102, 107, 113, 117, 138, 161, 165, 194, 200, 230
Pat Rossi: 43
Sandra Sevigny: 21, 39, 51, 101, 118, 197
Tim Spransy: 23
Walter Stuart: 103, 133
J/B Woolsey Associates: 84, 105, 131, 137, 201, 207, 217, 219, 236

Photography

Photo Research by - Paula Wehde
Cover image - David Job/TSI

Nature of Science
Page 10, Courtesy of Alex Martinez; **11t**, Lawrence Migdale/Stock Boston; **11b**, Josh Mitchell/TSI; **12t,mt,b**, PhotoDisc; **12m**, Russ Lappa; **12mb**, Steven Maus; **14**, Steven Mays.

Chapter 1
Pages 14–15, Jean Francois Causse/TSI; **16t**, Richard Haynes; **16b**, Russ Lappa; **19tl**, Robert Becker/Custom Medical Stock; **19bl**, Fred Hossler/Visuals Unlimited; **19m**, Clive Brunckill/Allsport; **19tr**, Biophoto Associates/Science Source/Photo Researchers; **19br**, John D. Cunningham/Visuals Unlimited; **20**, Wayne Hoy/The Picture Cube; **22, 23**, Richard Haynes; **24**, Lori Adamski Peek/TSI; **25**, Paul J. Sutton/Duomo; **27**, Michael P. Manheim/ MidwestStock; **28–29**, Charles Gupton/TSI; **29tr**, Melanie Carr/Zephyr Pictures; **29br**, Bob Daemmrich/Stock Boston; **31**, Superstock; **32**, Betsy Fuchs/The Picture Cube; **33**, Charles Gupton/TSI.

Chapter 2
Pages 36–37, Globus, Holway & Lobel/The Stock Market; **38t**, Russ Lappa; **38b**, Cathy Cheney/Stock Boston; **39**, Richard Haynes; **41**, Andrew Syred/Science Photo Library/Photo Researchers; **42**, Salisbury District Hospital/Science Photo Library/Photo Researchers; **43**, William R. Sallaz/Duomo; **44**, The Granger Collection, NY; **45 both**, Superstock; **46**, John Meyer/Custom Medical Stock; **47l**, Michael Acliolo/International Stock; **47r**, Simon Fraser/Science Photo Library/Photo Researchers; **48**, Ted Horowitz/The Stock Market; **49**, Adamski–Peek/TSI; **50t**, Richard Haynes; **50b**, Superstock; **51tl**, Astrid & Hanns–Frieder Michler/Science Photo Library/Photo Researchers; **51bl**, Eric Grave/Photo Researchers; **51m**, Richard Haynes; **51r**, Ed Reschke/Peter Arnold; **52l**, Richard Haynes; **52r**, Jim Cummins/FPG International; **54**, Superstock; **55**, Richard Haynes; **56t**, Richard Haynes; **56b**, Jed Jacobson/Allsport; **57l**, David Young Wolff/TSI; **57r**, Lennart Nilsson/Behold Man; **59l**, Prof. P. Motta/Dept. of Anatomy/University "La Sapienza", Rome/Science Photo Library/Photo Researchers; **59r**, Russ Lappa; **60,61**, Richard Haynes; **62**, Bob Daemmrich/Stock Boston; **63l**, Superstock; **63r**, Ed Reschke/Peter Arnold.

Chapter 3
Pages 66–67, Superstock; **68**, Bob Daemmrich/Stock Boston; **69l**, Richard Haynes; **69r,70,71,72–73,73 all, 74 all**, Russ Lappa; **75**, Joan Baron/The Stock Market; **76, 77t**, Richard Haynes; **77b**, David Young-Wolff/PhotoEdit; **78**, David Young Wolff/TSI; **81**, David Young-Wolff/PhotoEdit; **82**, The Granger Collection, NY; **83, 84**, Richard Haynes; **87**, CNRI/Science Photo Library/Photo Researchers; **89, 90t**, Richard Haynes; **90b**, Llewellyn/Uniphoto; **92**, Prof. P. Motta/Dept. of Anatomy/University "La Sapienza", Rome/Science Photo Library/Photo Researchers; **93**, CNRI/Science Photo Library/Photo Researchers; **94**, Donna Day/TSI; **95**, Joan Baron/The Stock Market.

Chapter 4
Pages 98–99, National Cancer Institute/Science Photo Library/Photo Researchers; **100, 101**, Richard Haynes; **102t**, Erich Lessing/Art Resource; **102b** Science Photo Library/Photo Researchers; **104–105**, Pete Saloutos/The Stock Market; **106**, Scott Weersing/Allsport; **107**, Richard Haynes; **109**, Prof. P. Motta/Dept. of Anatomy/University "La Sapienza", Rome/Science Photo Library/Photo Researchers; **110**, Cabisco/Visuals Unlimited; **111**, Matt Meadows/Peter Arnold; **112**, Richard Haynes; **113**, Andrew Syred/Science Photo Library/Photo Researchers; **114**, Bill Longcore/Science Source/Photo Researchers; **115t**, Andrew Syred/Science Photo Library/Photo Researchers; **115b**, National Cancer Institute/Science Photo Library/Photo Researchers; **116**, Oliver Meckes/Photo Researchers; **118**, Richard Haynes; **120t**, Daemmrich/Stock Boston; **120b**, Thom Duncan/Adventure Photo; **121 both**, Custom Medical Stock; **122t** AP/Wide World Photos; **122b**, The Granger Collection, NY; **123t**, Liaison International; **123b**, Brad Nelson/Custom Medical Stock; **124**, Nicole Katodo/TSI; **125**, Prof. P. Motta/Dept. of Anatomy/University "La Sapienza", Rome/Science Photo Library/Photo Researchers.

Chapter 5
Pages 128–129, Mark Gibson/The Stock Market; **130t**, Richard Haynes; **130b**, Dick Dickinson/Photo Network; **132l**, Richard Haynes; **132 inset**, Eddy Gray/Science Photo Library/Photo Researchers; **133**, Richard Haynes; **136**, Paul Harris/TSI; **138**, J. Sohm/The Image Works; **139**, Russ Lappa; **140**, Spencer Jones/FPG International; **141**, Ken Karp; **142**, Al Bello/TSI; **143l**, Clark Overton/Phototake; **143m**, SIV/Photo Researchers; **143r**, Martin Rotker/Phototake; **144**, Smoke Free Educational Services; **145,148**, Richard Haynes; **150**, Ken Karp; **151**, Eddy Gray/Science Photo Library/Photo Researchers.

Chapter 6
Pages 154–155, Microworks/Phototake; **156t**, Richard Haynes; **156b**, The Granger Collection, NY; **157**, Pete Saloutos/The Stock Market; **158t**, CNRI/Science Photo Library/Photo Researchers; **158m**, Biozentrum/Science Photo Library/Photo Researchers; **158b**, Gucho/CNRI/Science Photo Library/Photo Researchers; **160t**, Mike Peres/Custom Medical Stock Photo; **160b**, Scott Camazine/Photo Researchers; **161**, Russ Lappa; **162**, Science Pictures Ltd./Science Photo Library/Photo Researchers; **163**, Lennart Nilsson/Boehringer Ingelheim International GmbH; **164**, Lori Adamski Peek/TSI; **166**, NIBSC/Science Photo Library/Photo Researchers; **167**, Jon Riley/TSI; **168, 169**, Richard Haynes; **170t**, Russ Lappa; **170b**, CNRI/Science Photo Library/Photo Researchers; **171**, Aaron Haupt/Photo Researchers; **172t**, Historical Picture Service/Custom Medical Stock; **172b**, The Granger Collection, NY; **173t**, Granger Collection, NY; **173b**, Giraudon/Art Resource; **175t**, Richard Haynes; **175b**, Richard Haynes; **176l**, Ron Kimball; **176r**, Andrew Syred/Science Photo Library/Photo Researchers; **177**, Therisa Stack/Tom Stack & Associates; **178**, Dept. of Clinical Radiology, Salisbury District Hospital/Science Photo Library/Photo Researchers; **179**, Yoav levy/Phototake; **180**, Stevie Grand/Science Photo Library/Photo Researchers; **182t**, Richard Haynes; **182bl,182–183**, The Granger Collection, NY; **184**, Phil Savoie/The Picture Cube; **185**, Biozentrum/Science Photo Library/Photo Researchers.

Chapter 7
Pages 188–189, 1998 Magic Eye Inc.; **190t**, Richard Haynes; **190b**, Lee Snider/The Image Works; **191**, Gordon R. Gainer/The Stock Market; **192**, Biophoto Associates/Photo Researchers; **195, 196t**, Richard Haynes; **196b**, Milton Feinberg/The Picture Cube; **197**, Richard Haynes; **199**, Art Resouce; **200**, Tom Stewart/The Stock Market; **202**, William Sallaz/Duomo; **203**, Robert E. Daemmrich/TSI; **204**, Superstock; **206t**, Prof. P. Motta/Dept. of Anatomy/U. "La Sapienza," Rome/Science Photo Library/Photo Researchers; **206b**, Lennart Nilsson; **208**, Renee Lynn/TSI; **210l**, Spencer Grant/The Picture Cube; **210r**, Lennart Nilsson; **211**, Mugshots/The Stock Market; **212t**, Russ Lappa; **212b**, Uniphoto; **213**, Tom Croke/Liaison International; **214**, David Young-Wolff/PhotoEdit; **218**, Index Stock; **220**, Bob Daemmrich/Stock Boston; **221**, Spencer Grant/The Picture Cube.

Chapter 8
Pages 224–225, Uniphoto; **226**, Keith Kent/Photo Researchers; **227l**, Chad Slattery/TSI; **227r**, Nancy Sheehan/The Picture Cube; **231**, Mitsuaki Iwago/Minden Pictures; **232 both**, Dr. Dennis Kunkel/Phototake; **235**, Prof. P.M. Motta & J. Van Blerkom/Science Photo Library/ Photo Researchers; **237tl**, Stephen R. Swinburne/Stock Boston; **237tm**, Stephen R. Swinburne/Stock Boston; **237b**, David Phillips/Science Photo Library/ Photo Researchers; **239**, Lennart Nilsson; **240**, Index Stock; **241l**, Roy Morsch/The Stock Market; **241r**, Frauke/Mauritius/H. Armstrong Roberts; **242l**, Penny Gentieu; **242r**, Elizabeth Hathol/The Stock Market; **243**, Don Semtzer/TSI; **244t**, Ken Karp; **244b**, Roy Morso/The Stock Market; **245l**, James D. Wilson/Liaison International; **245r**, Robert E. Daemmrich/TSI; **246**, Mark Burnett/Photo Researchers; **247**, Bruce Dale/National Geographic Society; **248**, David Young-Wolff/Photo Edit; **249**, David Young Wolff/TSI; **251t** David Phillips/Science Photo Library/ Photo Researchers; **251b**, Penny Gentieu.

Interdisciplinary Exploration
Page 254t, Duomo; **254b**, Scala/Art Resource; **255**, Louvre, Dpt. des Antiquités Grecques/Romaines, Paris, France. Photograph by Erich Lessing/Art Resource; **256**, Tony Duffy/Allsport USA; **257**, Pascal Rondeau/Allsport USA; **258–259**, Mark C. Burnett/Stock Boston/PNI;

Skills Handbook
Page 260, Mike Moreland/Photo Network; **261t**, Foodpix; **261m**, Richard Haynes; **261b**, Russ Lappa, **264**, Richard Haynes; **266**, Ron Kimball; **267**, Renee Lynn/Photo Researchers.